College Chemistry Part 1

Author

Hein

ISBN 9781119192152

Printed in the United States of America 10 9 8 7 6 5 4 3 2 1

List of Titles

Introduction to General, Organic, and Biochemistry, 11th edition
by Morris Hein, Scott Pattison, Susan Arena, and Leo R. Best
Copyright © 2015, ISBN: 978-1-118-50189-4

Table of Contents

INTRODUCTION TO
GENERAL, ORGANIC, AND BIOCHEMISTRY

ELEVENTH EDITION

Morris Hein

Mount San Antonio College

Scott Pattison

Ball State University

Susan Arena

University of Illinois, Urbana-Champaign

WILEY

ON THE COVER:
Buckminsterfullerine (or Buckyball) is an allotropic form of carbon with a formula of C_{60}. It consists of five- and six-membered cyclic rings of carbon in a cage-like structure that resembles a soccer ball. It was named after the renowned inventor Buckminster Fuller, who designed the world-famous geodesic dome.

Vice President & Executive Publisher: Kaye Pace
Vice President & Publisher: Petra Recter
Acquisitions Editor: Nicholas Ferrari
Editorial Assistant: Mallory Fryc
Content Editor: Alyson Rentrop
Senior Marketing Manager: Kristine Ruff
Design Director: Harry Nolan
Senior Content Manager: Kevin Holm
Senior Designer: Maureen Eide
Senior Photo Editor: Lisa Gee
Senior Production Editor: Elizabeth Swain

Cover photo: © Laguna Design/Oxford Scientific/Getty Images

This book was typeset in 10/12 Times New Roman at Prepare and printed and bound by R. R. Donnelley (Willard). The cover was printed by R. R. Donnelley (Willard).

Founded in 1807, John Wiley & Sons, Inc. has been a valued source of knowledge and understanding for more than 200 years, helping people around the world meet their needs and fulfill their aspirations. Our company is built on a foundation of principles that include responsibility to the communities we serve and where we live and work. In 2008, we launched a Corporate Citizenship Initiative, a global effort to address the environmental, social, economic, and ethical challenges we face in our business. Among the issues we are addressing are carbon impact, paper specifications and procurement, ethical conduct within our business and among our vendors, and community and charitable support. For more information, please visit our website: www.wiley.com/go/citizenship.

The paper in this book was manufactured by a mill whose forest management programs include sustained yield-harvesting of its timberlands. Sustained yield harvesting principles ensure that the number of trees cut each year does not exceed the amount of new growth.

This book is printed on acid-free paper. ∞

Main text   ISBN 978-1-118-50189-4
Binder Version   ISBN 978-1-118-41389-0

Printed in the United States of America
10 9 8 7 6 5 4 3 2 1

Dedicated to the great-great grandchildren of Morris Hein:
Dillion Brayden Prum
Amber Jordyn Prum
The young will create our future.
The future is in their hands.

Dedicated to the mother of Scott Pattison:
Margaret Pattison
Striving is the heart of life.

ABOUT THE AUTHORS

Morris Hein earned a BS and MS in Chemistry at the University of Denver and his PhD at the University of Colorado, Boulder. He is Professor Emeritus of Chemistry at Mt. San Antonio College, where he regularly taught the preparatory chemistry course and organic chemistry. He is the original author of *Foundations of College Chemistry*, and his name has become synonymous with clarity, meticulous accuracy, and a step-by-step approach that students can follow. Over the years, more than three million students have learned chemistry using a text by Morris Hein. In addition to *Introduction to General, Organic, and Biochemistry*, Eleventh Edition, he is co-author of *Foundations of College Chemistry*, Fourteenth Edition. He is also co-author of *Foundations of Chemistry in the Laboratory*, Fourteenth Edition, and *Introduction to General, Organic, and Biochemistry in the Laboratory*, Eleventh Edition.

Scott E. Pattison earned a BA in chemistry from the University of California, Santa Cruz, an MA in chemistry from the University of Washington, and a PhD in biochemistry from the University of California, Riverside. He is currently Professor of Chemistry at Ball State University. A dedicated teacher at the university level for thirty-seven years, his primary area of instruction is biochemistry; however, he greatly enjoys teaching medical/nursing chemistry and general chemistry. Scott became a co-author with Morris Hein on the Third Edition of *Introduction to General, Organic, and Biochemistry*, and he brings his knowledge of students, subject matter, and current research to the text. In addition to his professional career, he volunteers in local schools from preschool through high school, providing extra science experiences for tomorrow's university students.

Susan Arena earned a BS and MA in Chemistry at California State University-Fullerton. She has taught science and mathematics at all levels, including middle school, high school, community college, and university. At the University of Illinois she developed a program for increasing the retention of minorities and women in science and engineering. This program focused on using active learning and peer teaching to encourage students to excel in the sciences. She has coordinated and led workshops and programs for science teachers from elementary through college levels that encourage and support active learning and creative science teaching techniques. For several years she was director of an Institute for Chemical Education (ICE) field center in Southern California. In addition to *Introduction to General, Organic, and Biochemistry*, Eleventh Edition, she is co-author of *Foundations of College Chemistry*, Fourteenth Edition. Susan enjoys reading, knitting, traveling, classic cars, and gardening in her spare time when she is not playing with her grandchildren.

PREFACE

It is our purpose to teach students the basic fundamentals of chemistry so that they understand and use this knowledge in their future science courses and in their everyday lives. Chemistry is everywhere. What pleasure it will give you when you read a science-related article on the internet or in the newspaper and you say to yourself: I understand what they are talking about. It is for you, the student, that we have written this book. It is our primary goal that you learn the subject matter presented so we can feel proud that we have helped further your career.

The central focus of this Eleventh Edition of *Introduction to General, Organic, and Biochemistry* is to present chemistry in a clear, engaging manner to stimulate students to see the relationship of chemistry to their chosen careers.

Development of Problem-Solving Skills

We all want our students to develop real skills in solving problems. We believe that a key to the success of this text is the fact that our problem-solving approach works for students. It is a step-by-step process that teaches the use of units and shows the change from one unit to the next. Section 4.3 emphasizes the general process of solving problems. In this edition we continue to use examples to incorporate fundamental mathematical skills, scientific notation, and significant figures. We have added Problem-Solving Strategy boxes in the text to highlight the steps needed to solve chemistry problems. We continue to use four significant figures for atomic and molar masses for consistency and for rounding off answers. We are meticulous in providing answers, correctly rounded, for students who have difficulty with mathematics.

FOSTERING STUDENT SKILLS *Attitude* plays a critical role in problem solving. We encourage students to learn that a systematic method approach to solving problems is better than memorization. Once we have laid the foundations of concepts, we highlight the steps so students can locate them easily. Important rules and equations are highlighted for emphasis and ready reference.

STUDENT PRACTICE Practice problems follow most examples in the text, with answers provided at the end of the chapter. The end of each chapter begins with *Review Questions*, which help students review key terms and concepts, as well as material presented in tables and figures. This is followed by *Paired Exercises*, covering concepts and numerical exercises, where two similar exercises are presented side by side. *Additional Exercises*, includes further practice problems presented in a more random order. Finally, *Challenge Exercises* present problems designed to take the student beyond the basic chapter material. This new edition includes many new exercises and problems. Answers for selected exercises appear in Appendix VI and answers for *Putting It Together* review exercises appear in Appendix VII.

Organization

The fundamentals of basic chemistry are covered in Chapters 1 through 18. The less theoretical aspects of chemistry are presented early in the book, leaving more abstract material for later. New material is presented at a level appropriate for beginning students by emphasizing the language of chemistry, equation writing and balancing, and calculations involving chemical reactions. The Periodic Table is first introduced in Chapter 3 along with elements, compounds, and chemical formulas. This subject is further discussed in detail in Chapters 10 and 11 with discussion of modern atomic theory and the Periodic Table. Instructors who want to teach atomic theory and chemical bonding early in the course can cover Chapters 10 and 11 immediately after Chapter 5.

Organic Chemistry and Biochemistry are studied in Chapters 19 to 26 and Chapters 27 to 35, respectively. We have reviewed and carefully selected organic reactions to illustrate the reactions of important functional groups. Three organic reactions—substitution, addition, and elimination—are introduced and, where possible, subsequent chapters present reactions within this framework.

IUPAC nomenclature is emphasized in this edition, but we have considered how organics are named in everyday usage. Thus we also use common names if they continue to be widely used. A full chapter (26) on Stereoisomerism unfolds the importance of chemical structure of organic and biochemical substances. Practical applications are pointed out in subsequent chapters.

Finally, we examine the principles of biochemistry and again strive to illustrate current, relevant applications such as DNA, gene therapy, nucleic acids and heredity, and use of industrial enzymes. Because biochemistry is increasingly a visual science, many new molecular models have been incorporated to help students better comprehend biochemical functions.

Highlights in This Edition

In this Eleventh Edition we have tried to build on the strengths of previous editions. We have worked to update the art and add more macro to molecular figures to help students clarify concepts visually. We continually strive to keep the material at the same level so students can easily read and use the text to learn chemistry. Some specific features and selected changes in this text are highlighted below:

- **CONCEPT MODULES** Each chapter was reviewed and reorganized into concept modules to facilitate student learning. Each module is structured to ensure that students are focused on learning the key concepts and skills presented within the module. While the chapters may look different in their section titles, the content remains essentially the same; it has simply been streamlined to improve the flow and place conceptual material together.

  - Each module begins with a **Learning Objective** that states the goal for the section and prompts students to recognize the important concepts, providing the scaffolding for understanding.
  - New examples model problem solving for students, and **Practice Problems** have been added to provide students with opportunities to apply their knowledge. **Key Terms** in each section are highlighted in bold and listed at the beginning of each section as well as in the **Chapter Review**. Each Key Term is also defined in the Glossary.
  - **Connecting organic chemistry to biochemistry** has been given added emphasis in this edition. The number of in-chapter practice problems that emphasize organic-biochemistry connections (the "Application to Biochemistry" practice problems in the organic chapters and the "Organic Review" practice problems in the biochemistry chapters) has been increased. Margin notes have been added in the organic chapters ("A Biochemical Perspective") that relate biochemical topics to organic functional group chemistry, and margin notes have been added to the biomolecule chapters ("Functional Group Biochemistry") to briefly refresh important functional group chemistries.

- **Molecular art**: Learning chemistry requires the ability to connect the macroscopic world of everyday life to the microscopic world of atoms and molecules. In this edition we have added molecular art to macroscopic pictures to emphasize this connection. Biochemical molecular art has been added and refined to further emphasize the importance of 3-D shape to biochemical function.
- **Design and Illustration Program**: This edition has a fresh new design, enhanced by an updated art and photo program. New photos appear throughout.
- **Organic/Biochemistry Problem Solving**: Organic and biochemistry require a different set of problem-solving skills than general chemistry. The organic problems are now organized by type (e.g., nomenclature, chemical reactions, etc.) to emphasize the subject continuity through all organic functional groups. In-chapter **Practice Problems** are paired with margin notes (**"More Practice?"**) to allow the student to rapidly access more problems of the same type.
- **Chemistry In Action** sections, show the impact of chemistry in a variety of practical applications. These essays cover a range of relevant topics and introduce experimental

information on new chemical discoveries and applications. To maintain currency with the rapidly growing biochemistry field, over 50% of the organic and biochemistry Chemistry in Action essays are new to this edition. In addition, all organic and biochemistry chapters now include a second Chemistry in Action that focuses on a health application.

- The organic and biochemistry chapters now contain short, health-related commentaries, called **Health Connections**. These focused subsections relate specific chapter concepts to everyday health issues.

Learning Aids

- **Learning Objectives** highlight the concept being taught in each section. These objectives are tied to **Example**, **Practice Problems**, **Review Exercises**, and **Exercises** to assist the student in mastering each concept module and objective.
- Important **terms** are set off in bold type where they are defined, and are listed in grey at the beginning of each section. All **Key Terms** listed in the **Chapter Review** are also defined in the Glossary.
- Worked **examples** show students the how of problem solving using **Problem-solving Strategies** and **Solution Maps** before they are asked to tackle problems on their own.
- **Practice problems** permit immediate reinforcement of a skill shown in the example problems. Answers are provided at the end of the chapter to encourage students to check their problem solving immediately.
- **Marginal notations** help students understand basic concepts and problem-solving techniques. These are printed in blue to clearly distinguish them from text and vocabulary terms.

LEARNING AIDS: MATH SKILLS For students who may need help with the mathematical aspects of chemistry, the following learning aids are available:

- A **Review of Mathematics**, covering the basic functions, is provided in Appendix I.
- **Math Survival Guide: Tips and Tricks for Science Students**, 2nd Edition, by Jeffrey R. Appling and Jean C. Richardson, a brief paperback summary of basic skills that can be packaged with the text, provides an excellent resource for students who need help with the mathematical aspects of chemistry.

Student and Instructor Supplements

FOR THE STUDENT **Student Solutions Manual** by Morris Hein, Scott Pattison, Susan Arena and Kathy Mitchell, ISBN 978-1-118-50191-7: includes answers and solutions to all End-Of-Chapter Questions and Exercises.

Introduction to General, Organic, and Biochemistry in the Laboratory, 10th Edition by Morris Hein, Judith Peisen and James M. Ritchey, ISBN 978-0-470-59881-8: includes 42 experiments for a laboratory program that may accompany the lecture course. The manual reflects the most current terminology and environmental standards, and features up-to-date information on waste disposal and safe laboratory procedures. The Manual also includes study aides and exercises.

Math Survival Guide: Tips and Tricks for Science Students, 2nd Edition, Jeffrey R. Appling and Jean C. Richardson, ISBN 978-0-471-27054-6 a brief paperback summary of basic skills with practice exercises in every chapter. This guide provides an excellent resource for students who need help with the mathematical aspects of chemistry.

Respondus Test Bank Network: Provides tests and quizzes for Wiley's leading titles for easy publication into your LMS course, as well as for printed tests.*

Instructor's Companion Web Site at www.wiley.com/college/hein Instructors have access to the following useful resources:

Test Bank, prepared by Thomas Gill, College of Southern Nevada, Lydia Martinez Rivera, University of Texas at San Antonio, Anthony Stellato, Suffolk County Community College and Paul D. Root, Henry Ford Community College. Includes more than 3,400 true-false, multiple-choice and open-ended questions and answers.

---

*For schools without a campus-wide license to Respondus, Wiley will provide one for no additional cost.

Respondus Test Bank, the test bank contains true-false, multiple-choice, open-ended questions, and answers to all test questions.

Instructor's Manual for Introduction to General, Organic, and Biochemistry in the Laboratory, 10e, by Morris Hein and Judith Peisen. Includes information on the management of the lab, evaluation of experiments, notes for individual experiments, a list of reagents and amounts needed for each experiment, and answer keys to each experiment report form and all exercises.

Digital Image Library: images from the text are available online in JPEG format. Instructors may use these to customize their presentations and to provide additional visual support for quizzes and exams.

Power Point Lecture Slides: created by Karin Hassenrueck, California State University Northridge, Karen Sanchez, Florida State College at Jacksonville and Marc Lord, Columbus State Community College. These slides contain lecture outlines and key topics from each chapter of the text, along with supporting artwork and figures from the text.

Acknowledgments

We very much appreciate the talented assistance and untiring efforts of the many publication professionals involved in this project. Thank you to the staff at John Wiley & Sons, especially to our editor, Nick Ferrari, and Production Editor, Elizabeth Swain, whose attention to detail kept this project on track. Thank you as well to Alyson Rentrop, Content Editor, Lisa Gee, Senior Photo Editor, and Editorial Assistants, Ashley Gayle, Katherine Bull and Mallory Fryc. Without your collective effort, this endeavor would not have been possible. Additionally, we thank our fine compositor, Assunta Petrone of codeMantra. We gratefully acknowledge the diligent, conscientious work from all on this collaborative project.

We are grateful for the many helpful comments from colleagues and students who, over the years, have made this book possible. We hope they will continue to share their ideas for change with us, either directly or through our publisher.

We are especially thankful for the support, friendship, and constant encouragement of our spouses, Joan and Steve.

Our sincere appreciation goes to the following reviewers who were kind enough to read and give their professional comments:

Ali O. Sezer
California University of Pennsylvania

Andrew Burns
Kent State University Stark

Beatriz E. Ruiz Silva
Los Angeles Trade-Technical College

David B. Shaw
Madison Area Technical College

Dawn Richardson
Collin College

Edward L. Barnes, Jr.
Fayetteville Technical Community College

Eugene F. Douglass
University of North Carolina-Pembroke

Gerald Ittenbach
Fayetteville Technical Community College

James D. Carr
University of Nebraska

Jing-Yi Chin
Suffolk Community College

Joe David Escobar, Jr.
Oxnard College

Joy Walker
Truman College

Karen Sanchez
Florida State College at Jacksonville

Larry Emme
Chemeketa Community College

Lisa Rezende
University of Arizona

Lucinda Spryn
Thomas Nelson Community College

Lydia Martinez Rivera
The University of Texas at San Antonio

Madeline Adamczeski
San Jose City College

Melodie Graber
Oakton Community College

Michael L. Kirby
Des Moines Area Community College

Mildred Hall
Clark State Community College

Myung-Hoon Kim
Georgia Perimeter College

Pearl Tsang
University of Cincinnati

Rebecca Barlag
Ohio University

Richard Hyslop
University of Northern Colorado

Roberta Sulk
Northeast Wisconsin Technical College

Sean Birke
Jefferson College

Sharon Sowa
Indiana University of PA

Stephen Milczanowski
Florida Community College-Jacksonville

Suzanne Williams
Northern Michigan University

Tara S. Carpenter
University of Maryland, Baltimore County

Theodore E. Fickel
Los Angeles Valley College

Velislava Karaivanova
Pittsburgh Community College

Morris Hein, Scott Pattison, and Susan Arena

Periodic Table of the Elements

Atomic masses are based on carbon-12. Elements marked with † have no stable isotopes. The atomic mass given is that of the isotope with the longest known half-life.

For practical use, atomic masses have been rounded to four figures.

Key:
Atomic number →
Symbol →
Name →
Atomic mass →

Example:
11
Na
Sodium
22.99

Current ACS and IUPAC – Preferred U.S.

Period	1 / 1A	2 / 2A	3 / 3B	4 / 4B	5 / 5B	6 / 6B	7 / 7B	8 / 8B	9 / 8B	10	11 / 1B	12 / 2B	13 / 3A	14 / 4A	15 / 5A	16 / 6A	17 / 7A	18 / 8A
1	1 **H** Hydrogen 1.008																	2 **He** Helium 4.003
2	3 **Li** Lithium 6.941	4 **Be** Beryllium 9.012											5 **B** Boron 10.81	6 **C** Carbon 12.01	7 **N** Nitrogen 14.01	8 **O** Oxygen 16.00	9 **F** Fluorine 19.00	10 **Ne** Neon 20.18
3	11 **Na** Sodium 22.99	12 **Mg** Magnesium 24.31											13 **Al** Aluminum 26.98	14 **Si** Silicon 28.09	15 **P** Phosphorus 30.97	16 **S** Sulfur 32.07	17 **Cl** Chlorine 35.45	18 **Ar** Argon 39.95
4	19 **K** Potassium 39.10	20 **Ca** Calcium 40.08	21 **Sc** Scandium 44.96	22 **Ti** Titanium 47.87	23 **V** Vanadium 50.94	24 **Cr** Chromium 52.00	25 **Mn** Manganese 54.94	26 **Fe** Iron 55.85	27 **Co** Cobalt 58.93	28 **Ni** Nickel 58.69	29 **Cu** Copper 63.55	30 **Zn** Zinc 65.39	31 **Ga** Gallium 69.72	32 **Ge** Germanium 72.61	33 **As** Arsenic 74.92	34 **Se** Selenium 78.96	35 **Br** Bromine 79.90	36 **Kr** Krypton 83.80
5	37 **Rb** Rubidium 85.47	38 **Sr** Strontium 87.62	39 **Y** Yttrium 88.91	40 **Zr** Zirconium 91.22	41 **Nb** Niobium 92.91	42 **Mo** Molybdenum 95.94	43 **Tc** Technetium 98.00†	44 **Ru** Ruthenium 101.1	45 **Rh** Rhodium 102.9	46 **Pd** Palladium 106.4	47 **Ag** Silver 107.9	48 **Cd** Cadmium 112.4	49 **In** Indium 114.8	50 **Sn** Tin 118.7	51 **Sb** Antimony 121.8	52 **Te** Tellurium 127.6	53 **I** Iodine 126.9	54 **Xe** Xenon 131.3
6	55 **Cs** Cesium 132.9	56 **Ba** Barium 137.3	57 **La** * Lanthanum 138.9	72 **Hf** Hafnium 178.5	73 **Ta** Tantalum 180.9	74 **W** Tungsten 183.8	75 **Re** Rhenium 186.2	76 **Os** Osmium 190.2	77 **Ir** Iridium 192.2	78 **Pt** Platinum 195.1	79 **Au** Gold 197.0	80 **Hg** Mercury 200.6	81 **Tl** Thallium 204.4	82 **Pb** Lead 207.2	83 **Bi** Bismuth 209.0	84 **Po** Polonium 209†	85 **At** Astatine 210†	86 **Rn** Radon 222†
7	87 **Fr** Francium 223†	88 **Ra** Radium 226†	89 **Ac** ** Actinium 227†	104 **Rf** Rutherfordium 261†	105 **Db** Dubnium 262†	106 **Sg** Seaborgium 266†	107 **Bh** Bohrium 264†	108 **Hs** Hassium 277†	109 **Mt** Meitnerium 268†	110 **Ds** Darmstadtium 271†	111 **Rg** Roentgenium 272†	112 **Cn** Copernicium	113 **Uut**	114 **Fl** Flerovium	115 **Uup**	116 **Lv** Livermorium	117 **Uus**	118 **Uuo**

Transition Elements

Inner Transition Elements

Lanthanide Series * 6

58 **Ce** Cerium 140.1	59 **Pr** Praseodymium 140.9	60 **Nd** Neodymium 144.2	61 **Pm** Promethium 145†	62 **Sm** Samarium 150.4	63 **Eu** Europium 152.0	64 **Gd** Gadolinium 157.3	65 **Tb** Terbium 158.9	66 **Dy** Dysprosium 162.5	67 **Ho** Holmium 164.9	68 **Er** Erbium 167.3	69 **Tm** Thulium 168.9	70 **Yb** Ytterbium 173.0	71 **Lu** Lutetium 175.0

Actinide Series ** 7

90 **Th** Thorium 232.0	91 **Pa** Protactinium 231.0	92 **U** Uranium 238.0	93 **Np** Neptunium 237	94 **Pu** Plutonium 244†	95 **Am** Americium 243†	96 **Cm** Curium 247†	97 **Bk** Berkelium 247†	98 **Cf** Californium 251†	99 **Es** Einsteinium 252†	100 **Fm** Fermium 257†	101 **Md** Mendelevium 258†	102 **No** Nobelium 259†	103 **Lr** Lawrencium 262†

colors indicate placement of the outermost electrons
☐ s orbitals ☐ p orbitals ☐ d orbitals ☐ f orbitals

Atomic Masses of the Elements
Based on the 2005 IUPAC Table of Atomic Masses

Name	Symbol	Atomic Number	Atomic Mass	Name	Symbol	Atomic Number	Atomic Mass
Actinium*	Ac	89	227	Manganese	Mn	25	54.938049
Aluminum	Al	13	26.981538	Meitnerium*	Mt	109	268
Americium*	Am	95	243	Mendelevium*	Md	101	258
Antimony	Sb	51	121.760	Mercury	Hg	80	200.59
Argon	Ar	18	39.948	Molybdenum	Mo	42	95.94
Arsenic	As	33	74.92160	Neodymium	Nd	60	144.24
Astatine*	At	85	210	Neon	Ne	10	20.1797
Barium	Ba	56	137.327	Neptunium*	Np	93	237
Berkelium*	Bk	97	247	Nickel	Ni	28	58.6934
Beryllium	Be	4	9.012182	Niobium	Nb	41	92.90638
Bismuth	Bi	83	208.98038	Nitrogen	N	7	14.00674
Bohrium*	Bh	107	264	Nobelium*	No	102	259
Boron	B	5	10.811	Osmium	Os	76	190.23
Bromine	Br	35	79.904	Oxygen	O	8	15.9994
Cadmium	Cd	48	112.411	Palladium	Pd	46	106.42
Calcium	Ca	20	40.078	Phosphorus	P	15	30.973762
Californium*	Cf	98	251	Platinum	Pt	78	195.078
Carbon	C	6	12.0107	Plutonium*	Pu	94	244
Cerium	Ce	58	140.116	Polonium*	Po	84	209
Cesium	Cs	55	132.90545	Potassium	K	19	39.0983
Chlorine	Cl	17	35.4527	Praseodymium	Pr	59	140.90765
Chromium	Cr	24	51.9961	Promethium*	Pm	61	145
Cobalt	Co	27	58.933200	Protactinium	Pa	91	231.03588
Copernicium	Cn	112		Radium*	Ra	88	226
Copper	Cu	29	63.546	Radon*	Rn	86	222
Curium*	Cm	96	247	Rhenium	Re	75	186.207
Darmstadtium*	Ds	110	271	Rhodium	Rh	45	102.90550
Dubnium*	Db	105	262	Roentgenium*	Rg	111	272
Dysprosium	Dy	66	162.500	Rubidium	Rb	37	85.4678
Einsteinium*	Es	99	252	Ruthenium	Ru	44	101.07
Erbium	Er	68	167.26	Rutherfordium*	Rf	104	261
Europium	Eu	63	151.964	Samarium	Sm	62	150.36
Fermium*	Fm	100	257	Scandium	Sc	21	44.955910
Flerovium	Fl	114		Seaborgium*	Sg	106	266
Fluorine	F	9	18.9984032	Selenium	Se	34	78.96
Francium*	Fr	87	233	Silicon	Si	14	28.0855
Gadolinium	Gd	64	157.25	Silver	Ag	47	107.8682
Gallium	Ga	31	69.723	Sodium	Na	11	22.989770
Germanium	Ge	32	72.61	Strontium	Sr	38	87.62
Gold	Au	79	196.96655	Sulfur	S	16	32.066
Hafnium	Hf	72	178.49	Tantalum	Ta	73	180.9479
Hassium*	Hs	108	277	Technetium*	Tc	43	98
Helium	He	2	4.002602	Tellurium	Te	52	127.60
Holmium	Ho	67	164.93032	Terbium	Tb	65	158.92534
Hydrogen	H	1	1.00794	Thallium	Tl	81	204.3833
Indium	In	49	114.818	Thorium	Th	90	232.0381
Iodine	I	53	126.90447	Thulium	Tm	69	168.93421
Iridium	Ir	77	192.217	Tin	Sn	50	118.710
Iron	Fe	26	55.845	Titanium	Ti	22	47.867
Krypton	Kr	36	83.80	Tungsten	W	74	183.94
Lanthanum	La	57	138.9055	Uranium	U	92	238.0289
Lawrencium*	Lr	103	262	Vanadium	V	23	50.9415
Lead	Pb	82	207.2	Xenon	Xe	54	131.29
Lithium	Li	3	6.941	Ytterbium	Yb	70	173.04
Livermorium	Lv	116		Yttrium	Y	39	88.90585
Lutetium	Lu	71	174.967	Zinc	Zn	30	65.39
Magnesium	Mg	12	24.3050	Zirconium	Zr	40	91.224

*This element has no stable isotopes. The atomic mass given is that of the isotope with the longest known half-life.

The spectacular colors of the aurora borealis are the result of chemistry in our atmosphere.

© Stocktrek Images/SuperStock

CHAPTER **1**

AN INTRODUCTION TO CHEMISTRY

Do you know how the beautiful, intricate fireworks displays are created? Have you ever wondered how a tiny seedling can grow into a cornstalk taller than you in just one season? Perhaps you have been mesmerized by the flames in your fireplace on a romantic evening as they change color and form. And think of your relief when you dropped a container and found that it was plastic, not glass. These phenomena are the result of chemistry that occurs all around us, all the time. Chemical changes bring us beautiful colors, warmth, light, and products to make our lives function more smoothly. Understanding, explaining, and using the diversity of materials we find around us is what chemistry is all about.

1.1 THE NATURE OF CHEMISTRY

KEY TERM

chemistry

Key terms are highlighted in bold
to alert you to new terms defined
in the text.

A knowledge of chemistry is useful to virtually everyone—we see chemistry occurring around us every day. An understanding of chemistry is useful to engineers, teachers, health care professionals, attorneys, homemakers, business people, firefighters, and environmentalists, just to name a few. Even if you're not planning to work in any of these fields, chemistry is important and is used by us every day. Learning about the benefits and risks associated with chemicals will help you to be an informed citizen, able to make intelligent choices concerning the world around you. Studying chemistry teaches you to solve problems and communicate with others in an organized and logical manner. These skills will be helpful in college and throughout your career.

What is chemistry? One dictionary gives this definition: "**Chemistry** is the science of the composition, structure, properties, and reactions of matter, especially of atomic and molecular systems." Another, somewhat simpler definition is "Chemistry is the science dealing with the composition of *matter* and the changes in composition that matter undergoes." Neither of these definitions is entirely adequate. Chemistry and physics form a fundamental branch of knowledge. Chemistry is also closely related to biology, not only because living organisms are made of material substances but also because life itself is essentially a complicated system of interrelated chemical processes.

The scope of chemistry is extremely broad. It includes the whole universe and everything, animate and inanimate, in it. Chemistry is concerned with the composition and changes in the composition of matter and also with the energy and energy changes associated with matter. Through chemistry we seek to learn and to understand the general principles that govern the behavior of all matter.

The chemist, like other scientists, observes nature and attempts to understand its secrets: What makes a tulip red? Why is sugar sweet? What is occurring when iron rusts? Why is carbon monoxide poisonous? Problems such as these—some of which have been solved, some of which are still to be solved—are all part of what we call chemistry.

A chemist may interpret natural phenomena, devise experiments that reveal the composition and structure of complex substances, study methods for improving natural processes, or synthesize substances. Ultimately, the efforts of successful chemists advance the frontiers of knowledge and at the same time contribute to the well-being of humanity.

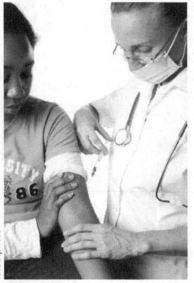

iStockphoto

A health care professional needs
to understand chemistry in order
to administer the correct dose of
medication.

Thinking Like a Chemist

Chemists take a special view of things in order to understand the nature of the chemical changes taking place. Chemists "look inside" everyday objects to see how the basic components are behaving. To understand this approach, let's consider a lake. When we view the lake from a distance, we get an overall picture of the water and shoreline. This overall view is called the *macroscopic* picture.

As we approach the lake we begin to see more details—rocks, sandy beach, plants submerged in the water, and aquatic life. We get more and more curious. What makes the rocks and sand? What kind of organisms live in the water? How do plants survive underwater? What lies hidden in the water? We can use a microscope to learn the answers to some of these questions. Within the water and the plants, we can see single cells and inside them organelles working to keep the organisms alive. For answers to other questions, we need to go even further inside the lake. A drop of lake water can itself become a mysterious and fascinating *microscopic* picture full of molecules and motion. (See **Figure 1.1**.) A chemist looks into the world of atoms and molecules and their motions. Chemistry makes

Image Source/SuperStock

Figure 1.1

Inside a drop of lake water we find water molecules,
some dissolved substances.

the connection between the *microscopic* world of molecules and the *macroscopic* world of everyday objects.

Think about the water in the lake. On the surface it has beauty and colors, and it gently laps the shore of the lake. What is the microscopic nature of water? It is composed of tiny molecules represented as

In this case H represents a hydrogen atom and O an oxygen atom. The water molecule is represented by H_2O since it is made up of two hydrogen atoms and one oxygen atom.

EXAMPLE 1.1

You are given eight oxygen atoms and fifteen hydrogen atoms. How many water molecules can you make from them?

SOLUTION

From the model shown above for a water molecule you can see that one molecule of water contains one atom of oxygen and two atoms of hydrogen. Using this model as reference, you can make eight water molecules from eight oxygen atoms. But you can make only seven water molecules from fifteen hydrogen atoms with one H atom and one O atom left over. The answer is seven water molecules.

PRACTICE 1.1

You are given ten hydrogen atoms and eight oxygen atoms. How many water molecules can you make from them?

1.2 A SCIENTIFIC APPROACH TO PROBLEM SOLVING

Describe the steps involved in the scientific method.

● LEARNING OBJECTIVE

KEY TERMS
scientific method
hypothesis
theory
scientific laws

One of the most common and important things we do every day is to solve problems. For example,

- You have two exams and a laboratory report due on Monday. How should you divide your time?
- You leave for school and learn from the radio that there is a big accident on the freeway. What is your fastest alternate route to avoid the traffic problem?
- You need to buy groceries, mail some packages, attend your child's soccer game, and pick up the dry cleaning. What is the most efficient sequence of events?

We all face these kinds of problems and decisions. A logical approach can be useful for solving daily problems:

1. Define the problem. We first need to recognize we have a problem and state it clearly, including all the known information. When we do this in science, we call it *making an observation.*

2. Propose possible solutions to the problem. In science this is called making a *hypothesis.*

3. Decide which is the best way to proceed or solve the problem. In daily life we use our memory of past experiences to help us. In the world of science we *perform an experiment.*

Using a scientific approach to problem solving is worthwhile. It helps in all parts of your life whether you plan to be a scientist, doctor, business person, or writer.

>CHEMISTRY *IN ACTION*

Egyptians, the First Medicinal Chemists

Look at any images of the ancient Egyptians and notice the black eyeliner commonly worn at that time. As chemists analyzed the composition of a sample of this eyeliner in the antiquities collection at the Louvre Museum in Paris, they were appalled to discover the high concentration of lead in the samples. Today lead is routinely removed from most consumer products because it is very toxic even in low concentrations. It is toxic to many organs and can cause symptoms such as abdominal pain, dementia, anemia, seizures, and even death. It turns out the lead compounds found in the Egyptian eyeliner are not found in nature but must be synthesized. The synthesis of these lead salts is complicated and the products are not lustrous. This led chemists to question why the Egyptians would add these compounds to their eyeliner. The answer was revealed after reading some of the ancient manuscripts from

that time. Lead salts were synthesized for use in treating eye ailments, scars, and discolorations. So even if the lead salts were not the best ingredients for beauty, they were added for the perceived health benefits.

Since we now know that lead compounds are very toxic, Christian Amatore, an analytical chemist at the Ecole Normale Supérieure in Paris, wondered if the lead compounds in Egyptian eyeliner could have actually conferred any health benefits. He introduced lead salts into samples of human tissue growing in the laboratory and observed that the cells began forming compounds that trigger an immune response. Perhaps the ancient Egyptians did know something about medicinal chemistry after all. So should we follow the Egyptians example and add lead to our cosmetics? This is probably not a good idea because the risks associated with prolonged lead exposure outweigh the benefits.

age fotostock/SuperStock

Terra cotta sculpture of Nefertiti

Scott Bauer/Courtesy USDA

Scientists employ the scientific method every day in their laboratory work.

The Scientific Method

Chemists work together and also with other scientists to solve problems. As scientists conduct studies they ask many questions, and their questions often lead in directions that are not part of the original problem. The amazing developments from chemistry and technology usually involve what we call the **scientific method**, which can generally be described as follows:

1. **Collect the facts or data** that are relevant to the problem or question at hand. This is usually done by planned experimentation. The data are then analyzed to find trends or regularities that are pertinent to the problem.
2. **Formulate a hypothesis** that will account for the data and that can be tested by further experimentation.
3. **Plan and do additional experiments to test the hypothesis.**
4. **Modify the hypothesis** as necessary so that it is compatible with all the pertinent data.

Confusion sometimes arises regarding the exact meanings of the words *hypothesis*, *theory*, and *law*. A **hypothesis** is a tentative explanation of certain facts that provides a basis for further experimentation. A well-established hypothesis is often called a **theory** or model. Thus, a theory is an explanation of the general principles of certain phenomena with considerable evidence or facts to support it. Hypotheses and theories explain natural phenomena, whereas **scientific laws** are simple statements of natural phenomena to which no exceptions are known under the given conditions.

These four steps are a broad outline of the general procedure that is followed in most scientific work, but they are not a "recipe" for doing chemistry or any other science (**Figure 1.2**). Chemistry is an experimental science, however, and much of its progress has been due to application of the scientific method through systematic research.

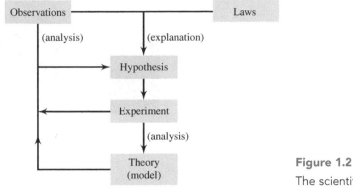

Figure 1.2
The scientific method.

We study many theories and laws in chemistry; this makes our task as students easier because theories and laws summarize important aspects of the sciences. Certain theories and models advanced by great scientists in the past have since been substantially altered and modified. Such changes do not mean that the discoveries of the past are any less significant. Modification of existing theories and models in the light of new experimental evidence is essential to the growth and evolution of scientific knowledge. Science is dynamic.

1.3 THE PARTICULATE NATURE OF MATTER

Describe the characteristics of matter, including the states of matter.

● **LEARNING OBJECTIVE**

The entire universe consists of matter and energy. Every day we come into contact with countless kinds of matter. Air, food, water, rocks, soil, glass, and this book are all different types of matter. Broadly defined, **matter** is *anything* that has mass and occupies space.

Matter may be quite invisible. For example, if an apparently empty test tube is submerged mouth downward in a beaker of water, the water rises only slightly into the tube. The water cannot rise further because the tube is filled with invisible matter: air (see **Figure 1.3**).

To the macroscopic eye, matter appears to be continuous and unbroken. We are impressed by the great diversity of matter. Given its many forms, it is difficult to believe that on a microscopic level all of matter is composed of discrete, tiny, fundamental particles called *atoms* (**Figure 1.4**). It is truly amazing to understand that the fundamental particles in ice cream are very similar to the particles in air that we breathe. Matter is actually discontinuous and is composed of discrete, tiny particles called *atoms*.

KEY TERMS

matter
solid
amorphous
liquid
gas

Figure 1.3

An apparently empty test tube is submerged, mouth downward, in water. Only a small volume of water rises into the tube, which is actually filled with invisible matter–air.

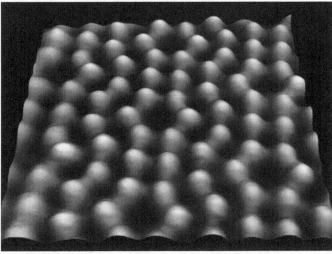

© Andrew Dunn/Alamy

Figure 1.4

Silicon atoms on a silicon chip produced this image using a scanning tunneling microscope.

Figure 1.5

The three states of matter.
(a) Solid—water molecules are held together rigidly and are very close to each other.
(b) Liquid—water molecules are close together but are free to move around and slide over each other. (c) Gas—water molecules are far apart and move freely and randomly.

Solid (Ice)
(a)

Liquid (Water)
(b)

Gas (Steam)
(c)

Physical States of Matter

Crystalline solid

Amorphous solid

Matter exists in three physical states: solid, liquid, and gas (see **Figure 1.5**). A **solid** has a definite shape and volume, with particles that cling rigidly to one another. The shape of a solid can be independent of its container. In Figure 1.5a we see water in its solid form. Another example, a crystal of sulfur, has the same shape and volume whether it is placed in a beaker or simply laid on a glass plate.

Most commonly occurring solids, such as salt, sugar, quartz, and metals, are *crystalline*. The particles that form crystalline materials exist in regular, repeating, three-dimensional, geometric patterns (see **Figure 1.6**). Some solids such as plastics, glass, and gels do not have any regular, internal geometric pattern. Such solids are called **amorphous** solids. (*Amorphous* means "without shape or form.")

A **liquid** has a definite volume but not a definite shape, with particles that stick firmly but not rigidly. Although the particles are held together by strong attractive forces and are in close contact with one another, they are able to move freely. Particle mobility gives a liquid fluidity and causes it to take the shape of the container in which it is stored. Note how water looks as a liquid in Figure 1.5b.

A **gas** has indefinite volume and no fixed shape, with particles that move independently of one another. Particles in the gaseous state have gained enough energy to overcome the attractive forces that held them together as liquids or solids. A gas presses continuously in all directions on the walls of any container. Because of this quality, a gas completely fills a container. The particles of a gas are relatively far apart compared with those of solids and liquids. The actual volume of the gas particles is very small compared with the volume of the space occupied by the gas. Observe the large space between the water molecules in Figure 1.5c compared to ice and liquid water. A gas therefore may be compressed into a very small volume or expanded almost indefinitely. Liquids cannot be compressed to any great extent, and solids are even less compressible than liquids.

If a bottle of ammonia solution is opened in one corner of the laboratory, we can soon smell its familiar odor in all parts of the room. The ammonia gas escaping from the solution demonstrates that gaseous particles move freely and rapidly and tend to permeate the entire area into which they are released.

Figure 1.6

A large crystal of table salt. A salt crystal is composed of a three-dimensional array of particles.

Na⁺ Cl⁻

Although matter is discontinuous, attractive forces exist that hold the particles together and give matter its appearance of continuity. These attractive forces are strongest in solids, giving them rigidity; they are weaker in liquids but still strong enough to hold liquids to definite volumes. In gases, the attractive forces are so weak that the particles of a gas are practically independent of one another. Table 1.1 lists common materials that exist as solids, liquids, and gases. Table 1.2 compares the properties of solids, liquids, and gases.

TABLE 1.1 Common Materials in the Solid, Liquid, and Gaseous States of Matter

Solids	Liquids	Gases
Aluminum	Alcohol	Acetylene
Copper	Blood	Air
Gold	Gasoline	Butane
Polyethylene	Honey	Carbon dioxide
Salt	Mercury	Chlorine
Sand	Oil	Helium
Steel	Vinegar	Methane
Sulfur	Water	Oxygen

TABLE 1.2 Physical Properties of Solids, Liquids, and Gases

State	Shape	Volume	Particles	Compressibility
Solid	Definite	Definite	Rigidly clinging; tightly packed	Very slight
Liquid	Indefinite	Definite	Mobile; adhering	Slight
Gas	Indefinite	Indefinite	Independent of each other and relatively far apart	High

1.4 CLASSIFYING MATTER

Distinguish among a pure substance, a homogeneous mixture, and a heterogeneous mixture.

● LEARNING OBJECTIVE

KEY TERMS
substance
homogeneous
heterogeneous
phase
system
mixture

The term *matter* refers to all materials that make up the universe. Many thousands of distinct kinds of matter exist. A **substance** is a particular kind of matter with a definite, fixed composition. Sometimes known as *pure substances*, substances are either elements or compounds. Familiar examples of elements are copper, gold, and oxygen. Familiar compounds are salt, sugar, and water. We'll discuss elements and compounds in more detail in Chapter 3.

We classify a sample of matter as either *homogeneous or heterogeneous* by examining it. **Homogeneous** matter is uniform in appearance and has the same properties throughout. Matter consisting of two or more physically distinct phases is **heterogeneous**. A **phase** is a homogeneous part of a system separated from other parts by physical boundaries. A **system** is simply the body of matter under consideration. Whenever we have a system in which visible boundaries exist between the parts or components, that system has more than one phase and is heterogeneous. It does not matter whether these components are in the solid, liquid, or gaseous states.

A pure substance may exist as different phases in a heterogeneous system. Ice floating in water, for example, is a two-phase system made up of solid water and liquid water. The water in each phase is homogeneous in composition, but because two phases are present, the system is heterogeneous.

A **mixture** is a material containing two or more substances and can be either heterogeneous or homogeneous. Mixtures are variable in composition. If we add a spoonful of sugar to a glass of water, a heterogeneous mixture is formed immediately. The two phases are a solid (sugar) and a liquid (water). But upon stirring, the sugar dissolves to form a homogeneous mixture or solution.

(a) Water is the liquid in the beaker, and the white solid in the spoon is sugar. (b) Sugar can be dissolved in the water to produce a solution.

(a)   (b)

Both substances are still present: All parts of the solution are sweet and wet. The proportions of sugar and water can be varied simply by adding more sugar and stirring to dissolve. Solutions do not have to be liquid. For example, air is a homogeneous mixture of gases. Solid solutions also exist. Brass is a homogeneous solution of copper and zinc.

Many substances do not form homogeneous mixtures. If we mix sugar and fine white sand, a heterogeneous mixture is formed. Careful examination may be needed to decide that the mixture is heterogeneous because the two phases (sugar and sand) are both white solids. Ordinary matter exists mostly as mixtures. If we examine soil, granite, iron ore, or other naturally occurring mineral deposits, we find them to be heterogeneous mixtures. **Figure 1.7** illustrates the relationships of substances and mixtures.

Flowcharts can help you to visualize the connections between concepts.

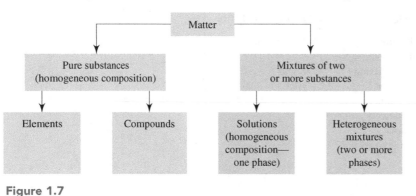

Figure 1.7

Classification of matter. A pure substance is always homogeneous in composition, whereas a mixture always contains two or more substances and may be either homogeneous or heterogeneous.

Distinguishing Mixtures from Pure Substances

Single substances—elements or compounds—seldom occur naturally in a pure state. Air is a mixture of gases; seawater is a mixture of a variety of dissolved minerals; ordinary soil is a complex mixture of minerals and various organic materials.

Mixture

1. A mixture always contains two or more substances that can be present in varying amounts.

2. The components of a mixture do not lose their identities and may be separated by physical means.

Pure Substance

1. A pure substance (element or compound) always has a definite composition by mass.

2. The elements in a compound lose their identities and may be separated only by chemical means.

PRACTICE 1.2

Which of the following is a mixture and which is a pure substance? Explain your answer.

(a) vinegar (4% acetic acid and 96% water)
(b) sodium chloride (salt) solution
(c) gold
(d) milk

How is a mixture distinguished from a pure substance? A mixture always contains two or more substances that can be present in varying concentrations. Let's consider two examples.

Homogeneous Mixture Homogeneous mixtures (solutions) containing either 5% or 10% salt in water can be prepared simply by mixing the correct amounts of salt and water. These mixtures can be separated by boiling away the water, leaving the salt as a residue.

Heterogeneous Mixture The composition of a heterogeneous mixture of sulfur crystals and iron filings can be varied by merely blending in either more sulfur or more iron filings. This mixture can be separated physically by using a magnet to attract the iron.

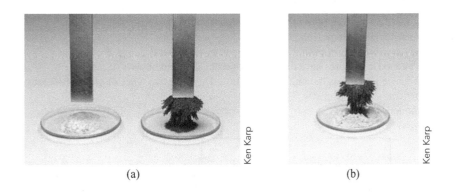

(a)   (b)

(a) When iron and sulfur exist as pure substances, only the iron is attracted to a magnet. (b) A mixture of iron and sulfur can be separated by using the difference in magnetic attraction.

CHAPTER **1 REVIEW**

1.1 THE NATURE OF CHEMISTRY

- Chemistry is important to everyone because chemistry occurs all around us in our daily lives.
- Chemistry is the science dealing with matter and the changes in composition that matter undergoes.
- Chemists seek to understand the general principles governing the behavior of all matter.
- Chemistry "looks inside" ordinary objects to study how their components behave.
- Chemistry connects the macroscopic and microscopic worlds.

KEY TERM

chemistry

1.2 A SCIENTIFIC APPROACH TO PROBLEM SOLVING

- Scientific thinking helps us solve problems in our daily lives.
- General steps for solving problems include:
    - Defining the problem
    - Proposing possible solutions
    - Solving the problem
- The scientific method is a procedure for processing information in which we:
    - Collect the facts
    - Formulate a hypothesis
    - Plan and do experiments
    - Modify the hypothesis if necessary

KEY TERMS

scientific method
hypothesis
theory
scientific laws

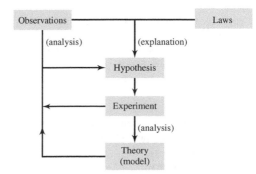

1.3 THE PARTICULATE NATURE OF MATTER

KEY TERMS

matter
solid
amorphous
liquid
gas

• Matter is anything with the following two characteristics:
  • Has mass
  • Occupies space
• On the macroscopic level matter appears continuous.
• On the microscopic level matter is discontinuous and composed of atoms.
• Solid—rigid substance with a definite shape
• Liquid—fluid substance with a definite volume that takes the shape of its container
• Gas—takes the shape and volume of its container

1.4 CLASSIFYING MATTER

KEY TERMS

substance
homogeneous
heterogeneous
phase
system
mixture

• Matter can be classified as a pure substance or a mixture.
• A mixture has variable composition:
  • Homogeneous mixtures have the same properties throughout.
  • Heterogeneous mixtures have different properties in different parts of the system.
• A pure substance always has the same composition. There are two types of pure substances:
  • Elements
  • Compounds

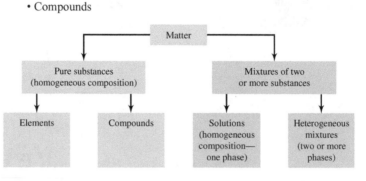

REVIEW QUESTIONS

1. Explain the difference between
   (a) a hypothesis and a theory
   (b) a theory and a scientific law
2. Consider each of the following statements and determine whether it represents an observation, a hypothesis, a theory, or a scientific law:
   (a) The battery in my watch must be dead since it is no longer keeping time.
   (b) My computer must have a virus since it is not working properly.
   (c) The air feels cool.
   (d) The candle burns more brightly in pure oxygen than in air because oxygen supports combustion.
   (e) My sister wears red quite often.
   (f) A pure substance has a definite, fixed composition.
3. Determine whether each of the following statements refers to a solid, a liquid, or a gas:
   (a) It has a definite volume but not a definite shape.
   (b) It has an indefinite volume and high compressibility.
   (c) It has a definite shape.
   (d) It has an indefinite shape and slight compressibility.
4. Some solids have a crystalline structure, while others have an amorphous structure. For each of the following 5 descriptions, determine whether it refers to a crystalline solid or an amorphous solid:
   (a) has a regular repeating pattern
   (b) plastic
   (c) has no regular repeating pattern
   (d) glass
   (e) gold

5. Define a phase.
6. How many phases are present in the graduated cylinder?
7. What is another name for a homogeneous mixture?
8. Which liquids listed in Table 1.1 are not mixtures?
9. Which of the gases listed in Table 1.1 are not pure substances?
10. When the stopper is removed from a partly filled bottle containing solid and liquid acetic acid at 16.7°C, a strong vinegar-like odor is noticeable immediately. How many acetic acid phases must be present in the bottle? Explain.
11. Is the system enclosed in the bottle in Question 10 homogeneous or heterogeneous? Explain.
12. Is a system that contains only one substance necessarily homogeneous? Explain.
13. Is a system that contains two or more substances necessarily heterogeneous? Explain.
14. Distinguish between homogeneous and heterogeneous mixtures.
15. Which of the following are pure substances?
    (a) sugar   (d) maple syrup
    (b) sand   (e) eggs
    (c) gold
16. Use the steps of the scientific method to help determine the reason that your cell phone has suddenly stopped working:
    (a) observation   (c) experiment
    (b) hypothesis   (d) theory

Richard Megna/ Fundamental Photographs

Most of the exercises in this chapter are available for assignment via the online homework management program, WileyPLUS (www.wileyplus.com)
All exercises with blue numbers have answers in Appendix VI.

PAIRED EXERCISES

1. Refer to the illustration and determine which state(s) of matter are present.

3. Look at the photo and determine whether it represents a homogeneous or heterogeneous mixture.

Richard Megna/Fundamental Photographs

5. For each of the following mixtures, state whether it is homogeneous or heterogeneous:
(a) tap water
(b) carbonated beverage
(c) oil and vinegar salad dressing
(d) people in a football stadium

2. Refer to the illustration and determine which states(s) of matter are present.

4. Look at the maple leaf below and determine whether it represents a homogeneous or heterogeneous mixture.

© Justin Horrocks/iStockphoto

6. For each of the following mixtures, state whether it is homogeneous or heterogeneous:
(a) stainless steel
(b) motor oil
(c) soil
(d) a tree

ADDITIONAL EXERCISES

7. At home, check your kitchen and bathroom cabinets for five different substances; then read the labels and list the first ingredient of each.

8. During the first week of a new semester, consider that you have enrolled in five different classes, each of which meets for 3 hours per week. For every 1 hour that is spent in class, a minimum of 1 hour is required

outside of class to complete assignments and study for exams. You also work 20 hours per week, and it takes you 1 hour to drive to the job site and back home. On Friday nights, you socialize with your friends. You are fairly certain that you will be able to successfully complete the semester with good grades. Show how the steps in the scientific method can help you predict the outcome of the semester.

Use the following food label to answer Exercises 9–10.

Nutrition Facts	Amount/serving	%DV*	Amount/serving	%DV*
Serv. Size 1 cup (249g)	Total Fat 12g	18%	Sodium 940mg	39%
	Sat. Fat 6g	30%	Total Carb. 24g	8%
Servings About 3	Polyunsat. Fat 1.5g		Dietary Fiber 1g	4%
Calories 250 Fat Cal. 110	Monounsat. Fat 2.5g		Sugars 1g	
*Percent Daily Values (DV) are based on a 2,000 calorie diet.	Cholest. 60mg	20%	Protein 10g	20%
	Vitamin A 0% • Vitamin C 0% • Calcium 6% • Iron 8%			

INGREDIENTS: WATER, CHICKEN STOCK, ENRICHED PASTA (SEMOLINA WHEAT FLOUR, EGG WHITE SOLIDS, NIACIN, IRON, THIAMINE MONONITRATE [VITAMIN B1], RIBOFLAVIN [VITAMIN B2] AND FOLIC ACID), CREAM (DERIVED FROM MILK), CHICKEN, CONTAINS LESS THAN 2% OF: CHEESES (GRANULAR, PARMESAN AND ROMANO PASTE [PASTERURIZED COW'S MILK, CULTURES, SALT, ENZYMES], WATER, SALT, LACTIC ACID, CITRIC ACID AND DISODIUM PHOSPHATE), BUTTER (PASTERURIZED SWEET CREAM [DERIVED FROM MILK] AND SALT), MODIFIED CORN STARCH, SALT, WHOLE EGG SOLIDS, SUGAR, RICE STARCH, GARLIC, SPICE, XANTHAM GUM, MUSTARD FLOUR, ISOLATED SOY PROTEIN AND SODIUM PHOSPHATE.

9. Identify the following ingredients as either a pure substance or a mixture.
   (a) water
   (b) chicken stock (the liquid that remains in the pot after cooking the chicken)
   (c) salt
   (d) mustard flour

10. Using the food label, make a hypothesis regarding the nutritional quality of this food. Propose a way to determine whether your hypothesis is valid.

11. Read the following passage (from *Science News*) and identify the observation and hypothesis.

    Could an invisibility cloak, like the one used by Harry Potter, really exist? For scientists in Cambridge, Massachusetts, it may be a reality. Researchers at MIT have developed an invisibility cloak for small objects such as an ant or a grain of sand. Calcite crystals have the ability to reflect light around an object, rendering it invisible, or at least "unseeable." If a larger crystal were to be used, it should be able to hide larger objects. The invisibility cloak works only with laser light aimed directly at the crystal. Future work will improve the effectiveness of these invisibility cloaks.

12. Various chemical elements are pictured. For each one a microscopic view is also shown. Determine the number of phases for each substance below and identify them.
    (a) iodine

© 2001 Richard Megna/ Fundamental Photographs

(b) bromine

© 1995 Richard Megna/ Fundamental Photographs

(c) sulfur

Stocktrek Images/Richard Roscoe/Getty Images, Inc.

ANSWERS TO PRACTICE EXERCISES

1.1 five water molecules: H_2O, H_2O, H_2O, H_2O, H_2O

1.2 (a) mixture; concentration can be changed by adding more acetic acid or more water. (b) mixture; concentration can be changed by adding more or less salt. (c) pure substance; gold is 100% gold. (d) mixture; milk contains several substances.

Careful and accurate measurements for each ingredient are essential when baking or cooking as well as in the chemistry laboratory.

Blend Images/SuperStock

CHAPTER **2**

STANDARDS FOR MEASUREMENT

D oing an experiment in chemistry is very much like cooking a meal in the kitchen. It's important to know the ingredients and the amounts of each in order to have a tasty product. Working on your car requires specific tools in exact sizes. Buying new carpeting or draperies is an exercise in precise and accurate measurement for a good fit. A small difference in the concentration or amount of medication a pharmacist gives you may have significant effects on your well-being. As we saw in Chapter 1, observation is an important part of the scientific process. Observations can be *qualitative* (the substance is a blue solid) or *quantitative* (the mass of the substance is 4.7 grams). A quantitative observation is called a **measurement**. Both a number and a unit are required for a measurement. For example, at home in your kitchen measuring 3 flour is not possible. We need to know the unit on the 3. Is it cups, grams, or tablespoons? A measurement of 3 cups tells us both the amount and the size of the measurement. In this chapter we will discuss measurements and the rules for calculations using these measurements.

2.1 SCIENTIFIC NOTATION

LEARNING OBJECTIVE ● Write decimal numbers in scientific notation.

KEY TERMS

measurement
scientific notation

Scientists often use numbers that are very large or very small in **measurements**. For example, the Earth's age is estimated to be about 4,500,000 (4.5 billion) years. Numbers like these are bulky to write, so to make them more compact scientists use powers of 10. Writing a number as the product of a number between 1 and 10 multiplied by 10 raised to some power is called **scientific notation**.

To learn how to write a number in scientific notation, let's consider the number 2468. To write this number in scientific notation:

1. Move the decimal point in the original number so that it is located after the first nonzero digit.

$$2468 \rightarrow 2.468 \qquad \text{(decimal moves three places to the left)}$$

2. Multiply this new number by 10 raised to the proper exponent (power). The proper exponent is equal to the number of places that the decimal point was moved.

$$2.468 \times 10^3$$

3. The sign on the exponent indicates the direction the decimal was moved.

$$\text{moved right} \rightarrow \text{negative exponent}$$

$$\text{moved left} \rightarrow \text{positive exponent}$$

Examples show you problem-solving techniques in a step-by-step form. Study each one and then try the Practice Exercises.

EXAMPLE 2.1

Write 5283 in scientific notation.

SOLUTION   5283.   Place the decimal between the 5 and the 2. Since the decimal was moved three places to the left, the power of 10 will be 3 and the number 5.283 is multiplied by 10^3.

$$5.283 \times 10^3$$

EXAMPLE 2.2

Write 4,500,000,000 in scientific notation (two digits).

SOLUTION   4 500 000 000.   Place the decimal between the 4 and the 5. Since the decimal was moved nine places to the left, the power of 10 will be 9 and the number 4.5 is multiplied by 10^9.

$$4.5 \times 10^9$$

Scientific notation is a useful way to write very large numbers, such as the distance between the Earth and the moon, or very small numbers, such as the length of these *E. coli* bacteria (shown here as a colored scanning electron micrograph $\times$ 14,000).

NASA

Dr. Gopal Murti/Photo Researchers, Inc.

EXAMPLE 2.3

Write 0.000123 in scientific notation.

SOLUTION   0.000123   Place the decimal between the 1 and the 2. Since the deci-
4   mal was moved four places to the right, the power of 10
will be -4 and the number 1.23 is multiplied by 10^{-4}.

1.23×10^{-4}

PRACTICE 2.1

Write the following numbers in scientific notation:

(a) 1200 (four digits)   (c) 0.0468
(b) 6,600,000 (two digits)   (d) 0.00003

Answers to Practice Exercises are
found at the end of each chapter.

2.2 MEASUREMENT AND UNCERTAINTY

Explain the significance of uncertainty in measurement in chemistry and how
significant figures are used to indicate a measurement's certainty.

● **LEARNING OBJECTIVE**

To understand chemistry, it is necessary to set up and solve problems. Problem solving requires
an understanding of the mathematical operations used to manipulate numbers. Measurements
are made in an experiment, and chemists use these data to calculate the extent of the physical and chemical changes occurring in the substances that are being studied. By appropriate
calculations, an experiment's results can be compared with those of other experiments and
summarized in ways that are meaningful.

A measurement is expressed by a numerical value together with a unit of that measurement.
For example,

KEY TERM
significant figures

A measurement always
requires a unit.

┌─ numerical value ─┐
70.0 kilograms $=$ 154 pounds
└──── unit ────┘

Whenever a measurement is made with an instrument
such as a thermometer or ruler, an estimate is required. We
can illustrate this by measuring temperature. Suppose we
measure temperature on a thermometer calibrated in degrees
and observe that the mercury stops between 21 and 22 (see
Figure 2.1a). We then know that the temperature is at least
21 degrees and is less than 22 degrees. To express the temperature with one more digit, we estimate that the mercury
is about two-tenths the distance between 21 and 22. The
temperature is therefore 21.2 degrees. The last digit (2) has
some uncertainty because it is an estimated value. Because
the last digit has some uncertainty (we made a visual estimate), it may be different when another person makes the
same measurement. If three more people make this same
reading, the results might be

Person	Measurement
1	21.2
2	21.3
3	21.1
4	21.2

(a)	(b)	(c)
21.2°C	22.0°C	22.11°C
precise to 0.1°C	precise to 0.1°C	precise to 0.01°C

Figure 2.1

Measuring temperature (°C) with various degrees of precision.

Notice that the first two digits of the measurements did not change (they are *certain*). The last digit in these measurements is *uncertain*. The custom in science is to record all of the certain digits and the first uncertain digit.

Numbers obtained from a measurement are never exact values. They always have some degree of uncertainty due to the limitations of the measuring instrument and the skill of the individual making the measurement. It is customary when recording a measurement to include all the digits that are known plus one digit that is estimated. This last estimated digit introduces some uncertainty. Because of this uncertainty, every number that expresses a measurement can have only a limited number of digits. These digits, used to express a measured quantity, are known as **significant figures**.

Now let's return to our temperature measurements. In Figure 2.1a the temperature is recorded as 21.2 degrees and is said to have three significant figures. If the mercury stopped exactly on the 22 (Figure 2.1b), the temperature would be recorded as 22.0 degrees. The zero is used to indicate that the temperature was estimated to a precision of one-tenth degree. Finally, look at Figure 2.1c. On this thermometer, the temperature is recorded as 22.11°C (four significant figures). Since the thermometer is calibrated to tenths of a degree, the first estimated digit is the hundredths.

EXAMPLE 2.4

The length of a ballpoint pen was recorded by three students as 14.30 cm, 14.33 cm, and 14.34 cm.

(a) What are the estimated digits in these measurements?
(b) How many figures are certain?

SOLUTION

(a) The estimated digits are 0, 3, and 4, respectively.
(b) Three figures are certain in each measurement

PRACTICE 2.2

Three measurements for the boiling point of water are 100.4°C, 100.1°C, and 100.0°C. The accepted boiling point is 100.0°C.

(a) What are the estimated digits?
(b) How many figures are certain?

2.3 SIGNIFICANT FIGURES

LEARNING OBJECTIVE • Determine the number of significant figures in a given measurement and round measurements to a specific number of significant figures.

KEY TERM
rounding off numbers

Because all measurements involve uncertainty, we must use the proper number of significant figures in each measurement. In chemistry we frequently do calculations involving measurements, so we must understand what happens when we do arithmetic on numbers containing uncertainties. We'll learn several rules for doing these calculations and figuring out how many significant figures to have in the result. You will need to follow these rules throughout the calculations in this text.

The first thing we need to learn is how to determine how many significant figures are in a number.

RULES FOR COUNTING SIGNIFICANT FIGURES

1. *Nonzero digits.* All nonzero digits are significant.

2. *Exact numbers.* Some numbers are exact and have an infinite number of significant figures. Exact numbers occur in simple counting operations; when you count 25 dollars, you have exactly 25 dollars. Defined numbers, such as

12 inches in 1 foot, 60 minutes in 1 hour, and 100 centimeters in 1 meter, are also considered to be exact numbers. Exact numbers have no uncertainty.

3. *Zeros.* A zero is *significant* when it is

Rules for significant figures should be memorized for use throughout the text.

- between nonzero digits:

  205 has three significant figures (2, 0, 5)

  2.05 has three significant figures (2, 0, 5)

  61.09 has four significant figures (6, 1, 0, 9)

- at the end of a number that includes a decimal point:

  0.500 has three significant figures (5, 0, 0)

  25.160 has five significant figures (2, 5, 1, 6, 0)

  3.00 has three significant figures (3, 0, 0)

  20. has two significant figures (2, 0)

A zero is *not significant* when it is

- before the first nonzero digit. These zeros are used to locate a decimal point:

  0.0025 has two significant figures (2, 5)

  0.0108 has three significant figures (1, 0, 8)

- at the end of a number without a decimal point:

  1000 has one significant figure (1)

  590 has two significant figures (5, 9)

One way of indicating that these zeros are significant is to write the number using scientific notation. Thus if the value 1000 has been determined to four significant figures, it is written as 1.000×10^3. If 590 has only two significant figures, it is written as 5.9×10^2.

EXAMPLE 2.5

How many significant figures are in each of the following measurements?

(a) 45 apples
(b) 0.02050 cm
(c) 3500 ft

SOLUTION

(a) The number is exact and has no uncertainty associated with it (Rule 2).
(b) Four significant figures. The zeroes before the 2 are not significant, the 2 is significant, the zero between the 2 and the 5 is significant, the 5 is significant, and the final zero is significant.
(c) Two significant figures. The zeroes at the end of a number without a decimal point are not significant.

PRACTICE 2.3

How many significant figures are in each of these measurements?

(a) 4.5 inches
(b) 3.025 feet
(c) 125.0 meters
(d) 0.001 mile

(e) 25.0 grams
(f) 12.20 liters
(g) 100,000 people
(h) 205 birds

Rounding Off Numbers

When we do calculations on a calculator, we often obtain answers that have more digits than are justified. It is therefore necessary to drop the excess digits in order to express the answer with the proper number of significant figures. When digits are dropped from a number, the value of the last digit retained is determined by a process known as **rounding off numbers**. Two rules will be used in this book for rounding off numbers.

Not all schools use the same rules for rounding. Check with your instructor for variations in these rules.

RULES FOR ROUNDING OFF

1. When the first digit after those you want to retain is 4 or less, that digit and all others to its right are dropped. The last digit retained is not changed. The following examples are rounded off to four digits:

74.693 = 74.69   1.00629 = 1.006
This digit is dropped.   These two digits are dropped.

2. When the first digit after those you want to retain is 5 or greater, that digit and all others to the right are dropped and the last digit retained is increased by one. These examples are rounded off to four digits:

1.026868 = 1.027   18.02500 = 18.03
These three digits are dropped.   These three digits are dropped.
This digit is changed to 7.   This digit is changed to 3.

12.899 = 12.90
This digit is dropped.
These two digits are changed to 90.

PRACTICE 2.4

Round off these numbers to the number of significant figures indicated:

(a) 42.246 (four)   (d) 0.08965 (two)
(b) 88.015 (three)   (e) 225.3 (three)
(c) 0.08965 (three)   (f) 14.150 (three)

2.4 SIGNIFICANT FIGURES IN CALCULATIONS

LEARNING OBJECTIVE ● Apply the rules for significant figures, in calculations involving addition, subtraction, multiplication, and division.

The results of a calculation based on measurements cannot be more precise than the least precise measurement.

Multiplication or Division

In calculations involving multiplication or division, the answer must contain the same number of significant figures as in the measurement that has the least number of significant figures. Consider the following examples:

Use your calculator to check your work in the examples. Compare your results to be sure you understand the mathematics.

EXAMPLE 2.6

(190.6)(2.3) = 438.38

SOLUTION
The value 438.38 was obtained with a calculator. The answer should have two significant figures because 2.3, the number with the fewest significant figures, has only two significant figures.

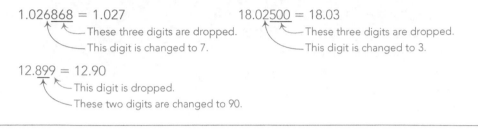

Round off this digit to 4.

Drop these three digits.

438.38

Move the decimal two places to the left to express in scientific notation.

The correct answer is 440 or 4.4×10^2.

EXAMPLE 2.7

$$\frac{(13.59)(6.3)}{12} = 7.13475$$

SOLUTION

The value 7.13475 was obtained with a calculator. The answer should contain two significant figures because 6.3 and 12 each have only two significant figures.

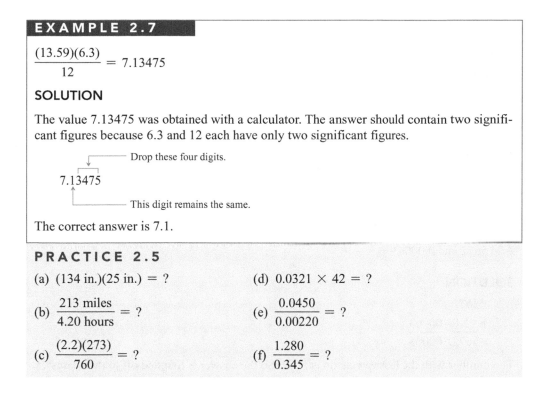

The correct answer is 7.1.

PRACTICE 2.5

(a) $(134 \text{ in.})(25 \text{ in.}) = ?$

(b) $\dfrac{213 \text{ miles}}{4.20 \text{ hours}} = ?$

(c) $\dfrac{(2.2)(273)}{760} = ?$

(d) $0.0321 \times 42 = ?$

(e) $\dfrac{0.0450}{0.00220} = ?$

(f) $\dfrac{1.280}{0.345} = ?$

Addition or Subtraction

The results of an addition or a subtraction must be expressed to the same precision as the least precise measurement. This means the result must be rounded to the same number of decimal places as the value with the fewest decimal places (blue line in examples).

EXAMPLE 2.8

Add 125.17, 129, and 52.2.

SOLUTION

The number with the least precision is 129. Therefore the answer is rounded off to the nearest unit: 306.

EXAMPLE 2.9

Subtract 14.1 from 132.56.

SOLUTION

```
    132.5|6
 −   14.1|
  ──────────
    118.4|6
```

The number with the least precision is 14.1. Therefore the answer is rounded off to the nearest tenth: 118.5.

EXAMPLE 2.10

Subtract 120 from 1587.

SOLUTION

$$
\begin{array}{r}
158\,|\,7 \\
-\ \ 12\,|\,0 \\
\hline
146\,|\,7
\end{array}
$$

The number with the least precision is 120. The zero is not considered significant; therefore the answer must be rounded to the nearest ten: 1470 or 1.47×10^3.

EXAMPLE 2.11

Add 5672 and 0.00063.

SOLUTION

$$
\begin{array}{r}
5672\ \ |\ \ \ \ \ \\
+\ \ \ \ 0.\,|00063 \\
\hline
5672.\,|00063
\end{array}
$$

Note: When a very small number is added to a large number, the result is simply the original number.

The number with the least precision is 5672. So the answer is rounded off to the nearest unit: 5672.

EXAMPLE 2.12

$$
\frac{1.039 - 1.020}{1.039} = ?
$$

SOLUTION

$$
\frac{1.039 - 1.020}{1.039} = 0.018286814
$$

The value 0.018286814 was obtained with a calculator. When the subtraction in the numerator is done,

$$
1.039 - 1.020 = 0.019
$$

the number of significant figures changes from four to two. Therefore the answer should contain two significant figures after the division is carried out:

Drop these six digits.

0.018286814

This digit remains the same.

The correct answer is 0.018, or 1.8×10^{-2}.

PRACTICE 2.6

If you need to brush up on your math skills, refer to the "Mathematical Review" in Appendix I.

How many significant figures should the answer in each of these calculations contain?

(a) $(14.0)(5.2)$

(b) $(0.1682)(8.2)$

(c) $\dfrac{(160)(33)}{4}$

(d) $8.2 + 0.125$

(e) $119.1 - 3.44$

(f) $\dfrac{94.5}{1.2}$

(g) $1200 + 6.34$

(h) $1.6 + 23 - 0.005$

RULES FOR SIGNIFICANT FIGURES IN CALCULATIONS

Multiplication or Division
The answer contains the same number of significant figures as the measurement with the *least number* of significant figures.

Addition or Subtraction
The answer contains the same number of significant figures as the *least precise* measurement.

Additional material on mathematical operations is given in Appendix I, "Mathematical Review." Study any portions that are not familiar to you. You may need to do this at various times during the course when additional knowledge of mathematical operations is required.

2.5 THE METRIC SYSTEM

Name the units for mass, length, and volume in the metric system and convert from one unit to another.

● LEARNING OBJECTIVE

The **metric system**, or **International System** (**SI**, from *Système International*), is a decimal system of units for measurements of mass, length, time, and other physical quantities. Built around a set of standard units, the metric system uses factors of 10 to express larger or smaller numbers of these units. To express quantities that are larger or smaller than the standard units, prefixes are added to the names of the units. These prefixes represent multiples of 10, making the metric system a decimal system of measurements. Table 2.1 shows the names, symbols, and numerical values of the common prefixes. Some examples of the more commonly used prefixes are

KEY TERMS
metric system or International
System (SI)
meter (m)
conversion factor
solution map
mass
weight
kilogram (kg)
volume
liter (L)

$$1 \textit{ kilo}\text{meter} = 1000 \text{ meters}$$
$$1 \textit{ kilo}\text{gram} = 1000 \text{ grams}$$
$$1 \textit{ milli}\text{meter} = 0.001 \text{ meter}$$
$$1 \textit{ micro}\text{second} = 0.000001 \text{ second}$$

The common standard units in the International System, their abbreviations, and the quantities they measure are given in Table 2.2. Other units are derived from these units. The metric system, or International System, is currently used by most of the countries in the world, not only in scientific and technical work but also in commerce and industry.

The prefixes most commonly used in chemistry are shown in bold in Table 2.1.

TABLE 2.1 Common Prefixes and Numerical Values for SI Units

Prefix	Symbol	Numerical value	Power of 10 equivalent
giga	G	1,000,000,000	10^9
mega	M	1,000,000	10^6
kilo	k	1,000	10^3
hecto	h	100	10^2
deka	da	10	10^1
—	—	1	10^0
deci	d	0.1	10^{-1}
centi	c	0.01	10^{-2}
milli	m	0.001	10^{-3}
micro	μ	0.000001	10^{-6}
nano	n	0.000000001	10^{-9}
pico	p	0.000000000001	10^{-12}
femto	f	0.000000000000001	10^{-15}

Kathleen Pepper/Copyright John Wiley & Sons, Inc.

Most products today list both systems of measurement on their labels.

Common length relationships:

$$1\ m = 10^6\ \mu m = 10^{10}\ \text{Å}$$
$$= 100\ cm = 1000\ mm$$
$$1\ cm = 10\ mm = 0.01\ m$$
$$1\ in. = 2.54\ cm$$
$$1\ mile = 1.609\ km$$

See inside back cover for a table of conversions.

TABLE 2.2 International System's Standard Units of Measurement

Quantity	Name of unit	Abbreviation
Length	meter	m
Mass	kilogram	kg
Temperature	kelvin	K
Time	second	s
Amount of substance	mole	mol
Electric current	ampere	A
Luminous intensity	candela	cd

Measurement of Length

The standard unit of length in the metric system is the **meter (m)**. When the metric system was first introduced in the 1790s, the meter was defined as one ten-millionth of the distance from the equator to the North Pole, measured along the meridian passing through Dunkirk, France. The latest definition describes a meter as the distance that light travels in a vacuum during 1/299,792,458 of a second.

A meter is 39.37 inches, a little longer than 1 yard. One meter equals 10 decimeters, 100 centimeters, or 1000 millimeters (see Figure 2.2). A kilometer contains 1000 meters. Table 2.3 shows the relationships of these units.

The nanometer (10^{-9} m) is used extensively in expressing the wavelength of light, as well as in atomic dimensions. See the inside back cover for a complete table of common conversions.

© tomograf/iStockphoto

1 in.   **Inches**

2.54 cm
25.4 mm   **Centimeters**

Figure 2.2

Comparison of the metric and American systems of length measurement: 2.54 cm = 1 in. A playing card measures 2 ½ in. or 6.3 cm.

TABLE 2.3 Metric Units of Length

Unit	Abbreviation	Meter equivalent	Exponential equivalent
kilometer	km	1000 m	10^3 m
meter	m	1 m	10^0 m
decimeter	dm	0.1 m	10^{-1} m
centimeter	cm	0.01 m	10^{-2} m
millimeter	mm	0.001 m	10^{-3} m
micrometer	μm	0.000001 m	10^{-6} m
nanometer	nm	0.000000001 m	10^{-9} m
angstrom	Å	0.0000000001 m	10^{-10} m

Unit Conversions

One of the benefits of using the metric system is the ease with which we can convert from one unit to another. We do this by using the relationships between units—math equations called equivalent units. Table 2.4 shows common equivalent units for length in the metric system.

To convert from one unit to another we must use a **conversion factor**. A conversion factor is a ratio of equivalent quantities. Where do we find these conversion factors? They are formed from equivalent units. For example, since 1 m = 100 cm (Table 2.4) we could write two ratios: $\dfrac{1 \text{ m}}{100 \text{ cm}}$ or $\dfrac{100 \text{ cm}}{1 \text{ m}}$. In both cases the ratio is 1 since the units are equal.

We can convert one metric unit to another by using conversion factors.

$$\textbf{unit}_1 \times \textbf{conversion factor} = \textbf{unit}_2$$

If you want to know how many millimeters are in 2.5 meters, you need to convert meters (m) to millimeters (mm). Start by writing

$$\text{m} \times \text{conversion factor} = \text{mm}$$

This conversion factor must accomplish two things: It must cancel (or eliminate) meters, *and* it must introduce millimeters—the unit wanted in the answer. Such a conversion factor will be in fractional form and have meters in the denominator and millimeters in the numerator:

$$\cancel{\text{m}} \times \frac{\text{mm}}{\cancel{\text{m}}} = \text{mm}$$

We know that 1 m = 1000 mm. From this relationship we can write two conversion factors.

$$\frac{1 \text{ m}}{1000 \text{ mm}} \quad \text{and} \quad \frac{1000 \text{ mm}}{1 \text{ m}}$$

Choosing the conversion factor $\dfrac{1000 \text{ mm}}{1 \text{ m}}$, we can set up the calculation for the conversion of 2.5 m to millimeters:

$$(2.5 \cancel{\text{ m}})\left(\frac{1000 \text{ mm}}{1 \cancel{\text{ m}}}\right) = 2500 \text{ mm} \quad \text{or} \quad 2.5 \times 10^3 \text{ mm} \quad \text{(two significant figures)}$$

Note that, in making this calculation, units are treated as numbers; meters in the numerator are canceled by meters in the denominator.

TABLE 2.4
Length Equivalent Units

1 m	=	10 dm
1 m	=	100 cm
1 m	=	1000 mm
1 kg	=	1000 g
1 cm	=	10 mm

Important equations and statements are boxed or highlighted in color.

We know that multiplying a measurement by 1 does not change its value. Since our conversion factors both equal 1, we can multiply the measurement by the appropriate one to convert units.

EXAMPLE 2.13

Change 215 centimeters to meters.

SOLUTION

We will use a **solution map** to outline our path for the conversion for this example:

Solution map: cm → m

We start with

$$\text{cm} \times \text{conversion factor} = \text{m}$$

The conversion factor must have centimeters in the denominator and meters in the numerator:

$$\cancel{\text{cm}} \times \frac{\text{m}}{\cancel{\text{cm}}} = \text{m}$$

From the relationship 100 cm = 1 m, we can write a factor that will accomplish this conversion:

$$\frac{1 \text{ m}}{100 \text{ cm}}$$

Now set up the calculation using all the data given:

$$(215 \ \cancel{cm})\left(\frac{1 \ m}{100 \ \cancel{cm}}\right) = 2.15 \ m$$

PRACTICE 2.7

Convert the following measurements:

(a) 567 mm to m
(b) 68 cm to mm
(c) 125 m to km

Measurement of Mass

Although we often use mass and weight interchangeably in our everyday lives, they have quite different meanings in chemistry. In science we define the **mass** of an object as the amount of matter in the object. Mass is measured on an instrument called a balance. The **weight** of an object is a measure of the effect of gravity on the object. Weight is determined by using an instrument called a scale, which measures force against a spring. This means mass is independent of the location of an object, but weight is not. In this text we will use the term *mass* for all of our metric mass measurements. The gram is a unit of mass measurement, but it is a tiny amount of mass; for instance, a U.S. nickel has a mass of about 5 grams. Therefore the *standard unit* of mass in the SI system is the **kilogram (kg)** (equal to 1000 g). The amount of mass in a kilogram is defined by international agreement as exactly equal to the mass of a platinum-iridium cylinder (international prototype kilogram) kept in a vault at Sèvres, France. Comparing this unit of mass to 1 lb (16 oz), we find that 1 kg is equal to 2.205 lb. A pound is equal to 453.6 g (0.4536 kg). The same prefixes used in length measurement are used to indicate larger and smaller gram units (see Table 2.5). A balance is used to measure mass. Two examples of balances are shown in Figure 2.3.

TABLE 2.5   Metric Units of Mass

Unit	Abbreviation	Gram equivalent	Exponential equivalent
kilogram	kg	1000 g	10^3 g
gram	g	1 g	10^0 g
decigram	dg	0.1 g	10^{-1} g
centigram	cg	0.01 g	10^{-2} g
milligram	mg	0.001 g	10^{-3} g
microgram	μg	0.000001 g	10^{-6} g

Figure 2.3

(a) Digital electronic, top-loading balance with a precision of 0.001 g (1 mg); and (b) a digital electronic analytical balance with a precision of 0.0001 g (0.1 mg).

© Sciencephotos/Alamy

© 2005 Richard Megna/Fundamental Photographs

(a)   (b)

>CHEMISTRY *IN ACTION*

Keeping Track of Units

Why do scientists worry about units? The National Aeronautics and Space Administration (NASA) recently was reminded of just why keeping track of units is so important. In 1999 a $125 million satellite was lost in the atmosphere of Mars because scientists made some improper assumptions about units. NASA's scientists at the Jet Propulsion Lab (JPL) in Pasadena, California, received thrust data from the satellite's manufacturer, Lockheed Martin Aeronautics in Denver, Colorado. Unfortunately, the Denver scientists used American units in their measurements and the JPL scientists assumed the units were metric. This mistake caused the satellite to fall 100 km lower into the Mars atmosphere than planned. The spacecraft burned up from the friction with the atmosphere.

Measuring and using units correctly is very important. In fact, it can be critical, as we have just seen. For example, a Canadian jet almost crashed when the tanks were filled with 22,300 pounds (instead of kilograms) of fuel. Calculations for distance were based on kilograms, and the jet almost ran out of fuel before landing at the destination. Correct units are also important to ensure perfect fits for household purchases such as drapes, carpet, or appliances. Be sure to pay attention to units in both your chemistry problems and in everyday life!

JPL/NASA

Mars climate orbiter

EXAMPLE 2.14

Change 25 grams to milligrams.

SOLUTION

We use the conversion factor 1000 mg/g.

Solution map: g → mg

$$(25 \text{ g})\left(\frac{1000 \text{ mg}}{1 \text{ g}}\right) = 25{,}000 \text{ mg} \qquad (2.5 \times 10^4 \text{ mg})$$

Note that multiplying a number by 1000 is the same as multiplying the number by 10^3 and can be done simply by moving the decimal point three places to the right:

$$(6.428)(1000) = 6428 \qquad (6.428)$$

Common mass relationships:
1 g = 1000 mg
1 kg = 1000 g
1 kg = 2.205 lb
1 lb = 453.6 g

PRACTICE 2.8

Convert the following measurements:
(a) 560 mg to g
(b) 525 g to kg
(c) 175 g to mg

To change milligrams to grams, we use the conversion factor 1 g/1000 mg. For example, we convert 155 mg to grams as follows:

$$(155 \text{ mg})\left(\frac{1 \text{ g}}{1000 \text{ mg}}\right) = 0.155 \text{ g}$$

Measurement of Volume

Volume, as used here, is the amount of space occupied by matter. The SI unit of volume is the *cubic meter* (m^3). However, the liter (pronounced *lee-ter* and abbreviated L) and the milliliter (abbreviated mL) are the standard units of volume used in most chemical laboratories. A **liter (L)** is usually defined as 1 cubic decimeter (1 kg) of water at 4°C.

The most common instruments or equipment for measuring liquids are the graduated cylinder, volumetric flask, buret, pipet, and syringe, which are illustrated in **Figure 2.4**. These pieces are usually made of glass and are available in various sizes. Let's try some examples.

Common volume relationships:
$$1 \text{ L} = 1000 \text{ mL} = 1000 \text{ cm}^3$$
$$1 \text{ mL} = 1 \text{ cm}^3$$
$$1 \text{ L} = 1.057 \text{ qt}$$
$$946.1 \text{ mL} = 1 \text{ qt}$$

| Graduated cylinder | Volumetric flask | Buret | Pipet | Syringe |

Figure 2.4

Calibrated glassware for measuring the volume of liquids.

EXAMPLE 2.15

How many milliliters are contained in 3.5 liters?

SOLUTION

The conversion factor to change liters to milliliters is 1000 mL/L:

Solution map: L → mL

$$(3.5 \text{ L})\left(\frac{1000 \text{ mL}}{\text{L}}\right) = 3500 \text{ mL} \qquad (3.5 \times 10^3 \text{ mL})$$

Liters may be changed to milliliters by moving the decimal point three places to the right and changing the units to milliliters:

$$1.500 \text{ L} = 1500. \text{ mL}$$

PRACTICE 2.9

Convert the following measurements:
(a) 25 mL to L
(b) 1.55 L to mL
(c) 4.5 L to dL

2.6 DIMENSIONAL ANALYSIS: A PROBLEM-SOLVING METHOD

Use dimensional analysis to solve problems involving unit conversions.

● LEARNING OBJECTIVE

See Appendix II for help in using a scientific calculator.

Many chemical principles can be illustrated mathematically. Learning how to set up and solve numerical problems in a systematic fashion is *essential* in the study of chemistry.

Usually a problem can be solved by several methods. But in all methods it is best to use a systematic, orderly approach. The *dimensional analysis method* is emphasized in this book because it

- provides a systematic, straightforward way to set up problems.
- gives a clear understanding of the principles involved.
- trains you to organize and evaluate data.
- helps to identify errors, since unwanted units are not eliminated if the setup of the problem is incorrect.

Dimensional analysis converts one unit to another unit by using conversion factors.

Label all factors with the proper units.

The following examples show the conversion between American units and metric units. Mass conversions from American to metric units are shown in Examples 2.16 and 2.21.

EXAMPLE 2.16

A 1.50-lb package contains how many grams of baking soda?

SOLUTION

We are solving for the number of grams equivalent to 1.50 lb. Since 1 lb = 453.6 g, the conversion factor is 453.6 g/lb:

Solution map: lb → g

$$(1.50 \ \cancel{lb})\left(\frac{453.6 \text{ g}}{1 \ \cancel{lb}}\right) = 680. \text{ g}$$

PRACTICE 2.10

A tennis ball has a mass of 65 g. Determine the American equivalent in pounds.

The volume of a cubic or rectangular container can be determined by multiplying its length × width × height. Thus a box 10 cm on each side has a volume of (10 cm)(10 cm)(10 cm) = 1000 cm³.

EXAMPLE 2.17

How many cubic centimeters are in a cube that is 11.1 inches on a side?

SOLUTION

First we change inches to centimeters; our conversion factor is 2.54 cm/in.:

Solution map: in. → cm

$$(11.1 \ \cancel{in.})\left(\frac{2.54 \text{ cm}}{1 \ \cancel{in.}}\right) = 28.2 \text{ cm on a side}$$

Then we determine volume (length × width × height):

$$(28.2 \text{ cm})(28.2 \text{ cm})(28.2 \text{ cm}) = 22,426 \text{ cm}^3 \qquad (2.24 \times 10^4 \text{ cm}^3)$$

When doing problems with multiple steps, you should round only at the end of the problem. We are rounding at the end of each step in example problems to illustrate the proper significant figures.

EXAMPLE 2.18

How many cubic centimeters (cm^3) are in a box that measures 2.20 in. by 4.00 in. by 6.00 in.?

SOLUTION

First we need to determine the volume of the box in cubic inches ($in.^3$) by multiplying the length $\times$ width $\times$ height:

$$(2.20 \text{ in.})(4.00 \text{ in.})(6.00 \text{ in.}) = 52.8 \text{ in.}^3$$

Now we convert $in.^3$ to cm^3 by using the inches and centimeters relationship (1 in. = 2.54 cm) three times:

Solution map: $(\text{in.} \rightarrow \text{cm})^3$

$$\text{in.}^3 \times \frac{\text{cm}}{\text{in.}} \times \frac{\text{cm}}{\text{in.}} \times \frac{\text{cm}}{\text{in.}} = \text{cm}^3$$

$$(52.8 \text{ in.}^3)\left(\frac{2.54 \text{ cm}}{1 \text{ in.}}\right)\left(\frac{2.54 \text{ cm}}{1 \text{ in.}}\right)\left(\frac{2.54 \text{ cm}}{1 \text{ in.}}\right) = 865 \text{ cm}^3$$

Units are emphasized in problems by using color and solution maps to help visualize the steps in the process.

Some problems require a series of conversions to reach the correct units in the answer. For example, suppose we want to know the number of seconds in 1 day. We need to convert from the unit of days to seconds using this solution map:

Solution map: day $\rightarrow$ hours $\rightarrow$ minutes $\rightarrow$ seconds

Each arrow in the solution map represents a conversion factor. This sequence requires three conversion factors, one for each step. We convert days to hours (hr), hours to minutes (min), and minutes to seconds (s). The conversions can be done individually or in a continuous sequence:

$$\text{day} \times \frac{\text{hr}}{\text{day}} \longrightarrow \text{hr} \times \frac{\text{min}}{\text{hr}} \longrightarrow \text{min} \times \frac{\text{s}}{\text{min}} = \text{s}$$

$$\text{day} \times \frac{\text{hr}}{\text{day}} \times \frac{\text{min}}{\text{hr}} \times \frac{\text{s}}{\text{min}} = \text{s}$$

Inserting the proper factors, we calculate the number of seconds in 1 day to be

$$(1 \text{ day})\left(\frac{24 \text{ hr}}{1 \text{ day}}\right)\left(\frac{60 \text{ min}}{1 \text{ hr}}\right)\left(\frac{60 \text{ s}}{1 \text{ min}}\right) = 86,400. \text{ s}$$

All five digits in 86,400. are significant, since all the factors in the calculation are exact numbers.

EXAMPLE 2.19

How many centimeters are in 2.00 ft?

SOLUTION

The stepwise conversion of units from feet to centimeters may be done in this sequence. Convert feet to inches; then convert inches to centimeters:

Solution map: ft $\rightarrow$ in. $\rightarrow$ cm

The conversion factors needed are

$$\frac{12 \text{ in.}}{1 \text{ ft}} \quad \text{and} \quad \frac{2.54 \text{ cm}}{1 \text{ in.}}$$

$$(2.00 \text{ ft})\left(\frac{12 \text{ in.}}{1 \text{ ft}}\right) = 24.0 \text{ in.}$$

$$(24.0 \text{ in.})\left(\frac{2.54 \text{ cm}}{1 \text{ in.}}\right) = 61.0 \text{ cm}$$

NOTE   Since 1 ft and 12 in. are exact numbers, the number of significant figures allowed in the answer is three, based on the number 2.00.

EXAMPLE 2.20

How many meters are in a 100.-yd football field?

SOLUTION

The stepwise conversion of units from yards to meters may be done by this sequence, using the proper conversion factors:

Solution map: yd → ft → in. → cm → m

$$(100. \text{ yd})\left(\frac{3 \text{ ft}}{1 \text{ yd}}\right) = 300. \text{ ft}$$

$$(300. \text{ ft})\left(\frac{12 \text{ in.}}{1 \text{ ft}}\right) = 3600 \text{ in.}$$

$$(3600 \text{ in.})\left(\frac{2.54 \text{ cm}}{1 \text{ in.}}\right) = 9144 \text{ cm}$$

$$(9144 \text{ cm})\left(\frac{1 \text{ m}}{100 \text{ cm}}\right) = 91.4 \text{ m} \quad \text{(three significant figures)}$$

PRACTICE 2.11

(a) How many meters are in 10.5 miles?
(b) What is the area of a 6.0-in. × 9.0-in. rectangle in square meters?

Examples 2.19 and 2.20 may be solved using a linear expression and writing down conversion factors in succession. This method often saves one or two calculation steps and allows numerical values to be reduced to simpler terms, leading to simpler calculations. The single linear expressions for Examples 2.19 and 2.20 are

$$(2.00 \text{ ft})\left(\frac{12 \text{ in.}}{1 \text{ ft}}\right)\left(\frac{2.54 \text{ cm}}{1 \text{ in.}}\right) = 61.0 \text{ cm}$$

$$(100. \text{ yd})\left(\frac{3 \text{ ft}}{1 \text{ yd}}\right)\left(\frac{12 \text{ in.}}{1 \text{ ft}}\right)\left(\frac{2.54 \text{ cm}}{1 \text{ in.}}\right)\left(\frac{1 \text{ m}}{100 \text{ cm}}\right) = 91.4 \text{ m}$$

Using the units alone (Example 2.20), we see that the stepwise cancellation proceeds in succession until the desired unit is reached:

$$\text{yd} \times \frac{\text{ft}}{\text{yd}} \times \frac{\text{in.}}{\text{ft}} \times \frac{\text{cm}}{\text{in.}} \times \frac{\text{m}}{\text{cm}} = \text{m}$$

EXAMPLE 2.21

A driver of a car is obeying the speed limit of 55 miles per hour. How fast is the car traveling in kilometers per second?

SOLUTION

Several conversions are needed to solve this problem:

Solution map: mi. → km

hr → min → s

To convert mi → km,

$$\left(\frac{55 \text{ mi}}{\text{hr}}\right)\left(\frac{1.609 \text{ km}}{1 \text{ mi}}\right) = 88\frac{\text{km}}{\text{hr}}$$

Next we must convert hr → min → s. Notice that hours is in the denominator of our quantity, so the conversion factor must have hours in the numerator:

$$\left(\frac{88 \text{ km}}{\text{hr}}\right)\left(\frac{1 \text{ hr}}{60 \text{ min}}\right)\left(\frac{1 \text{ min}}{60 \text{ s}}\right) = 0.024\frac{\text{km}}{\text{s}}$$

PRACTICE 2.12

How many cubic meters of air are in a room measuring 8 ft × 10 ft × 12 ft?

EXAMPLE 2.22

Suppose four ostrich feathers weigh 1.00 lb. Assuming that each feather is equal in mass, how many milligrams does a single feather weigh?

SOLUTION

The unit conversion in this problem is from 1.00 lb/4 feathers to milligrams per feather. Since the unit *feathers* occurs in the denominator of both the starting unit and the desired unit, the unit conversions are

Solution map: lb → g → mg

$$\left(\frac{1.00 \text{ lb}}{4 \text{ feathers}}\right)\left(\frac{453.6 \text{ g}}{1 \text{ lb}}\right)\left(\frac{1000 \text{ mg}}{1 \text{ g}}\right) = \frac{113,400 \text{ mg}}{\text{feather}}(1.13 \times 10^5 \text{ mg/feather})$$

PRACTICE 2.13

You are traveling in Europe and wake up one morning to find your mass is 75.0 kg. Determine the American equivalent (in pounds) to see whether you need to go on a diet before you return home.

PRACTICE 2.14

A bottle of excellent Chianti holds 750 mL. What is its volume in quarts?

PRACTICE 2.15

Milk is often purchased by the half gallon. Determine the number of liters equal to this amount.

2.7 MEASUREMENT OF TEMPERATURE

LEARNING OBJECTIVE ● Convert measurements among the Fahrenheit, Celsius, and Kelvin temperature scales.

KEY TERMS

thermal energy
temperature
heat

Thermal energy is a form of energy associated with the motion of small particles of matter. Depending on the amount of thermal energy present, a given system is said to be hot or cold. **Temperature** is a measure of the intensity of thermal energy, or how hot a system is, regardless of its size. The term **heat** refers to the flow of energy due to a temperature difference. Heat always flows from a region of higher temperature to one of lower temperature. The SI unit of temperature is the kelvin. The common laboratory instrument for measuring temperature is a thermometer (see **Figure 2.5**).

Figure 2.5

Comparison of Celsius, Kelvin, and Fahrenheit temperature scales.

The temperature of a system can be expressed by several different scales. Three commonly used temperature scales are Celsius (pronounced *sell-see-us*), Kelvin (also called absolute), and Fahrenheit. The unit of temperature on the Celsius and Fahrenheit scales is called a *degree*, but the size of the Celsius and the Fahrenheit degree is not the same. The symbol for the Celsius and Fahrenheit degrees is °, and it is placed as a superscript after the number and before the symbol for the scale. Thus, 10.0°C means 10.0 *degrees Celsius*. The degree sign is not used with Kelvin temperatures:

$$\text{degrees Celsius} = °C$$
$$\text{Kelvin (absolute)} = K$$
$$\text{degrees Fahrenheit} = °F$$

On the Celsius scale the interval between the freezing and boiling temperatures of water is divided into 100 equal parts, or degrees. The freezing point of water is assigned a temperature of 0°C and the boiling point of water a temperature of 100°C. The Kelvin temperature scale is known as the absolute temperature scale because 0 K is the lowest temperature theoretically attainable. The Kelvin zero is 273.15 kelvins below the Celsius zero. A kelvin is equal in size to a Celsius degree. The freezing point of water on the Kelvin scale is 273.15 K. The Fahrenheit scale has 180 degrees between the freezing and boiling temperatures of water. On this scale the freezing point of water is 32°F and the boiling point is 212°F:

$$0°C \cong 273\ K \cong 32°F \qquad 100°C \cong 373\ K \cong 212°F$$

The three scales are compared in Figure 2.5. Although absolute zero (0 K) is the lower limit of temperature on these scales, temperature has no upper limit. Temperatures of several million degrees are known to exist in the sun and in other stars.

By examining Figure 2.5, we can see that there are 100 Celsius degrees and 100 kelvins between the freezing and boiling points of water, but there are 180 Fahrenheit degrees between these two temperatures. Hence, the size of the Celsius degree and the kelvin are the same, but 1 Celsius degree is equal to 1.8 Fahrenheit degrees.

>CHEMISTRY *IN ACTION*

Setting Standards

The kilogram is the standard base unit for mass in the SI system. But who decides just what a kilogram is? Before 1880, a kilogram was defined as the mass of a cubic decimeter of water. But this is difficult to reproduce very accurately since impurities and air are dissolved in water. The density of water also changes with temperature, leading to inaccuracy. So in 1885 a Pt-Ir cylinder was made with a mass of exactly 1 kilogram. This cylinder is kept in a vault at Sèvres, France, outside Paris, along with six copies. In 1889 the kilogram was determined to be the base unit of mass for the metric system and has been weighed against its copies three times in the past 100 years (1890, 1948, 1992) to make sure that it is accurate. The trouble with all this is that the cylinder itself can vary. Experts in the science of measurement want to change the definition of the kilogram to link it to a property of matter that does not change.

The kilogram is the only one of seven SI base units defined in terms of a physical object instead of a property of matter. The meter (redefined in 1983) is defined in terms of the speed of light (1 m = distance light travels in $\frac{1}{299,792,458}$ s). The second is defined in terms of the natural vibration of the cesium atom. Unfortunately, three of the SI base units (mole, ampere, and candela) depend on the definition of the kilogram. If the mass of the kilogram is uncertain, then all of these units are uncertain.

How else could we define a kilogram? Scientists have several ideas. They propose to fix the kilogram to a set value of a physical constant (which does not change). These constants connect experiment to theory. Right now they are continuing to struggle to find a new way to determine the mass of the kilogram.

Official contribution of the National Institute of Standards and Technology, not subject to copyright in the United States. Sissy Riley, Information Services division/NIST

Kilogram artifact in Sèvres, France.

From these data, mathematical formulas have been derived to convert a temperature on one scale to the corresponding temperature on another scale:

$$K = °C + 273.15$$
$$°F = (1.8 \times °C) + 32$$
$$°C = \frac{°F - 32}{1.8}$$

EXAMPLE 2.23

The temperature at which table salt (sodium chloride) melts is 800.°C. What is this temperature on the Kelvin and Fahrenheit scales?

SOLUTION

To calculate K from °C, we use the formula

$$K = °C + 273.15$$
$$K = 800.°C + 273.15 = 1073 \text{ K}$$

To calculate °F from °C, we use the formula

$$°F = (1.8 \times °C) + 32$$
$$°F = (1.8)(800.°C) + 32$$
$$°F = 1440 + 32 = 1472°F$$

Summarizing our calculations, we see that

$$800.°C = 1073 \text{ K} = 1472°F$$

Remember that the original measurement of 800.°C was to the units place, so the converted temperature is also to the units place.

>CHEMISTRY *IN ACTION*

Taking the Temperature of Old Faithful

If you have ever struggled to take the temperature of a sick child, imagine the difficulty in taking the temperature of a geyser. Such are the tasks scientists set for themselves! In 1984, James A. Westphal and Susan W. Keiffer, geologists from the California Institute of Technology, measured the temperature and pressure inside Old Faithful during several eruptions in order to learn more about how a geyser functions. The measurements, taken at eight depths along the upper part of the geyser were so varied and complicated that the researchers returned to Yellowstone in 1992 to further investigate Old Faithful's structure and functioning. To see what happened between eruptions, Westphal and Keiffer lowered an insulated 2-in. video camera into the geyser. Keiffer had assumed that the vent (opening in the ground) was a uniform vertical tube, but this is not the case. Instead, the geyser appears to be an east–west crack in the Earth that extends downward at least 14 m. In some places it is over 1.8 m wide, and in other places it narrows to less than 15 cm. The walls of the vent contain many cracks, allowing water to enter at several depths. The complicated nature of the temperature data is explained by these cracks. Cool water enters the vent at depths of 5.5 m and 7.5 m. Superheated water and steam blast into the vent 14 m underground. According to Westphal, temperature increases of up to 130°C at the beginning of an eruption suggest that water and steam also surge into the vent from deeper geothermal sources.

During the first 20–30 seconds of an eruption, steam and boiling water shoot through the narrowest part of the vent at near the speed of sound. The narrow tube limits the rate at which the water can shoot from the geyser. When the pressure falls below a critical value, the process slows and Old Faithful begins to quiet down again.

The frequency of Old Faithful's eruptions is not on a precise schedule, but varies from 45 to 105 minutes—the average is about 79 minutes. The variations in time between eruptions depend on the amount of boiling water left in the fissure. Westphal says, "There's no real pattern except that a short eruption is always followed by a long one." Measurements of temperatures inside Old Faithful have given scientists a better understanding of what causes a geyser to erupt.

Old Faithful eruptions shoot into the air an average of 130 feet.

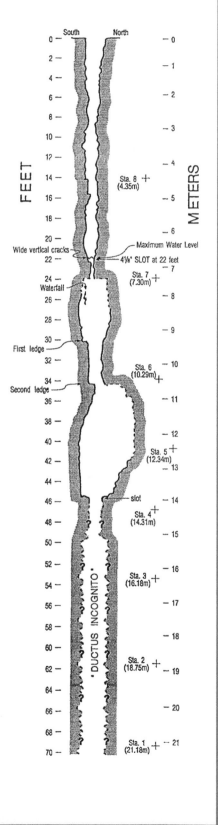

EXAMPLE 2.24

The temperature on December 1 in Honolulu, Hawaii, was 110.°F, a new record. Convert this temperature to °C.

SOLUTION

We use the formula

$$°C = \frac{°F - 32}{1.8}$$

$$°C = \frac{110. - 32}{1.8} = \frac{78}{1.8} = 43°C$$

EXAMPLE 2.25

What temperature on the Fahrenheit scale corresponds to −8.0°C? (Notice the negative sign in this problem.)

SOLUTION

$$°F = (1.8 × °C) + 32$$

$$°F = (1.8)(-8.0) + 32 = -14 + 32$$

$$°F = 18°F$$

Temperatures used throughout this book are in degrees Celsius (°C) unless specified otherwise. The temperature after conversion should be expressed to the same precision as the original measurement.

PRACTICE 2.16

Helium boils at 4 K. Convert this temperature to °C and then to °F.

PRACTICE 2.17

"Normal" human body temperature is 98.6°F. Convert this to °C and K.

2.8 DENSITY

LEARNING OBJECTIVE • Solve problems involving density

KEY TERMS

density
specific gravity

Density (d) is the ratio of the mass of a substance to the volume occupied by that mass; it is the mass per unit of volume and is given by the equation

$$d = \frac{mass}{volume}$$

Density is a physical characteristic of a substance and may be used as an aid to its identification. When the density of a solid or a liquid is given, the mass is usually expressed in grams and the volume in milliliters or cubic centimeters.

$$d = \frac{mass}{volume} = \frac{g}{mL} \quad or \quad d = \frac{g}{cm^3}$$

Since the volume of a substance (especially liquids and gases) varies with temperature, it is important to state the temperature along with the density. For example, the volume of 1.0000 g of water at 4°C is 1.0000 mL; at 20°C, it is 1.0018 mL; and at 80°C, it is 1.0290 mL. Density therefore also varies with temperature.

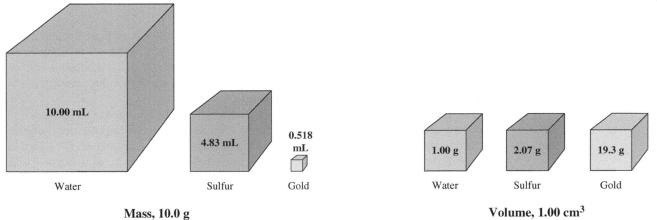

Figure 2.6

Comparison of mass and volume.

The density of water at 4°C is 1.0000 g/mL, but at 80°C the density of water is 0.9718 g/mL:

$$d^{4°C} = \frac{1.0000 \text{ g}}{1.0000 \text{ mL}} = 1.0000 \text{ g/mL}$$

$$d^{80°C} = \frac{1.0000 \text{ g}}{1.0290 \text{ mL}} = 0.97182 \text{ g/mL}$$

The density of iron at 20°C is 7.86 g/mL.

$$d^{20°C} = \frac{7.86 \text{ g}}{1.00 \text{ mL}} = 7.86 \text{ g/mL}$$

The densities of a variety of materials are compared in Figure 2.6.

Densities for liquids and solids are usually represented in terms of grams per milliliter (g/mL) or grams per cubic centimeter (g/cm³). The density of gases, however, is expressed in terms of grams per liter (g/L). Unless otherwise stated, gas densities are given for 0°C and 1 atmosphere pressure (discussed further in Chapter 13). Table 2.6 lists the densities of some common materials.

TABLE 2.6   Densities of Some Selected Materials

Liquids and solids		Gases	
Substance	**Density (g/mL at 20°C)**	**Substance**	**Density (g/L at 0°C)**
Wood (Douglas fir)	0.512	Hydrogen	0.090
Ethyl alcohol	0.789	Helium	0.178
Vegetable oil	0.91	Methane	0.714
Water (4°C)	1.000*	Ammonia	0.771
Sugar	1.59	Neon	0.90
Glycerin	1.26	Carbon monoxide	1.25
Karo syrup	1.37	Nitrogen	1.251
Magnesium	1.74	Air	1.293*
Sulfuric acid	1.84	Oxygen	1.429
Sulfur	2.07	Hydrogen chloride	1.63
Salt	2.16	Argon	1.78
Aluminum	2.70	Carbon dioxide	1.963
Silver	10.5	Chlorine	3.17
Lead	11.34		
Mercury	13.55		
Gold	19.3		

*For comparing densities, the density of water is the reference for solids and liquids; air is the reference for gases.

When an insoluble solid object is dropped into water, it will sink or float, depending on its density. If the object is less dense than water, it will float, displacing a *mass* of water equal to the mass of the object. If the object is more dense than water, it will sink, displacing a *volume* of water equal to the volume of the object. This information can be used to determine the volume (and density) of irregularly shaped objects.

The **specific gravity** (sp gr) of a substance is the ratio of the density of that substance to the density of another substance, usually water at 4°C. Specific gravity has no units because the density units cancel. The specific gravity tells us how many times as heavy a liquid, a solid, or a gas is as compared to the reference material. Since the density of water at 4°C is 1.00 g/mL, the specific gravity of a solid or liquid is the same as its density in g/mL without the units.

$$\text{sp gr} = \frac{\text{density of a liquid or solid}}{\text{density of water}}$$

Sample calculations of density problems follow.

EXAMPLE 2.26

What is the density of a mineral if 427 g of the mineral occupy a volume of 35.0 mL?

SOLUTION

We need to solve for density, so we start by writing the formula for calculating density:

$$d = \frac{\text{mass}}{\text{volume}}$$

Then we substitute the data given in the problem into the equation and solve:

mass = 427 g   volume = 35.0 mL

$$d = \frac{\text{mass}}{\text{volume}} = \frac{427 \text{ g}}{35.0 \text{ mL}} = 12.2 \text{ g/mL}$$

EXAMPLE 2.27

The density of gold is 19.3 g/mL. What is the mass of 25.0 mL of gold? Use density as a conversion factor, converting

Solution map: mL → g

The conversion of units is

$$\text{mL} \times \frac{\text{g}}{\text{mL}} = \text{g}$$

$$(25.0 \text{ mL})\left(\frac{19.3 \text{ g}}{\text{mL}}\right) = 483 \text{ g}$$

EXAMPLE 2.28

Calculate the volume (in mL) of 100. g of ethyl alcohol.

SOLUTION

From Table 2.6 we see that the density of ethyl alcohol is 0.789 g/mL. This density also means that 1 mL of the alcohol has a mass of 0.789 g (1 mL/0.789 g).

For a conversion factor, we can use either

$$\frac{\text{g}}{\text{mL}} \quad \text{or} \quad \frac{\text{mL}}{\text{g}}$$

Solution map: g → mL,

$$(100. \, \cancel{g}) \left(\frac{1 \, \text{mL}}{0.789 \, \cancel{g}} \right) = 127 \, \text{mL of ethyl alcohol}$$

EXAMPLE 2.29

The water level in a graduated cylinder stands at 20.0 mL before and at 26.2 mL after a 16.74-g metal bolt is submerged in the water. (a) What is the volume of the bolt? (b) What is the density of the bolt?

SOLUTION

(a) The bolt will displace a volume of water equal to the volume of the bolt. Thus, the increase in volume is the volume of the bolt:

$$
\begin{aligned}
26.2 \, \text{mL} &= \text{volume of water plus bolt} \\
-20.0 \, \text{mL} &= \text{volume of water} \\
\hline
6.2 \, \text{mL} &= \text{volume of bolt}
\end{aligned}
$$

(b) $d = \dfrac{\text{mass of bolt}}{\text{volume of bolt}} = \dfrac{16.74 \, \text{g}}{6.2 \, \text{mL}} = 2.7 \, \text{g/mL}$

PRACTICE 2.18

Pure silver has a density of 10.5 g/mL. A ring sold as pure silver has a mass of 18.7 g. When it is placed in a graduated cylinder, the water level rises 2.0 mL. Determine whether the ring is actually pure silver or whether the customer should contact the Better Business Bureau.

PRACTICE 2.19

The water level in a metric measuring cup is 0.75 L before the addition of 150. g of shortening. The water level after submerging the shortening is 0.92 L. Determine the density of the shortening.

CHAPTER 2 REVIEW

2.1 SCIENTIFIC NOTATION

- Quantitative observations consist of a number and a unit and are called measurements.
- Very large and very small numbers can be represented compactly by using scientific notation:
  - The number is represented as a decimal between 1 and 10 and is multiplied by 10 raised to the appropriate exponent.
  - The sign on the exponent is determined by the direction the decimal point is moved in the original number.

KEY TERMS
measurement
scientific notation

2.2 MEASUREMENT AND UNCERTAINTY

- All measurements reflect some amount of uncertainty, which is indicated by the number of significant figures in the measurement.
- The significant figures include all those known with certainty plus one estimated digit.

KEY TERM
significant figures

2.3 SIGNIFICANT FIGURES

- Rules exist for counting significant figures in a measurement:
  - Nonzero numbers are always significant.
  - Exact numbers have an infinite number of significant figures.
  - The significance of a zero in a measurement is determined by its position within the number.
- Rules exist for rounding off the result of a calculation to the correct number of significant figures.
  - If the first number after the one you want to retain is 4 or less, that digit and all those after it are dropped.
  - If the first number after the one you want to retain is 5 or greater, that digit and all those after it are dropped and the last digit retained is increased by one.

2.4 SIGNIFICANT FIGURES IN CALCULATIONS

- The results of a calculation cannot be more precise than the least precise measurement.
- Rules exist for determining the correct number of significant figures in the result of a calculation.

2.5 THE METRIC SYSTEM

- The metric system uses factors of 10 and a set of standard units for measurements.
- Length in the metric system is measured by the standard unit of the meter.
- The standard unit for mass in the metric system is the kilogram. In chemistry we often use the gram instead, as we tend to work in smaller quantities.
- Volume is the amount of space occupied by matter.
- The standard unit for volume is the cubic meter. In chemistry we usually use the volume unit of the liter or the milliliter.

2.6 DIMENSIONAL ANALYSIS: A PROBLEM-SOLVING METHOD

- Dimensional analysis is a common method used to convert one unit to another.
  - Conversion factors are used to convert one unit into another:

$$\text{unit}_1 \times \text{conversion factor} = \text{unit}_2$$

  - A solution map is used to outline the steps in the unit conversion.

2.7 MEASUREMENT OF TEMPERATURE

- There are three commonly used temperature scales: Fahrenheit, Celsius, and Kelvin.
- We can convert among the temperature scales by using mathematical formulas:
  - $K = {}^{\circ}C + 273.15$
  - ${}^{\circ}F = (1.8 \times {}^{\circ}C) + 32$
  - ${}^{\circ}C = \dfrac{{}^{\circ}F - 32}{1.8}$

2.8 DENSITY

- The density of a substance is the amount of matter (mass) in a given volume of the substance:

$$d = \frac{\text{mass}}{\text{volume}}$$

- Specific gravity is the ratio of the density of a substance to the density of another reference substance (usually water).

REVIEW QUESTIONS

1. When a very large number is written in scientific notation, should the exponent be a positive or a negative number?
2. To write 635.2×10^{-8} in the proper scientific notation form, should the exponent increase or decrease?
3. Explain why the last digit in a measurement is uncertain.
4. How can the number 642,000 g be written to indicate that there are four significant figures?
5. How are significant zeroes identified?

6. State the rules used in this text for rounding off numbers.
7. Is it possible for the calculated answer from a multiplication or division problem to contain more significant figures than the measurements used in the calculation?
8. Is it possible for the calculated answer from an addition or subtraction problem to contain more significant figures than the measurements used in the calculation?
9. How many nanometers are in 1 cm? (Table 2.3)
10. How many milligrams are in 1 kg?
11. Why does an astronaut weigh more on Earth than in space when his or her mass remains the same in both places?
12. What is the relationship between milliliters and cubic centimeters?
13. What is the metric equivalent of 3.5 in.?
14. Distinguish between heat and temperature.
15. Compare the number of degrees between the freezing point of water and its boiling point on the Fahrenheit, Kelvin, and Celsius temperature scales. (Figure 2.5)

16. Describe the order of the following substances (top to bottom) if these three substances were placed in a 100-mL graduated cylinder: 25 mL glycerin, 25 mL mercury, and a cube of magnesium 2.0 cm on an edge. (Table 2.6)
17. Arrange these materials in order of increasing density: salt, vegetable oil, lead, and ethyl alcohol. (Table 2.6)
18. Ice floats in vegetable oil and sinks in ethyl alcohol. The density of ice must lie between what numerical values? (Table 2.6)
19. Distinguish between density and specific gravity.
20. Ice floats in water, yet ice is simply frozen water. If the density of water is 1.0 g/mL, how is this possible?
21. If you collect a container of oxygen gas, should you store it with the mouth up or down? Explain your answer. (Table 2.6)
22. Which substance has the greater volume; 25 g gold or 25 g silver? (Table 2.6)

Most of the exercises in this chapter are available for assignment via the online homework management program, WileyPLUS (www.wileyplus.com). All exercises with blue numbers have answers in Appendix VI.

PAIRED EXERCISES

1. What is the numerical meaning of each of the following?
   (a) kilogram
   (b) centimeter
   (c) microliter
   (d) millimeter
   (e) deciliter

2. What is the correct unit of measurement for each of the following?
   (a) 1000 m
   (b) 0.1 g
   (c) 0.000001 L
   (d) 0.01 m
   (e) 0.001 L

3. State the abbreviation for each of the following units:
   (a) gram
   (b) microgram
   (c) centimeter
   (d) micrometer
   (e) milliliter
   (f) deciliter

4. State the abbreviation for each of the following units:
   (a) milligram
   (b) kilogram
   (c) meter
   (d) nanometer
   (e) angstrom
   (f) microliter

5. Determine whether the zeros in each number are significant:
   (a) 2050
   (b) 9.00×10^2
   (c) 0.0530
   (d) 0.075
   (e) 300.
   (f) 285.00

6. Determine whether the zeros in each number are significant:
   (a) 0.005
   (b) 1500
   (c) 250.
   (d) 10.000
   (e) 6.070×10^4
   (f) 0.2300

7. How many significant figures are in each of the following numbers?
   (a) 0.025
   (b) 22.4
   (c) 0.0404
   (d) 5.50×10^3

8. State the number of significant figures in each of the following numbers:
   (a) 40.0
   (b) 0.081
   (c) 129,042
   (d) 4.090×10^{-3}

9. Round each of the following numbers to three significant figures:
   (a) 93.246
   (b) 0.02857
   (c) 4.644
   (d) 34.250

10. Round each of the following numbers to three significant figures:
   (a) 8.8726
   (b) 21.25
   (c) 129.509
   (d) 1.995×10^6

11. Express each of the following numbers in exponential notation:
   (a) 2,900,000
   (b) 0.587
   (c) 0.00840
   (d) 0.0000055

12. Write each of the following numbers in exponential notation:
   (a) 0.0456
   (b) 4082.2
   (c) 40.30
   (d) 12,000,000

13. Solve the following problems, stating answers to the proper number of significant figures:
   (a) $12.62 + 1.5 + 0.25 = ?$
   (b) $(2.25 \times 10^3)(4.80 \times 10^4) = ?$
   (c) $\dfrac{(452)(6.2)}{14.3} = ?$
   (d) $(0.0394)(12.8) = ?$
   (e) $\dfrac{0.4278}{59.6} = ?$
   (f) $10.4 + 3.75(1.5 \times 10^4) = ?$

14. Evaluate each of the following expressions. State the answer to the proper number of significant figures:
   (a) $15.2 - 2.75 + 15.67$
   (b) $(4.68)(12.5)$
   (c) $\dfrac{182.6}{4.6}$
   (d) $1986 + 23.84 + 0.012$
   (e) $\dfrac{29.3}{(284)(415)}$
   (f) $(2.92 \times 10^{-3})(6.14 \times 10^5)$

15. Change these fractions into decimals. Express each answer to three significant figures:

(a) $\dfrac{5}{6}$ (b) $\dfrac{3}{7}$ (c) $\dfrac{12}{16}$ (d) $\dfrac{9}{18}$

16. Change each of the following decimals to fractions in lowest terms:
(a) 0.25   (b) 0.625   (c) 1.67   (d) 0.8888

17. Solve each of these equations for x:

(a) $3.42x = 6.5$ (c) $\dfrac{0.525}{x} = 0.25$

(b) $\dfrac{x}{12.3} = 7.05$

18. Solve each equation for the variable:

(a) $x = \dfrac{212 - 32}{1.8}$ (c) $72°F = 1.8x + 32$

(b) $8.9\dfrac{g}{mL} = \dfrac{40.90\ g}{x}$

Unit Conversions

19. Complete the following metric conversions using the correct number of significant figures:
(a) 28.0 cm to m
(b) 1000. m to km
(c) 9.28 cm to mm
(d) 10.68 g to mg
(e) 6.8×10^4 mg to kg
(f) 8.54 g to kg
(g) 25.0 mL to L
(h) 22.4 L to μL

20. Complete the following metric conversions using the correct number of significant figures:
(a) 4.5 cm to Å
(b) 12 nm to cm
(c) 8.0 km to mm
(d) 164 mg to g
(e) 0.65 kg to mg
(f) 5.5 kg to g
(g) 0.468 L to mL
(h) 9.0 μL to mL

21. Complete the following American/metric conversions using the correct number of significant figures:
(a) 42.2 in. to cm
(b) 0.64 m to in.
(c) 2.00 in.^{2} to cm^2
(d) 42.8 kg to lb
(e) 3.5 qt to mL
(f) 20.0 L to gal

22. Make the following conversions using the correct number of significant figures:
(a) 35.6 m to ft
(b) 16.5 km to mi
(c) 4.5 in.^{3} to mm^3
(d) 95 lb to g
(e) 20.0 gal to L
(f) 4.5×10^4 ft^3 to m^3

23. After you have worked out at the gym on a stationary bike for 45 min, the distance gauge indicates that you have traveled 15.2 mi. What was your rate in km/hr?

24. A competitive college runner ran a 5-K (5.0-km) race in 15 min, 23 s. What was her pace in miles per hour?

25. A pharmacy technician is asked to prepare an antibiotic IV solution that will contain 500. mg of cephalosporin for every 100. mL of normal saline solution. The total volume of saline solution will be 1 L. How many grams of the cephalosporin will be needed for this IV solution?

26. An extra-strength aspirin tablet contains 0.500 g of the active ingredient, acetylsalicylic acid. Aspirin strength used to be measured in grains. If 1 grain = 60 mg, how many grains of the active ingredient are in 1 tablet? (Report your answer to three significant figures.)

27. The maximum speed recorded for a giant tortoise is 0.11 m/sec. How many miles could a gaint tortoise travel in 5.0 hr?

28. How many days would it take for a crepe myrtle tree to grow 1 cm in height if it grows 3.38 feet per year? (Report your answer to three significant figures.)

29. A personal trainer uses calipers on a client to determine his percent body fat. After taking the necessary measurements, the personal trainer determines that the client's body contains 11.2% fat by mass (11.2 lb of fat per 100 lb of body mass). If the client weighs 225 lb, how many kg of fat does he have?

30. The weight of a diamond is measured in carats. How many pounds does a 5.75-carat diamond weigh? (1 carat = 200. mg)

31. A competitive high school swimmer takes 52 s to swim 100. yards. What is his rate in m/min?

32. In 2005, Jarno Trulli was the pole winner of the U.S. Grand Prix Race with a speed of 133 mi per hr. What was his speed in cm/s?

33. In 2006, Christian Stengl climbed to the top of Mount Everest, elevation 29,035 ft, from a starting point of 21,002 ft in a record time of 16 hr, 42 min. Determine his average rate of climb in
(a) miles per minute   (b) meters per second

34. The *Alvin*, a submersible research vessel, can descend into the ocean to a depth of approximately 4500 m in just over 5 hr. Determine its average rate of submersion in
(a) feet per minute   (b) kilometers per second

35. The world's record for the largest cup of coffee was broken on October 15, 2010, with a 2010-gal cup of coffee in Las Vegas, Nevada. If a cup of coffee contains 473 mL of coffee, how many cups of coffee would be required to fill this coffee cup?

36. Tilapia is rapidly becoming an important source of fish around the world. This is because it can be farmed easily and sustainably. In 2011, 475 million lb of tilapia were consumed by Americans. If the average tilapia has a mass of 535 g, how many tilapia were consumed in 2011?

PRNewsFoto/GourmetGift Baskets.com/AP/Wide World Photos

37. Assuming that there are 20. drops in 1.0 mL, how many drops are in 1.0 gallon?

38. How many liters of oil are in a 42-gal barrel of oil?

39. Calculate the number of milliliters of water in a cubic foot of water.

40. Oil spreads in a thin layer on water called an "oil slick." How much area in m^2 will 200 cm^3 of oil cover if it forms a layer 0.5 nm thick?

41. A textbook is 27 cm long, 21 cm wide and 4.4 cm thick. What is the volume in:
(a) cubic centimeters?   (c) cubic inches?
(b) liters?

42. An aquarium measures 16 in. × 8 in. × 10 in. How many liters of water does it hold? How many gallons?

43. A toddler in Italy visits the family doctor. The nurse takes the child's temperature, which reads 38.8°C.
(a) Convert this temperature to °F.
(b) If 98.6°F is considered normal, does the child have a fever?

44. Driving to the grocery store, you notice the temperature is 45°C. Determine what this temperature is on the Fahrenheit scale and what season of the year it might be.

45. Make the following conversions and include an equation for each one:
(a) 162°F to °C   (c) −18°C to °F
(b) 0.0°F to K   (d) 212 K to °C

46. Make the following conversions and include an equation for each one:
(a) 32°C to °F   (c) 273°C to K
(b) −8.6°F to °C   (d) 100 K to °F

47. At what temperature are the Fahrenheit and Celsius temperatures exactly equal?

48. At what temperature are Fahrenheit and Celsius temperatures the same in value but opposite in sign?

49. The average temperature on Venus is 460°C. What is this temperature in °F?

50. The average temperature at the top of Jupiter's clouds is −244°F. What is this temperature in °C?

51. What is the density of a sample of 65.0 mL of automobile oil having a mass of 59.82 g?

52. A 25.2-mL sample of kerosene was determined to have a mass of 20.41 g. What is the density of kerosene?

53. A student weighed an empty graduated cylinder and found that it had a mass of 25.23 g. When filled with 25.0 mL of an unknown liquid, the total mass was 50.92 g. What is the density of the liquid?

54. A total of 32.95 g of mossy zinc was placed into a graduated cylinder containing 50.0 mL of water. The water level rose to 54.6 mL. Determine the density of the zinc.

55. Linseed oil has a density of 0.929 g/mL. How many mL are in 15 g of the oil?

56. Glycerol has a density of 1.20 g/mL. How many mL are in 75 g of glycerol?

ADDITIONAL EXERCISES

57. You calculate that you need 10.0123576 g of NaCl for an experiment. What amount should you measure out if the precision of the balance is
(a) + or − 0.01 g?   (c) + or − 0.0001 g?
(b) + or − 0.001 g?

58. Often small objects are measured by mass in order to count them.
(a) If the mass of 1 Skittle is 1.134, what mass of Skittles should be packaged in a bag containing 175 Skittles?
(b) The volume of exactly 6 Skittles is 5.3 mL as measured in a 10.0-mL graduated cylinder. What volume (in liters) of Skittles should be packaged in a bag containing 175 Skittles?
(c) Determine the number of Skittles expected in 325.0-g bag of Skittles.
(d) Determine the number of Skittles expected in a beaker containing 0.550 L of Skittles.
(e) Five bags were filled with 350.0 g of Skittles and 5 more bags were filled with 0.325 L of Skittles. The Skittles in each bag were then counted and the data are tabulated below:

Mass Skittles	Number of Skittles	Volume Skittles	Number of Skittles
350.0 g	310	0.325 L	392
350.0 g	313	0.325 L	378
350.0 g	308	0.325 L	401
350.0 g	309	0.325 L	369
350.0 g	312	0.325 L	382

Which measurement method is more accurate? More precise? Explain your reasoning.

59. Suppose you want to add 100 mL of solvent to a reaction flask. Which piece of glassware shown in Figure 2.3 would be the **best** choice for accomplishing this task and why?

60. A reaction requires 21.5 g of $CHCl_3$. No balance is available, so it will have to be measured by volume. How many mL of $CHCl_3$ need to be taken? (Density of $CHCl_3$ is 1.484 g/mL.)

61. A 25.27-g sample of pure sodium was prepared for an experiment. How many mL of sodium is this? (Density of sodium is 0.97 g/mL.)

62. In the United States, coffee consumption averages 4.00×10^8 cups per day. If each cup of coffee contains 160 mg caffeine, how many pounds of caffeine are being consumed each day?

63. In a role-playing video game (RPG) your character is a Human Paladin that can carry 115 lb of gear. Your character is carrying 92 lb of gear and a vial of strength potion (which allows you to carry an additional 50.0 lb of gear). If you find a cave filled with mass potions (used for resisting strong winds), after using the strength potion, how many vials can you collect if the vials each contain 50.0 mL of mass potion with a density of 193 g/mL? The vials have negligible mass.

64. A cape is designed for Lady Gaga's concert with 4560 sequins. If a sequin has a volume of 0.0241 cm^3 and the sequins have a density of 41.6 g/cm^3, what is the mass in lb and kg of sequins on Lady Gaga's cape?

65. Will a hollow cube with sides of length 0.50 m hold 8.5 L of solution? Depending on your answer, how much additional solution would be required to fill the container or how many times would the container need to be filled to measure the 8.5 L?

66. The accepted toxic dose of mercury is 300 µg/day. Dental offices sometimes contain as much as 180 µg of mercury per cubic meter of air. If a nurse working in the office ingests 2×10^4 L of air per day, is he or she at risk for mercury poisoning?

67. Hydrogen becomes a liquid at 20.27 K. What is this temperature in (a)°C?   (b) °F?

68. Scientists led by Rob Eagle at CalTech have examined 150-million-year-old fossilized teeth of sauropods, huge four-legged dinosaurs, to determine their average body temperature. They analyzed the type and number of carbon-oxygen bonds, leading them to conclude that the sauropods' internal temperature was between 36 and 38°C. Determine this temperatue range in °F and compare the body temperature to other modern animals. Which of the following animals do these dinosaurs most closely resemble?

Animal	Temperature
dogs	100.5–102.5°F
tropical fish	78°F
bottlenose dolphin	97–99°F
tortoises	78–82°F
humans	99°F
birds	105°F
cows	102°F

69. According to the National Heart, Lung, and Blood Institute, LDL-cholesterol levels of less than 130 mg of LDL-cholesterol per deciliter of blood are desirable for heart health in humans. On the average, a human has 4.7 L of whole blood. What is the maximum number if grams of LDL-cholesterol that a human should have?

70. You have been sent to buy gold from prospectors in the West. You have no balance but you do have a flask full of mercury. You have been told that many prospectors will bring you fool's gold or iron pyrite in the hopes that you cannot tell the difference. Given the following densities for gold, mercury, and iron pyrite, how could you determine whether the samples brought to you are really gold?

gold	18.3 g/mL
mercury	13.6 g/mL
iron pyrite	5.00 g/mL

71. The height of a horse is measured in hands (1 hand = exactly 4 in.). How many meters is a horse that measures 14.2 hands?

72. Camels have been reported to drink as much as 22.5 gal of water in 12 hr. How many liters can they drink in 30. days?

73. You are given three cubes, A, B, and C; one is magnesium, one is aluminum, and the third is silver. All three cubes have the same mass, but cube A has a volume of 25.9 mL, cube B has a volume of 16.7 mL, and cube C has a volume of 4.29 mL. Identify cubes A, B, and C.

74. When a chunk of wood burns, much more than just smoke is produced. In addition nanotubes made of pure carbon are formed that they have a structure resembling a roll of chicken wire. These nanotubes are stronger than steel, resistant to fire, and make good heat conductors. If a typical carbon nanotube has a diameter of 1.3 nm, how many nanotubes would need to be laid side by side to construct a bridge 40.0 feet wide?

75. In the United States, land is measured in acres. There are 43,560 ft^2 in each acre. How many km^2 are in 125 acres?

76. A cube of aluminum has a mass of 500. g. What will be the mass of a cube of gold of the same dimensions?

77. A 25.0-mL sample of water at 90°C has a mass of 24.12 g. Calculate the density of water at this temperature.

78. The mass of an empty container is 88.25 g. The mass of the container when filled with a liquid ($d = 1.25$ g/mL) is 150.50 g. What is the volume of the container?

79. Which liquid will occupy the greater volume, 50 g of water or 50 g of ethyl alcohol? Explain.

80. The Sacagawea gold-colored dollar coin has a mass of 8.1 g and contains 3.5% manganese. What is its mass in ounces (1 lb = 16 oz), and how many ounces of Mn are in this coin?

81. The density of sulfuric acid is 1.84 g/mL. What volume of this acid will weigh 100. g?

82. Dark-roasted coffee contains increased amonts of N-methylpyridinium, or NMP, a ringed compound that is not present in green unroasted coffee beans. This compound seems to decrease the stomach acid production normally associated with drinking coffee. In coffee made from dark-roasted coffee, the concentration of NMP is 31.4 mg/L. How many milligrams of NMP would you consume if you drank 2.00 large cups of dark-roasted coffee? (One coffee cup contains 10.0 fluid ounces of liquid.)

83. The density of palladium at 20°C is 12.0 g/mL, and at 1550°C the density is 11.0 g/mL. What is the change in volume (in mL) of 1.00 kg Pd in going from 20°C to 1550°C?

84. As a solid substance is heated, its volume increases, but its mass remains the same. Sketch a graph of density versus temperature showing the trend you expect. Briefly explain.

85. The first Apple computer had 5.0 Mbytes of storage space on its hard drive and the cost of this computer was $9995. An Apple iPad II has 64 Gbytes of storage for a cost of $699. Calculate the cost per byte for each of these two Apple products. Which is a better buy?

(a) Apple II computer   (b) iPad

Rama & Musée Bolo/Wikimedia/http://en.wikipedia.org/wiki/File: Apple-II.jpg

© Christine Glade/iStockphoto

86. A gold bullion dealer advertised a bar of pure gold for sale. The gold bar had a mass of 3300 g and measured 2.00 cm × 15.0 cm × 6.00 cm. Was the bar pure gold? Show evidence for your answer.

87. A 35.0-mL sample of ethyl alcohol (density 0.789 g/mL) is added to a graduated cylinder that has a mass of 49.28 g. What will be the mass of the cylinder plus the alcohol?

88. Several years ago, pharmacists used the Apothecary System of Measurement. In this system, 1 scruple is equal to 20 grains (gr). There are 480 gr in 1 oz, and in this system, there are 373 g in 12 oz. How many scruples would be in 695 g?

CHALLENGE EXERCISES

89. You have just purchased a 500-mL bottle of a decongestant medication. The doctor prescribed 2 teaspoons 4 times a day for 10 days. Have you purchased enough medication? (1 teaspoon (tsp) = 5 mL)

90. Your boss found a piece of metal in the lab and wants you to determine what the metal is. She is pretty sure that the metal is either lead, aluminum, or silver. The lab bench has a balance and a 100-mL graduated cylinder with 50 mL of water in it. You decide to weigh the metal and find that it has a mass of 20.25 g. After dropping the piece of metal into the graduated cylinder containing water, you observe that the volume increased to 57.5 mL. Identify the metal.

91. Forgetful Freddie placed 25.0 mL of a liquid in a graduated cylinder with a mass of 89.450 g when empty. When Freddie placed a metal slug with a mass of 15.454 g into the cylinder, the volume rose to 30.7 mL. Freddie was asked to calculate the density of the liquid and of the metal slug from his data, but he forgot to obtain the mass of the liquid. He was told that if he found the mass of the cylinder containing the liquid and the slug, he would have enough data for the calculations. He did so and found its mass to be 125.934 g. Calculate the density of the liquid and of the metal slug.

92. Neutrinos are subatomic particles with a very low mass. Recent work at CERN, Europe's particle-physics lab near Geneva, Switzerland, suggests that neutrinos may have the ability to travel faster than the speed of light. If the speed of light is 1.86×10^8 mi/hr, how many nanoseconds should it take for light to travel from CERN to the Gran Sasso National Lab in Italy, a 730.0-km journey? If a neutrino can travel the same distance 60 nsec faster, how many significant figures would you need to detect the difference in speed?

ANSWERS TO PRACTICE EXERCISES

2.1 (a) $1200 = 1.200 \times 10^3$ (left means positive exponent)

(b) $6,600,000 = 6.6 \times 10^6$ (left means positive exponent)

(c) $0.0468 = 4.68 \times 10^{-2}$ (right means negative exponent)

(d) $0.00003 = 3 \times 10^{-5}$ (right means negative exponent)

2.2 (a) the estimated digits are 4, 1, 0; (b) 3

2.3 (a) 2; (b) 4; (c) 4; (d) 1; (e) 3; (f) 4; (g) 1; (h) 3

2.4 (a) 42.25 (Rule 2); (b) 88.0 (Rule 1); (c) 0.0897 (Rule 2); (d) 0.090 (Rule 2); (e) 225 (Rule 1); (f) 14.2 (Rule 2)

2.5 (a) 3350 in.$^2 = 3.4 \times 10^3$ in.^{2}; (b) 50.7 mi/hr; (c) 0.79; (d) 1.3; (e) 20.5; (f) 3.71

2.6 (a) 2; (b) 2; (c) 1; (d) 2; (e) 4; (f) 2; (g) 2; (h) 2

2.7 (a) 0.567 m; (b) 680; (c) 0.125

2.8 (a) 0.560 g; (b) 0.525 kg; (c) 1.75×10^5 mg

2.9 (a) 0.025 L; (b) 1550 mL; (c) 45 dL

2.10 0.14 lb

2.11 (a) 1.69×10^4 m; (b) 3.5×10^{-2} m^2

2.12 30 m^3 or 3×10^1 m^3

2.13 165 lb

2.14 0.793 qt

2.15 1.89 L (the number of significant figures is arbitrary)

2.16 $-269°C$, $-452°F$

2.17 37.0°C, 310. K

2.18 The density is 9.35 g/mL; therefore the ring is not pure silver. The density of silver is 10.5 g/mL.

2.19 0.88 g/mL

This reclining Buddha in the Grand Palace in Bangkok, Thailand, is made of gold.

CHAPTER **3**

ELEMENTS AND COMPOUNDS

In Chapter 1 we learned that matter can be divided into the broad categories of pure substances and mixtures. We further learned that pure substances are either elements or compounds. The chemical elements are very important to us in our daily lives. In tiny amounts they play a large role in our health and metabolism. Metallic elements are used for the skin of airplanes, buildings, and sculpture. In this chapter we explore the nature of the chemical elements and begin to learn how chemists classify them.

3.1 ELEMENTS

Define an element and write the chemical symbol for an element when given its name.

● LEARNING OBJECTIVE

KEY TERMS
element
atom
symbols

See the periodic table on the inside front cover.

All words in English are formed from an alphabet consisting of only 26 letters. All known substances on Earth—and most probably in the universe, too—are formed from a sort of "chemical alphabet" consisting of over 100 known elements. An **element** is a fundamental or elementary substance that cannot be broken down by chemical means to simpler substances. Elements are the building blocks of all substances. The elements are numbered in order of increasing complexity beginning with hydrogen, number 1. Of the first 92 elements, 88 are known to occur in nature. The other four—technetium (43), promethium (61), astatine (85), and francium (87)—either do not occur in nature or have only transitory existences during radioactive decay. With the exception of number 94, plutonium, elements above number 92 are not known to occur naturally but have been synthesized, usually in very small quantities, in laboratories. The discovery of trace amounts of element 94 (plutonium) in nature has been reported. No elements other than those on Earth have been detected on other bodies in the universe.

Most substances can be decomposed into two or more simpler substances. Water can be decomposed into hydrogen and oxygen. Sugar can be decomposed into carbon, hydrogen, and oxygen. Table salt is easily decomposed into sodium and chlorine. An element, however, cannot be decomposed into simpler substances by ordinary chemical changes.

If we could take a small piece of an element, say copper, and divide it and subdivide it into smaller and smaller particles, we would finally come to a single unit of copper that we could no longer divide and still have copper (see **Figure 3.1**). This smallest particle of an element that can exist is called an **atom**, which is also the smallest unit of an element that can enter into a chemical reaction. Atoms are made up of still smaller subatomic particles. However, these subatomic particles (described in Chapter 5) do not have the properties of elements.

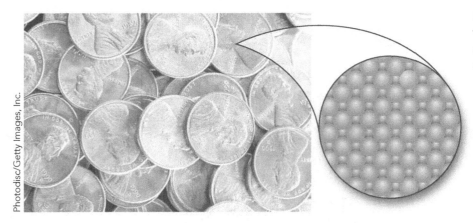

Photodisc/Getty Images, Inc.

Figure 3.1
The surface of a penny is made up of tiny identical copper atoms packed tightly together.

Natural States of the Elements

Most substances around us are mixtures or compounds. Elements tend to be reactive, and they combine with other elements to form compounds. It is rare to find elements in nature in pure form. There are some exceptions, however. Gold, for example, can be found as nuggets. Silver and platinum can also be found in nature in pure form. In fact, these metals are sometimes called the *noble metals* since they have a low reactivity. The noble gases are also not reactive and can be found in nature in uncombined form. Helium gas, for example, consists of tiny helium atoms moving independently.

Nitrogen and oxygen gases are composed of molecules (N_2, ●) and (O_2, ●).

David Muir/Getty Images, Inc.

Gold is one of the few elements found in nature in an uncombined state.

© Ashok Rodrigues/iStockphoto

Helium causes these balloons to float in air.

Air can also be divided into its component gases. It is mainly composed of nitrogen and oxygen gases. But when we "look inside" these gases, we find tiny molecules (N_2 and O_2) instead of independent atoms like we see in the noble gases.

Distribution of Elements

At the present time, 118 elements are known and only 88 of these occur naturally. At normal room temperature only two of the elements, bromine and mercury, are liquids (see Figure 3.2a). Eleven elements—hydrogen, nitrogen, oxygen, fluorine, chlorine, helium, neon, argon, krypton, xenon, and radon—are gases (see Figure 3.2b). The elements are distributed unequally in nature.

Ten elements make up about 99% of the mass of the Earth's crust, seawater, and atmosphere. The distribution of the elements is listed in order of their abundance in Table 3.1.

Oxygen, the most abundant of these elements, accounts for about 20% of the atmosphere and is found in virtually all rocks, sand, and soil. In these places, oxygen is not present as O_2 molecules but as part of compounds usually containing silicon and aluminum atoms. The mass percents given in Table 3.1 include the Earth's crust to a depth of 10 miles, the oceans, fresh

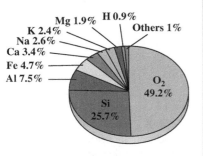

TABLE 3.1   Mass Percent of the Most Abundant Elements in the Earth's Crust, Oceans, and Atmosphere

Element	Mass percent	Element	Mass percent
Oxygen	49.2	Titanium	0.6
Silicon	25.7	Chlorine	0.19
Aluminum	7.5	Phosphorus	0.11
Iron	4.7	Manganese	0.09
Calcium	3.4	Carbon	0.08
Sodium	2.6	Sulfur	0.06
Potassium	2.4	Barium	0.04
Magnesium	1.9	Nitrogen	0.03
Hydrogen	0.9	Fluorine	0.03
		All others	0.49

© Valerie Loiseleux/iStockphoto

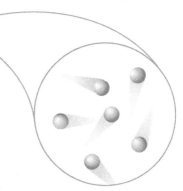

(b) Neon creates the light in these signs.

Mark Evans/iStockphoto

(a) Mercury is sometimes used in thermometers.

Figure 3.2

Examples of a liquid and a gaseous element.

water, and the atmosphere. It does not include the mantle and core of the Earth, which consist primarily of nickel and iron.

The list of elements found in living matter is very different from those of the Earth's crust, oceans, and atmosphere. The major elements in living organisms are shown in Table 3.2.

The major biologically important molecules are formed primarily from oxygen, carbon, hydrogen, and nitrogen. Some elements found in the body are crucial for life, although they are present in very tiny amounts (trace elements). Some of these trace elements include chromium, copper, fluorine, iodine, and selenium.

Names of the Elements

The names of the elements come to us from various sources. Many are derived from early Greek, Latin, or German words that describe some property of the element. For example, iodine is taken from the Greek word *iodes*, meaning "violetlike," and iodine is certainly violet in the vapor state. The name of the metal bismuth originates from the German words *weisse masse*, which means "white mass." Miners called it *wismat*; it was later changed to *bismat*, and finally to bismuth. Some elements are named for the location of their discovery—for example, germanium, discovered in 1886 by a German chemist. Others are named in commemoration of famous scientists, such as einsteinium and curium, named for Albert Einstein and Marie Curie, respectively.

Symbols of the Elements

We all recognize Mr., N.Y., and Ave. as abbreviations for mister, New York, and avenue, respectively. In a like manner, each element also has an abbreviation; these are called **symbols** of the elements. Fourteen elements have a single letter as their symbol, and the rest have two letters. A symbol stands for the element itself, for one atom of the element, and (as we shall see later) for a particular quantity of the element.

RULES FOR SYMBOLS OF ELEMENTS

1. Symbols have either one or two letters.

2. If one letter is used, it is capitalized.

3. If two letters are used, only the first is capitalized.

Examples: Iodine I   Barium Ba

The symbols and names of all the elements are given in the table on the inside front cover of this book. Table 3.3 lists the more commonly used elements and their symbols. Examine

TABLE 3.2 Mass Percent of the Elements in the Human Body

Element	Mass percent
Oxygen	65
Carbon	18
Hydrogen	10
Nitrogen	3
Calcium	1.4
Phosphorus	1
Magnesium	0.5
Potassium	0.34
Sulfur	0.26
Sodium	0.14

TABLE 3.3 Symbols of the Most Common Elements

Element	Symbol	Element	Symbol	Element	Symbol
Aluminum	Al	Gold	Au	Platinum	Pt
Antimony	Sb	Helium	He	Plutonium	Pu
Argon	Ar	Hydrogen	H	Potassium	K
Arsenic	As	Iodine	I	Radium	Ra
Barium	Ba	Iron	Fe	Silicon	Si
Bismuth	Bi	Lead	Pb	Silver	Ag
Boron	B	Lithium	Li	Sodium	Na
Bromine	Br	Magnesium	Mg	Strontium	Sr
Cadmium	Cd	Manganese	Mn	Sulfur	S
Calcium	Ca	Mercury	Hg	Tin	Sn
Carbon	C	Neon	Ne	Titanium	Ti
Chlorine	Cl	Nickel	Ni	Tungsten	W
Chromium	Cr	Nitrogen	N	Uranium	U
Cobalt	Co	Oxygen	O	Xenon	Xe
Copper	Cu	Palladium	Pd	Zinc	Zn
Fluorine	F	Phosphorus	P		

Aluminum is used for recyclable cans.

© Getty Images, Inc.

© Photononstop/SuperStock

Chunks of sulfur are transported in baskets from a mine in East Java.

TABLE 3.4 Symbols of the Elements Derived from Early Names*

Present name	Symbol	Former name
Antimony	Sb	Stibium
Copper	Cu	Cuprum
Gold	Au	Aurum
Iron	Fe	Ferrum
Lead	Pb	Plumbum
Mercury	Hg	Hydrargyrum
Potassium	K	Kalium
Silver	Ag	Argentum
Sodium	Na	Natrium
Tin	Sn	Stannum
Tungsten	W	Wolfram

*These symbols are in use today even though they do not correspond to the current name of the element.

Table 3.3 carefully and you will note that most of the symbols start with the same letter as the name of the element that is represented. A number of symbols, however, appear to have no connection with the names of the elements they represent (see Table 3.4). These symbols have been carried over from earlier names (usually in Latin) of the elements and are so firmly implanted in the literature that their use is continued today.

Special care must be taken in writing symbols. Capitalize only the first letter, and use a lowercase second letter if needed. This is important. For example, consider Co, the symbol for the element cobalt. If you write CO (capital C and capital O), you will have written the two elements carbon and oxygen (the *formula* for carbon monoxide), *not* the single element cobalt. Also, make sure that you write the letters distinctly; otherwise, Co (for cobalt) may be misread as Ca (for calcium).

Knowledge of symbols is essential for writing chemical formulas and equations and will be needed in the remainder of this book and in any future chemistry courses you may take. One

>CHEMISTRY *IN ACTION*

Naming Elements

Have you ever wondered where the names of the elements came from? Some of the elements were named for famous scientists or where they were first discovered and others for their characteristics. Some of the elemental symbols refer to old and rarely used names for the elements.

Elements named for places
- Americium (Am)—first created in America.
- Berkelium (Bk)—first created in Berkeley, Califorina.
- Francium (Fr)—discovered at Curie Institute in France.
- Scandium (Sc)—discovered and mined in Scandinavia.

Elements named for planets and the sun
- Helium (He)—named for the sun (helios) because this was the first place helium was detected.
- Uranium (U)—named for Uranus, which was discovered just before uranium.
- Plutonium (Pu)—named for the former planet Pluto.

Elements named for mythological characters
- Thorium (Th)—named after Thor, the Scandinavian god of war. Thorium is used as a fuel for nuclear weapons.

- Titanium (Ti)—named after Titans, supermen of Greek mythology. Titanium is a super-element because it is very resistant to acid.
- Vanadium (V)—named after the Scandinavian goddess of beauty, Vandis, because vanadium compounds form such beautiful colors.
- Tantalum (Ta) and Niobium (Nb)—named after the mythological Greek king, Tantalus, and his daughter, Princess Niobe. Like the king and his daughter, tantalum and niobium are often found together.

Elements named for their properties
- Chlorine (Cl)—from Greek *chloros* meaning "green." Chlorine is a greenish yellow gas.
- Iodine (I)—from Greek *iodos* meaning "violet."
- Argon (Ar)—from Greek *argos* meaning "lazy." Argon is an extremely unreactive gas, so it was thought too lazy to react.
- Cobalt (Co)—from Greek *kobold* meaning "goblin" or "evil spirit." Cobalt miners often died suddenly and unexpectedly, which was probably due to ingesting arsenic found with the cobalt ore in the German mines.

way to learn the symbols is to practice a few minutes a day by making flash cards of names and symbols and then practicing daily. Initially, it is a good plan to learn the symbols of the most common elements shown in Table 3.3.

EXAMPLE 3.1

Write the names and symbols for the elements that have only one letter as their symbol. (Use the periodic table on the inside front cover of your text.)

SOLUTION

Boron, B; Carbon, C; Fluorine, F; Hydrogen, H; Iodine, I; Nitrogen, N; Oxygen, O; Phosphorus, P; Potassium, K; Sulfur, S; Uranium, U; Vanadium, V; Tungsten, W; Yttrium, Y.

PRACTICE 3.1

Write the name, symbol, and vertical column location for the elements whose symbols begin with C. [Use the periodic table on the inside front cover of your text. (1A, 2A, etc.)]

3.2 INTRODUCTION TO THE PERIODIC TABLE

Explain the arrangement of the elements on the periodic table and classify elements as metal, nonmetal, or metalloid.

LEARNING OBJECTIVE

KEY TERMS
groups
noble gases
alkali metals
alkaline earth metals
halogens
representative elements
transition elements
metals
nonmetals
metalloids
diatomic molecules

Almost all chemistry classrooms have a chart called the *periodic table* hanging on the wall. It shows all the chemical elements and contains a great deal of useful information about them. As we continue our study of chemistry, we will learn much more about the periodic table. For now let's begin with the basics.

A simple version of the periodic table is shown in Table 3.5. Notice that in each box there is the symbol for the element and, above it, a number called the *atomic number*. For example nitrogen is $\begin{array}{c} 7 \\ N \end{array}$ and gold is $\begin{array}{c} 79 \\ Au \end{array}$.

TABLE 3.5   The Periodic Table

Noble gases

1 H																	2 He
3 Li	4 Be	☐ Metals										5 B	6 C	7 N	8 O	9 F	10 Ne
11 Na	12 Mg	▨ Metalloids										13 Al	14 Si	15 P	16 S	17 Cl	18 Ar
19 K	20 Ca	21 Sc	22 Ti	23 V	24 Cr	25 Mn	26 Fe	27 Co	28 Ni	29 Cu	30 Zn	31 Ga	32 Ge	33 As	34 Se	35 Br	36 Kr
37 Rb	38 Sr	39 Y	40 Zr	41 Nb	42 Mo	43 Tc	44 Ru	45 Rh	46 Pd	47 Ag	48 Cd	49 In	50 Sn	51 Sb	52 Te	53 I	54 Xe
55 Cs	56 Ba	57 La*	72 Hf	73 Ta	74 W	75 Re	76 Os	77 Ir	78 Pt	79 Au	80 Hg	81 Tl	82 Pb	83 Bi	84 Po	85 At	86 Rn
87 Fr	88 Ra	89 Ac†	104 Rf	105 Db	106 Sg	107 Bh	108 Hs	109 Mt	110 Ds	111 Rg	112 Cn	113 Uut	114 Fl	115 Uup	116 Lv	117 Uus	118 Uuo

(☐ Nonmetals)

	58 Ce	59 Pr	60 Nd	61 Pm	62 Sm	63 Eu	64 Gd	65 Tb	66 Dy	67 Ho	68 Er	69 Tm	70 Yb	71 Lu
*														
†	90 Th	91 Pa	92 U	93 Np	94 Pu	95 Am	96 Cm	97 Bk	98 Cf	99 Es	100 Fm	101 Md	102 No	103 Lr

Figure 3.3

Some groups of elements have special names.

Noble Gases

2 He
10 Ne
18 Ar
36 Kr
54 Xe
86 Rn

The elements are placed in the table in order of increasing atomic number in a particular arrangement designed by Dimitri Mendeleev in 1869. His arrangement organizes the elements with similar chemical properties in columns called families or **groups**. An example of this is the column in the margin.

These elements are all gases and nonreactive. The group is called the **noble gases**. Other groups with special names are the **alkali metals** (under 1A on the table), **alkaline earth metals** (Group 2A), and **halogens** (Group 7A).

The tall columns of the periodic table (1A–7A and the noble gases) are known as the **representative elements**. Those elements in the center section of the periodic table are called **transition elements**. Figure 3.3 shows these groups on a periodic table.

Metals, Nonmetals, and Metalloids

The elements can be classified as metals, nonmetals, and metalloids. Most of the elements are metals. We are familiar with them because of their widespread use in tools, construction materials, automobiles, and so on. But nonmetals are equally useful in our everyday life as major components of clothing, food, fuel, glass, plastics, and wood. Metalloids are often used in the electronics industry.

The **metals** are solids at room temperature (mercury is an exception). They have high luster, are good conductors of heat and electricity, are *malleable* (can be rolled or hammered into sheets), and are *ductile* (can be drawn into wires). Most metals have a high melting point and a high density. Familiar metals are aluminum, chromium, copper, gold, iron, lead, magnesium, mercury, nickel, platinum, silver, tin, and zinc. Less familiar but still important metals are calcium, cobalt, potassium, sodium, uranium, and titanium.

Metals have little tendency to combine with each other to form compounds. But many metals readily combine with nonmetals such as chlorine, oxygen, and sulfur to form compounds such as metallic chlorides, oxides, and sulfides. In nature, minerals are composed of the more reactive metals combined with other elements. A few of the less reactive metals such as copper, gold, and silver are sometimes found in a native, or free, state. Metals are often mixed with one another to form homogeneous mixtures of solids called alloys. Some examples are brass, bronze, steel, and coinage metals.

Nonmetals, unlike metals, are not lustrous, have relatively low melting points and densities, and are generally poor conductors of heat and electricity. Carbon, phosphorus, sulfur, selenium, and iodine are solids; bromine is a liquid; and the rest of the nonmetals are gases. Common nonmetals found uncombined in nature are carbon (graphite and diamond), nitrogen, oxygen, sulfur, and the noble gases (helium, neon, argon, krypton, xenon, and radon).

Nonmetals combine with one another to form molecular compounds such as carbon dioxide (CO_2), methane (CH_4), butane (C_4H_{10}), and sulfur dioxide (SO_2). Fluorine, the most reactive nonmetal, combines readily with almost all other elements.

Several elements (boron, silicon, germanium, arsenic, antimony, tellurium, and polonium) are classified as **metalloids** and have properties that are intermediate between those of metals and those of nonmetals. The intermediate position of these elements is shown in Table 3.5. Certain metalloids, such as boron, silicon, and germanium, are the raw materials for the semiconductor devices that make the electronics industry possible.

EXAMPLE 3.2

Which of the following elements are not metals?

Na, Mo, Cl, S, Mg, Pt, Kr, I, C, Cu

SOLUTION

Nonmetals are generally found on the right-hand side of the periodic table: Cl, S, Kr, I, and C.

PRACTICE 3.2

Write the chemical symbols for
(a) five elements that are metals.
(b) two elements that are liquids at normal room temperature.
(c) five elements that are gases (not noble gases) at normal room temperature.

Diatomic Elements

Diatomic molecules each contain exactly two atoms (alike or different). Seven elements in their uncombined state are **diatomic molecules**. Their symbols, formulas, and brief descriptions are listed in Table 3.6. Whether found free in nature or prepared in the laboratory, the molecules of these elements always contain two atoms. The formulas of the free elements are therefore always written to show this molecular composition: H_2, N_2, O_2, F_2, Cl_2, Br_2, and I_2.

Container of hydrogen molecules.

TABLE 3.6   Elements That Exist as Diatomic Molecules

Element	Symbol	Molecular formula	Normal state
Hydrogen	H	H_2	Colorless gas
Nitrogen	N	N_2	Colorless gas
Oxygen	O	O_2	Colorless gas
Fluorine	F	F_2	Pale yellow gas
Chlorine	Cl	Cl_2	Greenish-yellow gas
Bromine	Br	Br_2	Reddish-brown liquid
Iodine	I	I_2	Bluish-black solid

It is important to see that symbols can designate either an atom or a molecule of an element. Consider hydrogen and oxygen. Hydrogen gas is present in volcanic gases and can be prepared by many chemical reactions. Regardless of their source, all samples of free hydrogen gas consist of diatomic molecules.

Free hydrogen is designated by the formula H_2, which also expresses its composition. Oxygen makes up about 20% by volume of the air that we breathe. This free oxygen is constantly being replenished by photosynthesis; it can also be prepared in the laboratory by several reactions. The majority of free oxygen is diatomic and is designated by the formula O_2. Now consider water, a compound designated by the formula H_2O (sometimes HOH). Water contains neither free hydrogen (H_2) nor free oxygen (O_2). The H_2 part of the formula H_2O simply indicates that two atoms of hydrogen are combined with one atom of oxygen to form water.

H_2 (gray) and O_2 (red) molecules.

Symbols are used to designate elements, show the composition of molecules of elements, and give the elemental composition of compounds.

Figure 3.4 summarizes the classification of elements.

Figure 3.4

Elements fall into two broad categories.

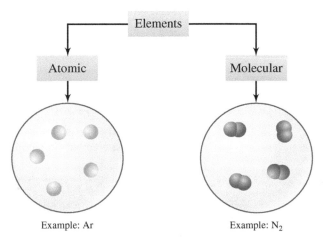

>CHEMISTRY *IN ACTION*

Atomic Oxygen, Friend or Foe?

When scientists at NASA first began sending spacecraft into orbit, they discovered that the spacecraft were being corroded by the environment of the upper atmosphere. The culprit was the atomic oxygen formed by the interaction of ultraviolet radiation with oxygen gas, or O_2. Researchers using atomic oxygen to test the durability of satellite coatings found that atomic oxygen could remove carbon-based materials from the surface of objects without damaging them. Furthermore, NASA engineers discovered that atomic oxygen would not react with and damage glass composed of silicon dioxide because this silicon had already reacted with oxygen and would not react further. Armed with this knowledge, they began to coat the space station and shuttle parts with a thin layer of silicon dioxide to protect them from the corrosive effects of atomic oxygen.

Back in the lab, NASA researchers looked for new ways to utilize the power of atomic oxygen. They discovered several useful applications.

SURGICAL IMPLANTS When implanting foreign objects in a patient, a surgeon must be sure the parts are clean and sterile. It is easy to sterilize these parts and kill all bacteria, but occasionally there is organic debris left behind from the dead bacteria. This organic material can cause postoperative inflammation. Treatment of the sterile implants with atomic oxygen dissolves away the organic matter, leading to more successful and less painful recovery times.

CLEANING OF DAMAGED ART Artwork that has been damaged by soot can be cleaned using atomic oxygen. The oxygen atoms react with the soot and cause it to vaporize away. The chief conservator at the Cleveland Museum of Art tried the atomic oxygen treatment on two paintings damaged in a church fire. Although the paintings were not extremely valuable (and so were good subjects for an experiment), all other attempts to restore them had failed. Atomic oxygen proved to work wonders, and the soot and char were removed to reveal the original image. Because the treatment is a gas, the underlying layers were not harmed. The treatment doesn't work on everything and won't replace other techniques altogether, but the conservator was impressed enough to continue to work with NASA on the process.

Damaged   Restored

NASA

PRACTICE 3.3

Identify the physical state of each of the following elements at room temperature (20°C):

H, Na, Ca, N, S, Fe, Cl, Br, Ne, Hg

Hint: You may need to use a resource (such as the Internet or a chemical handbook) to assist you.

PRACTICE 3.4

Identify each of the following elements as a nonmetal, metal, or metalloid:

Na, F, Cr, Mo, Kr, Si, Cu, Sb, I, S

3.3 COMPOUNDS AND FORMULAS

LEARNING OBJECTIVE ● Distinguish between molecular and ionic compounds and write chemical formulas for compounds.

KEY TERMS

compound
molecule
ion
cation
anion
chemical formula
subscripts
natural law
law of definite composition
law of multiple proportions

A **compound** is a distinct substance that contains two or more elements chemically combined in a definite proportion by mass. Compounds, unlike elements, can be decomposed chemically into simpler substances—that is, into simpler compounds and/or elements. Atoms of the elements in a compound are combined in whole-number ratios, never as fractional parts.

Molecular and Ionic Compounds

Compounds fall into two general types, *molecular* and *ionic*. **Figure 3.5** illustrates the classification of compounds.

A **molecule** is the smallest uncharged individual unit of a compound formed by the union of two or more atoms. Water is a typical molecular compound. If we divide a drop of water into smaller and smaller particles, we finally obtain a single molecule of water consisting of two hydrogen atoms bonded to one oxygen atom, as shown in Figure 3.6. This molecule is the ultimate particle of water; it cannot be further subdivided without destroying the water molecule and forming hydrogen and oxygen.

An **ion** is a positively or negatively charged atom or group of atoms. An ionic compound is held together by attractive forces that exist between positively and negatively charged ions. A positively charged ion is called a **cation** (pronounced *cat-eye-on*); a negatively charged ion is called an **anion** (pronounced *an-eye-on*).

Sodium chloride is a typical ionic compound. The ultimate particles of sodium chloride are positively charged sodium ions and negatively charged chloride ions, shown in Figure 3.6. Sodium chloride is held together in a crystalline structure by the attractive forces existing between these oppositely charged ions. Although ionic compounds consist of large aggregates of cations and anions, their formulas are normally represented by the simplest possible ratio of the atoms in the compound. For example, in sodium chloride the ratio is one sodium ion to one chloride ion, so the formula is NaCl.

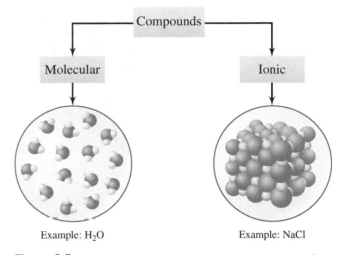

Example: H_2O Example: NaCl

Figure 3.5

Compounds can be classified as molecular and ionic. Ionic compounds are held together by attractive forces between their positive and negative charges. Molecular compounds are held together by covalent bonds.

Two hydrogen atoms combined with an oxygen atom to form a molecule of water (H_2O).

A positively charged sodium ion and a negatively charged chloride ion form the compound sodium chloride (NaCl).

Figure 3.6

Representation of molecular and ionic (nonmolecular) compounds.

There are more than 50 million known registered compounds, with no end in sight as to the number that will be prepared in the future. Each compound is unique and has characteristic properties. Let's consider two compounds, water and sodium chloride, in some detail. Water is a colorless, odorless, tasteless liquid that can be changed to a solid (ice) at 0°C and to a gas (steam) at 100°C. Composed of two atoms of hydrogen and one atom of oxygen per molecule, water is 11.2% hydrogen and 88.8% oxygen by mass. Water reacts chemically with sodium to produce hydrogen gas and sodium hydroxide, with lime to produce calcium hydroxide, and with sulfur trioxide to produce sulfuric acid. When water is decomposed, it forms hydrogen and oxygen molecules (see Figure 3.7). No other compound has all these exact physical and chemical properties; they are characteristic of water alone.

Sodium chloride is a colorless crystalline substance with a ratio of one atom of sodium to one atom of chlorine. Its composition by mass is 39.3% sodium and 60.7% chlorine. It does not conduct electricity in its solid state; it dissolves in water to produce a solution that conducts electricity. When a current is passed through molten sodium chloride, solid sodium and

Figure 3.7

A representation of the decomposition of water into oxygen and hydrogen molecules.

Water molecules $\longrightarrow$ Oxygen molecule + Hydrogen molecules

Andrew Lambert Photography/
Photo Researchers, Inc.

Sodium chloride ⟶ Sodium metal + Chlorine gas

Figure 3.8
When sodium chloride is decomposed, it forms sodium metal and chlorine gas.

gaseous chlorine are produced (see **Figure 3.8**). These specific properties belong to sodium chloride and to no other substance. Thus, a compound may be identified and distinguished from all other compounds by its characteristic properties. We consider these chemical properties further in Chapter 4.

Writing Formulas of Compounds

Chemical formulas are used as abbreviations for compounds. A **chemical formula** shows the symbols and the ratio of the atoms of the elements in a compound. Sodium chloride contains one atom of sodium per atom of chlorine; its formula is NaCl. The formula for water is H_2O; it shows that a molecule of water contains two atoms of hydrogen and one atom of oxygen.

The formula of a compound tells us which elements it is composed of and how many atoms of each element are present in a formula unit. For example, a unit of sulfuric acid is composed of two atoms of hydrogen, one atom of sulfur, and four atoms of oxygen. We could express this compound as HHSOOOO, but this is cumbersome, so we write H_2SO_4 instead. The formula may be expressed verbally as "H-two-S-O-four." Numbers that appear partially below the line and to the right of a symbol of an element are called **subscripts**. Thus, the 2

Figure 3.9

Explanation of the formulas NaCl, H_2SO_4, and $Ca(NO_3)_2$.

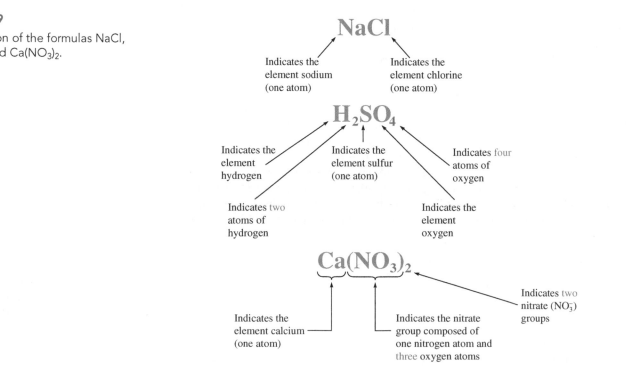

NaCl

Indicates the
element sodium
(one atom)

Indicates the
element chlorine
(one atom)

H_2SO_4

Indicates the
element
hydrogen

Indicates the
element sulfur
(one atom)

Indicates four
atoms of
oxygen

Indicates two
atoms of
hydrogen

Indicates the
element
oxygen

$Ca(NO_3)_2$

Indicates the
element calcium
(one atom)

Indicates the nitrate
group composed of
one nitrogen atom and
three oxygen atoms

Indicates two
nitrate (NO_3^-)
groups

and the 4 in H_2SO_4 are subscripts (see **Figure 3.9**). Characteristics of chemical formulas are as follows:

1. The formula of a compound contains the symbols of all the elements in the compound.

2. When the formula contains one atom of an element, the symbol of that element represents that one atom. The number 1 is not used as a subscript to indicate one atom of an element.

3. When the formula contains more than one atom of an element, the number of atoms is indicated by a subscript written to the right of the symbol of that atom. For example, the 2 in H_2O indicates two atoms of H in the formula.

4. When the formula contains more than one of a group of atoms that occurs as a unit, parentheses are placed around the group, and the number of units of the group is indicated by a subscript placed to the right of the parentheses. Consider the nitrate group, NO_3^-. The formula for sodium nitrate, $NaNO_3$, has only one nitrate group, so no parentheses are needed. Calcium nitrate, $Ca(NO_3)_2$, has two nitrate groups, as indicated by the use of parentheses and the subscript 2. $Ca(NO_3)_2$ has a total of nine atoms: one Ca, two N, and six O atoms. The formula $Ca(NO_3)_2$ is read as "C-A [pause] N-O-three taken twice."

5. Formulas written as H_2O, H_2SO_4, $Ca(NO_3)_2$, and $C_{12}H_{22}O_{11}$ show only the number and kind of each atom contained in the compound; they do not show the arrangement of the atoms in the compound or how they are chemically bonded to one another.

PRACTICE 3.5

How would you read these formulas aloud?
(a) KBr   (b) $PbCl_2$ (c) $CaCO_3$ (d) $Mg(OH)_2$

EXAMPLE 3.3

Write formulas for the following compounds; the atomic composition is given.

(a) hydrogen chloride: 1 atom hydrogen + 1 atom chlorine;
(b) methane: 1 atom carbon + 4 atoms hydrogen;
(c) glucose: 6 atoms carbon + 12 atoms hydrogen + 6 atoms oxygen.

SOLUTION

(a) First write the symbols of the atoms in the formula: H Cl.
   Since the ratio of atoms is one to one, we bring the symbols together to give the formula for hydrogen chloride as HCl.
(b) Write the symbols of the atoms: C H.
   Now bring the symbols together and place a subscript 4 after the hydrogen atom. The formula is CH_4.
(c) Write the symbols of the atoms: C H O.
   Now write the formula, bringing together the symbols followed by the correct subscripts according to the data given (six C, twelve H, six O). The formula is $C_6H_{12}O_6$.

PRACTICE 3.6

Write formulas for the following compounds from the compositions given.

(a) potassium bromide: 1 atom potassium + 1 atom bromine
(b) sodium chlorate: 1 atom sodium + 1 atom chlorine + 3 atoms oxygen
(c) sulfurous acid: 2 atoms hydrogen + 1 atom sulfur + 3 atoms oxygen
(d) aluminum carbonate: 2 aluminum atoms + 3 carbonate ions

Composition of Compounds

A large number of experiments extending over a long period have established the fact that a particular compound always contains the same elements in the same proportions by mass. For example, water always contains 11.2% hydrogen and 88.8% oxygen by mass

Figure 3.10

(a) Dalton's atoms were individual particles, the atoms of each element being alike in mass and size but different in mass and size from other elements. (b) and (c) Dalton's atoms combine in specific ratios to form compounds.

(see Figure 3.10). The fact that water contains hydrogen and oxygen in this particular ratio does not mean that hydrogen and oxygen cannot combine in some other ratio but rather that a compound with a different ratio would not be water. In fact, hydrogen peroxide is made up of two atoms of hydrogen and two atoms of oxygen per molecule and contains 5.9% hydrogen and 94.1% oxygen by mass; its properties are markedly different from those of water (see Figure 3.10).

	Water	Hydrogen peroxide
	11.2% H	5.9% H
	88.8% O	94.1% O
Atomic composition	2 H + 1 O	2 H + 2 O

We often summarize our general observations regarding nature into a statement called a **natural law**. In the case of the composition of a compound, we use the **law of definite composition**, which states that a compound always contains two or more elements chemically combined in a definite proportion by mass.

Let's consider two elements, oxygen and hydrogen, that form more than one compound. In water, 8.0 g of oxygen are present for each gram of hydrogen. In hydrogen peroxide, 16.0 g of oxygen are present for each gram of hydrogen. The masses of oxygen are in the ratio of small whole numbers, 16:8 or 2:1. Hydrogen peroxide has twice as much oxygen (by mass) as does water. Using Dalton's atomic model, we deduce that hydrogen peroxide has twice as many oxygen atoms per hydrogen atom as water. In fact, we now write the formulas for water as H_2O and for hydrogen peroxide as H_2O_2. See Figure 3.10b and c.

The **law of multiple proportions** states that atoms of two or more elements may combine in different ratios to produce more than one compound.

Some examples of the law of multiple proportions are given in Table 3.7. The reliability of this law and the law of definite composition is the cornerstone of the science of chemistry. In essence, these laws state that (1) the composition of a particular substance will always be the same no matter what its origin or how it is formed, and (2) the composition of different compounds formed from the same elements will always be unique.

TABLE 3.7   Selected Compounds Showing Elements That Combine to Give More Than One Compound

Compound	Formula	Percent composition
Copper(I) chloride	CuCl	64.2% Cu, 35.8% Cl
Copper(II) chloride	$CuCl_2$	47.3% Cu, 52.7% Cl
Methane	CH_4	74.9% C, 25.1% H
Octane	C_8H_{18}	85.6% C, 14.4% H
Methyl alcohol	CH_4O	37.5% C, 12.6% H, 49.9% O
Ethyl alcohol	C_2H_6O	52.1% C, 13.1% H, 34.7% O
Glucose	$C_6H_{12}O_6$	40.0% C, 6.7% H, 53.3% O

You need to recognize the difference between a *law* and a *model* (*theory*). A law is a summary of observed behavior. A model (theory) is an attempt to explain the observed behavior. This means that laws remain constant—that is, they do not undergo modification—while theories (models) sometimes fail and are modified or discarded over time.

CHAPTER **3 REVIEW**

3.1 ELEMENTS

- All matter consists of about 100 elements.
- An element is a fundamental chemical substance.
- The smallest particle of an element is an atom.
- Elements cannot be broken down by chemical means to a simpler substance.
- Most elements are found in nature combined with other elements.
- Elements that are found in uncombined form in nature include gold, silver, copper, and platinum as well as the noble gases (He, Ne, Ar, Kr, Xe, Rn).
- Chemical elements are not distributed equally in nature.
- Hydrogen is the most abundant element in the universe.
- Oxygen is the most abundant element on the Earth and in the human body.
- Names for the chemical elements come from a variety of sources, including Latin, location of discovery, and famous scientists.
- Rules for writing symbols for the elements are:
  - One or two letters
  - If one letter, use a capital
  - If two letters, only the first is a capital

KEY TERMS
element
atom
symbols

3.2 INTRODUCTION TO THE PERIODIC TABLE

- The periodic table was designed by Dimitri Mendeleev and arranges the elements according to their atomic numbers and in groups by their chemical properties.
- Elements can be classified as representative or as transition elements.
- Elements can also be classified by special groups with similar chemical properties. Such groups include the noble gases, alkali metals, alkaline earth metals, and halogens.
- Elements can be classified as metals, nonmetals, or metalloids.
  - Most elements are metals.
  - Metals have the following properties:
    - High luster
    - Good conductors of heat and electricity
    - Malleable
  - Nonmetals have the following properties:
    - Not lustrous
    - Poor conductors of heat and electricity
- Diatomic molecules contain exactly two atoms (alike or different).
- Seven elements exist as diatomic molecules—H_2, N_2, O_2, F_2, Cl_2, Br_2, and I_2.

KEY TERMS
groups
noble gases
alkali metals
alkaline earth metals
halogens
representative elements
transition elements
metals
nonmetals
metalloids
diatomic molecules

Elements

Atomic

Molecular

Example: Ar

Example: N_2

3.3 COMPOUNDS AND FORMULAS

- A compound is a substance that contains two or more elements chemically combined in a definite proportion by mass.
- There are two general types of compounds:
  - Molecular—formed of individual molecules composed of atoms
  - Ionic—formed from ions that are either positive or negative
    - Cation—positively charged ion
    - Anion—negatively charged ion
- A chemical formula shows the symbols and the ratios of atoms for the elements in a chemical compound.
- Characteristics of a chemical formula include:
  - It contains symbols of all elements in the compound.
  - The symbol represents one atom of the element.
  - If more than one atom of an element is present, the number of atoms is indicated by a subscript.
  - Parentheses are used to show multiple groups of atoms occurring as a unit in the compound.
  - A formula does not show the arrangement of the atoms in the compound.
- The law of definite composition states that a compound always contains two or more elements combined in a definite proportion by mass.
- The law of multiple proportions states that atoms of two or more elements may combine in different ratios to form more than one compound.

Compounds

Molecular

Ionic

Example: H_2O

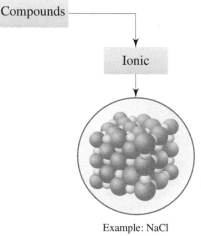

Example: NaCl

REVIEW QUESTIONS

1. Are there more atoms of silicon or hydrogen in the Earth's crust, seawater, and atmosphere? Use Table 3.1 and the fact that the mass of a silicon atom is about 28 times that of a hydrogen atom.
2. Give the symbols for each of the following elements:
   (a) manganese   (e) chlorine
   (b) fluorine   (f) vanadium
   (c) sodium   (g) zinc
   (d) helium   (h) nitrogen
3. Give the names for each of the following elements:
   (a) Fe   (e) Be
   (b) Mg   (f) Co
   (c) C   (g) Ar
   (d) P   (h) Hg
4. What does the symbol of an element stand for?
5. List six elements and their symbols in which the first letter of the symbol is different from that of the name. (Table 3.4)
6. Write the names and symbols for the 14 elements that have only one letter as their symbol. (See periodic table on inside front cover.)
7. Of the six most abundant elements in the human body, how many are metals? nonmetals? metalloids? (Table 3.2)

8. Write the names and formulas for the elements that exist as diatomic molecules. (Table 3.6)
9. Interpret the difference in meaning for each pair:
   (a) CO and Co   (c) S_8 and 8 S
   (b) H_2 and 2 H   (d) CS and Cs
10. Distinguish between an element and a compound.
11. How many metals are there? nonmetals? metalloids? (Table 3.5)
12. Of the ten most abundant elements in the Earth's crust, seawater, and atmosphere, how many are metals? nonmetals? metalloids? (Table 3.1)
13. Give the names of (a) the solid diatomic nonmetal and (b) the liquid diatomic nonmetal. (Table 3.6)
14. Distinguish between a compound and a mixture.
15. What are the two general types of compounds? How do they differ from each other?
16. What is the basis for distinguishing one compound from another?
17. What is the major difference between a cation and an anion?

Most of the exercises in this chapter are available for assignment via the online homework management program, WileyPLUS (www.wileyplus.com). All exercises with blue *numbers have answers in Appendix VI.*

PAIRED EXERCISES

1. Which of the following are diatomic molecules?
   (a) HCl
   (b) O_2
   (c) N_2O
   (d) P_4
   (e) SiO_2
   (f) H_2O_2
   (g) CH_4
   (h) ClF

2. Which of the following are diatomic molecules?
   (a) O_3
   (b) H_2O
   (c) CO_2
   (d) HI
   (e) S_8
   (f) Cl_2
   (g) CO
   (h) NH_3

3. What elements are present in each compound?
   (a) potassium iodide KI
   (b) sodium carbonate Na_2CO_3
   (c) aluminum oxide Al_2O_3
   (d) calcium bromide $CaBr_2$
   (e) acetic acid $HC_2H_3O_2$

4. What elements are present in each compound?
   (a) magnesium bromide $MgBr_2$
   (b) carbon tetrachloride CCl_4
   (c) nitric acid HNO_3
   (d) barium sulfate $BaSO_4$
   (e) aluminum phosphate $AlPO_4$

5. Write the formula for each compound (the composition is given after each name):
   (a) zinc oxide   1 atom Zn, 1 atom O
   (b) potassium chlorate 1 atom K, 1 atom Cl, 3 atoms O
   (c) sodium hydroxide   1 atom Na, 1 atom O, 1 atom H
   (d) ethyl alcohol   2 atoms C, 6 atoms H, 1 atom O

6. Write the formula for each compound (the composition is given after each name):
   (a) aluminum bromide   1 atom Al, 3 atoms Br
   (b) calcium fluoride   1 atom Ca, 2 atoms F
   (c) lead(II) chromate 1 atom Pb, 1 atom Cr, 4 atoms O
   (d) benzene   6 atoms C, 6 atoms H

7. Many foods contain interesting compounds that give them their flavors and smells. Some of these compounds are listed below with the chemical composition given after each name. Write the formulas for these compounds.
   (a) Allicin gives garlic its flavor (6 carbons, 10 hydrogens, 1 oxygen, and 2 sulfurs).
   (b) Capsaicin gives peppers their heat (18 carbons, 27 hydrogens, 1 nitrogen, and 3 oxygens).
   (c) Limonene gives oranges their fragrance (10 carbons and 16 hydrogens).

8. Many plants contain interesting compounds that sometimes have medicinal properties. Some of these compounds are listed below with the chemical composition given after each name. Write the formulas for these compounds.
   (a) Aescin from horse chestnuts has anti-inflammatory properties (55 carbons, 86 hydrogens, and 24 oxygens).
   (b) Proanthocyanidins found in cranberries help to prevent urinary tract infections. Proanthocyanidins are polymers composed of epicatechin units (15 carbons, 14 hydrogens, and 6 oxygens).
   (c) Betulinic acid found in the common birch tree is an antimalarial drug (30 carbons, 48 hydrogens, and 3 oxygens).

9. Write the name and number of atoms of each element in each of the following compounds:
   (a) Fe_2O_3
   (b) $Ca(NO_3)_2$
   (c) $Co(C_2H_3O_2)_2$
   (d) CH_3COCH_3
   (e) K_2CO_3
   (f) $Cu_3(PO_4)_2$
   (g) C_2H_5OH
   (h) $Na_2Cr_2O_7$

10. Write the name and number of atoms of each element in each of the following compounds:
   (a) $HC_2H_3O_2$
   (b) $(NH_4)_3PO_4$
   (c) $Mg(HSO_3)_2$
   (d) $ZnCl_2$
   (e) $NiCO_3$
   (f) $KMnO_4$
   (g) $CH_3CH_2CH_2CH_3$
   (h) $PbCrO_4$

11. How many total atoms are represented in each formula?
   (a) $Co(ClO_3)_2$
   (b) $(NH_4)_2SO_3$
   (c) CH_3CH_2COOH
   (d) $C_{12}H_{22}O_{11}$

12. How many total atoms are represented in each formula?
   (a) CH_3CH_2OH
   (b) $KAl(SO_4)_2$
   (c) $NH_4C_2H_3O_2$
   (d) $C_6H_4Cl_2$

13. How many hydrogen atoms are represented in each formula?
   (a) $Al(C_2H_3O_2)_3$
   (b) $CH_3CH_2CH_2OH$
   (c) NH_4OH
   (d) $C_6H_5CH_2CH_3$

14. How many oxygen atoms are represented in each formula?
   (a) $Fe(C_2H_3O_2)_3$
   (b) H_3PO_4
   (c) $Ba(ClO_3)_2$
   (d) $Fe_2(Cr_2O_7)_3$

15. Determine whether each of the following is a pure substance or a mixture:
   (a) hot tea
   (b) beach sand
   (c) carbon dioxide
   (d) cement
   (e) zinc
   (f) vinegar

16. Determine whether each of the following is a pure substance or a mixture:
   (a) dirt
   (b) salad dressing
   (c) tungsten
   (d) dinitrogen monoxide
   (e) brass
   (f) egg

17. For Question 15, state whether each pure substance is an element or a compound.

18. For Question 16, state whether each pure substance is an element or a compound.

19. Classify each of the following as an element, a compound, or a mixture:

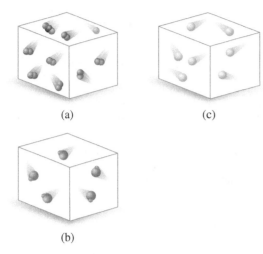

(a)

(c)

(b)

20. Classify each of the following as an element, a compound, or a mixture:

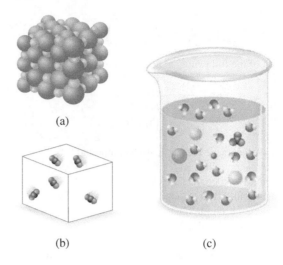

(a)

(b)

(c)

21. Is there a pattern to the location of the gaseous elements on the periodic table? If so, describe it.

22. Is there a pattern to the location of the liquid elements on the periodic table? If so, describe it.

23. What percent of the first 36 elements on the periodic table are metals?

24. What percent of the first 36 elements on the periodic table are solids at room temperature?

25. In Section 3.3, there is a statement about the composition of water. It says that water (H_2O) contains 8 grams of oxygen for every 1 gram of hydrogen. Show why this statement is true.

26. In Section 3.3, there is a statement about the composition of hydrogen peroxide. It says that hydrogen peroxide (H_2O_2) contains 16 grams of oxygen for every 1 gram of hydrogen. Show why this statement is true.

ADDITIONAL EXERCISES

27. You accidentally poured salt into your large grind pepper shaker. This is the only pepper that you have left and you need it to cook a meal, but you don't want the salt to be mixed in. How can you successfully separate these two components?

28. On the periodic table at the front of this book, do you notice anything about the atoms that make up the following ionic compounds: NaCl, KI, and $MgBr_2$? (*Hint*: Look at the position of the atoms in the given compounds on the periodic table.)

29. How many total atoms are present in each of the following compounds?
    (a) CO
    (b) BF_3
    (c) HNO_3
    (d) $KMnO_4$
    (e) $Ca(NO_3)_2$
    (f) $Fe_3(PO_4)_2$

30. The formula for vitamin B_{12} is $C_{63}H_{88}CoN_{14}O_{14}P$.
    (a) How many atoms make up one molecule of vitamin B_{12}?
    (b) What percentage of the total atoms are carbon?
    (c) What fraction of the total atoms are metallic?

31. It has been estimated that there is 4×10^{-4} mg of gold per liter of seawater. At a price of $19.40/g, what would be the value of the gold in 1 km^3 (1×10^{15} cm^3) of the ocean?

32. Calcium dihydrogen phosphate is an important fertilizer. How many atoms of hydrogen are there in ten formula units of $Ca(H_2PO_4)_2$?

33. How many total atoms are there in one molecule of $C_{145}H_{293}O_{168}$?

34. Name the following:
    (a) three elements, all metals, beginning with the letter M
    (b) four elements, all solid nonmetals
    (c) five elements, all solids in the first five rows of the periodic table, whose symbols start with letters different from the element name

35. How would you separate a mixture of sugar and sand and isolate each in its pure form?

36. How many total atoms are there in seven dozen formulas of nitric acid, HNO_3?

37. Make a graph using the following data. Plot the density of air in grams per liter along the *x*-axis and temperature along the *y*-axis.

Temperature (°C)	Density (g/L)
0	1.29
10	1.25
20	1.20
40	1.14
80	1.07

(a) What is the relationship between density and temperature according to your graph?
(b) From your plot, find the density of air at these temperatures:
    5°C   25°C   70°C

38. These formulas look similar but represent different things.
    8 S S_8
Compare and contrast them. How are they alike? How are they different?

39. Write formulas for the following compounds that a colleague read to you:
    (a) NA–CL
    (b) H2–S–O4
    (c) K2–O
    (d) Fe2–S3
    (e) K3–P–O4
    (f) CA (pause) CN taken twice
    (g) C6–H12–O6
    (h) C2–H5 (pause) OH
    (i) CR (pause) NO3 taken three times

40. The abundance of iodine in seawater is 5.0×10^{-8} percent by mass. How many kilograms of seawater must be treated to obtain 1.0 g of iodine?

41. When the tongue detects something sweet, it begins a chain of reactions to tell the body to expect calorie-containing foods. If we consume noncaloric foods containing artificial sweeteners, our bodies expect food and will tell our brains to find more if the sweet food does not contain anything to digest. Some common sweeteners are listed below. Write the name and number of atoms of each element in the sweeteners.

Compound	Common name	Chemical formula
(a) Sucrose	Table sugar	$C_{12}H_{22}O_{11}$
(b) Saccharin	Sweet 'N Low	$C_7H_5O_3NS$
(c) Aspartame	NutraSweet, Equal	$C_{14}H_{18}O_5N_2$
(d) Acesulfame-K	Sunett, Sweet One	$C_4H_4O_3NS\text{-}K$
(e) Sucralose	Splenda	$C_{12}H_{19}O_8Cl_3$

42. Should the elemental symbol for cobalt be written as Co or CO? What confusion could arise if the wrong notation were used?

43. Caffeine has the chemical structure illustrated in the image given below. Carbon atoms are represented as grey spheres, nitrogen atoms as blue spheres, oxygen atoms as red spheres, and hydrogen atoms as white spheres. Write a chemical formula for caffeine.

CHALLENGE EXERCISES

44. Write the chemical formulas of the neutral compounds that would result if the following ions were combined. Use the Charges of Common Ions table on the inside back cover of the book to help you.
(a) ammonium ion and chloride ion
(b) hydrogen ion and hydrogen sulfate ion
(c) magnesium ion and iodide ion
(d) iron(II) ion and fluoride ion
(e) lead(II) ion and phosphate ion
(f) aluminum ion and oxide ion

45. Write formulas of all the compounds that will form between the first five of the Group 1A and 2A metals and the oxide ion.

46. Unsaturated fats and oils are often used in cooking. For each pair of fatty acids listed below, tell the number of carbon and hydrogen atoms in each molecule.
(a) arachidic acid (saturated) $CH_3(CH_2)_{18}COOH$ and arachidonic acid (unsaturated) $CH_3(CH_2)_4(CH{=}CHCH_2)_4(CH_2)_2COOH$
(b) stearic acid (saturated) $CH_3(CH_2)_{16}COOH$ and linoleic acid (unsaturated) $CH_3(CH_2)_4(CH{=}CHCH_2)_2(CH_2)_6COOH$
(c) What is the ratio of hydrogen to carbon atoms for each pair?
(d) Propose a possible explanation for describing linoleic and stearic acids as being saturated.

ANSWERS TO PRACTICE EXERCISES

3.1 Cesium, Cs, IA; Calcium, Ca, 2A; Chromium, Cr, 6B; Cobalt, Co, 8B; Copper, Cu, 1B; Cadmium, Cd, 2B; Carbon, C, 4A; Chlorine, Cl, 7A; Cerium, Ce, 4B; Copernicium, Cn, 2B; Curium, Cm, 8B; Californium, Cf, 1B.

3.2 (a) any of the transition metals
(b) Br and Hg
(c) H, N, O, F, Cl

3.3 gases　　H, N, Cl, Ne
liquids　　Br, Hg
solids　　Na, Ca, S, Fe

3.4 nonmetal　　F, Kr, I, S
metal　　Na, Cr, Mo, Cu
metalloid　　Si, Sb

3.5 (a) K–BR
(b) PB–CL2
(c) CA (pause) CO3
(d) MG (pause) OH taken twice

3.6 (a) KBr
(b) $NaClO_3$
(c) H_2SO_3
(d) $Al_2(CO_3)_3$

A burning log undergoes chemical change resulting in the release of energy in the form of heat and light. The physical properties of the log change during the chemical reaction.

CHAPTER **4**

PROPERTIES OF MATTER

The world we live in is a kaleidoscope of sights, sounds, smells, and tastes. Our senses help us to describe these objects in our lives. For example, the smell of freshly baked cinnamon rolls creates a mouthwatering desire to gobble down a sample. Just as sights, sounds, smells, and tastes form the properties of the objects around us, each substance in chemistry has its own unique properties that allow us to identify it and predict its interactions.

These interactions produce both physical and chemical changes. When you eat an apple, the ultimate metabolic result is carbon dioxide and water. These same products are achieved by burning logs. Not only does a chemical change occur in these cases, but an energy change occurs as well. Some reactions release energy (as does the apple or the log) whereas others require energy, such as the production of steel or the melting of ice. Over 90% of our current energy comes from chemical reactions.

4.1 PROPERTIES OF SUBSTANCES

Compare the physical and chemical properties of a substance.

● LEARNING OBJECTIVE

KEY TERMS

properties
physical properties
chemical properties

How do we recognize substances? Each substance has a set of **properties** that is characteristic of that substance and gives it a unique identity. Properties—the "personality traits" of substances—are classified as either physical or chemical. **Physical properties** are the inherent characteristics of a substance that can be determined without altering its composition; they are associated with its physical existence. Common physical properties include color, taste, odor, state of matter (solid, liquid, or gas), density, melting point, and boiling point (see Figure 4.1). **Chemical properties** describe the ability of a substance to form new substances, either by reaction with other substances or by decomposition.

Let's consider a few of the physical and chemical properties of chlorine. Physically, chlorine is a gas at room temperature about 2.4 times heavier than air. It is greenish yellow in color and has a disagreeable odor. Chemically, chlorine will not burn but will support the combustion of certain other substances. It can be used as a bleaching agent, as a disinfectant for water, and in many chlorinated substances such as refrigerants and insecticides. When chlorine combines with the metal sodium, it forms a salt called sodium chloride (see Figure 4.2). These properties, among many others, help us characterize and identify chlorine.

Figure 4.1

Physical property. The boiling point of water is a physical property. At its boiling point water changes from a liquid to a gas, but the molecules remain water molecules. They are still water but are farther apart.

Sodium metal   +   Chlorine gas   ⟶   Sodium chloride

Na atom

Cl_2 molecules

Cl^-
Na^+

Na⁺ Cl^-

Figure 4.2

Chemical property. When sodium metal reacts with chlorine gas, a new substance called sodium chloride forms.

TABLE 4.1   Physical Properties of Selected Substances

Substance	Color	Odor	Physical state	Melting point (°C)	Boiling point (°C)
Chlorine	Greenish yellow	Sharp, suffocating	Gas (20°C)	−101.6	−34.6
Water	Colorless	Odorless	Liquid	0.0	100.0
Sugar	White	Odorless	Solid	—	Decomposes 170–186
Acetic acid	Colorless	Like vinegar	Liquid	16.7	118.0
Nitrogen dioxide	Reddish brown	Sharp, suffocating	Gas	−11.2	21.2
Oxygen	Colorless	Odorless	Gas	−218.4	−183

Substances, then, are recognized and differentiated by their properties. Table 4.1 lists six substances and several of their common physical properties. Information about physical properties, such as that given in Table 4.1, is available in handbooks of chemistry and physics. Scientists don't pretend to know all the answers or to remember voluminous amounts of data, but it is important for them to know where to look for data in the literature and on the Internet.

Many chemists have reference books such as the Handbook of Chemistry and Physics to use as a resource.

No two substances have identical physical and chemical properties.

>CHEMISTRY *IN ACTION*

Making Money

Chemists are heavily involved in the manufacture of our currency. In fact, in a very real way, the money industry depends on chemistry and finding substances with the correct properties. The most common paper currency in the United States is the dollar bill. Chemistry is used to form the ink and paper and in processes used to defeat counterfeiters. The ink used on currency has to do a variety of things. It must be just the right consistency to fill the fine lines of the printing plate and release onto the paper without smearing. The ink must dry almost immediately, since the sheets of currency fly out of the press and into stacks 10,000 sheets tall. The pressure at the bottom of the stack is large, and the ink must not stick to the back of the sheet above it.

The security of our currency also depends on substances in the ink, which is optically variable. This color-changing ink shifts from green to black depending on how the bill is tilted. The ink used for the numbers in the lower right corner on the front of $10, $20, $50, and $100 bills shows this color change.

Once the currency is printed, it has to undergo durability tests. The bills are soaked in different solvents for 24 hours to make sure that they can stand dry cleaning and chemical exposure to household items such as gasoline. Then the bills must pass a washing-machine test to be sure that, for example, your $20 bill is still intact in your pocket after the washer is through with it. Paper currency is a blend of 75% cotton and 25% linen. Last, the bills must pass the crumple test, in which they are rolled up, put in a metal tube, crushed by a plunger, removed, and flattened. This process is repeated up to 50 times.

Once a bill is in circulation, Federal Reserve banks screen it using light to measure wear. If the bill gets too dirty, it is shredded and sent to a landfill. The average $1 bill stays in circulation for only 18 months. No wonder Congress decided in 1997 to revive the dollar coin by creating a new dollar coin to succeed the Susan B. Anthony dollar.

Sacagawea dollar coin, which succeeded the Susan B. Anthony dollar, is still not in wide circulation today.

Ryan McVay/Getty Images, Inc.

Currency in stacks.

Corbis Digital Stock

EXAMPLE 4.1

You have three flasks that contain chlorine gas, nitrogen dioxide gas, and oxygen gas. Describe how you would use physical properties to identify the contents in each flask.

SOLUTION

Use Table 4.1 to compare the compounds and note their colors. You will find that chlorine is a greenish yellow color, nitrogen dioxide is reddish brown, and oxygen is colorless. Now you have the information to identify the contents in each flask.

PRACTICE 4.1

You are given three samples of silver compounds: AgCl, AgBr, and AgI. Arrange these silver compounds in the order of their percent silver by mass (highest to lowest). Describe how you arrived at your arrangement. *Hint:* Use the periodic table inside the front cover of your text.

4.2 PHYSICAL AND CHEMICAL CHANGES

Compare the physical and chemical changes in a substance.

● LEARNING OBJECTIVE

KEY TERMS
physical change
chemical change
chemical equation
reactants
products

Matter can undergo two types of changes, physical and chemical. **Physical changes** are changes in physical properties (such as size, shape, and density) or changes in the state of matter without an accompanying change in composition. The changing of ice into water and water into steam are physical changes from one state of matter into another. No new substances are formed in these physical changes.

When a clean platinum wire is heated in a burner flame, the appearance of the platinum changes from silvery metallic to glowing red. This change is physical because the platinum can be restored to its original metallic appearance by cooling and, more importantly, because the composition of the platinum is not changed by heating and cooling.

In a **chemical change**, new substances are formed that have different properties and composition from the original material. The new substances need not resemble the original material in any way.

When a clean copper wire is heated in a burner flame, the appearance of the copper changes from coppery metallic to glowing red. Unlike the platinum wire, the copper wire is not restored to its original appearance by cooling but instead becomes a black material. This black material is a new substance called copper(II) oxide. It was formed by a chemical change when copper combined with oxygen in the air during the heating process. The unheated wire

Sawing wood produces physical change.

© Josh McCulloch/All Canada Photos/SuperStock

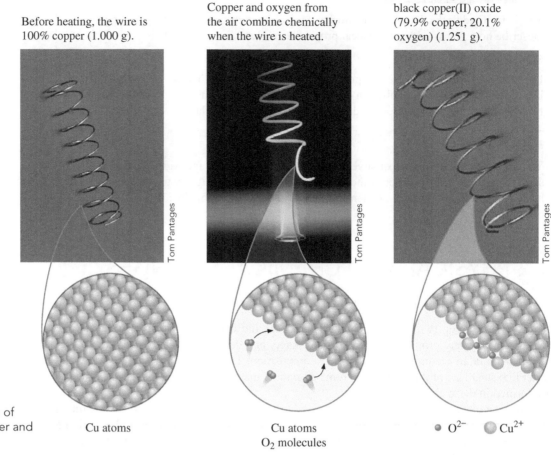

Before heating, the wire is 100% copper (1.000 g).

Copper and oxygen from the air combine chemically when the wire is heated.

After heating, the wire is black copper(II) oxide (79.9% copper, 20.1% oxygen) (1.251 g).

Cu atoms

Cu atoms
O_2 molecules

● O^{2-} ● Cu^{2+}

Figure 4.3

Chemical change: Forming of copper(II) oxide from copper and oxygen.

was essentially 100% copper, but the copper(II) oxide is 79.9% copper and 20.1% oxygen. One gram of copper will yield 1.251 g of copper(II) oxide (see **Figure 4.3**). The platinum is changed only physically when heated, but the copper is changed both physically and chemically when heated.

Water can be decomposed chemically into hydrogen and oxygen. This is usually accomplished by passing electricity through the water in a process called *electrolysis*. Hydrogen collects at one electrode while oxygen collects at the other (see **Figure 4.4**). The composition and the physical appearance of the hydrogen and the oxygen are quite different from those of water. They are both colorless gases, but each behaves differently when a burning wooden splint is placed into the sample: The hydrogen explodes with a pop while the flame brightens considerably in the oxygen (oxygen supports and intensifies

O_2 molecules

H_2 molecules

H_2O molecules

Figure 4.4

Electrolysis of water produces hydrogen gas (on the right) and oxygen gas (on the left). Note the ratio of the gases is 2:1.

the combustion of the wood). From these observations, we conclude that a chemical change has taken place.

Chemists have devised a shorthand method for expressing chemical changes in the form of **chemical equations**. The two previous examples of chemical changes can be represented by the following molecular representations, word and symbol equations. In the electrolysis reaction, water decomposes into hydrogen and oxygen when electrolyzed. In the formation reaction, copper plus oxygen when heated produce copper(II) oxide. The arrow means "produces," and it points to the products. The Greek letter delta (Δ) represents heat. The starting substances (water, copper, and oxygen) are called the **reactants**, and the substances produced [hydrogen, oxygen, and copper(II) oxide] are called the **products**. We will learn more about writing chemical equations in later chapters.

Formation of Copper(II) Oxide

Type of equation	Reactants			Products
Word	copper	+	oxygen $\xrightarrow{\Delta}$	copper(II) oxide
Molecular		+	$\xrightarrow{\Delta}$	
Symbol (formula)	2 Cu	+	O_2 $\xrightarrow{\Delta}$	2 CuO

Electrolysis of Water

Type of equation	Reactants		Products		
Word	water	$\xrightarrow[\text{energy}]{\text{electrical}}$	hydrogen	+	oxygen
Molecular		$\xrightarrow[\text{energy}]{\text{electrical}}$		+	
Symbol (formula)	2 H_2O	$\xrightarrow[\text{energy}]{\text{electrical}}$	2 H_2	+	O_2

Physical change usually accompanies a chemical change. Table 4.2 lists some common physical and chemical changes; note that wherever a chemical change occurs, a physical change also occurs. However, wherever a physical change is listed, only a physical change occurs.

TABLE 4.2   Physical or Chemical Changes of Some Common Processes

Process taking place	Type of change	Accompanying observations
Rusting of iron	Chemical	Shiny, bright metal changes to reddish brown rust.
Boiling of water	Physical	Liquid changes to vapor.
Burning of sulfur in air	Chemical	Yellow, solid sulfur changes to gaseous, choking sulfur dioxide.
Boiling of an egg	Chemical	Liquid white and yolk change to solids.
Combustion of gasoline	Chemical	Liquid gasoline burns to gaseous carbon monoxide, carbon dioxide, and water.
Digestion of food	Chemical	Food changes to liquid nutrients and partially solid wastes.
Sawing of wood	Physical	Smaller pieces of wood and sawdust are made from a larger piece of wood.
Burning of wood	Chemical	Wood burns to ashes, gaseous carbon dioxide, and water.
Heating of glass	Physical	Solid becomes pliable during heating, and the glass may change its shape.

> **EXAMPLE 4.2**
>
> In a distillation, a chemist is boiling pure ethyl alcohol and observes that the boiling point is 78.5°C. Using an apparatus to condense and recover the alcohol vapors back to a liquid, she finds that the boiling point of the condensed liquid also is 78.5°C. Describe whether this experiment is a physical or chemical change.
>
> **SOLUTION**
>
> The process of changing a liquid to a vapor and back to a liquid is a physical change verified by the fact that both liquids have the same boiling points.

PRACTICE 4.2

When ice melts, is this a physical or chemical change?

4.3 LEARNING TO SOLVE PROBLEMS

LEARNING OBJECTIVE ● List the basic steps in solving chemistry problems.

Now that we have learned some of the basics of chemistry including names and symbols for the elements, dimensional analysis, and a good amount of chemical terminology, we are ready to begin learning to solve chemistry problems.

One of the great joys of studying chemistry is learning to be a good problem solver. The ability to solve complicated problems is a skill that will help you greatly throughout your life. It is our goal to help you learn to solve problems by thinking through the problems on your own. To this end the basic steps in solving problems are:

Read Read the problem carefully. Determine what is known and what is to be solved for and write them down. It is important to label all factors and measurements with the proper units.

Plan Determine which principles are involved and which unit relationships are needed to solve the problem. You may refer to tables for needed data. Set up the problem in a neat, organized, and logical fashion, making sure all unwanted units cancel. Use the examples as guides for setting up the problem.

Calculate Proceed with the necessary mathematical operations. Make certain that your answer contains the proper number of significant figures.

Check Check the answer to see if it is reasonable.

At first we will help you through this process in each example. Then later in the text as you learn more about solving problems and have lots of practice, we'll help you less. By the end of your course you'll be solving problems on your own.

A few more words about problem solving. Don't allow any formal method of problem solving to limit your use of common sense and intuition. If a problem is clear to you and its solution seems simpler by another method, by all means use it.

If you approach problem solving using this general method, you will be able to learn to solve more and more difficult problems on your own. As you gain confidence you will become an independent, creative problem solver and be able to use this skill wherever you go in "real life."

4.4 ENERGY

LEARNING OBJECTIVE ● List the various forms of energy, explain the role of energy in chemical changes, and state the law of conservation of energy.

KEY TERMS

energy
potential energy
kinetic energy
law of conservation of energy

From the early discovery that fire can warm us and cook our food to our discovery that nuclear reactors can be used to produce vast amounts of controlled energy, our technical progress has been directed by our ability to produce, harness, and utilize energy. **Energy** is the capacity of matter to do work. Energy exists in many forms; some of the more familiar forms are mechanical, chemical, electrical, heat, nuclear, and radiant or light energy. Matter can have both potential and kinetic energy.

Potential energy (PE) is stored energy, or energy that an object possesses due to its relative position. For example, a ball located 20 ft above the ground has more potential energy than when located 10 ft above the ground and will bounce higher when allowed to fall. Water backed up behind a dam represents potential energy that can be converted into useful work in the form of electrical or mechanical energy. Gasoline is a source of chemical potential energy. When gasoline burns (combines with oxygen), the heat released is associated with a decrease in potential energy. The new substances formed by burning have less chemical potential energy than the gasoline and oxygen.

Kinetic energy (KE) is energy that matter possesses due to its motion. When the water behind the dam is released and allowed to flow, its potential energy is changed into kinetic energy, which can be used to drive generators and produce electricity. Moving bodies possess kinetic energy. We all know the results when two moving vehicles collide: Their kinetic energy is expended in the crash that occurs. The pressure exerted by a confined gas is due to the kinetic energy of rapidly moving gas particles.

Energy can be converted from one form to another form. Some kinds of energy can be converted to other forms easily and efficiently. For example, mechanical energy can be converted to electrical energy with an electric generator at better than 90% efficiency. On the other hand, solar energy has thus far been directly converted to electrical energy at an efficiency approaching 30%. In chemistry, energy is most frequently released as heat.

Brian Yaruin/The Image Works

The mechanical energy of falling water is converted to electrical energy at the hydroelectric plant at Niagara Falls. As the water falls, potential energy is converted to kinetic energy and turns a turbine to produce electrical energy.

Energy in Chemical Changes

In all chemical changes, matter either absorbs or releases energy. Chemical changes can produce different forms of energy. For example, electrical energy to start automobiles is produced by chemical changes in the lead storage battery. Light energy is produced by the chemical change that occurs in a light stick. Heat and light are released from the combustion of fuels. For example, the space shuttle uses the reaction between hydrogen and oxygen-producing water vapor to help power it (see Figure 4.5). All the energy needed for our life processes—breathing, muscle contraction, blood circulation, and so on—is produced by chemical changes occurring within the cells of our bodies.

Conversely, energy is used to cause chemical changes. For example, a chemical change occurs in the electroplating of metals when electrical energy is passed through a salt solution in which the metal is submerged. A chemical change occurs when radiant energy from the sun is used by green plants in the process of photosynthesis. And as we saw, a chemical change occurs when electricity is used to decompose water into hydrogen and oxygen. Chemical changes are often used primarily to produce energy rather than to produce new substances. The heat or thrust generated by the combustion of fuels is more important than the new substances formed.

NASA

Figure 4.5
The external fuel tank (orange) contained liquid hydrogen and liquid oxygen which fueled the shuttle's main engine. The exhaust gas from the shuttle was water.

EXAMPLE 4.3

Methane (CH_4) is the major compound in natural gas and is used in our homes for heat and cooking. The combustion of methane in oxygen (air) produces considerable heat energy. The chemical reaction is

$$CH_4 \quad + \quad 2\,O_2 \quad \rightarrow \quad CO_2 \quad + \quad 2\,H_2O \quad + \quad 802.5\ kJ$$

methane   oxygen   carbon dioxide   water   heat

If it were possible to make methane from carbon dioxide and water, how much heat energy would it take to make methane? Write the equation.

SOLUTION

From the equation it takes 802.5 kJ to make methane. The chemical equation for the reaction is

$$CO_2 + 2\,H_2O + 802.5\ kJ \rightarrow CH_4 + 2\,O_2$$

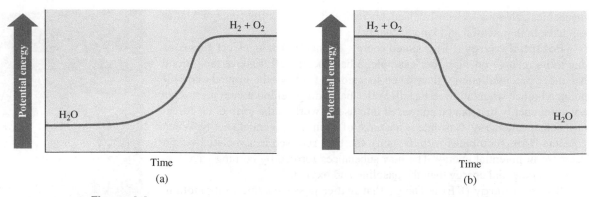

Figure 4.6

(a) In electrolysis of water, energy is absorbed by the system, so the products H_2 and O_2 have a higher potential energy. (b) When hydrogen is used as a fuel, energy is released and the product (H_2O) has lower potential energy.

Conservation of Energy

An energy transformation occurs whenever a chemical change occurs (see **Figure 4.6**). If energy is absorbed during the change, the products will have more chemical potential energy than the reactants. Conversely, if energy is given off in a chemical change, the products will have less chemical potential energy than the reactants. Water can be decomposed in an electrolytic cell by absorbing electrical energy. The products, hydrogen and oxygen, have a greater chemical potential energy level than that of water (see Figure 4.6a). This potential energy is released in the form of heat and light when the hydrogen and oxygen are burned to form water again (see Figure 4.6b). Thus, energy can be changed from one form to another or from one substance to another and, therefore, is not lost.

The energy changes occurring in many systems have been thoroughly studied. No system has ever been found to acquire energy except at the expense of energy possessed by another system. This is the **law of conservation of energy**: Energy can be neither created nor destroyed, though it can be transformed from one form to another.

4.5 HEAT: QUANTITATIVE MEASUREMENT

LEARNING OBJECTIVE ● Calculate the amount of heat lost or gained in a given system.

KEY TERMS
joule
calorie
specific heat

The SI-derived unit for energy is the joule (pronounced *jool*, rhyming with *tool*, and abbreviated J). Another unit for heat energy, which has been used for many years, is the calorie (abbreviated cal). The relationship between joules and calories is

$$4.184 \text{ J} = 1 \text{ cal} \quad \text{(exactly)}$$

To give you some idea of the magnitude of these heat units, 4.184 **joules**, or 1 **calorie**, is the quantity of heat energy required to change the temperature of 1 gram of water by 1°C, usually measured from 14.5°C to 15.5°C.

Since joules and calories are rather small units, kilojoules (kJ) and kilocalories (kcal) are used to express heat energy in many chemical processes. The kilocalorie is also known as the nutritional Calorie (spelled with a capital C and abbreviated Cal). In this book, heat energy will be expressed in joules.

1 kJ = 1000 J
1 kcal = 1000 cal = 1 Cal

The difference in the meanings of the terms *heat* and *temperature* can be seen by this example: Visualize two beakers, A and B. Beaker A contains 100 g of water at 20°C, and beaker B contains 200 g of water also at 20°C. The beakers are heated until the temperature of the water in each reaches 30°C. The temperature of the water in the beakers was raised by exactly the same amount, 10°C. But twice as much heat (8368 J) was required to raise the temperature of the water in beaker B as was required in beaker A (4184 J).

TABLE 4.3   Specific Heat of Selected Substances

Substance	Specific heat (J/g°C)	Specific heat (cal/g°C)
Water	4.184	1.000
Ethyl alcohol	2.138	0.511
Ice	2.059	0.492
Aluminum	0.900	0.215
Iron	0.473	0.113
Copper	0.385	0.0921
Gold	0.131	0.0312
Lead	0.128	0.0305

In the middle of the eighteenth century, Joseph Black (1728–1799), a Scottish chemist, was experimenting with the heating of elements. He heated and cooled equal masses of iron and lead through the same temperature range. Black noted that much more heat was needed for the iron than for the lead. He had discovered a fundamental property of matter—namely, that every substance has a characteristic heat capacity. Heat capacities may be compared in terms of specific heats. The **specific heat** of a substance is the quantity of heat (lost or gained) required to change the temperature of 1 g of that substance by 1°C. It follows then that the specific heat of liquid water is 4.184 J/g°C (or 1.000 cal/g°C). The specific heat of water is high compared with that of most substances. Aluminum and copper, for example, have specific heats of 0.900 J/g°C and 0.385 J/g°C, respectively (see Table 4.3). The relation of mass, specific heat, temperature change (Δt), and quantity of heat lost or gained by a system is expressed by this general equation:

The greek letter Δ is used to mean "change in."

Lowercase t is used for Celsius and upper case T for Kelvin.

$$\left(\begin{array}{c}\text{mass of}\\ \text{substance}\end{array}\right)\left(\begin{array}{c}\text{specific heat}\\ \text{of substance}\end{array}\right)(\Delta t) = \text{heat}$$

Mass is in grams, specific heat is in cal/g°C or J/g°C and Δt is in °C.

Thus the amount of heat needed to raise the temperature of 200. g of water by 10.0°C can be calculated as follows:

$$(200. \ \cancel{g})\left(\frac{4.184 \ J}{\cancel{g}\cancel{°C}}\right)(10.0 \ \cancel{°C}) = 8.37 \times 10^3 \ J$$

EXAMPLE 4.4

Calculate the specific heat of a solid in J/g°C and cal/g°C if 1638 J raises the temperature of 125 g of the solid from 25.0°C to 52.6°C.

SOLUTION

Read •   **Knowns:**   125 g of the solid
$\Delta t = 52.6 - 25.0 = 27.6$°C
Heat $= 1638$ J

Solving for: specific heat of the solid

Plan •   Use the equation

(mass)(specific heat)(Δt) = heat

solving for specific heat

$$\text{specific heat} = \frac{\text{heat}}{g \times \Delta t}$$

Calculate •   specific heat $= \dfrac{1638 \ J}{125 \ g \times 27.6°C} = 0.475$ J/g°C

Convert joules to calories using 1.00 cal/4.184 J

$$\text{specific heat} = \left(\frac{0.475 \ \cancel{J}}{g°C}\right)\left(\frac{1.000 \ cal}{4.184 \ \cancel{J}}\right) = 0.114 \text{ cal/g°C}$$

Check •   Note that the units in the answer agree with the units for specific heat.

EXAMPLE 4.5

A sample of a metal with a mass of 212 g is heated to 125.0°C and then dropped into 375 g water at 24.0°C. If the final temperature of the water is 34.2°C, what is the specific heat of the metal? (Assume no heat losses to the surroundings.)

SOLUTION

Read • **Knowns:**   mass (metal) = 212 g

mass (water) = 375 g

Δt (water) = 34.2 − 24.0 = 10.2°C

Δt (metal) = 125.0 − 34.2 = 90.8°C

Solving for: specific heat of the metal

Plan • When the metal enters the water, it begins to cool, losing heat to the water. At the same time, the temperature of the water rises. This continues until the temperature of the metal and the water is equal (34.2°C), after which no net flow of heat occurs.

Heat lost or gained by a system is given by

(mass)(specific heat)(Δt) = energy change (heat)

heat gained by the water = heat lost by the metal

heat gained by the water = (mass water)(specific heat)(Δt)

$$= (375\ \cancel{g})\left(\frac{4.184\ J}{\cancel{g}\,\cancel{°C}}\right)(10.2\,\cancel{°C}) = 1.60 \times 10^4\ J$$

Calculate • heat gained by the water = heat lost by the metal = 1.60×10^4 J

(mass metal)(specific heat metal)(Δt) = 1.60×10^4 J

(212 g)(specific heat metal)(90.8°C) = 1.60×10^4 J

To determine the specific heat of the metal, we rearrange the equation

(mass)(specific heat)(Δt) = heat

solving for the specific heat of the metal

$$\text{specific heat metal} = \frac{1.60 \times 10^4\ J}{(212\ g)(90.8°C)} = 0.831\ J/g°C$$

Check • Note the units in the answer agree with units for specific heat.

PRACTICE 4.3

Calculate the quantity of energy needed to heat 8.0 g of water from 42.0°C to 45.0°C.

PRACTICE 4.4

A 110.0-g sample of metal at 55.5°C raises the temperature of 150.0 g of water from 23.0°C to 25.5°C. Determine the specific heat of the metal in J/g°C.

4.6 ENERGY IN THE REAL WORLD

LEARNING OBJECTIVE • Define a hydrocarbon compound and explain its role in the world's energy supply.

Coal, petroleum, natural gas, and woody plants provide us with a vast resource of energy, all of which is derived from the sun. Plants use the process of photosynthesis to store the sun's energy, and we harvest that energy by burning the plants or using the decay products of the plants. These decay products have been converted over millions of years to fossil fuels. As the plants died and decayed, natural processes changed them into petroleum deposits that we now use in the forms of gasoline and natural gas.

>CHEMISTRY *IN ACTION*

Popping Popcorn

What's the secret to getting all those kernels in a bag of microwave popcorn to pop? Food scientists have looked at all sorts of things to improve the poppability of popcorn. In every kernel of popcorn there is starch and a little moisture. As the kernel heats up, the water vaporizes and the pressure builds up in the kernel. Finally, the kernel bursts and the starch expands into the white foam of popped corn.

Researchers in Indiana tested 14 types of popcorn to determine the most poppable. They found a range of 4–47% of unpopped kernels and determined that the kernels that held moisture the best produced the fewest unpopped kernels. Further analysis led them to the conclusion that the determining factor was the pericarp.

The pericarp is the hard casing on the popcorn kernel. It is made of long polymers of cellulose. When the kernel is heated up, the long chains of cellulose line up and make a strong crystalline structure. This strong structure keeps the water vapor inside the kernel, allowing the pressure to rise high enough to pop the kernel.

Getting the most pops comes from the molecular changes resulting from heating the kernel. Energy and chemistry combine to produce a tasty snack!

Popcorn

Although we do not really understand completely how petroleum deposits were formed, they most likely came from the remains of marine organisms living over 500 million years ago. Petroleum is composed of hydrocarbon compounds (which contain only carbon and hydrogen). Carbon is a unique element in that it can produce chains of atoms in a molecule of different lengths. Table 4.4 gives the names and formulas of some simple hydrocarbons. Natural gas is associated with petroleum deposits and consists mainly of methane with some ethane, propane, and butane mixed in. Large resources of natural gas are now being made available in the United States through a process called fracking, (hydraulic fracturing).

Coal was formed from the remains of plants that were buried and subjected to high pressure and heat over many years. Chemical changes lowered the oxygen and hydrogen content of these plant tissues and produced the black solid we recognize as coal. The energy available from a mass of coal increases as the carbon content increases. Coal is an important energy source in the United States.

TABLE 4.4 Names and Formulas for Simple Hydrocarbons

Names	Formula
Methane	CH_4
Ethane	C_2H_6
Propane	C_3H_8
Butane	C_4H_{10}
Pentane	C_5H_{12}
Hexane	C_6H_{14}
Heptane	C_7H_{16}
Octane	C_8H_{18}
Nonane	C_9H_{20}
Decane	$C_{10}H_{22}$

Alternative energy sources include wind, solar, and biofuels.

We are currently facing an energy crisis that has caused us to search for new renewable energy sources for our future. We will need to consider economic, supply, and climatic factors to find fuels to serve us as we continue to grow our human population. There are a variety of potential resources: solar, nuclear, biomass, wind, and synthetic fuels. We now are beginning to focus on developing these resources and using them in the most economic way to lower our energy dependence globally.

EXAMPLE 4.6

Much of the energy used in the world is dependent on coal. Large deposits of coal are found all over the world. Coal supplies about 20% of the energy used in the United States. The combustion of coal, which is mainly carbon and reacts with oxygen in the air, produces carbon dioxide and much heat energy. Write the chemical equation for this reaction.

SOLUTION

$$C + O_2 \rightarrow CO_2 + \text{heat (393 kJ)}$$

PRACTICE 4.5

The major compounds in gasoline are hydrocarbons. Without petroleum (from which hydrocarbons are distilled to make gasoline), industry would come to a halt and millions of automobiles would be idled. Devise a general formula (C_xH_y) that represents the hydrocarbons in Table 4.4.

CHAPTER **4 REVIEW**

4.1 PROPERTIES OF SUBSTANCES

- Each substance has a set of properties that is characteristic of the substance and gives it a unique identity.
- Physical properties are inherent in the substance and can be determined without altering the composition of the substance:
    - Color
    - Taste
    - Odor
    - State of matter
    - Density
    - Melting point
    - Boiling point
- Chemical properties describe the ability of a substance to interact with other substances to form different substances.

4.2 PHYSICAL AND CHEMICAL CHANGES

- A physical change is a change in the physical properties or a change in the state of matter for a substance without altering the composition of the substance.
- In a chemical change different substances are formed that have different properties and composition from the original material.
- Chemical changes can be represented by chemical equations:
    - Word equation
    - Molecular equation
    - Symbol (formula) equation

4.3 LEARNING TO SOLVE PROBLEMS

Read   Read the problem carefully, determining what is known and what is to be solved for .

Plan   Determine what is required to solve the problem and set up the problem in a neat, organized manner using the examples as guides.

Calculate Complete the necessary calculations making sure your answer contains the proper units and significant figures.

Check   Check to see if your answer is reasonable.

4.4 ENERGY

- Energy is the capacity to do work.
- Potential energy is energy that results from position or is stored within a substance.
- Kinetic energy is the energy matter possesses as a result of its motion.
- Energy can be converted from one form to another.
- Common forms of energy:
  - Mechanical
  - Chemical
  - Electrical
  - Heat
  - Nuclear
  - Light
- In chemistry, energy is most frequently expressed as heat.
- In all chemical changes matter either absorbs or releases energy.
- Energy can be used to cause chemical change.
- Chemical changes are often used to produce energy rather than new substances.
- Energy can neither be created nor destroyed. It can be transformed from one form to another.
- The energy released or absorbed in a chemical reaction can be summarized in graphical form.

KEY TERMS

energy
potential energy
kinetic energy
law of conservation of energy

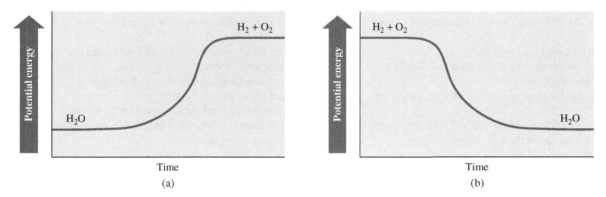

(a)   (b)

4.5 HEAT: QUANTITATIVE MEASUREMENT

- The SI unit for heat is the joule
  $4.184 \text{ J} = 1 \text{ cal}$
- The calorie is defined as the amount of heat required to change the temperature of 1 gram of water 1°C.
- Every substance has a characteristic heat capacity:
  - The specific heat of a substance is a measure of its heat capacity.
  - The specific heat is the quantity of heat required to change the temperature of 1 gram of the substance by 1°C.
- Heat lost or gained by a system can be calculated by
  heat $=$ (mass of substance)(specific heat of substance)(Δt).

KEY TERMS

joule
calorie
specific heat

REVIEW QUESTIONS

1. In what physical state does acetic acid exist at 393 K? (Table 4.1)
2. In what physical state does chlorine exist at −65°C? (Table 4.1)
3. Calculate the boiling point of acetic acid in
   (a) kelvins
   (b) degrees Fahrenheit (Table 4.1)
4. Calculate the melting point of acetic acid in (Table 4.1)
   (a) degrees Fahrenheit
   (b) kelvins
5. What evidence of chemical change is visible when electricity is run through water? (Figure 4.4)
6. What is the fundamental difference between a chemical change and a physical change?
7. What is the critical first step in solving any chemistry problem?
8. Is the calculation step the last step in solving a chemistry problem? Why or why not?

9. Distinguish between potential and kinetic energy.
10. How is chemistry calorie (cal) different from a food calorie (Cal)?
11. Which requires more energy to heat from 20°C to 30°C, iron or gold? (See Table 4.3.)
12. Predict which molecule would produce more carbon dioxide when burned, a molecule of ethane or a molecule of octane.
13. What is the common characteristic of all hydrocarbons?
14. Which is the most common element used to produce energy for human use?
15. Why might the combustion of fossil fuels not be the best solution to the planet's energy needs? What are some other energy sources that may become important in the future?

Most of the exercises in this chapter are available for assignment via the online homework management program, WileyPLUS (www.wileyplus.com). All exercises with blue *numbers have answers in Appendix VI.*

PAIRED EXERCISES

1. Determine whether each of the following represents a physical property or a chemical property:
   (a) Vinegar has a pungent odor.
   (b) Carbon cannot be decomposed.
   (c) Sulfur is a bright yellow solid.
   (d) Sodium chloride is a crystalline solid.
   (e) Water does not burn.
   (f) Mercury is a liquid at 25°C.
   (g) Oxygen is not combustible.
   (h) Aluminum combines with oxygen to form a protective oxide coating.

2. Determine whether each of the following represents a physical property or a chemical property:
   (a) Chlorine gas has a greenish-yellow tint.
   (b) The density of water at 4°C is 1.000 g/mL.
   (c) Hydrogen gas is very flammable.
   (d) Aluminum is a solid at 25°C.
   (e) Water is colorless and odorless.
   (f) Lemon juice tastes sour.
   (g) Gold does not tarnish.
   (h) Copper cannot be decomposed.

3. Cite the evidence that indicates that only physical changes occur when a platinum wire is heated in a Bunsen burner flame.

4. Cite the evidence that indicates that both physical and chemical changes occur when a copper wire is heated in a Bunsen burner flame.

5. Identify the reactants and products when a copper wire is heated in air in a Bunsen burner flame.

6. Identify the reactants and products for the electrolysis of water.

7. State whether each of the following represents a chemical change or a physical change:
   (a) A steak is cooked on a grill until well done.
   (b) In the lab, students firepolish the end of a glass rod. The jagged edge of the glass has become smooth.
   (c) Chlorine bleach is used to remove a coffee stain on a white lab coat.
   (d) When two clear and colorless aqueous salt solutions are mixed together, the solution turns cloudy and yellow.
   (e) One gram of an orange crystalline solid is heated in a test tube, producing a green powdery solid whose volume is 10 times the volume of the original substance.
   (f) In the lab, a student cuts a 20-cm strip of magnesium metal into 1-cm pieces.

8. State whether each of the following represents a chemical change or a physical change:
   (a) A few grams of sucrose (table sugar) are placed in a small beaker of deionized water; the sugar crystals "disappear," and the liquid in the beaker remains clear and colorless.
   (b) A copper statue, over time, turns green.
   (c) When a teaspoon of baking soda (sodium bicarbonate) is placed into a few ounces of vinegar (acetic acid), volumes of bubbles (effervescence) are produced.
   (d) When a few grams of a blue crystalline solid are placed into a beaker of deionized water, the crystals "disappear" and the liquid becomes clear and blue in color.
   (e) In the lab, a student mixes 2 mL of sodium hydroxide with 2 mL of hydrochloric acid in a test tube. He notices that the test tube has become very warm to the touch.
   (f) A woman visits a hairdresser and has her hair colored a darker shade of brown. After several weeks the hair, even though washed several times, has not changed back to the original color.

9. Are the following examples of potential energy or kinetic energy?
   (a) fan blades spinning   (d) a person napping
   (b) a bird flying   (e) ocean waves rippling
   (c) sodium hydroxide in a sealed jar

10. Are the following examples of potential energy or kinetic energy?
    (a) a fish swimming   (d) water starting to boil
    (b) a skier at the top of a hill   (e) a leaf unfolding
    (c) a bird's egg in a nest

11. What happens to the kinetic energy of a speeding car when the car is braked to a stop?

12. What energy transformation is responsible for the fiery reentry of the space shuttle into Earth's atmosphere?

13. Indicate with a plus sign (+) any of these processes that require energy and a negative sign (−) any that release energy.
    (a) arctic ice melting   (d) dry ice changing to vapor
    (b) starting a car   (e) blowing up a balloon
    (c) flash of lightning

14. Indicate with a plus sign (+) any of these processes that require energy and a negative sign (−) any that release energy.
    (a) riding a bike   (d) tires deflating
    (b) fireworks bursting   (e) wood burning in a fireplace
    (c) water evaporating

15. How many joules of heat are required to heat 125 g aluminum from 19.0°C to 95.5°C? (Table 4.3)

16. How many joules of heat are required to heat 65 g lead from 22.0°C to 98.5°C? (Table 4.3)

17. How many joules of heat are required to heat 25.0 g of ethyl alcohol from the prevailing room temperature, 22.5°C, to its boiling point, 78.5°C?

18. How many joules of heat are required to heat 35.0 g of isopropyl alcohol from the prevailing room temperature, 21.2°C, to its boiling point, 82.4°C? (The specific heat of isopropyl alcohol is 2.604 J/g°C.)

19. A 135-g sample of a metal requires 2.50 kJ to change its temperature from 19.5°C to 100.0°C. What is the specific heat of this metal?

20. A 275-g sample of a metal requires 10.75 kJ to change its temperature from 21.2°C to its melting temperature, 327.5°C. What is the specific heat of this metal?

21. A 155-g sample of copper was heated to 150.0°C, then placed into 250.0 g water at 19.8°C. (The specific heat of copper is 0.385 J/g°C.) Calculate the final temperature of the mixture. (Assume no heat loss to the surroundings.)

22. A 225-g sample of aluminum was heated to 125.5°C, then placed into 500.0 g water at 22.5°C. (The specific heat of aluminum is 0.900 J/g°C). Calculate the final temperature of the mixture. (Assume no heat loss to the surroundings.)

ADDITIONAL EXERCISES

23. Read the following passage and identify at least two physical and two chemical properties of zeolites.

> Zeolites are crystalline solids composed of silicon, aluminum, and oxygen with very porous structures. They are very useful in a variety of applications. Zeolites are formed naturally when volcanic rocks and ash react with alkaline groundwater. They may also be synthesized in the laboratory by allowing aluminosilicate crystals to form around small organic molecules. Zeolites generally have very low density due to their porous nature. They are often used as molecular sieves because they have large pores that can trap molecules of certain sizes and shapes while excluding others. Bandages used by the military sometimes contain zeolites, which absorb water from the blood, thus accelerating the natural clotting process. Zeolites have also replaced phosphates in many detergents, which is an ecological benefit, because zeolites do not encourage the growth of algae. Interestingly, the name *zeolite* comes from the fact that zeolites give off water in the form of steam when they are heated; thus, they are called boiling (zeo) stones (lithos).

24. A 110.0-g sample of a gray-colored, unknown, pure metal was heated to 92.0°C and put into a coffee-cup calorimeter containing 75.0 g of water at 21.0°C. When the heated metal was put into the water, the temperature of the water rose to a final temperature of 24.2°C. The specific heat of water is 4.184 J/g°C. (a) What is the specific heat of the metal. (b) Is it possible that the metal is either iron or lead? Explain.

25. The specific heat of a human is approximately 3.47 J/g°C. Given this information,
    (a) If a 165-lb man eats a candy bar containing 262 Cal, how much will his body temperature increase if all the calories from the candy bar are converted into heat energy? Remember that a food calorie (Cal) is equal to 1 kcal.
    (b) If a 165-lb man eats a roll of candy containing 25.0 Cal, how much will his body temperature increase if all the calories from the candy bar are converted into heat energy?

26. A sample of water at 23.0°C required an input of 1.69×10^4 J of heat to reach its boiling point, 100°C. What was the mass of the water? (Table 4.3)

27. A sample of gold required 3.25×10^4 J of heat to melt it from room temperature, 23.2°C, to its melting point, 1064.4°C. How many pounds of gold were in the sample?

28. If 40.0 kJ of energy are absorbed by 500.0 g of water at 10.0°C, what is the final temperature of the water?

29. A sample of iron was heated to 125.0°C, then placed into 375 g of water at 19.8°C. The temperature of the water rose to 25.6°C. How many grams of iron were in the sample? (Table 4.3)

30. A sample of copper was heated to 275.1°C and placed into 272 g of water at 21.0°C. The temperature of the water rose to 29.7°C. How many grams of copper were in the sample? (Table 4.3)

31. A 100.0-g sample of copper is heated from 10.0°C to 100.0°C.
    (a) Determine the number of calories needed. (The specific heat of copper is 0.0921 cal/g°C.)
    (b) The same amount of heat is added to 100.0 g of Al at 10.0°C. (The specific heat of Al is 0.215 cal/g°C.) Which metal gets hotter, the copper or the aluminum?

32. A 500.0-g piece of iron is heated in a flame and dropped into 400.0 g of water at 10.0°C. The temperature of the water rises to 90.0°C. How hot was the iron when it was first removed from the flame? (The specific heat of iron is 0.473 J/g°C.)

33. A 20.0-g piece of metal at 203°C is dropped into 100.0 g of water at 25.0°C. The water temperature rose to 29.0°C. Calculate the specific heat of the metal (J/g°C). Assume that all of the heat lost by the metal is transferred to the water and no heat is lost to the surroundings.

34. Assuming no heat loss by the system, what will be the final temperature when 50.0 g of water at 10.0°C are mixed with 10.0 g of water at 50.0°C?

35. Three 500.0-g pans of iron, aluminum, and copper are each used to fry an egg. Which pan fries the egg (105°C) the quickest? Explain.

36. At 6:00 P.M., you put a 300.0-g copper pan containing 800.0 g of water (all at room temperature, which is 25°C) on the stove. The stove supplies 628 J/s. When will the water reach the boiling point? (Assume no heat loss.)

37. Why does blowing gently across the surface of a cup of hot coffee help to cool it? Why does inserting a spoon into the coffee do the same thing?

38. If you are boiling some potatoes in a pot of water, will they cook faster if the water is boiling vigorously than if the water is only gently boiling? Explain your reasoning.

39. Homogenized whole milk contains 4% butterfat by volume. How many milliliters of fat are there in a glass (250 mL) of milk? How many grams of butterfat ($d = 0.8$ g/mL) are in this glass of milk?

40. Gloves are often worn to protect the hands from being burned when they come in contact with very hot or very cold objects. Gloves are often made of cotton or wool, but many of the newer heat-resistant gloves are made of silicon rubber. The specific heats of these materials are listed below:

Material	Specific heat (J/g°C)
wool felt	1.38
cotton	1.33
paper	1.33
rubber	3.65
silicon rubber	1.46

    (a) If a glove with a mass of 99.3 grams composed of cotton increases in temperature by 15.3°F, how much energy was absorbed by the glove?
    (b) A glove with a mass of 86.2 grams increases in temperature by 25.9°F when it absorbs 1.71 kJ of energy. Calculate the specific heat of the glove and predict its composition.
    (c) If a glove with a mass of 50.0 grams needs to absorb 1.65 kJ of energy, how much will the temperature of the glove increase for each of the materials listed above?
    (d) Which is the best material for a heat-resistant glove?
    (e) If you were designing a heat-resistant glove, what kind of specific heat would you look for?

41. If solar panels are placed in the Mojave Desert in California that generate 100 megawatts on a 1.3-square-mile site with an average of 7.50 hours of productive daylight each day, how many tons of coal are equivalent to the energy produced in one day by the solar panels? (One ton of coal will produce 26.6 gigajoules of energy, 1 Watt = 1 J/s.)

CHALLENGE EXERCISES

42. Suppose a ball is sitting at the top of a hill. At this point, the ball has potential energy. The ball rolls down the hill, so the potential energy is converted into kinetic energy. When the ball reaches the bottom of the hill, it goes halfway up the hill on the other side and stops. If energy is supposed to be conserved, then why doesn't the ball go up the other hill to the same level as it started from?

43. From the following molecular picture, determine whether a physical or a chemical change has occurred. Justify your answer.

44. From the illustration below (a) describe the change that has occurred and (b) determine whether the change was a physical change or a chemical change. Justify your answer.

45. Describe the change(s) that you see in the following illustration. Was this a physical or a chemical change?

ANSWERS TO PRACTICE EXERCISES

4.1 Each compound has one atom of silver to one atom of the other elements. Using the periodic table, we find the atomic masses of these elements to be Ag (107.9), Cl (35.45), Br (79.90), and I (126.8). Each compound has the same amount of silver, but the percent of silver will be different. The highest percent of silver will be in AgCl, the middle will be in AgBr, and the lowest will be in AgI. So the order is AgCl, AgBr, AgI.

4.2 Physical change

4.3 1.0×10^2 J = 24 cal

4.4 0.477 J/g°C

4.5 C_nH_{2n+2} where n is the number of carbons in each formula

PUTTING IT TOGETHER:
Review for Chapters 1–4

Answers for Putting It Together Reviews are found in Appendix VII.

Multiple Choice

Choose the correct answer to each of the following.

1. 1.00 cm is equal to how many meters?
   (a) 2.54   (b) 100.   (c) 10.0   (d) 0.0100

2. 1.00 cm is equal to how many inches?
   (a) 0.394   (b) 0.10   (c) 12   (d) 2.54

3. 4.50 ft is how many centimeters?
   (a) 11.4   (b) 21.3   (c) 454   (d) 137

4. The number 0.0048 contains how many significant figures?
   (a) 1   (b) 2   (c) 3   (d) 4

5. Express 0.00382 in scientific notation.
   (a) 3.82×10^3 (c) 3.82×10^{-2}
   (b) 3.8×10^{-3} (d) 3.82×10^{-3}

6. 42.0°C is equivalent to
   (a) 273 K   (c) 108°F
   (b) 5.55°F   (d) 53.3°F

7. 267°F is equivalent to
   (a) 404 K   (c) 540 K
   (b) 116°C   (d) 389 K

8. An object has a mass of 62 g and a volume of 4.6 mL. Its density is
   (a) 0.074 mL/g   (c) 7.4 g/mL
   (b) 285 g/mL   (d) 13 g/mL

9. The mass of a block is 9.43 g and its density is 2.35 g/mL. The volume of the block is
   (a) 4.01 mL   (c) 22.2 mL
   (b) 0.249 mL   (d) 2.49 mL

10. The density of copper is 8.92 g/mL. The mass of a piece of copper that has a volume of 9.5 mL is
    (a) 2.6 g   (c) 0.94 g
    (b) 85 g   (d) 1.1 g

11. An empty graduated cylinder has a mass of 54.772 g. When filled with 50.0 mL of an unknown liquid, it has a mass of 101.074 g. The density of the liquid is
    (a) 0.926 g/mL   (c) 2.02 g/mL
    (b) 1.08 g/mL   (d) 1.85 g/mL

12. The conversion factor to change grams to milligrams is
    (a) $\dfrac{100\ mg}{1\ g}$ (c) $\dfrac{1\ g}{1000\ mg}$
    (b) $\dfrac{1\ g}{100\ mg}$ (d) $\dfrac{1000\ mg}{1\ g}$

13. What Fahrenheit temperature is twice the Celsius temperature?
    (a) 64°F   (c) 200°F
    (b) 320°F   (d) 546°F

14. A gold alloy has a density of 12.41 g/mL and contains 75.0% gold by mass. The volume of this alloy that can be made from 255 g of pure gold is
    (a) 4.22×10^3 mL   (c) 27.4 mL
    (b) 2.37×10^3 mL   (d) 20.5 mL

15. A lead cylinder ($V = \pi r^2 h$) has radius 12.0 cm and length 44.0 cm and a density of 11.4 g/mL. The mass of the cylinder is
    (a) 2.27×10^5 g   (c) 1.78×10^3 g
    (b) 1.89×10^5 g   (d) 3.50×10^5 g

16. The following units can all be used for density *except*
    (a) g/cm^3 (b) kg/m^3 (c) g/L (d) kg/m^2

17. 37.4 cm × 2.2 cm equals
    (a) 82.28 cm²   (c) 82 cm²
    (b) 82.3 cm²   (d) 82.2 cm²

18. The following elements are among the five most abundant by mass in the Earth's crust, seawater, and atmosphere *except*
    (a) oxygen   (c) silicon
    (b) hydrogen   (d) aluminum

19. Which of the following is a compound?
    (a) lead   (c) potassium
    (b) wood   (d) water

20. Which of the following is a mixture?
    (a) water   (c) wood
    (b) chromium   (d) sulfur

21. How many atoms are represented in the formula Na_2CrO_4?
    (a) 3   (b) (5)   (c) (7)   (d) 8

22. Which of the following is a characteristic of metals?
    (a) ductile   (c) extremely strong
    (b) easily shattered   (d) dull

23. Which of the following is a characteristic of nonmetals?
    (a) always a gas
    (b) poor conductor of electricity
    (c) shiny
    (d) combines only with metals

24. When a pure substance was analyzed, it was found to contain carbon and chlorine. This substance must be classified as
    (a) an element
    (b) a mixture
    (c) a compound
    (d) both a mixture and a compound

25. Chromium, fluorine, and magnesium have the symbols
    (a) Ch, F, Ma   (c) Cr, F, Mg
    (b) Cr, Fl, Mg   (d) Cr, F, Ma

26. Sodium, carbon, and sulfur have the symbols
    (a) Na, C, S   (c) Na, Ca, Su
    (b) So, C, Su   (d) So, Ca, Su

27. Coffee is an example of
    (a) an element   (c) a homogeneous mixture
    (b) a compound   (d) a heterogeneous mixture

28. The number of oxygen atoms in $Al(C_2H_3O_2)_3$ is
    (a) 2   (b) 3   (c) 5   (d) 6

29. Which of the following is a mixture?
    (a) water   (c) sugar solution
    (b) iron(II) oxide   (d) iodine

79

30. Which is the most compact state of matter?
    (a) solid   (c) gas
    (b) liquid   (d) amorphous
31. Which is not characteristic of a solution?
    (a) a homogeneous mixture
    (b) a heterogeneous mixture
    (c) one that has two or more substances
    (d) one that has a variable composition
32. A chemical formula is a combination of
    (a) symbols   (c) elements
    (b) atoms   (d) compounds
33. The number of nonmetal atoms in $Al_2(SO_3)_3$ is
    (a) 5   (b) 7   (c) 12   (d) 14
34. Which of the following is not a physical property?
    (a) boiling point   (c) bleaching action
    (b) physical state   (d) color
35. Which of the following is a physical change?
    (a) A piece of sulfur is burned.
    (b) A firecracker explodes.
    (c) A rubber band is stretched.
    (d) A nail rusts.
36. Which of the following is a chemical change?
    (a) Water evaporates.
    (b) Ice melts.
    (c) Rocks are ground to sand.
    (d) A penny tarnishes.
37. The changing of liquid water to ice is known as a
    (a) chemical change
    (b) heterogeneous change
    (c) homogeneous change
    (d) physical change
38. Which of the following does not represent a chemical change?
    (a) heating of copper in air
    (b) combustion of gasoline
    (c) cooling of red-hot iron
    (d) digestion of food
39. Heating 30. g of water from 20.°C to 50.°C requires
    (a) 30. cal   (c) 3.8×10^3 J
    (b) 50. cal   (d) 6.3×10^3 J
40. The specific heat of aluminum is 0.900 J/g°C. How many joules of energy are required to raise the temperature of 20.0 g of Al from 10.0°C to 15.0°C?
    (a) 79 J   (b) 90. J   (c) 100. J   (d)   112 J
41. A 100.-g iron ball (specific heat = 0.473 J/g°C) is heated to 125°C and is placed in a calorimeter holding 200. g of water at 25.0°C. What will be the highest temperature reached by the water?
    (a) 43.7°C   (c) 65.3°C
    (b) 30.4°C   (d) 35.4°C
42. Which has the highest specific heat?
    (a) ice   (b) lead   (c) water   (d) aluminum
43. When 20.0 g of mercury are heated from 10.0°C to 20.0°C, 27.6 J of energy are absorbed. What is the specific heat of mercury?
    (a) 0.726 J/g°C   (c) 2.76 J/g°C
    (b) 0.138 J/g°C   (d) no correct answer given
44. Changing hydrogen and oxygen into water is a
    (a) physical change
    (b) chemical change
    (c) conservation reaction
    (d) no correct answer given

Free Response Questions

Answer each of the following. Be sure to include your work and explanations in a clear, logical form.

1. You decide to go sailing in the tropics with some friends. Once there, you listen to the marine forecast, which predicts in-shore wave heights of 1.5 m, offshore wave heights of 4 m, and temperature of 27°C. Your friend the captain is unfamiliar with the metric system, and he needs to know whether it is safe for your small boat and if it will be warm. He asks you to convert the measurements to feet and degrees Fahrenheit, respectively.

2. Jane is melting butter in a copper pot on the stove. If she knows how much heat her stove releases per minute, what other measurements does she need to determine how much heat the butter absorbed? She assumes that the stove does not lose any heat to the surroundings.

3. Julius decided to heat 75 g $CaCO_3$ to determine how much carbon dioxide is produced. (*Note:* When $CaCO_3$ is heated, it produces CaO and carbon dioxide.) He collected the carbon dioxide in a balloon. Julius found the mass of the CaO remaining was 42 g. If 44 g of carbon dioxide take up 24 dm^3 of space, how many *liters* of gas were trapped in the balloon?

Use these pictures to answer Question 4.

(1)   (2)   (3)   (4)

4. (a) Which picture best describes a homogeneous mixture?
   (b) How would you classify the contents of the other containers?
   (c) Which picture contains a compound? Explain how you made your choice.

Use these pictures to answer Question 5.

(1)   (2)   (3)   (4)

5. (a) Which picture best represents fluorine gas? Why?
   (b) Which other elements could that picture also represent?
   (c) Which of the pictures could represent SO_3 gas?

6. Sue and Tim each left a one-quart bowl outside one night. Sue's bowl was full of water and covered, while Tim's was empty and open. The next day there was a huge snowstorm that filled Tim's bowl with snow. The temperature that night went down to 12°F.
   (a) Which bowl would require less energy to bring its contents to room temperature (25°C)? Why?
   (b) What temperature change (°C) is required to warm the bowls to 25°C?
   (c) How much heat (in kJ) is required to raise the temperature of the contents of Sue's bowl to 0°C (without converting the ice to water)?
   (d) Did the water in Sue's bowl undergo chemical or physical changes or both?

7. One cup of Raisin Bran provides 60.% of the U.S. recommended daily allowance (RDA) of iron.
   (a) If the cereal provides 11 mg of iron, what is the U.S. RDA for Fe?
   (b) When the iron in the cereal is extracted, it is found to be the pure element. What is the volume of iron in a cup of the cereal?

8. Absent-minded Alfred put down a bottle containing silver on the table. When he went to retrieve it, he realized he had forgotten to label the bottle. Unfortunately, there were two full bottles of the same size side-by-side. Alfred realized he had placed a bottle of mercury on the same table last week. State two ways Alfred can determine which bottle contains silver without opening the bottles.

9. Suppose 25 g of solid sulfur and 35 g of oxygen gas are placed in a sealed container.
   (a) Does the container hold a mixture or a compound?
   (b) After heating, the container was weighed. From a comparison of the total mass before heating to the total mass after heating, can you tell whether a reaction took place? Explain.
   (c) After the container is heated, all the contents are gaseous. Has the density of the container including its contents changed? Explain.

Lightning occurs when electrons move to neutralize a charge difference between the clouds and the Earth.

SuperStock

CHAPTER **5**

EARLY ATOMIC THEORY AND STRUCTURE

Pure substances are classified as elements or compounds, but just what makes a substance possess its unique properties? How small a piece of salt will still taste salty? Carbon dioxide puts out fires, is used by plants to produce oxygen, and forms dry ice when solidified. But how small a mass of this material still behaves like carbon dioxide? Substances are in their simplest identifiable form at the atomic, ionic, or molecular level. Further division produces a loss of characteristic properties.

What particles lie within an atom or ion? How are these tiny particles alike? How do they differ? How far can we continue to divide them? Alchemists began the quest, early chemists laid the foundation, and modern chemists continue to build and expand on models of the atom.

5.1 DALTON'S MODEL OF THE ATOM

Describe Dalton's model of the atom and compare it to the earlier concepts of matter. ● **LEARNING OBJECTIVE**

KEY TERM

Dalton's atomic model

The structure of matter has long intrigued and engaged us. The earliest models of the atom were developed by the ancient Greek philosophers. About 440 B.C. Empedocles stated that all matter was composed of four "elements"—earth, air, water, and fire. Democritus (about 470–370 B.C.) thought that all forms of matter were composed of tiny indivisible particles, which he called atoms, derived from the Greek word *atomos*, meaning "indivisible." He held that atoms were in constant motion and that they combined with one another in various ways. This hypothesis was not based on scientific observations. Shortly thereafter, Aristotle (384–322 B.C.) opposed the theory of Democritus and instead endorsed and advanced the Empedoclean theory. So strong was the influence of Aristotle that his theory dominated the thinking of scientists and philosophers until the beginning of the seventeenth century.

More than 2000 years after Democritus, the English schoolmaster John Dalton (1766–1844) revived the concept of atoms and proposed an atomic model based on facts and experimental evidence (Figure 5.1). His theory, described in a series of papers published from 1803 to 1810, rested on the idea of a different kind of atom for each element. The essence of **Dalton's atomic model** may be summed up as follows:

1. Elements are composed of minute, indivisible particles called atoms.
2. Atoms of the same element are alike in mass and size.
3. Atoms of different elements have different masses and sizes.
4. Chemical compounds are formed by the union of two or more atoms of different elements.
5. Atoms combine to form compounds in simple numerical ratios, such as one to one, one to two, two to three, and so on.
6. Atoms of two elements may combine in different ratios to form more than one compound.

(a)   (b)   (c)

Figure 5.1

(a) Dalton's atoms were individual particles, the atoms of each element being alike in mass and size but different in mass and size from other elements; (b) and (c) Dalton's atoms combine in specific ratios to form compounds.

Dalton's atomic model stands as a landmark in the development of chemistry. The major premises of his model are still valid, but some of his statements must be modified or qualified because later investigations have shown that (1) atoms are composed of subatomic particles; (2) not all the atoms of a specific element have the same mass; and (3) atoms, under special circumstances, can be decomposed.

In chemistry we use models (theories) such as Dalton's atomic model to explain the behavior of atoms, molecules, and compounds. Models are modified to explain new information. We frequently learn the most about a system when our models (theories) fail. That is the time when we must rethink our explanation and determine whether we need to modify our model or propose a new or different model to explain the behavior.

EXAMPLE 5.1

Which statement of Dalton's model of the atom does this series of compounds represent: NO_2, N_2O, N_2O_3, N_2O_5?

SOLUTION

Atoms combine to form compounds in simple numerical ratios. Atoms of two elements combine in different ratios to form more than one compound.

PRACTICE 5.1

List another series of compounds that illustrates the statements in Example 5.1.

5.2 ELECTRIC CHARGE

LEARNING OBJECTIVE ● Recognize the force between particles and distinguish between a cation and an anion.

You've probably received a shock after walking across a carpeted area on a dry day. You may have also experienced the static electricity associated with combing your hair and have had your clothing cling to you. These phenomena result from an accumulation of *electric charge*. This charge may be transferred from one object to another. The properties of electric charge are as follows:

1. Charge may be of two types, positive and negative.

2. Unlike charges attract (positive attracts negative), and like charges repel (negative repels negative and positive repels positive).

3. Charge may be transferred from one object to another by contact or induction.

4. The less the distance between two charges, the greater the force of attraction between unlike charges (or repulsion between identical charges). The force of attraction (*F*) can be expressed using the following equation:

$$F = \frac{kq_1q_2}{r^2}$$

where q_1 and q_2 are the charges, r is the distance between the charges, and k is a constant.

Discovery of Ions

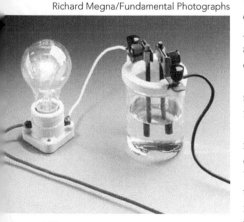

Richard Megna/Fundamental Photographs

English scientist Michael Faraday (1791–1867) made the discovery that certain substances when dissolved in water conduct an electric current. He also noticed that certain compounds decompose into their elements when an electric current is passed through the compound. Atoms of some elements are attracted to the positive electrode, while atoms of other elements are attracted to the negative electrode. Faraday concluded that these atoms are electrically charged. He called them *ions* after the Greek word meaning "wanderer."

Any moving charge is an electric current. The electrical charge must travel through a substance known as a conducting medium. The most familiar conducting media are metals formed into wires.

The Swedish scientist Svante Arrhenius (1859–1927) extended Faraday's work. Arrhenius reasoned that an ion is an atom (or a group of atoms) carrying a positive or negative charge. When a compound such as sodium chloride (NaCl) is melted, it conducts electricity. Water is unnecessary. Arrhenius's explanation of this conductivity was that upon melting, the sodium chloride dissociates, or breaks up, into charged ions, Na^+ and Cl^-. The Na^+ ions move toward the negative electrode (cathode), whereas the Cl^- ions migrate toward the positive electrode (anode). Thus positive ions are called *cations*, and negative ions are called *anions*.

When ions are present in a solution of salt water and an electric current is passed through the solution, the light bulb glows.

From Faraday's and Arrhenius's work with ions, Irish physicist G. J. Stoney (1826–1911) realized there must be some fundamental unit of electricity associated with atoms.

He named this unit the electron in 1891. Unfortunately, he had no means of supporting his idea with experimental proof. Evidence remained elusive until 1897, when English physicist J. J. Thomson (1856–1940) was able to show experimentally the existence of the electron.

EXAMPLE 5.2

What is a cation? What is an anion?

SOLUTION

A cation is a positively charged ion. An anion is a negatively charged ion.

PRACTICE 5.2

Which of the following ions are cations and which are anions?

$Na^+, Cl^-, NH_4^+, Ca^{2+}, Br^-, Al^{3+}, NO_3^-, SO_4^{2-}, PO_4^{3-}, K^+, Ag^+, Fe^{2+}, Fe^{3+}, S^{2-}$

5.3 SUBATOMIC PARTS OF THE ATOM

Describe the three basic subatomic particles and how they changed Dalton's model of the atom.

● **LEARNING OBJECTIVE**

KEY TERMS
subatomic particles
electron
proton
Thomson model of the atom
neutron

The concept of the atom—a particle so small that until recently it could not be seen even with the most powerful microscope—and the subsequent determination of its structure stand among the greatest creative intellectual human achievements.

Any visible quantity of an element contains a vast number of identical atoms. But when we refer to an atom of an element, we isolate a single atom from the multitude in order to present the element in its simplest form. **Figure 5.2** shows individual atoms as we can see them today.

What is this tiny particle we call the atom? The diameter of a single atom ranges from 0.1 to 0.5 nanometer (1 nm $= 1 \times 10^{-9}$ m). Hydrogen, the smallest atom, has a diameter of about 0.1 nm. To arrive at some idea of how small an atom is, consider this dot (•), which has a diameter of about 1 mm, or 1×10^6 nm. It would take 10 million hydrogen atoms to form a line of atoms across this dot. As inconceivably small as atoms are, they contain even smaller particles, the **subatomic particles**, including electrons, protons, and neutrons.

The development of atomic theory was helped in large part by the invention of new instruments. For example, the Crookes tube, developed by Sir William Crookes (1832–1919) in 1875, opened the door to the subatomic structure of the atom (**Figure 5.3**). The emissions generated in a Crookes tube are called *cathode rays*. J. J. Thomson demonstrated in 1897 that cathode rays (1) travel in straight lines, (2) are negative in charge, (3) are deflected by electric and magnetic fields, (4) produce sharp shadows, and (5) are capable of moving a small paddle wheel. This was the experimental discovery of the fundamental unit of charge—the electron.

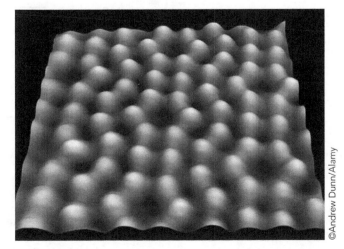

©Andrew Dunn/Alamy

Figure 5.2

A scanning tunneling microscope shows an array of copper atoms.

Figure 5.3

Cathode ray tube. A stream of electrons passes between electrodes. The fast-moving particles excite the gas inside the tube, creating a greenish glow between the electrodes.

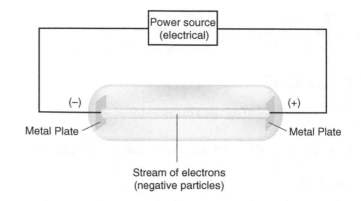

The **electron** (e^-) is a particle with a negative electrical charge and a mass of 9.110×10^{-28} g. This mass is 1/1837 the mass of a hydrogen atom. Although the actual charge of an electron is known, its value is too cumbersome for practical use and has therefore been assigned a relative electrical charge of -1. The size of an electron has not been determined exactly, but its diameter is believed to be less than 10^{-12} cm.

Protons were first observed by German physicist Eugen Goldstein (1850–1930) in 1886. However, it was Thomson who discovered the nature of the proton. He showed that the proton is a particle, and he calculated its mass to be about 1837 times that of an electron. The **proton** (p) is a particle with actual mass of 1.673×10^{-24} g. Its relative charge ($+1$) is equal in magnitude, but opposite in sign, to the charge on the electron. The mass of a proton is only very slightly less than that of a hydrogen atom.

Thomson had shown that atoms contain both negatively and positively charged particles. Clearly, the Dalton model of the atom was no longer acceptable. Atoms are not indivisible but are instead composed of smaller parts. Thomson proposed a new model of the atom.

In the **Thomson model of the atom**, the electrons are negatively charged particles embedded in the positively charged atomic sphere (see **Figure 5.4**). A neutral atom could become an ion by gaining or losing electrons.

Positive ions were explained by assuming that a neutral atom loses electrons. An atom with a net charge of $+1$ (for example, Na^+ or Li^+) has lost one electron. An atom with a net charge of $+3$ (for example, Al^{3+}) has lost three electrons (**Figure 5.5a**).

Negative ions were explained by assuming that additional electrons can be added to atoms. A net charge of -1 (for example, Cl^- or F^-) is produced by the addition of one electron. A net charge of -2 (for example, O^{2-} or S^{2-}) requires the addition of two electrons (**Figure 5.5b**).

The third major subatomic particle was discovered in 1932 by James Chadwick (1891–1974). This particle, the **neutron** (n), has neither a positive nor a negative charge and

Figure 5.4

Thomson model of the atom. In this early model of the atom, negative particles (electrons) were thought to be embedded in a positively charged sphere. It is sometimes called the plum pudding model.

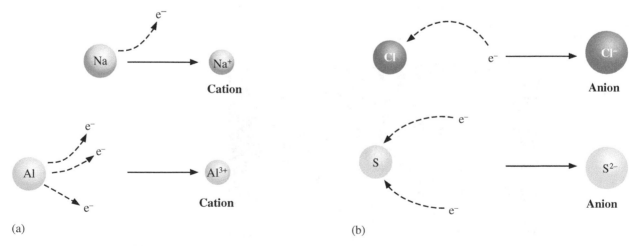

(a)   (b)

Figure 5.5

(a) When one or more electrons are lost from a neutral atom, a cation is formed. (b) When one or more electrons are added to a neutral atom, an anion is formed.

		Relative	Actual mass
Particle	Symbol	electrical charge	(g)
Electron	e^-	-1	9.110×10^{-28}
Proton	p	$+1$	1.673×10^{-24}
Neutron	n	0	1.675×10^{-24}

TABLE 5.1   Electrical Charge and Relative Mass of Electrons, Protons, and Neutrons

has an actual mass (1.675×10^{-24} g) that is only very slightly greater than that of a proton. The properties of these three subatomic particles are summarized in Table 5.1.

Nearly all the ordinary chemical properties of matter can be explained in terms of atoms consisting of electrons, protons, and neutrons. The discussion of atomic structure that follows is based on the assumption that atoms contain only these principal subatomic particles. Many other subatomic particles, such as mesons, positrons, neutrinos, and antiprotons, have been discovered, but it is not yet clear whether all these particles are actually present in the atom or whether they are produced by reactions occurring within the nucleus. The fields of atomic and high-energy physics have produced a long list of subatomic particles. Descriptions of the properties of many of these particles are to be found in physics textbooks.

EXAMPLE 5.3

The mass of a helium atom is 6.65×10^{-24} g. How many atoms are in a 4.0-g sample of helium?

SOLUTION

$$(4.0 \text{ g})\left(\frac{1 \text{ atom He}}{6.65 \times 10^{-24} \text{ g}}\right) = 6.0 \times 10^{23} \text{ atoms He}$$

PRACTICE 5.3

The mass of an atom of hydrogen is 1.673×10^{-24} g. How many atoms are in a 10.0-g sample of hydrogen?

5.4 THE NUCLEAR ATOM

Explain how the nuclear model of the atom differs from Dalton's and Thomson's models.   ● **LEARNING OBJECTIVE**

KEY TERMS
nucleus
atomic number

The discovery that positively charged particles are present in atoms came soon after the discovery of radioactivity by Henri Becquerel (1852–1908) in 1896. Radioactive elements spontaneously emit alpha particles, beta particles, and gamma rays from their nuclei (see Chapter 18).

By 1907 Ernest Rutherford (1871–1937) had established that the positively charged alpha particles emitted by certain radioactive elements are ions of the element helium. Rutherford used these alpha particles to establish the nuclear nature of atoms. In experiments performed in 1911, he directed a stream of positively charged helium ions (alpha particles) at a very thin sheet of gold foil (about 1000 atoms thick). See Figure 5.6a. He observed that most of the alpha particles passed through the foil with little or no deflection; but a few of the particles were deflected at large angles, and occasionally one even bounced back from the foil (Figure 5.6b). It was known that like charges repel each other and that an electron with a mass of 1/1837 that of a proton could not possibly have an appreciable effect on the path of an alpha particle, which is about 7350 times more massive than an electron. Rutherford therefore reasoned that each gold atom must contain a positively charged mass occupying a relatively tiny volume and that, when an alpha particle approaches close enough to this positive mass, it is deflected. Rutherford spoke of this positively charged mass as the *nucleus* of the atom. Because alpha particles have relatively high masses, the extent of the deflections (some actually

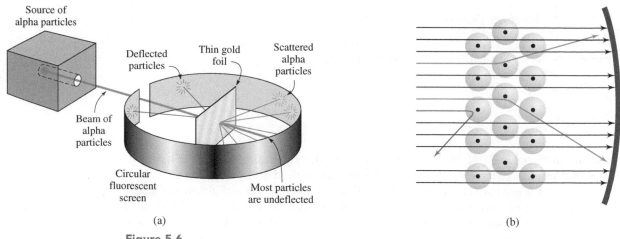

Figure 5.6

(a) Rutherford's experiment on alpha-particle scattering, where positive alpha particles (α), emanating from a radioactive source, were directed at a thin gold foil. (b) Deflection (red) and scattering (blue) of the positive alpha particles by the positive nuclei of the gold atoms.

bounced back) indicated to Rutherford that the nucleus is very heavy and dense. (The density of the nucleus of a hydrogen atom is about 10^{12} g/cm^3—about 1 trillion times the density of water.) Because most of the alpha particles passed through the thousand or so gold atoms without any apparent deflection, he further concluded that most of an atom consists of empty space.

When we speak of the mass of an atom, we are referring primarily to the mass of the nucleus. The nucleus contains all the protons and neutrons, which represent more than 99.9% of the total mass of any atom. By way of illustration, the largest number of electrons known to exist in an atom is 118. The mass of even 118 electrons is only about 1/17 of the mass of a single proton or neutron. The mass of an atom therefore is primarily determined by the combined masses of its protons and neutrons.

General Arrangement of Subatomic Particles

The alpha-particle scattering experiments of Rutherford established that the atom contains a dense, positively charged nucleus. The later work of Chadwick demonstrated that the atom contains neutrons, which are particles with mass, but no charge. Rutherford also noted that light, negatively charged electrons are present and offset the positive charges in the nucleus. Based on this experimental evidence, a model of the atom and the location of its subatomic particles was devised in which each atom consists of a **nucleus** surrounded by electrons (see Figure 5.7). The nucleus contains protons and neutrons but does not contain electrons. In a neutral atom the positive charge of the nucleus (due to protons) is exactly offset by the negative electrons. Because the charge of an electron is equal to, but of opposite sign than, the charge of a proton, a neutral atom must contain exactly the same number of electrons as protons. However, this model of atomic structure provides no information on the arrangement of electrons within the atom.

A neutral atom contains the same number of protons and electrons.

Figure 5.7

In the nuclear model of the atom, protons and neutrons are located in the nucleus. The electrons are found in the remainder of the atom (which is mostly empty space because electrons are very tiny).

EXAMPLE 5.4

What are the major subatomic particles and where are they located in an atom?

SOLUTION

Protons, neutrons, and electrons are the three major subatomic particles in an atom. The protons and neutrons are located in the nucleus and the electrons are located outside the nucleus and around the nucleus.

Atomic Numbers of the Elements

The **atomic number (Z)** of an element is the number of protons in the nucleus of an atom of that element. The atomic number determines the identity of an atom. For example, every atom with an atomic number of 1 is a hydrogen atom; it contains one proton in its nucleus. Every atom with an atomic number of 6 is a carbon atom; it contains 6 protons in its nucleus. Every atom with an atomic number of 92 is a uranium atom; it contains 92 protons in its nucleus. The atomic number tells us not only the number of positive charges in the nucleus but also the number of electrons in the neutral atom, since a neutral atom contains the same number of electrons and protons.

atomic number = number of protons in the nucleus

You don't need to memorize the atomic numbers of the elements because a periodic table is usually provided in texts, in laboratories, and on examinations. The atomic numbers of all elements are shown in the periodic table on the inside front cover of this book and are also listed in the table of atomic masses on the inside front endpapers.

PRACTICE 5.4

Look in the periodic table and determine how many protons and electrons are in a Cu atom and an Xe atom.

5.5 ISOTOPES OF THE ELEMENTS

Define the terms *atomic number*, *mass number*, and *isotope*.

● **LEARNING OBJECTIVE**

KEY TERMS
isotope
mass number

Shortly after Rutherford's conception of the nuclear atom, experiments were performed to determine the masses of individual atoms. These experiments showed that the masses of nearly all atoms were greater than could be accounted for by simply adding up the masses of all the protons and electrons that were known to be present in an atom. This fact led to the concept of the neutron, a particle with no charge but with a mass about the same as that of a proton. Because this particle has no charge, it was very difficult to detect, and the existence of the neutron was not proven experimentally until 1932. All atomic nuclei except that of the simplest hydrogen atom contain neutrons.

All atoms of a given element have the same number of protons. Experimental evidence has shown that, in most cases, all atoms of a given element do not have identical masses. This is because atoms of the same element may have different numbers of neutrons in their nuclei.

Atoms of an element having the same atomic number but different atomic masses are called **isotopes** of that element. Atoms of the various isotopes of an element therefore have the same number of protons and electrons but different numbers of neutrons.

Three isotopes of hydrogen (atomic number 1) are known. Each has one proton in the nucleus and one electron. The first isotope (protium), without a neutron, has a mass number of 1; the second isotope (deuterium), with one neutron in the nucleus, has a mass number of 2; the third isotope (tritium), with two neutrons, has a mass number of 3 (see **Figure 5.8**).

The three isotopes of hydrogen may be represented by the symbols ^1_1H, ^2_1H and ^3_1H, indicating an atomic number of 1 and mass numbers of 1, 2, and 3, respectively. This method

© 2010 Paul Silverman/Fundamental Photographs

An uncut diamond from a Colorado mine. Diamonds are composed of carbon.

Figure 5.8

The isotopes of hydrogen. The number of protons (purple) and neutrons (blue) are shown within the nucleus. The electron (e^-) exists outside the nucleus.

^1_1H
Protium

^2_1H or D
Deuterium

^3_1H or T
Tritium

of representing atoms is called *isotopic notation*. The subscript (Z) is the atomic number; the superscript (A) is the **mass number**, which is the sum of the number of protons and the number of neutrons in the nucleus. The hydrogen isotopes may also be referred to as hydrogen-1, hydrogen-2, and hydrogen-3.

The mass number of an element is the sum of the protons and neutrons in the nucleus.

Mass number (sum of protons and neutrons in the nucleus) ↘

$$^A_Z\mathbf{E}$$ ⟵ **Symbol of element**

Atomic number (number of protons in the nucleus) ↗

Most of the elements occur in nature as mixtures of isotopes. However, not all isotopes are stable; some are radioactive and are continuously decomposing to form other elements. For example, of the seven known isotopes of carbon, only two, carbon-12 and carbon-13, are stable. Of the seven known isotopes of oxygen, only three—$^{16}_8O$, $^{17}_8O$, and $^{18}_8O$—are stable. Of the fifteen known isotopes of arsenic, $^{75}_{33}As$ is the only one that is stable.

The relationship between mass number and atomic number is such that if we subtract the atomic number from the mass number of a given isotope, we obtain the number of neutrons in the nucleus of an atom of that isotope. Table 5.2 shows this method of determining the number of neutrons. For example, the fluorine atom ($^{19}_9F$), atomic number 9, having a mass of 19 contains 10 neutrons:

mass number	−	atomic number	=	number of neutrons
19	−	9	=	10

Use four significant figures for atomic masses in this text.

The atomic masses given in the table on the front endpapers of this book are values accepted by international agreement. You need not memorize atomic masses. In the calculations in this book, the use of atomic masses rounded to four significant figures will give results of sufficient accuracy. (See periodic table.)

TABLE 5.2   Determination of the Number of Neutrons in an Atom by Subtracting Atomic Number from Mass Number

	Hydrogen (^1_1H)	Oxygen ($^{16}_8O$)	Sulfur ($^{32}_{16}S$)	Fluorine ($^{19}_9F$)	Iron ($^{56}_{26}Fe$)
Mass number	1	16	32	19	56
Atomic number	$(-)1$	$(-)8$	$(-)16$	$(-)9$	$(-)26$
Number of neutrons	0	8	16	10	30

EXAMPLE 5.5

How many protons, neutrons, and electrons are found in an atom of $^{14}_{6}C$?

SOLUTION

The element is carbon, atomic number 6. The number of protons or electrons equals the atomic number and is 6. The number of neutrons is determined by subtracting the atomic number from the mass number: $14 - 6 = 8$.

PRACTICE 5.5

How many protons, neutrons, and electrons are in each of these isotopes?

(a) $^{16}_{8}O$ (b) $^{80}_{35}Br$ (c) $^{235}_{92}U$ (d) $^{64}_{29}Cu$

PRACTICE 5.6

What are the atomic number and the mass number of the elements that contain

(a) 9 electrons   (b) 24 protons and 28 neutrons   (c) $^{197}_{79}X$

What are the names of these elements?

>CHEMISTRY *IN ACTION*

Isotope Detectives

Scientists are learning to use isotopes to determine the origin of drugs and gems. It turns out that isotope ratios similar to those used in carbon dating can also identify the source of cocaine or the birthplace of emeralds.

Researchers with the Drug Enforcement Agency (DEA) have created a database of the origin of coca leaves that pinpoints the origin of the leaves with a 90% accuracy. Cocaine keeps a chemical signature of the environment where it grew. Isotopes of carbon and nitrogen are found in a particular ratio based on climatic conditions in the growing region. These ratios correctly identified the source of 90% of the samples tested, according to James Ehleringer of the University of Utah, Salt Lake City. This new method can trace drugs a step further back than current techniques, which mainly look at chemicals introduced by processing practices in different locations. This could aid in tracking the original exporters and stopping production at the source.

It turns out that a similar isotopic analysis of oxygen has led researchers in France to be able to track the birthplace of emeralds. Very high quality emeralds have few inclusions (microscopic cavities). Gemologists use these inclusions and the material trapped in them to identify the source of the gem. High-quality gems can now also be identified by using an oxygen isotope ratio. These tests use an ion microscope that blasts a few atoms from the gems' surface (with virtually undetectable damage). The tiny sample is analyzed for its oxygen isotope ratio and then compared to a database from emerald mines around the world. Using the information, gemologists can determine the mine from which the emerald came. Since emeralds from Colombian mines are valued much more highly than those from other countries, this technique can be used to help collectors know just what they are paying for, as well as to identify the history of treasured emeralds.

Raw and cut emeralds

© PjrStudio/Alamy

5.6 ATOMIC MASS

LEARNING OBJECTIVE • Explain the relationship between the atomic mass of an element and the masses of its isotopes.

KEY TERMS

atomic mass unit (amu)
atomic mass

$$1 \text{ amu} = 1.6606 \times 10^{-24} \text{ g}$$

Tetra Images /Getty Images, Inc.

The copper used in casting the Liberty Bell contains a mixture of the isotopes of copper.

The mass of a single atom is far too small to measure on a balance, but fairly precise determinations of the masses of individual atoms can be made with an instrument called a *mass spectrometer*. The mass of a single hydrogen atom is 1.673×10^{-24} g. However, it is neither convenient nor practical to compare the actual masses of atoms expressed in grams; therefore, a table of relative atomic masses using *atomic mass units* was devised. (The term *atomic weight* is sometimes used instead of *atomic mass*.) The carbon isotope having six protons and six neutrons and designated carbon-12, or $^{12}_{6}\text{C}$, was chosen as the standard for atomic masses. This reference isotope was assigned a value of exactly 12 atomic mass units (amu). Thus, 1 **atomic mass unit (amu)** is defined as equal to exactly 1/12 of the mass of a carbon-12 atom. The actual mass of a carbon-12 atom is 1.9927×10^{-23} g and that of one atomic mass unit is 1.6606×10^{-24} g. In the table of atomic masses, all elements then have values that are relative to the mass assigned to the reference isotope, carbon-12.

A table of atomic masses is given on the inside front cover of this book. Hydrogen atoms, with a mass of about 1/12 that of a carbon atom, have an average atomic mass of 1.00794 amu on this relative scale. Magnesium atoms, which are about twice as heavy as carbon, have an average mass of 24.305 amu. The average atomic mass of oxygen is 15.9994 amu.

Since most elements occur as mixtures of isotopes with different masses, the atomic mass determined for an element represents the average relative mass of all the naturally occurring isotopes of that element. The atomic masses of the individual isotopes are approximately whole numbers, because the relative masses of the protons and neutrons are approximately 1.0 amu each. Yet we find that the atomic masses given for many of the elements deviate considerably from whole numbers.

For example, the atomic mass of rubidium is 85.4678 amu, that of copper is 63.546 amu, and that of magnesium is 24.305 amu. The deviation of an atomic mass from a whole number is due mainly to the unequal occurrence of the various isotopes of an element.

The two principal isotopes of copper are $^{63}_{29}\text{Cu}$ and $^{65}_{29}\text{Cu}$. Copper used in everyday objects and the Liberty Bell contains a mixture of these two isotopes. It is apparent that copper-63 atoms are the more abundant isotope, since the atomic mass of copper, 63.546 amu, is closer to 63 than to 65 amu (see **Figure 5.9**). The actual values of the copper isotopes observed by mass spectra determination are shown in the following table:

Isotope	Isotopic mass (amu)	Abundance (%)	Average atomic mass (amu)
$^{63}_{29}\text{Cu}$	62.9298	69.09	63.55
$^{65}_{29}\text{Cu}$	64.9278	30.91	

The average atomic mass is a weighted average of the masses of all the isotopes present in the sample.

The average atomic mass can be calculated by multiplying the atomic mass of each isotope by the fraction of each isotope present and adding the results. The calculation for copper is

$$(62.9298 \text{ amu})(0.6909) = 43.48 \text{ amu}$$

$$(64.9278 \text{ amu})(0.3091) = \underline{20.07 \text{ amu}}$$
$$63.55 \text{ amu}$$

The **atomic mass** of an element is the average relative mass of the isotopes of that element compared to the atomic mass of carbon-12 (exactly 12.0000... amu).

Figure 5.9
A typical reading from a mass spectrometer. The two principal isotopes of copper are shown with the abundance (%) given.

EXAMPLE 5.6

Chlorine is found in nature as two isotopes, $^{37}_{17}Cl$ (24.47%) and $^{35}_{17}Cl$ (75.53%). The atomic masses are 36.96590 and 34.96885 amu, respectively. Determine the average atomic mass of chlorine.

SOLUTION

Multiply each mass by its percentage and add the results to find the average:

$(0.2447)(36.96590$ amu$) + (0.7553)(34.96885$ amu$)$

$= 35.4575$ amu

$= 35.46$ amu (four significant figures)

PRACTICE 5.7

Silver occurs as two isotopes with atomic masses 106.9041 and 108.9047 amu, respectively. The first isotope represents 51.82% and the second 48.18%. Determine the average atomic mass of silver.

CHAPTER **5 REVIEW**

5.1 DALTON'S MODEL OF THE ATOM

- Greek model of matter:
  - Four elements—earth, air, water, fire
  - Democritus—atoms (indivisible particles) make up matter
  - Aristotle—opposed atomic ideas
- Summary of Dalton's model of the atom:
  - Elements are composed of atoms.
  - Atoms of the same element are alike (mass and size).
  - Atoms of different elements are different in mass and size.
  - Compounds form by the union of two or more atoms of different elements.
  - Atoms form compounds in simple numerical ratios.
  - Atoms of two elements may combine in different ratios to form different compounds.

KEY TERM
Dalton's atomic model

5.2 ELECTRIC CHARGE

- The properties of electric charge:
  - Charges are one of two types—positive or negative.
  - Unlike charges attract and like charges repel.

• Charge is transferred from one object to another by contact or by induction.
• The force of attraction between charges is expressed by

$$F = \frac{kq_1q_2}{r^2}$$

• Michael Faraday discovered electrically charged ions.
• Svante Arrhenius explained that conductivity results from the dissociation of compounds into ions:
    • Cation—positive charge—attracted to negative electrode (cathode)
    • Anion—negative charge—attracted to positive electrode (anode)

5.3 SUBATOMIC PARTS OF THE ATOM

KEY TERMS

subatomic particles
electron
proton
Thomson model of the atom
neutron

• Atoms contain smaller subatomic particles:
    • Electron—negative charge, 1/1837 mass of proton
    • Proton—positive charge, 1.673×10^{-24} g
    • Neutron—no charge, 1.675×10^{-24} g
• Thomson model of the atom:
    • Negative electrons are embedded in a positive atomic sphere.
• Number of protons = number of electrons in a neutral atom.
• Ions are formed by losing or gaining electrons.

5.4 THE NUCLEAR ATOM

KEY TERMS

nucleus
atomic number

• Rutherford gold foil experiment modified the Thomson model to a nuclear model of the atom:
    • Atoms are composed of a nucleus containing protons and/or neutrons surrounded by electrons, which occupy mostly empty space.
    • Neutral atoms contain equal numbers of protons and electrons.

5.5 ISOTOPES OF THE ELEMENTS

KEY TERMS

isotope
mass number

• The mass number of an element is the sum of the protons and neutrons in the nucleus.

**Mass number
(sum of protons and
neutrons in the nucleus)** ↘

$$^{A}_{Z}\mathbf{E}$$ ←— **Symbol of element**

**Atomic number
(number of protons
in the nucleus)** ↗

• The number of neutrons in an atom is determined by

mass number − atomic number = number of neutrons
A − Z = neutrons

5.6 ATOMIC MASS

KEY TERMS

atomic mass unit (amu)
atomic mass

• The average atomic mass is a weighted average of the masses of all the isotopes present in the sample.

REVIEW QUESTIONS

1. List the main features of Dalton's model of the atom.
2. What elements of Democritus' theory did Dalton incorporate into his model of the atom?
3. How does Dalton's theory explain why chemical formulas are always written with whole-number values?
4. Distinguish between an atom and an ion.
5. Does the force of attraction increase, decrease, or stay the same as two oppositely charged particles approach each other?
6. How do cations and anions differ?

7. A neutron is approximately how many times heavier than an electron?
8. From the chemist's point of view, what are the essential differences among a proton, a neutron, and an electron?
9. What are the atomic numbers of (a) copper, (b) nitrogen, (c) phosphorus, (d) radium, and (e) zinc?
10. What letters are used to designate atomic number and mass number in isotopic notation of atoms?
11. In what ways are isotopes alike? In what ways are they different?
12. Explain why the mass number of an element is always a whole number.

Most of the exercises in this chapter are available for assignment via the online homework management program, WileyPLUS (www.wileyplus. com). All exercises with blue numbers have answers in Appendix VI.

PAIRED EXERCISES

1. Identify the ions in a mixture containing Cu^{2+}, N^{3-}, O^{2-}, Ca^{2+}, Al^{3+}, Te^{3-}, and H^+ that would be attracted to the positive end of an electric field.

2. Identify the ions in a mixture containing Mg^{2+}, Br^-, Cr^{3+}, Ba^{2+}, P^{3-}, Ca^{2+}, Se^{2-}, and Y^{3+} that would be attracted to the anode of a battery.

3. Explain why, in Rutherford's experiments, some alpha particles were scattered at large angles by the gold foil or even bounced back.

4. What experimental evidence led Rutherford to conclude the following?
   (a) The nucleus of the atom contains most of the atomic mass.
   (b) The nucleus of the atom is positively charged.
   (c) The atom consists of mostly empty space.

5. Describe the general arrangement of subatomic particles in the atom.

6. What part of the atom contains practically all its mass?

7. What contribution did these scientists make to atomic models of the atom?
   (a) Dalton   (b) Thomson   (c) Rutherford

8. Consider the following models of the atom: (a) Dalton, (b) Thomson, (c) Rutherford. How does the location of the electrons in an atom vary? How does the location of the atom's positive matter compare?

9. Explain why the atomic masses of elements are not whole numbers.

10. Is the isotopic mass of a given isotope ever an exact whole number? Is it always? (Consider the masses of $^{12}_{6}C$ and $^{63}_{29}Cu$.)

11. What special names are given to the isotopes of hydrogen?

12. List the similarities and differences in the three isotopes of hydrogen.

13. What is the nuclear composition of the five naturally occurring isotopes of germanium having mass numbers 70, 72, 73, 74, and 76?

14. What is the nuclear composition of the five naturally occurring isotopes of zinc having mass numbers 64, 66, 67, 68, and 70?

15. Write isotopic notation symbols for each of the following:
   (a) $Z = 29$, $A = 65$
   (b) $Z = 20$, $A = 45$
   (c) $Z = 36$, $A = 84$

16. Write isotopic notation symbols for each of the following:
   (a) $Z = 47$, $Z = 109$
   (b) $Z = 8$, $A = 18$
   (c) $Z = 26$, $A = 57$

17. Give the number of protons, neutrons, and electrons in the following isotopes.
   (a) ^{63}Cu
   (b) ^{32}S
   (c) manganese-55 (^{55}Mn)
   (d) potassium-39 (^{39}K)

18. Tell the number of protons, neutrons, and electrons in the following isotopes.
   (a) ^{54}Fe
   (b) ^{23}Na
   (c) bromine-79 (^{79}Br)
   (d) phosphorus-31 (^{31}P)

19. An unknown element contains 33 protons, 36 electrons, and has a mass number 76. Answer the following questions:
   (a) What is the atomic number of this element?
   (b) What is the name and symbol of this element?
   (c) How many neutrons does it contain?
   (d) What is the charge on this ion? Is it a cation or an anion?
   (e) Write the symbolic notation for this element.

20. An unknown element contains 56 protons, 54 electrons, and has a mass number 135. Answer the following questions:
   (a) What is the atomic number of this element?
   (b) What is the name and symbol of this element?
   (c) How many neutrons does it contain?
   (d) What is the charge on this ion? Is it a cation or an anion?
   (e) Write the symbolic notation for this element.

21. Naturally occurring zirconium exists as five stable isotopes: ^{90}Zr with a mass of 89.905 amu (51.45%); ^{91}Zr with a mass of 90.906 amu (11.22%); ^{92}Zr with a mass of 91.905 amu (17.15%); ^{94}Zr with a mass of 93.906 amu (17.38%); and ^{96}Zr with a mass of 95.908 amu (2.80%). Calculate the average mass of zirconium.

22. Naturally occurring titanium exists as five stable isotopes. Four of the isotopes are ^{46}Ti with a mass of 45.953 amu (8.0%); ^{47}Ti with a mass of 46.952 amu (7.3%); ^{48}Ti with a mass of 47.948 amu (73.8%); and ^{49}Ti with a mass of 48.948 amu (5.5%). The average mass of an atom of titanium is 47.9 amu. Determine the mass of the fifth isotope of titanium.

23. A particular element exists in two stable isotopic forms. One isotope has a mass of 62.9296 amu (69.17% abundance). The other isotope has a mass of 64.9278 amu. Calculate the average mass of the element and determine its identity.

24. A particular element exists in two stable isotopic forms. One isotope has a mass of 34.9689 amu (75.77% abundance). The other isotope has a mass of 36.9659 amu. Calculate the average mass of the element and determine its identity.

25. An average dimension for the radius of an atom is 1.0×10^{-8} cm, and the average radius of the nucleus is 1.0×10^{-13} cm. Determine the ratio of atomic volume to nuclear volume. Assume that the atom is spherical [$V = (4/3)\pi r^3$ for a sphere].

26. An aluminum atom has an average diameter of about 3.0×10^{-8} cm. The nucleus has a diameter of about 2.0×10^{-13} cm. Calculate the ratio of the atom's diameter to its nucleus.

ADDITIONAL EXERCISES

27. What experimental evidence supports these statements?
    (a) The nucleus of an atom is small.
    (b) The atom consists of both positive and negative charges.
    (c) The nucleus of the atom is positive.
28. Given the following information, determine which, if any, elements are isotopes.
    (a) mass number = 32; number of neutrons = 17
    (b) mass number = 32; number of protons = 16
    (c) number of protons = 15; number of neutrons = 16
29. The diameter of a silicon atom is 2.34×10^{-8} cm. If the silicon atoms were placed next to each other in a straight line across an 8.5-in. width of paper, how many silicon atoms would be there?
30. How is it possible for there to be more than one kind of atom of the same element?
31. Place each of the following elements in order of increasing number of neutrons (least to most); ^{156}Dy, ^{160}Gd, ^{162}Er, ^{165}Ho. Does this order differ from the elements' positions on the periodic table?
32. An unknown element Q has two known isotopes: ^{60}Q and ^{63}Q. If the average atomic mass is 61.5 amu, what are the relative percentages of the isotopes?

33. The actual mass of one atom of an element is 3.27×10^{-19} mg.
    (a) Calculate the atomic mass of the element.
    (b) Identify the element, giving the symbol and the name. (There is only one stable isotope of this element.)
34. The mass of an atom of silver is 1.79×10^{-22} g. How many atoms would be in a 0.52-lb sample of silver?
35. Using the periodic table inside the front cover of the book, determine which of the first 20 elements have isotopes that you would expect to have the same number of protons, neutrons, and electrons.
36. Solar winds that send streams of charged particles toward the Earth cause the aurora borealis or the northern lights. As these charged particles hit the upper atmosphere of the Earth or the ionosphere (so named because it is composed of a plasma or gaseous soup of ions), they collide with ions located in this region. These high-energy ions then lose energy in the form of light, which is visible in the northernmost and southernmost regions of the planet as ribbons of light in the night sky. Some of the ions responsible for the colors seen are C^+, O^+, and O^{2+}. Determine the number of protons and electrons in each of these ions.

37. Often the minerals we need in our diet are provided to us in vitamin tablets as cations. Following is a list of ingredients for a vitamin and mineral supplement. The table below highlights some of these minerals and identifies the ion provided for each mineral. Determine the number of protons and electrons in each of these ions.

Mineral supplement	Mineral use	Ion provided	Number of protons	Number of electrons
Calcium carbonate	Bones and Teeth	Ca^{2+}		
Iron(II) sulfate	Hemoglobin	Fe^{2+}		
Chromium(III) nitrate	Insulin	Cr^{3+}		
Magnesium sulfate	Bones	Mg^{2+}		
Zinc sulfate	Cellular metabolism	Zn^{2+}		
Potassium iodide	Thyroid function	I^-		

38. Complete the following table with the appropriate data for each isotope given (all are neutral atoms):

Element	Symbol	Atomic number	Mass number	Number of protons	Number of neutrons	Number of electrons
	^{36}Cl					
Gold			197			
		56			79	
					20	18
			58	28		

39. Complete the following table with the appropriate data for each isotope given (all are neutral atoms):

Element	Symbol	Atomic number	Mass number	Number of protons	Number of neutrons	Number of electrons
	^{134}Xe					
Silver			107			
				9		
		92			143	92
			41	19		

40. Draw diagrams similar to those shown in Figure 5.5 for the following ions:
    (a) O^{2-} (b) Na^+ (c) P^{3-} (d) Ca^{2+}
41. Draw pictures similar to those in Figure 5.8 for the following isotopes:
    (a) ^3He and ^4He (c) ^{10}B and ^{11}B
    (b) ^6Li and ^7Li (d) ^{12}C and ^{13}C
42. What percent of the total mass of one atom of each of the following elements comes from electrons?
    (a) aluminum (mass of one atom $= 4.480 \times 10^{-23}$ g)
    (b) phosphorus (mass of one atom $= 5.143 \times 10^{-23}$ g)
    (c) krypton (mass of one atom $= 1.392 \times 10^{-22}$ g)
    (d) platinum (mass of one atom $= 3.240 \times 10^{-22}$ g)

43. What percent of the total mass of one atom of each of the following elements comes from protons?
    (a) selenium (mass of one atom $= 1.311 \times 10^{-22}$ g)
    (b) xenon (mass of one atom $= 2.180 \times 10^{-22}$ g)
    (c) chlorine (mass of one atom $= 5.887 \times 10^{-23}$ g)
    (d) barium (mass of one atom $= 2.280 \times 10^{-22}$ g)
44. Figure 5.7 is a representation of the nuclear model of the atom. The area surrounding the nucleus is labeled as the electron region. What is the electron region?

CHALLENGE EXERCISE

45. You have discovered a new element and are trying to determine where on the periodic table it would fit. You decide to do a mass spectrometer analysis of the sample and discover that it contains three isotopes with masses of 270.51 amu, 271.23 amu, and 269.14 amu and relative abundances of 34.07%, 55.12%, and 10.81%, respectively. Sketch the mass spectrometer reading, determine the average atomic mass of the element, estimate its atomic number, and determine its approximate location on the periodic table.

ANSWERS TO PRACTICE EXERCISES

5.1 $CH_4, C_2H_2, C_2H_4, C_2H_6$

5.2 cations: $Na^+, NH_4^+, Ca^{2+}, Al^{3+}, K^+, Ag^+, Fe^{2+}, Fe^{3+}$
anions: $Cl^-, Br^-, NO_3^-, S^{2-}, SO_4^{2-}, PO_4^{3-}$

5.3 5.98×10^{24} atoms

5.4 Cu, 29 protons and 29 electrons; Xe, 36 protons and 36 electrons

5.5
	protons	neutrons	electrons
(a)	8	8	8
(b)	35	45	35
(c)	92	143	92
(d)	29	35	29

5.6 (a) atomic number 9
mass number 19
name fluorine
(b) atomic number 24
mass number 52
name chromium
(c) atomic number 79
mass number 179
name gold

5.7 107.9 amu

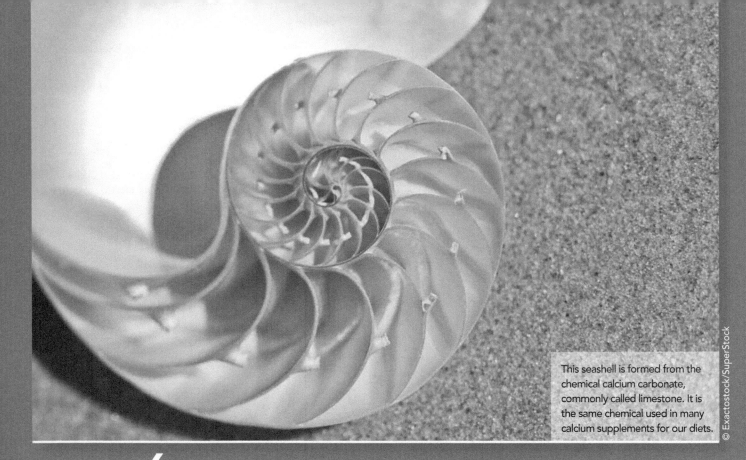

This seashell is formed from the chemical calcium carbonate, commonly called limestone. It is the same chemical used in many calcium supplements for our diets.

© Exactostock/SuperStock

CHAPTER **6**

NOMENCLATURE OF INORGANIC COMPOUNDS

As children, we begin to communicate with other people in our lives by learning the names of objects around us. As we continue to develop, we learn to speak and use language to complete a wide variety of tasks. As we enter school, we begin to learn of other languages—the languages of mathematics, of other cultures, of computers. In each case, we begin by learning the names of the building blocks and then proceed to more abstract concepts. Chemistry has a language all its own—a whole new way of describing the objects so familiar to us in our daily lives. Once we learn the language, we can begin to understand the macroscopic and microscopic world of chemistry.

6.1 COMMON AND SYSTEMATIC NAMES

Distinguish between the common and systematic names of chemical substances.   ● **LEARNING OBJECTIVE**

Chemical nomenclature is the system of names that chemists use to identify compounds. When a new substance is formulated, it must be named in order to distinguish it from all other substances (see **Figure 6.1**). In this chapter, we will restrict our discussion to the nomenclature of inorganic compounds—compounds that do not generally contain carbon.

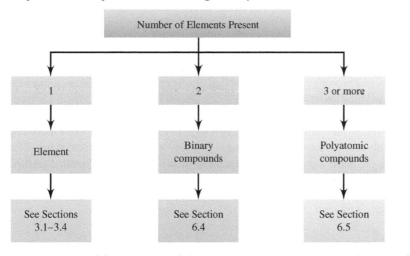

Figure 6.1

Where to find rules for naming inorganic substances in this book.

    Common names are arbitrary names that are not based on the chemical composition of compounds. Before chemistry was systematized, a substance was given a name that generally associated it with one of its outstanding physical or chemical properties. For example, *quicksilver* is a common name for mercury, and nitrous oxide (N_2O), used as an anesthetic in dentistry, has been called *laughing gas* because it induces laughter when inhaled. Water and ammonia are also common names because neither provides any information about the chemical composition of the compounds. If every substance were assigned a common name, the amount of memorization required to learn over 50 million names would be astronomical.
    Common names have distinct limitations, but they remain in frequent use. Common names continue to be used because the systematic name is too long or too technical for everyday use. For example, calcium oxide (CaO) is called *lime* by plasterers; photographers refer to *hypo* rather than sodium thiosulfate ($Na_2S_2O_3$); and nutritionists use the name *vitamin D_3*, instead of 9,10-secocholesta-5,7,10(19)-trien-3-ß-ol ($C_{27}H_{44}O$). **Table 6.1** lists the common names, formulas, and systematic names of some familiar substances.

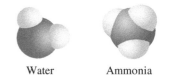

Water   Ammonia

Water (H_2O) and ammonia (NH_3) are almost always referred to by their common names.

TABLE 6.1   Common Names, Formulas, and Chemical Names of Familiar Substances

Common names	Formula	Chemical names	Common names	Formula	Chemical names
Acetylene	C_2H_2	ethyne	Gypsum	$CaSO_4 \cdot 2\ H_2O$	calcium sulfate dihydrate
Lime	CaO	calcium oxide	Grain alcohol	C_2H_5OH	ethanol, ethyl alcohol
Slaked lime	$Ca(OH)_2$	calcium hydroxide	Hypo	$Na_2S_2O_3$	sodium thiosulfate
Water	H_2O	water	Laughing gas	N_2O	dinitrogen monoxide
Galena	PbS	lead(II) sulfide	Lye, caustic soda	NaOH	sodium hydroxide
Alumina	Al_2O_3	aluminum oxide	Milk of magnesia	$Mg(OH)_2$	magnesium hydroxide
Baking soda	$NaHCO_3$	sodium hydrogen carbonate	Muriatic acid	HCl	hydrochloric acid
Cane or beet sugar	$C_{12}H_{22}O_{11}$	sucrose	Plaster of paris	$CaSO_4 \cdot \frac{1}{2}\ H_2O$	calcium sulfate hemihydrate
Borax	$Na_2B_4O_7 \cdot 10\ H_2O$	sodium tetraborate decahydrate	Potash	K_2CO_3	potassium carbonate
Brimstone	S	sulfur	Pyrite (fool's gold)	FeS_2	iron disulfide
Calcite, marble, limestone	$CaCO_3$	calcium carbonate	Quicksilver	Hg	mercury
			Saltpeter (chile)	$NaNO_3$	sodium nitrate
			Table salt	NaCl	sodium chloride
Cream of tartar	$KHC_4H_4O_6$	potassium hydrogen tartrate	Vinegar	$HC_2H_3O_2$	acetic acid
Epsom salts	$MgSO_4 \cdot 7\ H_2O$	magnesium sulfate heptahydrate	Washing soda	$Na_2CO_3 \cdot 10\ H_2O$	sodium carbonate decahydrate
			Wood alcohol	CH_3OH	methanol, methyl alcohol

Chemists prefer systematic names that precisely identify the chemical composition of chemical compounds. The system for inorganic nomenclature was devised by the International Union of Pure and Applied Chemistry (IUPAC), which was founded in 1921. The IUPAC meets regularly and constantly reviews and updates the system.

6.2 ELEMENTS AND IONS

LEARNING OBJECTIVE • Discuss the formation, charge, and naming of simple ions.

In Chapter 3, we studied the names and symbols for the elements as well as their location on the periodic table. In Chapter 5, we investigated the composition of the atom and learned that all atoms are composed of protons, electrons, and neutrons; that a particular element is defined by the number of protons it contains; and that atoms are uncharged because they contain equal numbers of protons and electrons.

The formula for most elements is simply the symbol of the element. In chemical reactions or mixtures, an element behaves as though it were a collection of individual particles. A small number of elements have formulas that are not single atoms at normal temperatures. Seven of the elements are *diatomic* molecules—that is, two atoms bonded together to form a molecule. These diatomic elements are hydrogen, H_2, oxygen, O_2, nitrogen, N_2, fluorine, F_2, chlorine, Cl_2, bromine, Br_2, and iodine, I_2. Three other elements that are commonly polyatomic are S_8, sulfur, Se_8, selenium and P_4, phosphorus.

Elements occurring as polyatomic molecules					
Hydrogen	H_2	Chlorine	Cl_2	Sulfur	S_8
Oxygen	O_2	Fluorine	F_2	Phosphorus	P_4
Nitrogen	N_2	Bromine	Br_2	Selenium	Se_8
		Iodine	I_2		

We have learned that a charged particle, known as an *ion*, can be produced by adding or removing one or more electrons from a neutral atom. For example, potassium atoms contain 19 protons and 19 electrons. To make a potassium ion, we remove one electron, leaving 19 protons and only 18 electrons. This gives an ion with a positive one ($+1$) charge:

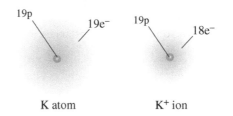

K atom K^+ ion

Written in the form of an equation, $K \rightarrow K^+ + e^-$. A positive ion is called a *cation*. Any neutral atom that *loses* an electron will form a cation. Sometimes an atom may lose one electron, as in the potassium example. Other atoms may lose more than one electron:

$$Mg \rightarrow Mg^{2+} + 2e^-$$

or

$$Al \rightarrow Al^{3+} + 3e^-$$

Cations are named the same as their parent atoms, as shown here:

Atom		Ion	
K	potassium	K^+	potassium ion
Mg	magnesium	Mg^{2+}	magnesium ion
Al	aluminum	Al^{3+}	aluminum ion

>CHEMISTRY *IN ACTION*

What's in a Name?

When a scientist discovered a new element in the early days of chemistry, he or she had the honor of naming it. Now researchers must submit their choices for a name to an international committee called the International Union of Pure and Applied Chemistry (IUPAC) before the name can be placed on the periodic table. Since 1997 the IUPAC has decided on names for 11 new elements from 104 through 118. The new elements are called rutherfordium (Rf), dubnium (Db), seaborgium (Sg), bohrium (Bh), hessium (Hs), meitnerium (Mt), darmstadtium (Ds), roentgenium (Rg), copernicium (Cn), flerovium (Fv), and livermorium (Lv).

The new names are compromises among the choices presented by different research teams. Some names given to the elements recognize places where much of the research to find these elements is done. The Russians gained recognition for work done at a laboratory in Dubna, the Germans for their laboratories in Darmstadt and Hesse, and the Americans for the Lawrence Livermore National Laboratory (LLNL).

Other names of elements recognize the contributions of great scientists and researchers such as the American Glenn Seaborg, the first living scientist to have an element named after him. The British recognized Ernest Rutherford, who discovered the atom's nucleus. The Germans recognized Lise Meitner who co-discovered atomic fusion. Both the Germans and the Russians won recognition for Niels Bohr whose model of the atom led to modern ideas about atomic structure. Wilhelm Roentgen was honored for discovering X-rays and winning the first Nobel Prize in physics. Most recently, the astronomer Copernicus was honored for changing our model of the solar system to a heliocentric model and to highlight the link between astronomy and nuclear science. The Russians honored Georgy Flerov, who developed the Soviet nuclear program, with the name for element 114.

Elements 113, 115, 117, and 118 do not yet have official names and are currently shown on the periodic table using three letter symbols representing their numbers.

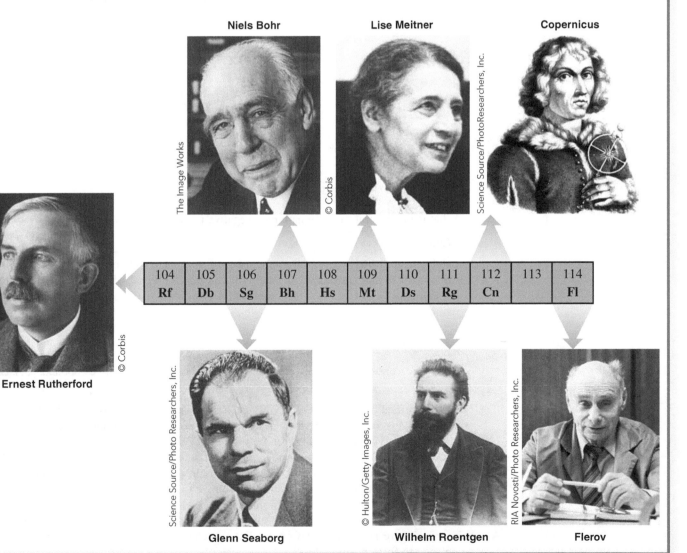

Niels Bohr

Lise Meitner

Copernicus

Ernest Rutherford

104 Rf	105 Db	106 Sg	107 Bh	108 Hs	109 Mt	110 Ds	111 Rg	112 Cn	113	114 Fl

Glenn Seaborg

Wilhelm Roentgen

Flerov

Ions can also be formed by adding electrons to a neutral atom. For example, the chlorine atom contains 17 protons and 17 electrons. The equal number of positive charges and negative charges results in a net charge of zero for the atom. If one electron is added to the chlorine atom, it now contains 17 protons and 18 electrons, resulting in a net charge of negative one (-1) on the ion:

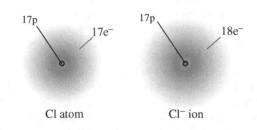

Cl atom   Cl⁻ ion

In a chemical equation, this process is summarized as $Cl + e^- \rightarrow Cl^-$. A negative ion is called an *anion*. Any neutral atom that *gains* an electron will form an anion. Atoms may gain more than one electron to form anions with different charges:

$$O + 2e^- \rightarrow O^{2-}$$
$$N + 3e^- \rightarrow N^{3-}$$

Anions are named differently from cations. To name an anion consisting of only one element, use the stem of the parent element name and change the ending to *-ide*. For example, the Cl^- ion is named by using the stem *chlor-* from chlorine and adding *-ide* to form chloride ion. Here are some examples:

Symbol	Name of atom	Ion	Name of ion
F	fluorine	F⁻	fluoride ion
Br	bromine	Br⁻	bromide ion
Cl	chlorine	Cl⁻	chloride ion
I	iodine	I⁻	iodide ion
O	oxygen	O²⁻	oxide ion
N	nitrogen	N³⁻	nitride ion

EXAMPLE 6.1

What is the general basis for naming a negative ion in a binary compound?

SOLUTION

Establish an identifying stem from the name of the negative element; then add the suffix *-ide* to that stem. For example, the stem for chlorine is *chlor-*. Add the suffix *-ide* to get the name of the ion, *chloride*. The stem for oxygen is *ox-*. Add the suffix *-ide* to get the name of the ion, *oxide*.

PRACTICE 6.1

Derive the names of these ions when used as the negative ion in a binary compound: P, N, B, C.

Ions are formed by adding or removing electrons from an atom. Atoms do not form ions on their own. Most often ions are formed when metals combine with nonmetals.

The charge on an ion can often be predicted from the position of the element on the periodic table. **Figure 6.2** shows the charges of selected ions from several groups on the periodic table. Notice that all the metals and hydrogen in the far left column (Group 1A) are ($1+$), all those in the next column (Group 2A) are ($2+$), and the metals in the next tall column (Group 3A) form ($3+$) ions. The elements in the lower center part of the table are called *transition metals*. These elements tend to form cations with various positive charges. There is no easy way to predict the charges on these cations. All metals lose electrons to form positive ions.

1A													3A	4A	5A	6A	7A	
H^+	2A																	
Li^+	Be^{2+}														N^{3-}	O^{2-}	F^-	
Na^+	Mg^{2+}												Al^{3+}		P^{3-}	S^{2-}	Cl^-	
K^+	Ca^{2+}				Cr^{2+} Cr^{3+}		Fe^{2+} Fe^{3+}			Cu^+ Cu^{2+}	Zn^{2+}						Br^-	
Rb^+	Sr^{2+}			Transition metals					Ag^+	Cd^{2+}							I^-	
Cs^+	Ba^{2+}																	

Figure 6.2
Charges of selected ions in the periodic table.

In contrast, the nonmetals form anions by gaining electrons. On the right side of the periodic table in Figure 6.2, you can see that the atoms in Group 7A form $(1-)$ ions. The nonmetals in Group 6A form $(2-)$ ions. It's important to learn the charges on the ions shown in Figure 6.2 and their relationship to the group number at the top of the column. For nontransition metals the charge is equal to the group number. For nonmetals, the charge is equal to the group number minus 8. We will learn more about why these ions carry their particular charges later in the course.

6.3 WRITING FORMULAS FROM NAMES OF IONIC COMPOUNDS

Write the chemical formula for an ionic compound from the name of the compound.

● LEARNING OBJECTIVE

In Chapters 3 and 5, we learned that compounds can be composed of ions. These substances are called *ionic compounds* and will conduct electricity when dissolved in water. An excellent example of an ionic compound is ordinary table salt composed of crystals of sodium chloride. When dissolved in water, sodium chloride conducts electricity very well, as shown in Figure 6.3.

A chemical compound must have a net charge of zero. If it contains ions, the charges on the ions must add up to zero in the formula for the compound. This is relatively easy in the case of sodium chloride. The sodium ion $(1+)$ and the chloride ion $(1-)$ add to zero, resulting in the formula NaCl. Now consider an ionic compound containing calcium (Ca^{2+}) and fluoride (F^-) ions. How can we write a formula with a net charge of zero? To do this we need one Ca^{2+} and two F^- ions. The correct formula is CaF_2. The subscript 2 indicates that two fluoride ions are needed for each calcium ion. Aluminum oxide is a bit more complicated because it consists of Al^{3+} and O^{2-} ions. Since 6 is the least common multiple of 3 and 2, we have $2(3+) + 3(2-) = 0$, or a formula containing 2 Al^{3+} ions and 3 O^{2-} ions for Al_2O_3. Here are a few more examples of formula writing for ionic compounds:

Name of compound	Ions	Least common multiple	Sum of charges on ions	Formula
Sodium bromide	Na^+, Br^-	1	$(+1) + (-1) = 0$	NaBr
Potassium sulfide	K^+, S^{2-}	2	$2(+1) + (-2) = 0$	K_2S
Zinc sulfate	Zn^{2+}, SO_4^{2-}	2	$(+2) + (-2) = 0$	$ZnSO_4$
Ammonium phosphate	NH_4^+, PO_4^{3-}	3	$3(+1) + (-3) = 0$	$(NH_4)_3PO_4$
Aluminum chromate	Al^{3+}, CrO_4^{2-}	6	$2(+3) + 3(-2) = 0$	$Al_2(CrO_4)_3$

Ken Karp

Na^+ ●
Cl^- ●
H_2O

Figure 6.3

A solution of salt water contains Na^+ and Cl^- ions in addition to water molecules. The ions cause the solution to conduct electricity, lighting the bulb.

RULES FOR WRITING FORMULAS FOR IONIC COMPOUNDS

1. Write the formula for the metal ion followed by the formula for the nonmetal ion.
2. Combine the smallest numbers of each ion needed to give the charge sum equal to zero.
3. Write the formula for the compound as the symbol for the metal and nonmetal, each followed by a subscript of the number determined in **2**.

EXAMPLE 6.2

Write formulas for (a) calcium chloride, (b) magnesium oxide, and (c) barium phosphide.

SOLUTION

(a) Use the following steps for calcium chloride.

1. From the name, we know that calcium chloride is composed of calcium and chloride ions. First write down the formulas of these ions:

$$Ca^{2+} \quad Cl^-$$

2. To write the formula of the compound, combine the smallest numbers of Ca^{2+} and Cl^- ions to give the charge sum equal to zero. In this case the lowest common multiple of the charges is 2:

$$(Ca^{2+}) + 2(Cl^-) = 0$$
$$(2+) + 2(1-) = 0$$

3. Therefore, the formula is $CaCl_2$.

(b) Use the same procedure for magnesium oxide:

1. From the name, we know that magnesium oxide is composed of magnesium and oxide ions. First write down the formulas of these ions:

$$Mg^{2+} \quad O^{2-}$$

2. To write the formula of the compound, combine the smallest numbers of Mg^{2+} and O^{2-} ions to give the charge sum equal to zero:

$$(Mg^{2+}) + (O^{2-}) = 0$$
$$(2+) + (2-) = 0$$

3. The formula is MgO.

(c) Use the same procedure for barium phosphide:

1. From the name, we know that barium phosphide is composed of barium and phosphide ions. First write down the formulas of these ions:

$$Ba^{2+} \quad P^{3-}$$

2. To write the formula of this compound, combine the smallest numbers of Ba^{2+} and P^{3-} ions to give the charge sum equal to zero. In this case the lowest common multiple of the charges is 6:

$$3(Ba^{2+}) + 2(P^{3-}) = 0$$
$$3(2+) + 2(3-) = 0$$

3. The formula is Ba_3P_2.

PRACTICE 6.2

Write formulas for compounds containing the following ions:

(a) K^+ and F^-
(b) Ca^{2+} and Br^-
(c) Mg^{2+} and N^{3-}
(d) Na^+ and S^{2-}
(e) Ba^{2+} and O^{2-}
(f) As^{5+} and CO_3^{2-}

6.4 NAMING BINARY COMPOUNDS

Name binary ionic and nonionic compounds.

● LEARNING OBJECTIVE

KEY TERMS
binary compounds
Stock System

Binary compounds contain only two different elements. Many binary compounds are formed when a metal combines with a nonmetal to form a *binary ionic compound*. The metal loses one or more electrons to become a cation while the nonmetal gains one or more electrons to become an anion. The cation is written first in the formula, followed by the anion.

Binary Ionic Compounds Containing a Metal Forming Only One Type of Cation

The chemical name is composed of the name of the metal followed by the name of the non-metal, which has been modified to an identifying stem plus the suffix *-ide*.

For example, sodium chloride, NaCl, is composed of one atom each of sodium and chlorine. The name of the metal, sodium, is written first and is not modified. The second part of the name is derived from the nonmetal, chlorine, by using the stem *chlor-* and adding the ending *-ide*; it is named *chloride*. The compound name is sodium chloride.

	NaCl
Elements:	Sodium (metal)
	Chlorine (nonmetal)
	name modified to the stem *chlor-* + *-ide*
Name of compound:	Sodium chloride

Stems of the more common negative-ion-forming elements are shown in Table 6.2.

TABLE 6.2   Examples of Elements Forming Anions

Symbol	Element	Stem	Anion name
Br	bromine	brom	bromide
Cl	chlorine	chlor	chloride
F	fluorine	fluor	fluoride
H	hydrogen	hydr	hydride
I	iodine	iod	iodide
N	nitrogen	nitr	nitride
O	oxygen	ox	oxide
P	phosphorus	phosph	phosphide
S	sulfur	sulf	sulfide

RULES FOR NAMING BINARY IONIC COMPOUNDS OF METAL FORMING ONE TYPE OF CATION

1. Write the name of the cation.
2. Write the stem for the anion and add the suffix *-ide*.

Compounds may contain more than one atom of the same element, but as long as they contain only two different elements and only one compound of these two elements exists, the name follows the rules for binary compounds:

Examples:

$CaBr_2$ Mg_3N_2 Li_2O
calcium bromide   magnesium nitride   lithium oxide

Table 6.3 lists some compounds with names ending in -ide.

TABLE 6.3	Examples of Compounds with Names Ending in -ide			
Formula	**Name**		**Formula**	**Name**
$AlCl_3$	aluminum chloride		BaS	barium sulfide
Al_2O_3	aluminum oxide		LiI	lithium iodide
CaC_2	calcium carbide		$MgBr_2$	magnesium bromide
HCl	hydrogen chloride		NaH	sodium hydride
HI	hydrogen iodide		Na_2O	sodium oxide

EXAMPLE 6.3

Name the compound CaF_2.

SOLUTION

From the formula it is a two-element compound and follows the rules for binary compounds.

1. The compound is composed of a metal, Ca, and a nonmetal, F. Elements in the 2A column of the periodic table form only one type of cation. Thus, we name the positive part of the compound *calcium*.

2. Modify the name of the second element to the stem *fluor-* and add the binary ending *-ide* to form the name of the negative part, *fluoride*.

Therefore, the name of the compound is *calcium fluoride*.

PRACTICE 6.3

Write formulas for these compounds:

(a) strontium chloride
(b) potassium iodide
(c) aluminum nitride

(d) calcium sulfide
(e) sodium oxide

Binary Ionic Compounds Containing a Metal That Can Form Two or More Types of Cations

The metals in the center of the periodic table (including the transition metals) often form more than one type of cation. For example, iron can form Fe^{2+} and Fe^{3+} ions, and copper can form Cu^+ and Cu^{2+} ions. This can be confusing when you are naming compounds. For example, copper chloride could be $CuCl_2$ or CuCl. To resolve this difficulty the IUPAC devised a system, known as the **Stock System**, to name these compounds. This system is currently recognized as the official system to name these compounds, although another older system is sometimes used. In the Stock System, when a compound contains a metal that can form more than one type of cation, the charge on the cation of the metal is designated by a Roman numeral placed in parentheses immediately following the name of the metal. The negative element is treated in the usual manner for binary compounds:

The Roman numeral is part of the cation name.

Cation charge	+1	+2	+3	+4	+5
Roman numeral	(I)	(II)	(III)	(IV)	(V)

Examples:			
	$FeCl_2$	iron(II) chloride	Fe^{2+}
	$FeCl_3$	iron(III) chloride	Fe^{3+}
	CuCl	copper(I) chloride	Cu^+
	$CuCl_2$	copper(II) chloride	Cu^{2+}

The fact that $FeCl_2$ has two chloride ions, each with a -1 charge, establishes that the charge on Fe is $+2$. To distinguish between the two iron chlorides, $FeCl_2$ is named iron(II) chloride and $FeCl_3$ is named iron(III) chloride:

	iron(II) chloride		iron(III) chloride	
	$FeCl_2$		$FeCl_3$	
charge:	$+2$	-1	$+3$	-1
name:	iron(II)	chloride	iron(III)	chloride

When a metal forms only one possible cation, we need not distinguish one cation from another, so Roman numerals are not needed. Thus we do not say calcium(II) chloride for $CaCl_2$, but rather calcium chloride, since the charge of calcium is understood to be $+2$.

RULES FOR NAMING BINARY IONIC COMPOUNDS OF METAL FORMING TWO OR MORE TYPES OF CATIONS (STOCK SYSTEM)

1. Write the name of the cation.
2. Write the charge on the cation as a Roman numeral in parentheses.
3. Write the stem of the anion and add the suffix -ide.

In classical nomenclature, when the metallic ion has only two cation types, the name of the metal (usually the Latin name) is modified with the suffixes -ous and -ic to distinguish between the two. The lower-charge cation is given the -ous ending, and the higher one, the -ic ending.

Examples:				
	$FeCl_2$	ferrous chloride	Fe^{2+}	(lower-charge cation)
	$FeCl_3$	ferric chloride	Fe^{3+}	(higher-charge cation)
	$CuCl$	cuprous chloride	Cu^+	(lower-charge cation)
	$CuCl_2$	cupric chloride	Cu^{2+}	(higher-charge cation)

Table 6.4 lists some common metals that have more than one type of cation.

TABLE 6.4 Names and Charges of Some Common Metal Ions That Have More Than One Type of Cation

Formula	Stock System name	Classical name	Formula	Stock System name	Classical name
Cu^{1+}	copper(I)	cuprous	Sn^{4+}	tin(IV)	stannic
Cu^{2+}	copper(II)	cupric	Pb^{2+}	lead(II)	plumbous
Hg^{1+} $(Hg_2)^{2+}$	mercury(I)	mercurous	Pb^{4+}	lead(IV)	plumbic
Hg^{2+}	mercury(II)	mercuric	As^{3+}	arsenic(III)	arsenous
Fe^{2+}	iron(II)	ferrous	As^{5+}	arsenic(V)	arsenic
Fe^{3+}	iron(III)	ferric	Ti^{3+}	titanium(III)	titanous
Sn^{2+}	tin(II)	stannous	Ti^{4+}	titanium(IV)	titanic

Notice that the *ous–ic* naming system does not give the charge of the cation of an element but merely indicates that at least two types of cations exist. The Stock System avoids any possible uncertainty by clearly stating the charge on the cation.

In this book we will use mainly the Stock System.

EXAMPLE 6.4

Name the compound FeS.

SOLUTION

This compound follows the rules for a binary compound.

1, 2. It is a compound of Fe, a metal, and S, a nonmetal, and Fe is a transition metal that has more than one type of cation. In sulfides, the charge on the S is -2. Therefore, the charge on Fe must be $+2$, and the name of the positive part of the compound is *iron(II)*.

3. We have already determined that the name of the negative part of the compound will be *sulfide*.

The name of FeS is *iron(II) sulfide*.

PRACTICE 6.4

Write the name for each of the following compounds using the Stock System:

(a) PbI_2 (b) SnF_4 (c) Fe_2O_3 (d) CuO

PRACTICE 6.5

Write formulas for the following compounds:

(a) tin(IV) chromate   (c) tin(II) fluoride
(b) chromium(III) bromide   (d) copper(I) oxide

Prefix	Number
mono	1
di	2
tri	3
tetra	4
penta	5
hexa	6
hepta	7
octa	8
nona	9
deca	10

Binary Compounds Containing Two Nonmetals

Compounds between nonmetals are molecular, not ionic. Therefore, a different system for naming them is used. In a compound formed between two nonmetals, the element that occurs first in this series is written and named first:

$$\text{Si, B, P, H, C, S, I, Br, N, Cl, O, F}$$

The name of the second element retains the *-ide* ending as though it were an anion. A Latin or Greek prefix (*mono-*, *di-*, *tri-*, and so on) is attached to the name of each element to indicate the number of atoms of that element in the molecule. The prefix *mono-* is rarely used for naming the first element. Some common prefixes and their numerical equivalences are as shown in the margin table.

RULES FOR NAMING BINARY COMPOUNDS CONTAINING TWO NONMETALS

1. Write the name for the first element using a prefix if there is more than one atom of this element.
2. Write the stem of the second element and add the suffix *-ide*. Use a prefix to indicate the number of atoms for the second element.

Here are some examples of compounds that illustrate this system:

$$N_2O_3$$

(di) nitrogen   (tri) oxide
Indicates two   Indicates three
nitrogen atoms   oxygen atoms

CO	carbon monoxide	N_2O	dinitrogen monoxide
CO_2	carbon dioxide	N_2O_4	dinitrogen tetroxide
PCl_3	phosphorus trichloride	NO	nitrogen monoxide
SO_2	sulfur dioxide	N_2O_3	dinitrogen trioxide
P_2O_5	diphosphorus pentoxide	S_2Cl_2	disulfur dichloride
CCl_4	carbon tetrachloride	S_2F_{10}	disulfur decafluoride

These examples illustrate that we sometimes drop the final *o* (mono) or *a* (penta) of the prefix when the second element is oxygen. This avoids creating a name that is awkward to pronounce. For example, CO is carbon monoxide instead of carbon monooxide.

EXAMPLE 6.5

Name the compound PCl_5.

SOLUTION

1. Phosphorus and chlorine are nonmetals, so the rules for naming binary compounds containing two nonmetals apply. Phosphorus is named first. Therefore, the compound is a chloride.

2. No prefix is needed for phosphorus because each molecule has only one atom of phosphorus. The prefix *penta-* is used with chloride to indicate the five chlorine atoms. (PCl_3 is also a known compound.)

The name for PCl_5 is *phosphorus pentachloride*.

Phosphorus pentachloride

PRACTICE 6.6

Name these compounds:
(a) Cl_2O (b) SO_2 (c) CBr_4 (d) N_2O_5 (e) NH_3 (f) ICl_3

PRACTICE 6.7

Name these compounds:
(a) KBr (b) Ca_3N_2 (c) SO_3 (d) SnF_2 (e) $CuCl_2$ (f) N_2O_4

6.5 NAMING COMPOUNDS CONTAINING POLYATOMIC IONS

Recognize names, formulas, and charges of polyatomic ions, name compounds containing polyatomic ions, and write formulas from names of compounds containing polyatomic ions.

● LEARNING OBJECTIVE

A **polyatomic ion** is an ion that contains two or more elements. Compounds containing polyatomic ions are composed of three or more elements and usually consist of one or more cations combined with a negative polyatomic ion. In general, naming compounds containing polyatomic ions is similar to naming binary compounds. The cation is named first, followed by the name for the negative polyatomic ion.

To name these compounds, you must learn to recognize the common polyatomic ions (Table 6.5) and know their charges. Consider the formula $KMnO_4$. You must be able to recognize that it consists of two parts $KMnO_4$. These parts are composed of a K^+ ion and a MnO_4^-

KEY TERM
polyatomic ion

TABLE 6.5   Names, Formulas, and Charges of Some Common Polyatomic Ions

Name	Formula	Charge	Name	Formula	Charge
Acetate	$C_2H_3O_2^-$	−1	Cyanide	CN^-	−1
Ammonium	NH_4^+	+1	Dichromate	$Cr_2O_7^{2-}$	−2
Arsenate	AsO_4^{3-}	−3	Hydroxide	OH^-	−1
Hydrogen carbonate	HCO_3^-	−1	Nitrate	NO_3^-	−1
Hydrogen sulfate	HSO_4^-	−1	Nitrite	NO_2^-	−1
Bromate	BrO_3^-	−1	Permanganate	MnO_4^-	−1
Carbonate	CO_3^{2-}	−2	Phosphate	PO_4^{3-}	−3
Chlorate	ClO_3^-	−1	Sulfate	SO_4^{2-}	−2
Chromate	CrO_4^{2-}	−2	Sulfite	SO_3^{2-}	−2

More ions are listed on the back endpapers.

Potassium permanganate
crystals are dark purple.

ion. The correct name for this compound is potassium permanganate. Many polyatomic ions that contain oxygen are called *oxy-anions* and generally have the suffix *-ate* or *-ite*. Unfortunately, the suffix doesn't indicate the number of oxygen atoms present. The *-ate* form contains more oxygen atoms than the *-ite* form. Examples include sulfate (SO_4^{2-}), sulfite (SO_3^{2-}), nitrate (NO_3^-), and nitrite (NO_2^-).

RULES FOR NAMING COMPOUNDS CONTAINING POLYATOMIC IONS

1. Write the name of the cation.
2. Write the name of the anion.

Only four of the common negatively charged polyatomic ions do not use the *ate–ite* system. These exceptions are hydroxide (OH^-) hydrogen sulfide (HS^-) peroxide (O_2^{2-}), and cyanide (CN^-). Care must be taken with these, as their endings can easily be confused with the *-ide* ending for binary compounds (Section 6.4).

There are three common positively charged polyatomic ions as well—the ammonium, the mercury(I) (Hg_2^{2+}), and the hydronium (H_3O^+) ions. The ammonium ion (NH_4^+) is frequently found in polyatomic compounds, whereas the hydronium ion (H_3O^+) is usually associated with aqueous solutions of acids (Chapter 15).

EXAMPLE 6.6

What is the minimum number of different elements in a compound that contains a polyatomic ion?

SOLUTION

Most polyatomic ions are anions and contain two different elements. Adding a cation to a polyatomic ion to form a compound means the minimum is three different elements in a polyatomic compound.

PRACTICE 6.8

Name these compounds:

(a) $NaNO_3$ (b) $Ca_3(PO_4)_2$ (c) KOH (d) Li_2CO_3 (e) $NaClO_3$

TABLE 6.6   Names of Selected Compounds That Contain More Than One Kind of Positive Ion

Formula	Name of compound
$KHSO_4$	potassium hydrogen sulfate
$Ca(HSO_3)_2$	calcium hydrogen sulfite
NH_4HS	ammonium hydrogen sulfide
$MgNH_4PO_4$	magnesium ammonium phosphate
NaH_2PO_4	sodium dihydrogen phosphate
Na_2HPO_4	sodium hydrogen phosphate
KHC_2O_4	potassium hydrogen oxalate
$KAl(SO_4)_2$	potassium aluminum sulfate
$Al(HCO_3)_3$	aluminum hydrogen carbonate

Inorganic compounds are also formed from more than three elements (see Table 6.6). In these cases, one or more of the ions is often a polyatomic ion. Once you have learned to recognize the polyatomic ions, naming these compounds follows the patterns we have already learned. First identify the ions. Name the cations in the order given and follow them with the names of the anions. Study the following examples:

Compound	Ions	Name
$NaHCO_3$	Na^+; HCO_3^-	sodium hydrogen carbonate
$NaHS$	Na^+; HS^-	sodium hydrogen sulfide
$MgNH_4PO_4$	Mg^{2+}; NH_4^+; PO_4^{3-}	magnesium ammonium phosphate
$NaKSO_4$	Na^+; K^+; SO_4^{2-}	sodium potassium sulfate

PRACTICE 6.9

Name these compounds:

(a) $KHCO_3$ (b) $NaHC_2O_4$ (c) $BaNH_4PO_4$ (d) $NaAl(SO_4)_2$

6.6 ACIDS

Use the rules to name an acid from its formula and to write the formula for an acid • LEARNING OBJECTIVE
from its name.

While we will learn much more about acids later (see Chapter 15), it is helpful to be able to recognize and name common acids both in the laboratory and in class. The simplest way to recognize many acids is to know that acid formulas often begin with hydrogen.

Binary Acids

Certain binary hydrogen compounds, when dissolved in water, form solutions that have *acid* properties. Because of this property, these compounds are given acid names in addition to their regular *-ide* names. For example, HCl is a gas and is called *hydrogen chloride*, but its water solution is known as *hydrochloric acid*. Binary acids are composed of hydrogen and one other nonmetallic element. However, not all binary hydrogen compounds are acids. To express the formula of a binary acid, it's customary to write the symbol of hydrogen first, followed by the symbol of the second element (e.g., HCl, HBr, or H_2S). When we see formulas such as CH_4 or NH_3, we understand that these compounds are not normally considered to be acids.

To name a binary acid, place the prefix *hydro-* in front of, and the suffix *-ic* after, the stem of the nonmetal name. Then add the word *acid*:

	HCl	H_2S
Examples:	*Hydro-*chlor-*ic acid*	*Hydro-*sulfur-*ic acid*
	(hydrochloric acid)	(hydrosulfuric acid)

RULES FOR NAMING BINARY ACIDS

1. Write the prefix *hydro-* followed by the stem of the second element and add the suffix *-ic.*

2. Add the word *acid.*

EXAMPLE 6.7

Name the acid HI.

SOLUTION

The compound follows the Rules for Naming Binary Acids.

1. Write the prefix *hydro-* and the stem of the second element with the suffix *-ic*: *hydro*iodic.

2. Add the word *acid*: hydroiodic *acid*.

PRACTICE 6.10

Name these binary acids:

(a) HCl   (b) HBr

Acids are hydrogen-containing substances that liberate hydrogen ions when dissolved in water. The same formula is often used to express binary hydrogen compounds, such as HCl, regardless of whether or not they are dissolved in water. Table 6.7 shows several examples of binary acids.

TABLE 6.7 Names and Formulas of Selected Binary Acids

Formula	Acid name
HF	Hydrofluoric acid
HCl	Hydrochloric acid
HBr	Hydrobromic acid
HI	Hydroiodic acid
H_2S	Hydrosulfuric acid
H_2Se	Hydroselenic acid

Figure 6.4 summarizes how to name binary compounds.

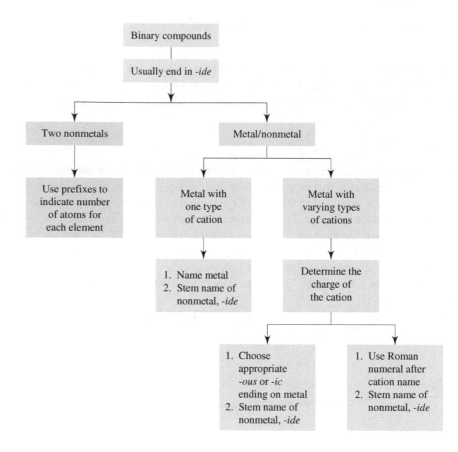

Figure 6.4

Flow diagram for naming binary compounds.

Naming Oxy-Acids

Inorganic compounds containing hydrogen, oxygen, and one other element are called *oxy-acids*. The first step in naming these acids is to determine that the compound in question is really an oxy-acid. The keys to identification are (1) hydrogen is the first element in the compound's formula and (2) the second part of the formula consists of a polyatomic ion containing oxygen.

Hydrogen in an oxy-acid is not specifically designated in the acid name. The presence of hydrogen in the compound is indicated by the use of the word *acid* in the name of the substance. To determine the particular type of acid, the polyatomic ion following hydrogen must be examined. The name of the polyatomic ion is modified in the following manner: (1) *-ate* changes to an *-ic* ending; (2) *-ite* changes to an *-ous* ending. (See Table 6.8.) The compound with the *-ic* ending contains more oxygen than the one with the *-ous* ending.

TABLE 6.8 Comparison of Acid and Anion Names for Selected Oxy-Acids

Acid	Anion	Acid	Anion	Acid	Anion
H_2SO_4	SO_4^{2-}	H_2CO_3	CO_3^{2-}	HIO_3	IO_3^{-}
Sulfuric acid	Sulfate ion	Carbonic acid	Carbonate ion	Iodic acid	Iodate ion
H_2SO_3	SO_3^{2-}	H_3BO_3	BO_3^{3-}	$HC_2H_3O_2$	$C_2H_3O_2^{-}$
Sulfurous acid	Sulfite ion	Boric acid	Borate ion	Acetic acid	Acetate ion
HNO_3	NO_3^{-}	H_3PO_4	PO_4^{3-}	$H_2C_2O_4$	$C_2O_4^{2-}$
Nitric acid	Nitrate ion	Phosphoric acid	Phosphate ion	Oxalic acid	Oxalate ion
HNO_2	NO_2^{-}	H_3PO_3	PO_3^{3-}	$HBrO_3$	BrO_3^{-}
Nitrous acid	Nitrite ion	Phosphorous acid	Phosphite ion	Bromic acid	Bromate ion

EXAMPLE 6.8

Name the acids H_2SO_4 and H_2SO_3.

SOLUTION

The names are written by modifying the name of the polyatomic ion in the acid.

For H_2SO_4 the polyatomic ion is the SO_4^{2-} sulfate ion. The *-ate* ending changes to an *-ic* ending in the acid. The stem of the sulfate ion is *sulfur* so the name for the compound is *sulfuric* and the word *acid* is added to show the presence of hydrogen in the compound: *sulfuric acid*.

For H_2SO_3 the polyatomic ion is the SO_3^{2-} sulfite ion. The *-ite* ending changes to an *-ous* ending in the acid, *sulfurous*, and the word *acid* is added to show the presence of hydrogen in the compound. *sulfurous acid*

PRACTICE 6.11

Name these polyatomic acids:

(a) H_2CO_3 (b) $HC_2H_3O_2$ (c) HNO_3 (d) HNO_2

Some elements form more than two different polyatomic ions containing oxygen. To name these ions, prefixes are used in addition to a suffix. To indicate more oxygen than in the *-ate* form we add the prefix *per-*, which is a short form of *hyper-* meaning "more." The prefix *hypo-*, meaning "less" (oxygen in this case), is used for the ion containing less oxygen than the *-ite* form. An example of this system is shown for the oxy-acids containing chlorine and oxygen in Table 6.9. The prefixes are also used with other similar ions, such as iodate (IO_3^-), bromate (BrO_3^-).

We have now looked at ways of naming a variety of inorganic compounds—binary compounds consisting of a metal and a nonmetal and of two nonmetals, acids, and polyatomic compounds. (See Figure 6.5.) These compounds are just a small part of the classified chemical compounds. Most of the remaining classes are in the broad field of organic chemistry under such categories as hydrocarbons, alcohols, ethers, aldehydes, ketones, phenols, and carboxylic acids.

TABLE 6.9	Oxy-Acids of Chlorine		
Acid formula	**Anion formula**	**Anion name**	**Acid name**
HClO	ClO^-	*hypo*chlor*ite*	*hypo*chlor*ous* acid
$HClO_2$	ClO_2^-	chlor*ite*	chlor*ous* acid
$HClO_3$	ClO_3^-	chlor*ate*	chlor*ic* acid
$HClO_4$	ClO_4^-	*per*chlor*ate*	*per*chlor*ic* acid

Figure 6.5

Flow diagram for naming acids.

CHAPTER 6 REVIEW

6.1 COMMON AND SYSTEMATIC NAMES

- Common names are arbitrary and do not describe the chemical composition of compounds.
  - Examples—ammonia, water
- A standard system of nomenclature was devised and is maintained by the IUPAC.

6.2 ELEMENTS AND IONS

- Diatomic elements—H_2, O_2, N_2, F_2, Cl_2, Br_2, I_2.
- Polyatomic elements—P_4, S_8.
- Ions form through the gain or loss of electrons from neutral atoms.
- The charge on ions can often be predicted from the periodic table.

6.3 WRITING FORMULAS FROM NAMES OF IONIC COMPOUNDS

- Compounds must have a net charge of zero.
- To write a formula from a name:
  - Identify and write the symbols for the elements in the compound.
  - Combine the smallest number of ions required to produce a net charge of zero.

6.4 NAMING BINARY COMPOUNDS

KEY TERMS

binary compounds
Stock System

- The rules for naming binary compounds can be summarized in the following chart.

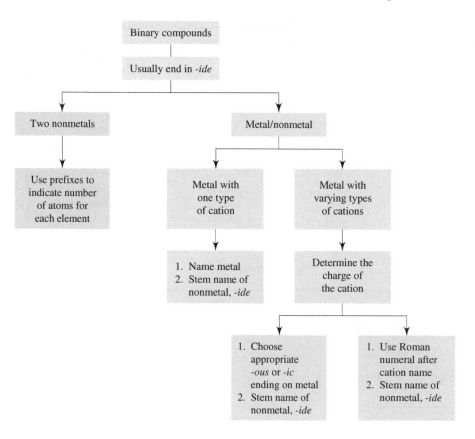

6.5 NAMING COMPOUNDS CONTAINING POLYATOMIC IONS

- The rules for naming these compounds:
  1. Write the name of the cation.
  2. Write the name of the anion.

KEY TERM

polyatomic ion

6.6 ACIDS

- The rules for naming acids can be summarized in the chart that follows:

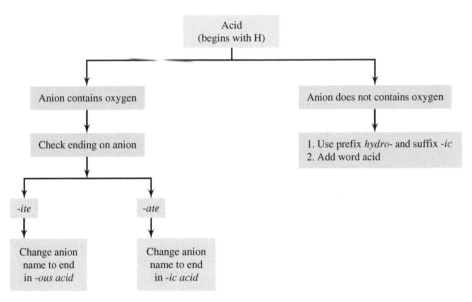

REVIEW QUESTIONS

1. List two compounds almost always referred to by their common names. What would be their systematic names?

2. What must happen in order to convert an atom into an anion? Into a cation?

3. Does the fact that two elements combine in a one-to-one atomic ratio mean that the charges on their ions are both 1? Explain.

4. When naming a binary ionic compound, how do you determine which element to name first?

5. Use the common ion table on the back endpapers of your text to determine the formulas for compounds composed of the following ions:
   (a) potassium and sulfide
   (b) cobalt(II) and bromate
   (c) ammonium and nitrate
   (d) hydrogen and phosphate
   (e) iron(III) oxide
   (f) magnesium and hydroxide

6. Explain why P_2O_5 is named dinitrogen pentoxide, using prefixes, but Al_2O_3 is named aluminum oxide, without prefixes.

7. Explain why $FeCl_2$ is named iron(II) chloride, using a Roman numeral, and $BaCl_2$ is named barium chloride, using no Roman numeral. Why does neither use prefixes?

8. The names of the nitrogen oxides are nitrogen dioxide (NO_2) and dinitrogen monoxide (N_2O). Why is the *mono-* prefix used only on the second molecule?

9. What is the advantage of using the Stock System for naming metals with variable charge instead of using the common name?

10. Write formulas for the compounds formed when a nickel(II) ion is combined with
    (a) sulfate   (f) acetate
    (b) phosphide   (g) dichromate
    (c) chromate   (h) bromide
    (d) hydroxide   (i) nitrate
    (e) iodite   (j) hypochlorite
    (Use the common ion table on the back endpapers of your text.)

11. Write the names and formulas for the four oxy-acids containing (a) bromine, (b) iodine.

12. How do you differentiate between different anions formed from a polyprotic acid?

Most of the exercises in this chapter are available for assignment via the online homework management program, WileyPLUS (www.wileyplus.com). All exercises with blue numbers have answers in Appendix VII.

PAIRED EXERCISES

1. Write the formula of the compound that will be formed between these elements:
   (a) Ba and S (d) Mg and N
   (b) Cs and P (e) Ca and I
   (c) Li and Br (f) H and Cl

2. Write the formula of the compound that will be formed between these elements:
   (a) Al and S (d) Sr and O
   (b) H and F (e) Cs and P
   (c) K and N (f) Al and Cl

3. Write formulas for the following cations:
   (a) potassium (h) calcium
   (b) ammonium (i) lead(II)
   (c) copper(I) (j) zinc
   (d) titanium(IV) (k) silver
   (e) nickel(III) (l) hydrogen
   (f) cesium (m) tin(II)
   (g) mercury(II) (n) iron(III)

4. Write formulas for the following anions:
   (a) fluoride (h) oxide
   (b) acetate (i) dichromate
   (c) iodide (j) hydrogen carbonate
   (d) carbonate (k) phosphate
   (e) sulfide (l) sulfate
   (f) nitrate (m) nitride
   (g) phosphide (n) chloride

5. Write the systematic names for the following:
   (a) baking soda ($NaHCO_3$) (d) vinegar ($HC_2H_3O_2$)
   (b) quicksilver (Hg) (e) Epsom salts ($MgSO_4 \cdot 7\,H_2O$)
   (c) lime (CaO) (f) lye (NaOH)

6. Write the systematic names for the following:
   (a) hypo ($Na_2S_2O_3$) (d) table salt (NaCl)
   (b) laughing gas (N_2O) (e) milk of magnesia ($Mg(OH)_2$)
   (c) alumina (Al_2O_3) (f) galena (PbS)

7. Complete the table, filling in each box with the proper formula.

			Anions		
Cations	Br^-	O^{2-}	NO_3^-	PO_4^{3-}	CO_3^{2-}
K^+	KBr				
Mg^{2+}					
Al^{3+}					
Zn^{2+}				$Zn_3(PO_4)_2$	
H^+					

8. Complete the table, filling in each box with the proper formula.

			Anions		
Cations	SO_4^{2-}	OH^-	AsO_4^{3-}	$C_2H_3O_2^-$	CrO_4^{2-}
NH_4^+			$(NH_4)_3AsO_4$		
Ca^{2+}					
Fe^{3+}	$Fe_2(SO_4)_3$				
Ag^+					
Cu^{2+}					

9. Write the names of each of the compounds formed in Question 7.

10. Write the names of each of the compounds formed in Question 8.

11. Write formulas for each of the following binary compounds, all of which are composed of nonmetals:
    (a) diphosphorus pentoxide (e) carbon tetrachloride
    (b) carbon dioxide (f) dichlorine heptoxide
    (c) tribromine octoxide (g) boron trifluoride
    (d) sulfur hexachloride (h) tetranitrogen hexasulfide

12. Write formulas for each of the following binary compounds, all of which are composed of a metal and nonmetal:
    (a) potassium nitride (e) calcium nitride
    (b) barium oxide (f) cesium bromide
    (c) iron(II) oxide (g) manganese(III) iodide
    (d) strontium phosphide (h) sodium selenide

13. Name each of the following binary compounds, all of which are composed of a metal and a nonmetal:
    (a) BaO (e) Al_2O_3
    (b) K_2S (f) $CaBr_2$
    (c) $CaCl_2$ (g) SrI_2
    (d) Cs_2S (h) Mg_3N_2

14. Name each of the following binary compounds, all of which are composed of nonmetals:
    (a) PBr_5 (e) $SiCl_4$
    (b) I_4O_9 (f) ClO_2
    (c) N_2S_5 (g) P_4S_7
    (d) S_2F_{10} (h) IF_6

15. Name these compounds by the Stock System (IUPAC):
    (a) $CuCl_2$ (d) $FeCl_3$
    (b) $FeCl_2$ (e) SnF_2
    (c) $Fe(NO_3)_2$ (f) VPO_4

16. Write formulas for these compounds:
    (a) tin(IV) bromide (d) mercury(II) nitrite
    (b) copper(I) sulfate (e) cobalt(III) carbonate
    (c) nickel(II) borate (f) iron(II) acetate

17. Write formulas for these acids:
    (a) hydrochloric acid (d) carbonic acid
    (b) chloric acid (e) sulfurous acid
    (c) nitric acid (f) phosphoric acid

18. Write formulas for these acids:
    (a) acetic acid (d) boric acid
    (b) hydrofluoric acid (e) nitrous acid
    (c) hydrosulfuric acid (f) hypochlorous acid

19. Name these acids:
    (a) HNO_2 (d) HBr   (g) HF
    (b) H_2SO_4 (e) H_3PO_3 (h) $HBrO_3$
    (c) $H_2C_2O_4$ (f) $HC_2H_3O_2$ (i) HIO_4

20. Name these acids:
    (a) H_3PO_4 (d) HCl   (g) HI
    (b) H_2CO_3 (e) HClO   (h) $HClO_4$
    (c) HIO_3 (f) HNO_3 (i) H_2SO_3

21. Write formulas for these compounds:
    (a) silver sulfite
    (b) cobalt(II) bromide
    (c) tin(II) hydroxide
    (d) aluminum sulfate
    (e) lead(II) chloride
    (f) ammonium carbonate
    (g) chromium(III) oxide
    (h) copper(II) chloride
    (i) potassium permanganate
    (j) arsenic(V) sulfite
    (k) sodium peroxide
    (l) iron(II) sulfate
    (m) potassium dichromate
    (n) bismuth(III) chromate

22. Write formulas for these compounds:
    (a) sodium chromate
    (b) magnesium hydride
    (c) nickel(II) acetate
    (d) calcium chlorate
    (e) magnesium bromate
    (f) potassium dihydrogen phosphate
    (g) manganese(II) hydroxide
    (h) cobalt(II) hydrogen carbonate
    (i) sodium hypochlorite
    (j) barium perchlorate
    (k) chromium(III) sulfite
    (l) antimony(III) sulfate
    (m) sodium oxalate
    (n) potassium thiocyanate

23. Write the name of each compound:
    (a) $ZnSO_4$ (f) CoF_2
    (b) Hg_2S (g) $Cr(ClO_3)_3$
    (c) $CuCO_3$ (h) Ag_3PO_4
    (d) $Cd(NO_3)_2$ (i) MnS
    (e) $Al(C_2H_3O_2)_3$ (j) $BaCrO_4$

24. Write the name of each compound:
    (a) $Ca(HSO_4)_2$ (f) $BiAsO_4$
    (b) $As_2(SO_3)_3$ (g) $(NH_4)_2CO_3$
    (c) $Sn(NO_2)_2$ (h) $(NH_4)_2HPO_4$
    (d) CuI   (i) NaClO
    (e) $KHCO_3$ (j) $KMnO_4$

25. Write the chemical formulas for these substances:
    (a) slaked lime   (e) cane sugar
    (b) fool's gold   (f) borax
    (c) washing soda   (g) wood alcohol
    (d) calcite   (h) acetylene

26. Write the chemical formulas for these substances:
    (a) grain alcohol   (e) muriatic acid
    (b) cream of tartar (f) plaster of paris
    (c) gypsum   (g) lye
    (d) brimstone   (h) laughing gas

ADDITIONAL EXERCISES

27. Write equations similar to those found in Section 6.2 for the formation of
    (a) potassium ion   (d) iron(II) ion
    (b) iodide ion   (e) calcium ion
    (c) bromide ion   (f) oxide ion

28. Name each of the following polyatomic ions:

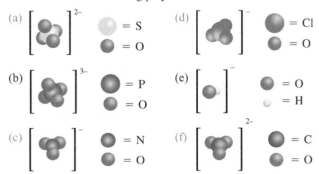

(a) $\left[\ \right]^{2-}$ = S = O
(b) $\left[\ \right]^{3-}$ = P = O
(c) $\left[\ \right]^{-}$ = N = O
(d) $\left[\ \right]^{-}$ = Cl = O
(e) $\left[\ \right]^{-}$ = O = H
(f) $\left[\ \right]^{2-}$ = C = O

29. Write formulas for all possible compounds formed between the calcium ion and the anions shown in Question 28.
30. Write formulas for all possible compounds formed between the potassium ion and the anions shown in Question 28.

31. Write the formula and name for each of the following compounds:

(a)   = Br   = C
(b)   = B   = F
(c)   = P   = Cl

32. Write the formula and name for the following compound:

K⁺   Cl⁻

33. State how each of the following is used in naming inorganic compounds: *ide, ous, ic, hypo, per, ite, ate*, Roman numerals.
34. Several excerpts from newspaper articles follow. Tell the chemical formula of the chemical spilled and indicate whether this spill should raise concern in the local area.

(a) A mistake at the Columbia Water and Light Department's West Ash Street pumping station sent an estimated 7200 gallons of calcium-carbonate-laden water into Harmony Creek early yesterday, forcing crews to spend hours cleaning up the mess.
(b) A tanker truck carrying 6000 gallons of acetic acid overturned on the I-5 freeway in San Diego, California.
(c) A university in New Hampshire was discovered dumping dihydrogen oxide into the local sewer system.

35. How many of each type of subatomic particle (protons and electrons) is in
(a) an atom of tin?
(b) a Sn^{2+} ion?
(c) a Sn^{4+} ion?

36. The compound X_2Y_3 is a stable solid. What ionic charge do you expect for X and Y? Explain.

37. The ferricyanide ion has the formula $Fe(CN)_6^{3-}$. Write the formula for the compounds that ferricyanide would form with the cations of elements 3, 13, and 30.

38. Compare and contrast the formulas of
(a) nitride with nitrite
(b) nitrite with nitrate
(c) nitrous acid with nitric acid

CHALLENGE EXERCISE

39. After studying chemistry, you should be able to recognize more of the substances listed on consumer products. A list of ingredients for dog food follows:

Chicken By-Product Meal (Natural source of Chondroitin Sulfate and Glucosamine), Corn Meal, Ground Whole Grain Sorghum, Ground Whole Grain Barley, Fish Meal (source of fish oil), Chicken, Chicken Fat (preserved with mixed Tocopherols, a source of Vitamin E), Dried Beet Pulp, Chicken Flavor, Dried Egg Product, Potassium Chloride, Brewers Dried Yeast, Salt, Sodium Hexametaphosphate, Fructooligosaccharides, Fish Oil (preserved with mixed Tocopherols, a source of Vitamin E), Calcium Carbonate, Flax Meal, Choline Chloride, Minerals (Ferrous Sulfate, Zinc Oxide, Manganese Sulfate, Copper Sulfate, Manganous Oxide, Potassium Iodide, Cobalt Carbonate), Vitamin E Supplement, Dried Chicken Cartilage (Natural source of Chondroitin Sulfate and Glucosamine), DL-Methionine, Vitamins (Ascorbic Acid, Vitamin A Acetate, Calcium Pantothenate, Biotin, Thiamine Mononitrate (source of Vitamin B1), Vitamin B12 Supplement, Niacin, Riboflavin Supplement (source of Vitamin B2), Inositol, Pyridoxine Hydrochloride (source of Vitamin B6), Vitamin D3 Supplement, Folic Acid), Beta-Carotene, L-Carnitine, Marigold, Citric Acid, Rosemary Extract.

Many of the substances in this bag of dog food are ionic compounds that you should be able to recognize. The manufacturers of this dog food did not completely identify some of the compounds. Write the chemical formula of the following compounds found in this ingredient list.
(a) potassium chloride   (f) copper sulfate
(b) calcium carbonate   (g) manganous oxide
(c) ferrous sulfate   (h) potassium iodide
(d) zinc oxide   (i) cobalt carbonate
(e) manganese sulfate   (j) sodium chloride

ANSWERS TO PRACTICE EXERCISES

6.1 phosphorus stem is *phosph-* + *-ide* = phosphide; nitrogen stem is *nitr-* + *-ide* = nitride; boron stem is *bor-* + *-ide* = boride; carbon stem is *carb-* + *-ide* = carbide

6.2 (a) KF; (b) $CaBr_2$; (c) Mg_3N_2; (d) Na_2S; (e) BaO; (f) $As_2(CO_3)_5$

6.3 (a) $SrCl_2$; (b) KI; (c) AlN; (d) CaS; (e) Na_2O

6.4 (a) lead(II) iodide; (b) tin(IV) fluoride; (c) iron(III) oxide; (d) copper(II) oxide

6.5 (a) $Sn(CrO_4)_2$; (b) $CrBr_3$; (c) SnF_2; (d) Cu_2O

6.6 (a) dichlorine monoxide; (b) sulfur dioxide; (c) carbon tetrabromide; (d) dinitrogen pentoxide; (e) ammonia; (f) iodine trichloride

6.7 (a) potassium bromide; (b) calcium nitride; (c) sulfur trioxide; (d) tin(II) fluoride; (e) copper(II) chloride; (f) dinitrogen tetroxide

6.8 (a) sodium nitrate; (b) calcium phosphate; (c) potassium hydroxide; (d) lithium carbonate; (e) sodium chlorate

6.9 (a) potassium hydrogen carbonate; (b) sodium hydrogen oxalate; (c) barium ammonium phosphate; (d) sodium aluminum sulfate

6.10 (a) hydrochloric acid; (b) hydrobromic acid

6.11 (a) carbonic acid; (b) acetic acid; (c) nitric acid; (d) nitrous acid

PUTTING IT TOGETHER:
Review for Chapters 5–6

Multiple Choice

Choose the correct answer to each of the following.

1. The concept of positive charge and a small, "heavy" nucleus surrounded by electrons was the contribution of
   (a) Dalton   (c) Thomson
   (b) Rutherford   (d) Chadwick

2. The neutron was discovered in 1932 by
   (a) Dalton   (c) Thomson
   (b) Rutherford   (d) Chadwick

3. An atom of atomic number 53 and mass number 127 contains how many neutrons?
   (a) 53   (c) 127
   (b) 74   (d) 180

4. How many electrons are in an atom of $^{40}_{18}Ar$?
   (a) 20   (c) 40
   (b) 22   (d) no correct answer given

5. The number of neutrons in an atom of $^{139}_{56}Ba$ is
   (a) 56   (c) 139
   (b) 83   (d) no correct answer given

6. The name of the isotope containing one proton and two neutrons is
   (a) protium   (c) deuterium
   (b) tritium   (d) helium

7. Each atom of a specific element has the same
   (a) number of protons   (c) number of neutrons
   (b) atomic mass   (d) no correct answer given

8. Which pair of symbols represents isotopes?
   (a) $^{23}_{11}Na$ and $^{23}_{12}Na$ (c) $^{63}_{29}Cu$ and $^{29}_{64}Cu$
   (b) $^{7}_{3}Li$ and $^{6}_{3}Li$ (d) $^{12}_{24}Mg$ and $^{12}_{26}Mg$

9. Two naturally occurring isotopes of an element have masses and abundance as follows: 54.00 amu (20.00%) and 56.00 amu (80.00%). What is the relative atomic mass of the element?
   (a) 54.20   (c) 54.80
   (b) 54.40   (d) 55.60

10. Substance X has 13 protons, 14 neutrons, and 10 electrons. Determine its identity.
    (a) ^{27}Mg (c) $^{27}Al^{3+}$
    (b) ^{27}Ne (d) ^{27}Al

11. The mass of a chlorine atom is 5.90×10^{-23}g. How many atoms are in a 42.0-g sample of chlorine?
    (a) 2.48×10^{-21} (c) 1.40×10^{-24}
    (b) 7.12×10^{23} (d) no correct answer given

12. The number of neutrons in an atom of $^{108}_{47}Ag$ is
    (a) 47   (c) 155
    (b) 108   (d) no correct answer given

13. The number of electrons in an atom of $^{27}_{13}Al$ is
    (a) 13   (c) 27
    (b) 14   (d) 40

14. The number of protons in an atom of $^{65}_{30}Zn$ is
    (a) 65   (c) 30
    (b) 35   (d) 95

15. The number of electrons in the nucleus of an atom of $^{24}_{12}Mg$ is
    (a) 12   (c) 36
    (b) 24   (d) no correct answer given

Names and Formulas

In which of the following is the formula correct for the name given?

1. copper(II) sulfate, $CuSO_4$

2. ammonium hydroxide, NH_4OH

3. mercury(I) carbonate, $HgCO_3$

4. phosphorus triiodide, PI_3

5. calcium acetate, $Ca(C_2H_3O_2)_2$

6. hypochlorous acid, $HClO$

7. dichlorine heptoxide, Cl_2O_7

8. magnesium iodide, MgI

9. sulfurous acid, H_2SO_3

10. potassium manganate, $KMnO_4$

11. lead(II) chromate, $PbCrO_4$

12. ammonium hydrogen carbonate, NH_4HCO_3

13. iron(II) phosphate, $FePO_4$

14. calcium hydrogen sulfate, $CaHSO_4$

15. mercury(II) sulfate, $HgSO_4$

16. dinitrogen pentoxide, N_2O_5

17. sodium hypochlorite, $NaClO$

18. sodium dichromate, $Na_2Cr_2O_7$

19. cadmium cyanide, $Cd(CN)_2$

20. bismuth(III) oxide, Bi_3O_2

21. carbonic acid, H_2CO_3

22. silver oxide, Ag_2O

23. ferric iodide, FeI_2

24. tin(II) fluoride, TiF_2

25. carbon monoxide, CO

26. phosphoric acid, H_3PO_3

119

27. sodium bromate, Na_2BrO_3

28. hydrosulfuric acid, H_2S

29. potassium hydroxide, POH

30. sodium carbonate, Na_2CO_3

31. zinc sulfate, $ZnSO_3$

32. sulfur trioxide, SO_3

33. tin(IV) nitrate, $Sn(NO_3)_4$

34. ferrous sulfate, $FeSO_4$

35. chloric acid, HCl

36. aluminum sulfide, Al_2S_3

37. cobalt(II) chloride, $CoCl_2$

38. acetic acid, $HC_2H_3O_2$

39. zinc oxide, ZnO_2

40. stannous fluoride, SnF_2

Free Response Questions

Answer each of the following. Be sure to include your work and explanations in a clear, logical form.

1. (a) What is an ion?
   (b) The average mass of a calcium atom is 40.08 amu. Why do we also use 40.08 amu as the average mass of a calcium ion (Ca^{2+})?

2. Congratulations! You discover a new element you name wyzzlebium (Wz). The average atomic mass of Wz was found to be 303.001 amu, and its atomic number is 120.
   (a) If the masses of the two isotopes of wyzzlebium are 300.9326 amu and 303.9303 amu, what is the relative abundance of each isotope?
   (b) What are the isotopic notations of the two isotopes? (e.g., ^A_ZWz)
   (c) How many neutrons are in one atom of the more abundant isotope?

3. How many protons are in one molecule of dichlorine heptoxide? Is it possible to determine precisely how many electrons and neutrons are in a molecule of dichlorine heptoxide? Why or why not?

4. An unidentified metal forms an ionic compound with phosphate. The metal forms a 2+ cation. If the minimum ratio of protons in the metal to the phosphorus is 6:5, what metal is it? (*Hint:* First write the formula for the ionic compound formed with phosphate anion.)

5. For each of the following compounds, indicate what is wrong with the name and why. If possible, fix the name.
   (a) iron hydroxide
   (b) dipotassium dichromium heptoxide
   (c) sulfur oxide

6. Sulfur dioxide is a gas formed as a by-product of burning coal. Sulfur trioxide is a significant contributor to acid rain. Does the existence of these two substances violate the law of multiple proportions? Explain.

7. (a) Which subatomic particles are not in the nucleus?
   (b) What happens to the size of an atom when it becomes an anion?
   (c) What do an ion of Ca and an atom of Ar have in common?

8. An unidentified atom is found to have an atomic mass 7.18 times that of the carbon-12 isotope.
   (a) What is the mass of the unidentified atom?
   (b) What are the possible identities of this atom?
   (c) Why are you unable to positively identify the element based on the atomic mass and the periodic table?
   (d) If the element formed a compound M_2O, where M is the unidentified atom, identify M by writing the isotopic notation for the atom.

9. Scientists such as Dalton, Thomson, and Rutherford proposed important models, which were ultimately challenged by later technology. What do we know to be false in Dalton's atomic model? What was missing in Thomson's model of the atom? What was Rutherford's experiment that led to the current model of the atom?

These black pearls are made of layers of calcium carbonate. They can be measured by counting or weighing.

© Hemis/Alamy

CHAPTER **7**

QUANTITATIVE COMPOSITION OF COMPOUNDS

Cereals, cleaning products, and pain remedies all list their ingredients on the package label. The ingredients are listed in order from most to least, but the amounts are rarely given. However, it is precisely these amounts that give products their desired properties and distinguish them from the competition. Understandably, manufacturers carefully regulate the amounts of ingredients to maintain quality and hopefully their customers' loyalty. In the medicines we purchase, these quantities are especially important for safety reasons—for example, they determine whether a medicine is given to children or is safe only for adults.

The composition of compounds is an important concept in chemistry. Determining numerical relationships among the elements in compounds and measuring exact quantities of particles are fundamental tasks that chemists routinely perform in their daily work.

7.1 THE MOLE

LEARNING OBJECTIVE ● Apply the concepts of the mole, molar mass, and Avogadro's number to solve chemistry problems.

KEY TERMS

Avogadro's number
mole
molar mass

PhotoDisc, Inc./Getty Images

Oranges can be "counted" by weighing them in the store.

The atom is an incredibly tiny object. Its mass is far too small to measure on an ordinary balance. In Chapter 5 (Section 5.6), we learned to compare atoms using a table of atomic mass units. These units are valuable when we compare the masses of individual atoms (mentally), but they have no practical use in the laboratory. The mass in grams for an "average" carbon atom (atomic mass 12.01 amu) would be 2.00×10^{-23} g, which is much too tiny for the best laboratory balance.

So how can we confidently measure masses for these very tiny atoms? We increase the number of atoms in a sample until we have an amount large enough to measure on a laboratory balance. The problem then is how to count our sample of atoms.

Consider for a moment the produce in a supermarket. Frequently, apples and oranges are sorted by size and then sold by weight, not by the piece of fruit. The grocer is counting by weighing. To do this, he needs to know the mass of an "average" apple (235 g) and the mass of an "average" orange (186 g). Now suppose he has an order from the local college for 275 apples and 350 oranges. It would take a long time to count and package this order. The grocer can quickly count fruit by weighing. For example,

$$(275 \text{ apples})\left(\frac{235 \text{ g}}{\text{apple}}\right) = 6.46 \times 10^4 \text{ g} = 64.6 \text{ kg}$$

$$(350 \text{ oranges})\left(\frac{186 \text{ g}}{\text{orange}}\right) = 6.51 \times 10^4 \text{ g} = 65.1 \text{ kg}$$

He can now weigh 64.6 kg of apples and 65.1 kg of oranges and pack them without actually counting them. Manufacturers and suppliers often count by weighing. Other examples of counting by weighing include nuts, bolts, and candy.

Chemists also count atoms by weighing. We know the "average" masses of atoms, so we can count atoms by defining a unit to represent a larger number of atoms. Chemists have chosen the mole (mol) as the unit for counting atoms. The mole is a unit for counting just as a dozen or a ream or a gross is used to count:

$$1 \text{ dozen} = 12 \text{ objects}$$
$$1 \text{ ream} = 500 \text{ objects}$$
$$1 \text{ gross} = 144 \text{ objects}$$
$$1 \text{ mole} = 6.022 \times 10^{23} \text{ objects}$$

Note that we use a unit only when it is appropriate. A dozen eggs is practical in our kitchen, a gross might be practical for a restaurant, but a ream of eggs would not be very practical. Chemists can't use dozens, grosses, or reams because atoms are so tiny that a dozen, gross, or ream of atoms still couldn't be measured in the laboratory.

Royalty-Free/Corbis Images

Eggs are measured by the dozen.

Copyright John Wiley & Sons, Inc.

Paper is measured by the ream (500 sheets).

Tom Pantages

Pencils are measured by the gross (144).

Units of measurement need to be appropriate for the object being measured.

The number represented by 1 mol, 6.022×10^{23}, is called **Avogadro's number**, in honor of Amadeo Avogadro (1776–1856), who investigated several quantitative aspects in chemistry. It's difficult to imagine how large Avogadro's number really is, but this example may help: If 10,000 people started to count Avogadro's number, and each counted at the rate of 100 numbers per minute each minute of the day, it would take them over 1 trillion (10^{12}) years to count the total number. So even the tiniest amount of matter contains extremely large numbers of atoms.

Symbol name	C (carbon)	Al (aluminum)	Pb (lead)
Element			
Average atomic mass	12.01 amu	26.98 amu	207.2 amu
Mass of sample	12.01 g	26.98 g	207.2 g
Number of atoms in sample	6.022×10^{23} atoms	6.022×10^{23} atoms	6.022×10^{23} atoms

Avogadro's number has been experimentally determined by several methods. How does it relate to atomic mass units? Remember that the atomic mass for an element is the average relative mass of all the isotopes for the element. The atomic mass (expressed in grams) of 1 mole of any element contains the same number of particles (Avogadro's number) as there are in exactly 12 g of ^{12}C. Thus, 1 **mole** of anything is the amount of the substance that contains the same number of items as there are atoms in exactly 12 g of ^{12}C.

Remember that ^{12}C is the reference isotope for atomic masses.

$$1 \text{ mole} = 6.022 \times 10^{23} \text{ items}$$

From the definition of mole, we can see that the atomic mass in grams of any element contains 1 mol of atoms. The term *mole* is so commonplace in chemistry that chemists use it as freely as the words *atom* or *molecule*. A mole of atoms, molecules, ions, or electrons represents Avogadro's number of these particles. If we can speak of a mole of atoms, we can also speak of a mole of molecules, a mole of electrons, or a mole of ions, understanding that in each case we mean 6.022×10^{23} particles:

The abbreviation for mole is mol, both singular and plural.

$$1 \text{ mol of atoms} = 6.022 \times 10^{23} \text{ atoms}$$
$$1 \text{ mol of molecules} = 6.022 \times 10^{23} \text{ molecules}$$
$$1 \text{ mol of ions} = 6.022 \times 10^{23} \text{ ions}$$

PRACTICE 7.1

How many atoms are in 1.000 mole of the following?
(a) Fe   (b) H_2 (c) H_2SO_4

The atomic mass of an element in grams contains Avogadro's number of atoms and is defined as the **molar mass** of that element. To determine molar mass, we change the units of the atomic mass (found in the periodic table) from atomic mass units to grams. For example, sulfur has an atomic mass of 32.07 amu, so 1 mol of sulfur has a molar mass of 32.07 g and contains 6.022×10^{23} atoms of sulfur. Here are some other examples:

Element	Atomic mass	Molar mass	Number of atoms
H	1.008 amu	1.008 g	6.022×10^{23}
Mg	24.31 amu	24.31 g	6.022×10^{23}
Na	22.99 amu	22.99 g	6.022×10^{23}

In this text molar masses of elements are given to four significant figures.

To summarize:

1. The atomic mass expressed in grams is the *molar mass* of an element. It is different for each element. In this text, molar masses are expressed to four significant figures.

$$1 \text{ molar mass} = \text{atomic mass of an element in grams}$$

2. One mole of any element contains Avogadro's number of atoms.

$$1 \text{ mol of atoms} = 6.022 \times 10^{23} \text{ atoms}$$

We can use these relationships to make conversions between number of atoms, mass, and moles, as shown in the following examples.

Sulfur	**Iodine**	**Iron**	**Mercury**
32.07 g	126.9 g	55.85 g	200.6 g
6.022×10^{23} atoms	6.022×10^{23} atoms	6.022×10^{23} atoms	6.022×10^{23} atoms

Richard Megna/Fundamental Photographs

EXAMPLE 7.1

How many moles of iron does 25.0 g of iron (Fe) represent?

SOLUTION

Plan • **Solution map:** g Fe → moles Fe

1 mole Fe = 55.85 g (from periodic table)

The conversion factor needed is

$$\frac{1 \text{ mole Fe}}{55.85 \text{ g Fe}} \quad \text{or} \quad \frac{55.85 \text{ g Fe}}{1 \text{ mole Fe}}$$

Calculate • $(25.0 \text{ g Fe})\left(\dfrac{1 \text{ mole Fe}}{55.85 \text{ g Fe}}\right) = 0.448 \text{ mol Fe}$

Check • Since 25.0 g has three significant figures, the number of significant figures allowed in the answer is three. The answer is reasonable since 0.448 mol is about ½ mole and 25.0 g is about ½ of 55.85 g (one mole Fe).

EXAMPLE 7.2

How many magnesium atoms are contained in 5.00 g Mg?

SOLUTION

Plan • **Solution map:** g Mg → atoms Mg

1 mol Mg = 24.31 g (from periodic table)

The conversion factor needed is

$$\frac{6.022 \times 10^{23} \text{ atoms Mg}}{24.31 \text{ g Mg}} \quad \text{or} \quad \frac{24.31 \text{ g Mg}}{6.022 \times 10^{23} \text{ atoms Mg}}$$

Calculate • $(5.00 \text{ g Mg})\left(\dfrac{6.022 \times 10^{23} \text{ atoms Mg}}{24.31 \text{ g Mg}}\right) = 1.24 \times 10^{23} \text{ atoms Mg}$

Check • Since 5.00 g has three significant figures, the number of significant figures allowed in the answer is three.

EXAMPLE 7.3

What is the mass, in grams, of one atom of carbon (C)?

SOLUTION

Plan •   **Solution map:** atoms C → grams C

        1 mol C = 12.01 g (from periodic table)

        The conversion factor needed is

$$\frac{6.022 \times 10^{23} \text{ atoms C}}{12.01 \text{ g C}} \quad \text{or} \quad \frac{12.01 \text{ g C}}{6.022 \times 10^{23} \text{ atoms C}}$$

Calculate • $(1 \text{ atom C})\left(\dfrac{12.01 \text{ g C}}{6.022 \times 10^{23} \text{ atoms C}}\right) = 1.994 \times 10^{-23} \text{ g C}$

Check •   Since 1 atom is an exact number, the number of significant figures allowed in the answer is four based on the number of significant figures in the molar mass of C.

EXAMPLE 7.4

What is the mass of 3.01×10^{23} atoms of sodium (Na)?

SOLUTION

Plan •   **Solution map:** atoms Na → grams Na

        1 mol Na = 22.99 g (from periodic table)

        The conversion factor needed is

$$\frac{6.022 \times 10^{23} \text{ atoms Na}}{22.99 \text{ g Na}} \quad \text{or} \quad \frac{22.99 \text{ g Na}}{6.022 \times 10^{23} \text{ atoms Na}}$$

Calculate • $(3.01 \times 10^{23} \text{ atoms Na})\left(\dfrac{22.99 \text{ g Na}}{6.022 \times 10^{23} \text{ atoms Na}}\right) = 11.5 \text{ g Na}$

Check •   Since 3.01×10^{23} has three significant figures, the answer (mass) should have three as well.

EXAMPLE 7.5

What is the mass of 0.252 mol of copper (Cu)?

SOLUTION

Plan •   **Solution map:** mol Cu → grams Cu

        1 mol Cu = 63.55 g (from periodic table)

        The conversion factor needed is

$$\frac{1 \text{ mol Cu}}{63.55 \text{ g Cu}} \quad \text{or} \quad \frac{63.55 \text{ g Cu}}{1 \text{ mol Cu}}$$

Calculate • $(0.252 \text{ mol Cu})\left(\dfrac{63.55 \text{ g Cu}}{1 \text{ mol Cu}}\right) = 16.0 \text{ g Cu}$

Check •   The number of significant figures in both the question and answer is three.

EXAMPLE 7.6

How many oxygen atoms are present in 1.00 mol of oxygen molecules?

SOLUTION

Plan •   Oxygen is a diatomic molecule with the formula O_2. Therefore, a molecule of oxygen contains 2 oxygen atoms: $\dfrac{2 \text{ atoms O}}{1 \text{ molecule O}_2}$.

Solution map: moles O_2 → molecules O_2 → atoms O

The conversion factors needed are:

$$\frac{6.022 \times 10^{23} \text{ molecules O}_2}{1 \text{ mole O}_2} \quad \text{and} \quad \frac{2 \text{ atoms O}}{1 \text{ molecule O}_2}$$

Calculate • $(1.00 \text{ mol O}_2)\left(\dfrac{6.022 \times 10^{23} \text{ molecules O}_2}{1 \text{ mole O}_2}\right)\left(\dfrac{2 \text{ atoms O}}{1 \text{ molecule O}_2}\right)$

$= 1.20 \times 10^{24} \text{ atoms O}$

PRACTICE 7.2

What is the mass of 2.50 mol of helium (He)?

PRACTICE 7.3

How many atoms are present in 0.025 mol of iron?

7.2 MOLAR MASS OF COMPOUNDS

LEARNING OBJECTIVE •   Calculate the molar mass of a compound.

A formula unit is indicated by the formula, for example, Mg, MgS, H_2O, NaCl.

One mole of a compound contains Avogadro's number of *formula units* of that compound. The terms *molecular weight*, *molecular mass*, *formula weight*, and *formula mass* have been used in the past to refer to the mass of 1 mol of a compound. However, the term *molar mass* is more inclusive because it can be used for all types of compounds.

If the formula of a compound is known, its molar mass can be determined by adding the molar masses of all the atoms in the formula. If more than one atom of any element is present, its mass must be added as many times as it appears in the compound.

EXAMPLE 7.7

The formula for water is H_2O. What is its molar mass?

SOLUTION

Read •   **Known:** H_2O

Plan •   The formula contains 1 atom O and 2 atoms H. We need to use the atomic masses from the inside front cover of the text.

Calculate •   O = 16.00 g   = 16.00 g
2 H = 2(1.008 g) = 2.016 g
18.02 g = molar mass of H_2O

EXAMPLE 7.8

Calculate the molar mass of calcium hydroxide, $Ca(OH)_2$.

SOLUTION

Read •   **Known:** $Ca(OH)_2$

Plan •   The formula contains 1 atom Ca and 2 atoms each of O and H. We need to use the atomic masses from the inside front cover of the text.

Calculate •
$$1\ Ca = 1(40.08\ g) = 40.08\ g$$
$$2\ O = 2(16.00\ g) = 32.00\ g$$
$$2\ H = 2(1.008\ g) = \underline{2.016\ g}$$
$$74.10\ g = \text{molar mass of } Ca(OH)_2$$

PRACTICE 7.4

Calculate the molar mass of KNO_3.

In this text we round all molar masses to four significant figures, although you may need to use a different number of significant figures for other work (in the lab).

The mass of 1 mol of a compound contains Avogadro's number of formula units. Consider the compound hydrogen chloride (HCl). One atom of H combines with one atom of Cl to form HCl. When 1 mol of H (1.008 g of H or 6.022×10^{23} H atoms) combines with 1 mol of Cl (35.45 g of Cl or 6.022×10^{23} Cl atoms), 1 mol of HCl (36.46 g of HCl or 6.022×10^{23} HCl molecules) is produced. These relationships are summarized in the following table:

H	Cl	HCl
6.022×10^{23} H *atoms*	6.022×10^{23} Cl *atoms*	6.022×10^{23} HCl *molecules*
1 mol H *atoms*	1 mol Cl *atoms*	1 mol HCl *molecules*
1.008 g H	34.45 g Cl	36.46 g HCl
1 molar mass H *atoms*	1 molar mass Cl *atoms*	1 molar mass HCl *molecules*

In dealing with diatomic elements (H_2, O_2, N_2, F_2, Cl_2, Br_2, and I_2), we must take special care to distinguish between a mole of atoms and a mole of molecules. For example, consider 1 mol of oxygen molecules, which has a mass of 32.00 g. This quantity is equal to 2 mol of

A mole of table salt (in front of a salt shaker) and a mole of water (in the plastic container) have different sizes but both contain Avogadro's number of formula units.

Tom Pantages

oxygen atoms. Remember that 1 mol represents Avogadro's number of the particular chemical entity that is under consideration:

$$1 \text{ mol } H_2O = 18.02 \text{ g } H_2O = 6.022 \times 10^{23} \text{ molecules}$$

$$1 \text{ mol NaCl} = 58.44 \text{ g NaCl} = 6.022 \times 10^{23} \text{ formula units}$$

$$1 \text{ mol } H_2 = 2.016 \text{ g } H_2 = 6.022 \times 10^{23} \text{ molecules}$$

$$1 \text{ mol } HNO_3 = 63.02 \text{ g } HNO_3 = 6.022 \times 10^{23} \text{ molecules}$$

$$1 \text{ mol } K_2SO_4 = 174.3 \text{ g } K_2SO_4 = 6.022 \times 10^{23} \text{ formula units}$$

$$1 \text{ mol} = 6.022 \times 10^{23} \text{ formula unit or molecules}$$
$$= 1 \text{ molar mass of a compound}$$

Formula units are often used in place of molecules for substances that contain ions.

EXAMPLE 7.9

What is the mass of 1 mol of sulfuric acid (H_2SO_4)?

SOLUTION

Read •   **Known:** H_2SO_4

Plan •   We need to use the atomic masses from the inside front cover of the text.

Calculate • $2 H = 2(1.008 \text{ g}) = 2.016 \text{ g}$

               $1 S = 32.07 \text{ g} = 32.07 \text{ g}$

               $4 O = 4(16.00 \text{ g}) = \underline{64.00 \text{ g}}$

                                   $98.09 \text{ g} = \text{mass of 1 mol of } H_2SO_4$

EXAMPLE 7.10

How many moles of sodium hydroxide (NaOH) are there in 1.00 kg of sodium hydroxide?

SOLUTION

Read •   **Known:**   1.00 kg NaOH

Plan •   We need to use the atomic masses from the inside front cover of the text to find the molar mass of NaOH.

               Na   O   H
            $22.99 \text{ g} + 16.00 \text{ g} + 1.008 \text{ g} = 40.00 \text{ g NaOH} = \text{Molar mass NaOH}$

            Solution map: kg NaOH → g NaOH → mol NaOH

Create the appropriate conversion factor by placing the unit desired in the numerator and the unit to be eliminated in the denominator.

            We need two conversion factors: $\dfrac{1000 \text{ g}}{1 \text{ kg}}$ and $\dfrac{1 \text{ mol NaOH}}{40.00 \text{ g NaOH}}$.

Calculate • $(1.00 \text{ kg NaOH})\left(\dfrac{1000 \text{ g NaOH}}{1 \text{ kg NaOH}}\right)\left(\dfrac{1 \text{ mol NaOH}}{40.00 \text{ g NaOH}}\right)$

            $= 25.00 \text{ mol NaOH}$

            Therefore, 1.00 kg NaOH = 25.00 mol NaOH.

EXAMPLE 7.11

What is the mass of 5.00 mol water?

SOLUTION

Read •   **Known:**   5.00 mol H_2O

Plan · We need to use the atomic masses from the inside front cover of the text to find the molar mass of H_2O.

Solution map: mol H_2O → g H_2O

$$\frac{18.02 \text{ g } H_2O}{1 \text{ mol } H_2O} \text{ (conversion factor)}$$

Calculate · $(5.00 \text{ mol } H_2O)\left(\dfrac{18.02 \text{ g } H_2O}{1 \text{ mol } H_2O}\right) = 90.1 \text{ g } H_2O$

Therefore, 5.00 mol H_2O = 90.1 g H_2O.

EXAMPLE 7.12

How many molecules of hydrogen chloride (HCl) are there in 25.0 g of hydrogen chloride?

SOLUTION

Read · **Known:** 25.0 g HCl

Plan · We need to use the atomic masses from the inside front cover of the text to find the molar mass of HCl.

$$\begin{matrix} \text{H} & & \text{Cl} \\ 1.008 \text{ g} & + & 34.45 \text{ g} = 36.46 \text{ g} = \text{molar mass HCl} \end{matrix}$$

Solution map: g HCl → mol HCl → molecules HCl

$$\frac{1 \text{ mol HCl}}{36.46 \text{ g HCl}} \text{ and } \frac{6.022 \times 10^{23} \text{ molecules HCl}}{1 \text{ mol HCl}} \text{ (conversion factors)}$$

Calculate · $(25.0 \text{ g HCl})\left(\dfrac{1 \text{ mol HCl}}{36.46 \text{ g HCl}}\right)\left(\dfrac{6.022 \times 10^{23} \text{ molecules HCl}}{1 \text{ mol HCl}}\right)$

$$= 4.13 \times 10^{23} \text{ molecules HCl}$$

PRACTICE 7.5

What is the mass of 0.150 mol of Na_2SO_4?

PRACTICE 7.6

How many moles and molecules are there in 500.0 g of $HC_2H_3O_2$?

7.3 PERCENT COMPOSITION OF COMPOUNDS

Calculate the percent composition of a compound from its chemical formula and from experimental data.

• **LEARNING OBJECTIVE**

KEY TERM
percent composition of a compound

Percent means parts per 100 parts. Just as each piece of pie is a percent of the whole pie, each element in a compound is a percent of the whole compound. The **percent composition of a compound** is the *mass percent* of each element in the compound. The molar mass represents the total mass, or 100%, of the compound. Thus, the percent composition of water, H_2O, is 11.19% H and 88.79% O by mass. According to the law of definite composition, the percent composition must be the same no matter what size sample is taken.

The percent composition of a compound can be determined (1) from knowing its formula or (2) from experimental data.

Percent Composition from Formula

If the formula of a compound is known, a two-step process is needed to determine the percent composition:

PROBLEM-SOLVING STRATEGY: For Calculating Percent Composition from Formula

1. Calculate the molar mass (Section 7.2).

2. Divide the total mass of each element in the formula by the molar mass and multiply by 100. This gives the percent composition:

$$\frac{\text{total mass of the element}}{\text{molar mass}} \times 100 = \text{percent of the element}$$

EXAMPLE 7.13

Calculate the percent composition of sodium chloride (NaCl).

SOLUTION

Read •   **Known:**   NaCl

Plan •   Use the Problem-Solving Strategy for Calculating Percent Composition from Formula.

Calculate • 1. We need to use the atomic masses from the inside front cover of the text to find the molar mass of NaCl.

$$\begin{array}{cc} \text{Na} & \text{Cl} \\ 22.99 \text{ g} + 34.45 \text{ g} = 58.44 \text{ g} = \text{molar mass NaCl} \end{array}$$

2. Calculate the percent composition for each element.

$$\text{Na:} \quad \left(\frac{22.99 \text{ g Na}}{58.44 \text{ g}}\right)(100) = \quad 39.34\% \text{ Na}$$

$$\text{Cl:} \quad \left(\frac{35.45 \text{ g Cl}}{58.44 \text{ g}}\right)(100) = \quad \underline{60.66\% \text{ Cl}} \\ 100.00\% \text{ total}$$

NOTE   In any two-component system, if the percent of one component is known, the other is automatically defined by difference; that is, if Na is 39.43%, then Cl is 100% − 39.34% = 60.66%. However, the calculation of the percent should be carried out for each component, since this provides a check against possible error. The percent composition should add to 100% ± 0.2%.

EXAMPLE 7.14

Calculate the percent composition of potassium chloride (KCl).

SOLUTION

Read •   **Known:**   KCl

Plan •   Use the Problem-Solving Strategy for Calculating Percent Composition from Formula.

Calculate • 1. We need to use the atomic masses from the inside front cover of the text to find the molar mass of KCl.

$$\begin{array}{cc} \text{K} & \text{Cl} \\ 39.10 \text{ g} + 35.45 \text{ g} = 74.55 \text{ g} = \text{molar mass KCl} \end{array}$$

2. Calculate the percent composition for each element.

K: $\left(\dfrac{39.10 \text{ g K}}{74.55 \text{ g}}\right)(100) = 52.45\% \text{ K}$

Cl: $\left(\dfrac{35.45 \text{ g Cl}}{74.55 \text{ g}}\right)(100) = \dfrac{47.55\% \text{ Cl}}{100.00\% \text{ total}}$

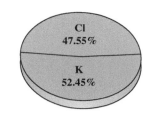

Comparing the results calculated for NaCl and for KCl, we see that NaCl contains a higher percentage of Cl by mass, although each compound has a one-to-one atom ratio of Cl to Na and Cl to K. The reason for this mass percent difference is that Na and K do not have the same atomic masses.

It is important to realize that when we compare *1 mol of NaCl with 1 mol of KCl*, each quantity contains the same number of Cl atoms—namely, 1 mol of Cl atoms. However, if we compare *equal masses* of NaCl and KCl, there will be more Cl atoms in the mass of NaCl, since NaCl has a higher mass percent of Cl.

1 mol NaCl contains	100.00 g NaCl contains	1 mol KCl contains	100.00 g KCl contains
1 mol Na	39.34 g Na	1 mol K	52.45 g K
1 mol Cl	60.66 g Cl	1 mol Cl	47.55 g Cl
	60.66% Cl		47.55% Cl

EXAMPLE 7.15

Calculate the percent composition of potassium sulfate (K_2SO_4).

SOLUTION

Read • **Known:** K_2SO_4

Plan • Use the Problem-Solving Strategy for Calculating Percent Composition from Formula.

Calculate • **1.** We need to use the atomic masses from the inside front cover of the text to find the molar mass of K_2SO_4.

$$\begin{array}{ccc} \text{K} & \text{S} & \text{O} \end{array}$$
$$2(39.10) \text{ g} + 32.07 \text{ g} + 4(16.00) = 174.3 \text{ g} = \text{molar mass } K_2SO_4$$

2. Calculate the percent composition for each element.

K: $\left(\dfrac{78.20 \text{ g K}}{174.3 \text{ g}}\right)(100) = 44.87\% \text{ K}$

S: $\left(\dfrac{32.07 \text{ g S}}{174.3 \text{ g}}\right)(100) = 18.40\% \text{ S}$

O: $\left(\dfrac{64.00 \text{ g O}}{174.3 \text{ g}}\right)(100) = \dfrac{36.72\% \text{ O}}{99.99\% \text{ total}}$

PRACTICE 7.7
Calculate the percent composition of $Ca(NO_3)_2$.

PRACTICE 7.8
Calculate the percent composition of K_2CrO_4.

PROBLEM-SOLVING STRATEGY: For Percent Composition from Experimental Data

1. Calculate the mass of the compound formed.

2. Divide the mass of each element by the total mass of the compound and multiply by 100.

EXAMPLE 7.16

Zinc oxide is a compound with many uses from preventing sunburn to a pigment in white paint. When heated in air, 1.63 g of zinc (Zn) combines with 0.40 g of oxygen (O_2) to form zinc oxide. Calculate the percent composition of the compound formed.

SOLUTION

Read •   **Knowns:**   1.63 g Zn

                              0.40 g O_2

Plan •   Use the Problem-Solving Strategy for Calculating Percent Composition from Experimental Data.

Calculate •   **1.** We need to calculate the mass of the product formed.

$$1.63 \text{ g Zn} + 0.40 \text{ g } O_2 = 2.03 \text{ g product}$$

2. Calculate the percent for each element.

$$\text{Zn: } \left(\frac{1.63 \text{ g Zn}}{2.03 \text{ g}} \right)(100) = \quad 80.3\% \text{ Zn}$$

$$\text{O: } \left(\frac{0.40 \text{ g O}}{2.03 \text{ g}} \right)(100) = \frac{20. \% \text{ O}}{100.3\% \text{ total}}$$

PRACTICE 7.9

Aluminum chloride is formed by reacting 13.43 g aluminum with 53.18 g chlorine. What is the percent composition of the compound?

> CHEMISTRY *IN ACTION*

Vanishing Coins?

Modern technology is changing our coins in some pretty interesting ways. The first U.S. coins were produced during the late 1700s from "coin silver," an alloy of 90% silver and 10% copper. Coins were made following a very simple rule: The mass of the coin reflects its relative value. Therefore, a half dollar weighed half as much as a dollar coin, and a quarter weighed ¼ as much as a dollar coin.

In the twentieth century our society began using machines to collect coins. We use vending machines, parking meters, toll baskets, laundromats, slot machines, and video games to make our lives more convenient and fun. This change produced a huge demand for coins. At the same time, the price of silver rose rapidly.

The solution? Make coins from a different alloy that would still work in all of our machines. This was a tricky process since the machines require a specific mass and electric "resistivity." In the mid-1960s new coins that sandwiched a layer of copper between layers of an alloy of copper and nickel began to replace quarters and dimes. And a new Susan B. Anthony dollar appeared briefly in 1979. Finally, in 1997 Congress decided to revive the dollar coin once more.

Congress specified that the new dollar coin had to look and feel different to consumers, be golden in color, and have a distinctive edge. At the same time, it needed to fool vending machines so that both the Susan B. Anthony dollar and the new coin would work. Designers decided on the portrait of Sacagawea, a Shoshone woman and her child. She was a guide on the Lewis and Clark expedition. On the back is an eagle. The chemists struggled to find a golden alloy for the coin. It is slightly larger than a quarter and weighs 8.1 grams. Vending machines determine a coin's value by its size, weight, and electromagnetic signature. This electromagnetic signature is hard to duplicate. All the golden coins tested had three times the conductivity of the silver Anthony coin. Metallurgists finally tried adding manganese and zinc to the copper core and found a "golden" alloy that fooled the vending machines! Sacagawea dollars are made of an alloy that is 77% copper, 12% zinc, 7% manganese, and 4% nickel. And on top of it all, the new coins only cost 12 cents each to make, leaving an 88 cent profit for the mint on each coin!

The future of coins is becoming less certain, however, as our machines are converted to electronic devices that use magnetic strips and a swipe of a card in place of "coins" and scan our cars for toll pass information. Some day soon, coins may vanish altogether from our pockets into collectors' albums.

7.4 CALCULATING EMPIRICAL FORMULAS

Determine the empirical formula for a compound from its percent composition.

KEY TERM
empirical formula

The **empirical formula**, or *simplest formula*, gives the smallest whole-number ratio of atoms present in a compound. This formula gives the relative number of atoms of each element in the compound.

We can establish empirical formulas because (1) individual atoms in a compound are combined in whole-number ratios and (2) each element has a specific atomic mass.

To calculate an empirical formula, we need to know (1) the elements that are combined, (2) their atomic masses, and (3) the ratio by mass or percentage in which they are combined. If elements A and B form a compound, we may represent the empirical formula as $A_x B_y$, where x and y are small whole numbers that represent the atoms of A and B. To write the empirical formula, we must determine x and y:

PROBLEM-SOLVING STRATEGY: For Calculating an Empirical Formula

1. Assume a definite starting quantity (usually 100.0 g) of the compound, if not given, and express the mass of each element in grams.

2. Convert the grams of each element into moles using each element's molar mass. This conversion gives the number of moles of atoms of each element in the quantity assumed in Step 1. At this point, these numbers will usually not be whole numbers.

3. Divide each value obtained in Step 2 by the smallest of these values. If the numbers obtained are whole numbers, use them as subscripts and write the empirical formula. If the numbers obtained are not whole numbers, go on to Step 4.

4. Multiply the values obtained in Step 3 by the smallest number that will convert them to whole numbers. Use these whole numbers as the subscripts in the empirical formula. For example, if the ratio of A to B is 1.0 : 1.5, multiply both numbers by 2 to obtain a ratio of 2 : 3. The empirical formula then is $A_2 B_3$.

In many of these calculations, results will vary somewhat from an exact whole number; this can be due to experimental errors in obtaining the data or from rounding off numbers. Calculations that vary by no more than ± 0.1 from a whole number usually are rounded off to the nearest whole number. Deviations greater than about 0.1 unit usually mean that the calculated ratios need to be multiplied by a factor to make them all whole numbers. For example, an atom ratio of 1 : 1.33 should be multiplied by 3 to make the ratio 3 : 4. Let's do a few examples to see how it works.

Some common fractions and their decimal equivalents are

$$1/4 = 0.25$$
$$1/3 = 0.333 \ldots$$
$$2/3 = 0.666 \ldots$$
$$1/2 = 0.5$$
$$3/4 = 0.75$$

Multiply the decimal equivalent by the number in the denominator of the fraction to get a whole number: $4(0.75) = 3$.

EXAMPLE 7.17

Calculate the empirical formula of a compound containing 11.19% hydrogen (H) and 88.79% oxygen (O).

SOLUTION

Read •   **Knowns:**   11.19% H
                      88.79% O

Plan •   Use the Problem-Solving Strategy for Calculating an Empirical Formula.

Calculate •   **1.** Assume 100.0 g of material. We know that the percent of each element equals the grams of each element:

           11.19 g H

           88.79 g O

2. Convert grams of each element to moles:

$$\text{H: } (11.19 \, \cancel{g})\left(\frac{1 \text{ mol H atoms}}{1.008 \, \cancel{g H}}\right) = 11.10 \text{ mol H atoms}$$

$$\text{O: } (88.79 \, \cancel{g})\left(\frac{1 \text{ mol O atoms}}{16.00 \, \cancel{g O}}\right) = 5.549 \text{ mol O atoms}$$

The formula could be expressed as $H_{11.10}O_{5.549}$. However, it's customary to use the smallest whole-number ratio of atoms.

3. Change the number of moles to whole numbers by dividing by the smallest number.

$$\text{H} = \frac{11.10 \text{ mol}}{5.549 \text{ mol}} = 2.000$$

$$\text{O} = \frac{5.549 \text{ mol}}{5.549 \text{ mol}} = 1.000$$

The simplest ratio of H to O is 2:1.

Empirical formula = H_2O

EXAMPLE 7.18

The analysis of a salt shows that it contains 56.58% potassium (K), 8.68% carbon (C), and 34.73% oxygen (O). Calculate the empirical formula for this substance.

SOLUTION

Read •   **Knowns:**   56.58% K
                        8.68% C
                      34.73% O

Plan •   Use the Problem-Solving Strategy for Calculating an Empirical Formula.

Calculate • **1.** Assume 100.0 g of material. We know that the percent of each element equals the grams of each element:

         56.58 g K

         8.68 g C

         34.73 g O

2. Convert the grams of each element to moles:

$$\text{K: } (56.58 \, \cancel{g K})\left(\frac{1 \text{ mol K atoms}}{39.10 \, \cancel{g K}}\right) = 1.447 \text{ mol K atoms}$$

$$\text{C: } (8.68 \, \cancel{g C})\left(\frac{1 \text{ mol C atoms}}{12.01 \, \cancel{g C}}\right) = 0.723 \text{ mol C atoms}$$

$$\text{O: } (34.73 \, \cancel{g O})\left(\frac{1 \text{ mol O atoms}}{16.00 \, \cancel{g O}}\right) = 2.171 \text{ mol O atoms}$$

3. Change the number of moles to whole numbers by dividing by the smallest number.

$$\text{K} = \frac{1.447 \text{ mol}}{0.723 \text{ mol}} = 2.00$$

$$\text{C} = \frac{0.723 \text{ mol}}{0.723 \text{ mol}} = 1.00$$

$$\text{O} = \frac{2.171 \text{ mol}}{0.723 \text{ mol}} = 3.00$$

The simplest ratio of K:C:O is 2:1:3.

Empirical formula = K_2CO_3

EXAMPLE 7.19

A sulfide of iron was formed by combining 2.233 g of iron (Fe) with 1.926 g of sulfur (S). What is the empirical formula for the compound?

SOLUTION

Read •   **Knowns:**   2.233 g Fe
                                    1.926 g S

Plan •   Use the Problem-Solving Strategy for Calculating an Empirical Formula.

Calculate • **1.** The mass of each element is known, so we use it directly.

2. Convert grams of each element to moles.

$$\text{Fe:} \quad (2.233 \ \cancel{g \ Fe})\left(\frac{1 \text{ mol Fe atoms}}{55.85 \ \cancel{g \ Fe}}\right) = 0.03998 \text{ mol Fe atoms}$$

$$\text{S:} \quad (1.926 \ \cancel{g \ S})\left(\frac{1 \text{ mol S atoms}}{32.07 \ \cancel{g \ S}}\right) = 0.06006 \text{ mol S atoms}$$

3. Change the number of moles to whole numbers by dividing by the smallest number.

$$\text{Fe} = \frac{0.03998 \text{ mol}}{0.03998 \text{ mol}} = 1.000$$

$$\text{S} = \frac{0.06006 \text{ mol}}{0.03998 \text{ mol}} = 1.502$$

4. We still have not reached a ratio that gives whole numbers in the formula, so we multiply by a number that will give us whole numbers.

Fe: $(1.000)2 = 2.000$

S: $(1.502)2 = 3.004$

Empirical formula $= Fe_2S_3$

PRACTICE 7.10

Calculate the empirical formula of a compound containing 52.14% C, 13.12% H, and 34.73% O.

PRACTICE 7.11

Calculate the empirical formula of a compound that contains 43.7% phosphorus and 56.3% O by mass.

7.5 CALCULATING THE MOLECULAR FORMULA FROM THE EMPIRICAL FORMULA

Compare an empirical formula to a molecular formula and calculate a molecular formula from the empirical formula of the compound and its molar mass.

LEARNING OBJECTIVE

KEY TERM
molecular formula

The **molecular formula** is the true formula, representing the total number of atoms of each element present in one molecule of a compound. It is entirely possible that two or more substances will have the same percent composition yet be distinctly different compounds. For example, acetylene (C_2H_2) is a common gas used in welding; benzene (C_6H_6) is an important solvent obtained from coal tar and is used in the synthesis of styrene and nylon. Both acetylene and benzene contain 92.3% C and 7.7% H. The smallest ratio of C and H corresponding to these percentages is CH (1:1) Therefore, the *empirical* formula for both acetylene and benzene is CH, even though the *molecular* formulas are C_2H_2 and

C_6H_6, respectively. Often the molecular formula is the same as the empirical formula. If the molecular formula is not the same, it will be an integral (whole number) multiple of the empirical formula. For example,

$$CH = \text{empirical formula}$$

$$(CH)_2 = C_2H_2 = \text{acetylene} \quad \text{(molecular formula)}$$

$$(CH)_6 = C_6H_6 = \text{benzene} \quad \text{(molecular formula)}$$

Table 7.1 compares the formulas of these substances. Table 7.2 shows empirical and molecular formula relationships of other compounds.

TABLE 7.1　Molecular Formulas of Two Compounds Having an Empirical Formula with a 1:1 Ratio of Carbon and Hydrogen Atoms

	Composition		
Formula	% C	% H	Molar mass
CH (empirical)	92.3	7.7	13.02 (empirical)
C_2H_2 (acetylene)	92.3	7.7	26.04 (2 × 13.02)
C_6H_6 (benzene)	92.3	7.7	78.12 (6 × 13.02)

TABLE 7.2　Some Empirical and Molecular Formulas

Substance	Empirical formula	Molecular formula	Substance	Empirical formula	Molecular formula
Acetylene	CH	C_2H_2	Diborane	BH_3	B_2H_6
Benzene	CH	C_6H_6	Hydrazine	NH_2	N_2H_4
Ethylene	CH_2	C_2H_4	Hydrogen	H	H_2
Formaldehyde	CH_2O	CH_2O	Chlorine	Cl	Cl_2
Acetic acid	CH_2O	$C_2H_4O_2$	Bromine	Br	Br_2
Glucose	CH_2O	$C_6H_{12}O_6$	Oxygen	O	O_2
Hydrogen chloride	HCl	HCl	Nitrogen	N	N_2
Carbon dioxide	CO_2	CO_2	Iodine	I	I_2

The molecular formula can be calculated from the empirical formula if the molar mass is known. The molecular formula will be equal either to the empirical formula or some multiple of it. For example, if the empirical formula of a compound of hydrogen and fluorine is HF, the molecular formula can be expressed as $(HF)_n$, where $n = 1, 2, 3, 4, \ldots$. This n means that the molecular formula could be HF, H_2F_2, H_3F_3, H_4F_4, and so on. To determine the molecular formula, we must evaluate n:

$$n = \frac{\text{molar mass}}{\text{mass of empirical formula}} = \text{number of empirical formula units}$$

What we actually calculate is the number of units of the empirical formula contained in the molecular formula.

EXAMPLE 7.20

A compound of nitrogen and oxygen with a molar mass of 92.00 g was found to have an empirical formula of NO_2. What is its molecular formula?

SOLUTION

Read • 　**Knowns:**　NO_2 = empirical formula

　　　　　　　　　　　Molar mass = 92.00

Plan • Let n be the number of NO_2 units in a molecule; then the molecular formula is $(NO_2)_n$. Find the molar mass of an NO_2 unit and determine the numbers of units needed for the molar mass of the compound.

Calculate • The molar mass of NO_2 is $14.01 \text{ g} + 2(16.00 \text{ g}) = 46.01 \text{ g}$.

$$n = \frac{92.00 \text{ g}}{46.01 \text{ g}} = 2 \text{ (empirical formula units)}$$

The molecular formula is $(NO_2)_2$ or N_2O_4.

N_2O_4

EXAMPLE 7.21

Propylene is a compound frequently polymerized to make polypropylene, which is used for rope, laundry bags, blankets, carpets, and textile fibers. Propylene has a molar mass of 42.08 g and contains 14.3% H and 85.7% C. What is its molecular formula?

SOLUTION

Read • **Knowns:**   Molar mass = 42.08 g

14.3% H

85.7% C

Plan • First find the empirical formula using the Problem-Solving Strategy for Calculating an Empirical Formula. Then use n to determine the molecular formula from the empirical formula.

Calculate • **1.** Assume 100.0 g of material. We know that the percent of each element equals the grams of each element:

14.3 g H

85.7 g C

2. Convert the grams of each element to moles:

H: $(14.3 \text{ g H})\left(\dfrac{1 \text{ mol H atoms}}{1.008 \text{ g H}}\right) = 14.2 \text{ mol H atoms}$

C: $(85.7 \text{ g C})\left(\dfrac{1 \text{ mol C atoms}}{12.01 \text{ g C}}\right) = 7.14 \text{ mol C atoms}$

3. Change the number of moles to whole numbers by dividing by the smallest number.

$$H = \frac{14.2 \text{ mol}}{7.14 \text{ mol}} = 1.99$$

$$C = \frac{7.14 \text{ mol}}{7.14 \text{ mol}} = 1.00$$

Empirical formula = CH_2

We determine the molecular formula from the empirical formula and the molar mass:

Molecular formula = $(CH_2)_n$

CH_2 molar mass = $12.01 \text{ g} + 2(1.008 \text{ g}) = 14.03 \text{ g}$

$$n = \frac{42.08 \text{ g}}{14.03 \text{ g}} = 3 \text{ (empirical formula units)}$$

The molecular formula is $(CH_2)_3 = C_3H_6$.

When propylene is polymerized into polypropylene, it can be used for rope and other recreational products.

raypauly/iStockphoto

C_3H_6

PRACTICE 7.12

Calculate the empirical and molecular formulas of a compound that contains 80.0% C, 20.0% H, and has a molar mass of 30.00 g.

CHAPTER 7 REVIEW

7.1 THE MOLE

- We count atoms by weighing them since they are so tiny.
- 1 mole $= 6.022 \times 10^{23}$ items.
- Avogadro's number is 6.022×10^{23}.

7.2 MOLAR MASS OF COMPOUNDS

- One mole of a compound contains Avogadro's number of formula units of that compound.
- The mass (grams) of one mole of a compound is the molar mass.
- Molar mass is determined by adding the molar masses of all the atoms in a formula.
- Molar masses are given to four significant figures in this text.

7.3 PERCENT COMPOSITION OF COMPOUNDS

- To determine the percent composition from a formula:
  - Calculate the molar mass.
  - For each element in the formula

$$\frac{\text{total mass of the element}}{\text{molar mass of the compound}} \times 100 = \text{percent of the element}$$

- To determine percent composition from experimental data:
  - Calculate the mass of the compound formed.
  - For each element in the formula

$$\frac{\text{mass of the element}}{\text{mass of the compound formed}} \times 100 = \text{percent of the element}$$

7.4 CALCULATING EMPIRICAL FORMULAS

- The empirical formula is the simplest formula giving the smallest whole-number ratio of atoms present in a compound.
- To determine the empirical formula for a compound you need to know:
  - The elements that are combined
  - Their atomic masses
  - The ratio of masses or percentage in which they are combined
- Empirical formulas are represented in the form $A_x B_y$. To determine the empirical formula of this compound:
  - Assume a starting quantity (100.0 g is a good choice).
  - Convert mass (g) to moles for each element.
  - Divide each element's moles by the smallest number of moles.
    - If the ratios are whole numbers, use them as subscripts and write the empirical formula.
  - If the ratios are not whole numbers, multiply them all by the smallest number, which will convert them to whole numbers.
  - Use the whole numbers to write the empirical formula.

7.5 CALCULATING THE MOLECULAR FORMULA FROM THE EMPIRICAL FORMULA

- The molecular formula is the true formula representing the total number of atoms of each element present in one molecule of the compound.
- Two or more substances may have the same empirical formulas but different molecular formulas.
- The molecular formula is calculated from the empirical formula when the molar mass is known:

  - $n = \dfrac{\text{molar mass}}{\text{mass of empirical formula}} = \text{number of empirical formula units}$

  - The molecular formula is $(A_x B_y)_n$.

REVIEW QUESTIONS

1. What is a mole?
2. Which would have a higher mass: a mole of K atoms or a mole of Au atoms?
3. Which would contain more atoms: a mole of K atoms or a mole of Au atoms?
4. Which would contain more electrons: a mole of K atoms or a mole of Au atoms?
5. What is the numerical value of Avogadro's number?
6. What is the relationship between Avogadro's number and the mole?
7. Which has the greater number of oxygen atoms, 1 mole of oxygen gas (O_2) or 1 mole of ozone gas (O_3)?
8. What is molar mass?
9. If the atomic mass scale had been defined differently, with an atom of $^{12}_6C$ defined as a mass of 50 amu, would this have any effect on the value of Avogadro's number? Explain.
10. Complete these statements, supplying the proper quantity.
    (a) A mole of O atoms contains _____ atoms.
    (b) A mole of O_2 molecules contains _____ molecules.
    (c) A mole of O_2 molecules contains _____ atoms.
    (d) A mole of O atoms has a mass of _____ grams.
    (e) A mole of O_2 molecules has a mass of _____ grams.

11. How many molecules are present in 1 molar mass of sulfuric acid (H_2SO_4)? How many atoms are present?
12. What are the two types of information that can be used to calculate the percent composition of a compound?
13. A compound is composed of only nitrogen and oxygen. If the compound contains 43.8% nitrogen, what is the percent oxygen in the compound?
14. Write the steps used to calculate percent composition of an element in a compound.
15. In calculating the empirical formula of a compound from its percent composition, why do we choose to start with 100.0 g of the compound?
16. Which of the following compounds have the same empirical formula? What is the empirical formula? CH_4, C_2H_4, C_4H_6, C_4H_{10}, C_8H_{12}, C_8H_{18}
17. What is the difference between an empirical formula and a molecular formula?
18. What data beyond the percent composition are generally used to determine the molecular formula of a compound?
19. What information does the ratio $\dfrac{\text{molar mass}}{\text{mass of emprical formula}}$ provide?

Most of the exercises in this chapter are available for assignment via the online homework management program, WileyPLUS (www.wileyplus.com). All exercises with blue numbers have answers in Appendix VI.

PAIRED EXERCISES

1. Determine the molar masses of these compounds:
    (a) KBr   (f) Fe_3O_4
    (b) Na_2SO_4 (g) $C_{12}H_{22}O_{11}$
    (c) $Pb(NO_3)_2$ (h) $Al_2(SO_4)_3$
    (d) C_2H_5OH (i) $(NH_4)_2HPO_4$
    (e) $HC_2H_3O_2$

2. Determine the molar masses of these compounds:
    (a) NaOH   (f) C_6H_5COOH
    (b) Ag_2CO_3 (g) $C_6H_{12}O_6$
    (c) Cr_2O_3 (h) $K_4Fe(CN)_6$
    (d) $(NH_4)_2CO_3$ (i) $BaCl_2 \cdot 2H_2O$
    (e) $Mg(HCO_3)_2$

3. How many moles of atoms are contained in the following?
    (a) 22.5 g Zn   (d) 382 g Co
    (b) 0.688 g Mg   (e) 0.055 g Sn
    (c) 4.5×10^{22} atoms Cu (f) 8.5×10^{24} molecules N_2

4. How many moles of atoms are contained in the following?
    (a) 25.0 g NaOH   (d) 14.8 g CH_3OH
    (b) 44.0 g Br_2 (e) 2.88 g Na_2SO_4
    (c) 0.684 g $MgCl_2$ (f) 4.20 lb ZnI_2

5. Calculate the number of grams in each of the following:
    (a) 0.550 mol Au   (c) 12.5 mol Cl_2
    (b) 15.8 mol H_2O (d) 3.15 mol NH_4NO_3

6. Calculate the number of grams in each of the following:
    (a) 4.25×10^{-4} mol H_2SO_4 (c) 0.00255 mol Ti
    (b) 4.5×10^{22} molecules CCl_4 (d) 1.5×10^{16} atoms S

7. How many molecules are contained in each of the following?
    (a) 2.5 mol S_8 (c) 17.5 g C_2H_5OH
    (b) 7.35 mol NH_3 (d) 225 g Cl_2

8. How many molecules are contained in each of the following?
    (a) 9.6 mol C_2H_4 (c) 23.2 g CH_3OH
    (b) 2.76 mol N_2O (d) 32.7 g CCl_4

9. How many atoms are contained in each of the following?
    (a) 25 molecules P_2O_5 (d) 1.25 g Na
    (b) 3.62 mol O_2 (e) 2.7 g CO_2
    (c) 12.2 mol CS_2 (f) 0.25 g CH_4

10. How many atoms are contained in each of the following?
    (a) 2 molecules CH_3COOH (d) 92.5 g Au
    (b) 0.75 mol C_2H_6 (e) 75 g PCl_3
    (c) 25 mol H_2O (f) 15 g $C_6H_{12}O_6$

11. Calculate the mass in grams of each of the following:
    (a) 1 atom He   (c) 4 molecules N_2O_5
    (b) 15 atoms C   (d) 11 molecules $C_6H_5NH_2$

12. Calculate the mass in grams of each of the following:
    (a) 1 atom Xe   (c) 9 molecules CH_3COOH
    (b) 22 atoms Cl   (d) 15 molecules $C_4H_4O_2(NH_2)_2$

13. Make the following conversions:
    (a) 25 kg CO_2 to mol CO_2 (c) 6 mol O_2 to atoms oxygen
    (b) 5 atoms Pb to mol Pb   (d) 25 molecules P_4 to g P_4

14. Make the following conversions:
    (a) 275 atoms W to mol W   (c) 12 molecules SO_2 to g SO_2
    (b) 95 atoms H_2O to kg H_2O (d) 25 mol Cl_2 to atoms chlorine

15. 1 molecule of tetraphosphorus decoxide contains
    (a) how many moles?   (d) how many oxygen atoms?
    (b) how many grams?   (e) how many total atoms?
    (c) how many phosphorus atoms?

16. 125 grams of disulfur decafluoride contain
    (a) how many moles?   (d) how many atoms of sulfur?
    (b) how many molecules?   (e) how many atoms of fluorine?
    (c) how many total atoms?

17. How many atoms of hydrogen are contained in each of the following?
    (a) 25 molecules $C_6H_5CH_3$ (c) 36 g CH_3CH_2OH
    (b) 3.5 mol H_2CO_3

18. How many atoms of hydrogen are contained in each of the following?
    (a) 23 molecules CH_3CH_2COOH (c) 57 g $C_6H_5ONH_2$
    (b) 7.4 mol H_3PO_4

19. Calculate the number of
    (a) grams of silver in 25.0 g AgBr
    (b) grams of nitrogen in 6.34 mol $(NH_4)_3PO_4$
    (c) grams of oxygen in 8.45×10^{22} molecules SO_3

20. Calculate the number of
    (a) grams of chlorine in 5.0 g $PbCl_2$
    (b) grams of hydrogen in 4.50 mol H_2SO_4
    (c) grams of hydrogen in 5.45×10^{22} molecules NH_3

21. Calculate the percent composition by mass of these compounds:
    (a) NaBr   (d) $SiCl_4$
    (b) $KHCO_3$ (e) $Al_2(SO_4)_3$
    (c) $FeCl_3$ (f) $AgNO_3$

22. Calculate the percent composition by mass of these compounds:
    (a) $ZnCl_2$ (d) $(NH_4)_2SO_4$
    (b) $NH_4C_2H_3O_2$ (e) $Fe(NO_3)_3$
    (c) MgP_2O_7 (f) ICl_3

23. Calculate the percent of iron in the following compounds:
    (a) FeO   (c) Fe_3O_4
    (b) Fe_2O_3 (d) $K_4Fe(CN)_6$

24. Which of the following chlorides has the highest and which has the lowest percentage of chlorine, by mass, in its formula?
    (a) KCl   (c) $SiCl_4$
    (b) $BaCl_2$ (d) LiCl

25. A 73.16-g sample of an interesting barium silicide reported to have superconducting properties was found to contain 33.62 g barium and the remainder silicon. Calculate the percent composition of the compound.

26. One of the compounds that give garlic its characteristic odor is ajoene. A 7.52-g sample of this compound contains 3.09 g sulfur, 0.453 g hydrogen, 0.513 g oxygen, and the remainder is carbon. Calculate the percent composition of ajoene.

27. Examine the following formulas. Which compound has the
    (a) higher percent by mass of hydrogen: H_2O or H_2O_2?
    (b) lower percent by mass of nitrogen: NO or N_2O_3?
    (c) higher percent by mass of oxygen: NO_2 or N_2O_4?

    Check your answers by calculation if you wish.

28. Examine the following formulas. Which compound has the
    (a) lower percent by mass of chlorine: $NaClO_3$ or $KClO_3$?
    (b) higher percent by mass of sulfur: $KHSO_4$ or K_2SO_4?
    (c) lower percent by mass of chromium: Na_2CrO_4 or $Na_2Cr_2O_7$?

    Check your answers by calculation if you wish.

29. Calculate the empirical formula of each compound from the percent compositions given:
    (a) 63.6% N, 36.4% O   (d) 43.4% Na, 11.3% C, 45.3% O
    (b) 46.7% N, 53.3% O   (e) 18.8% Na, 29.0% Cl, 52.3% O
    (c) 25.9% N, 74.1% O   (f) 72.02% Mn, 27.98% O

30. Calculate the empirical formula of each compound from the percent compositions given:
    (a) 64.1% Cu, 35.9% Cl   (d) 55.3% K, 14.6% P, 30.1% O
    (b) 47.2% Cu, 52.8% Cl   (e) 38.9% Ba, 29.4% Cr, 31.7% O
    (c) 51.9% Cr, 48.1% S   (f) 3.99% P, 82.3% Br, 13.7% Cl

31. Determine the empirical formula for each of the following, using the given masses:
    (a) a compound containing 26.08 g zinc, 4.79 g carbon, and 19.14 g oxygen
    (b) a 150.0-g sample of a compound containing 57.66 g carbon, 7.26 g hydrogen, and the rest, chlorine
    (c) a 75.0-g sample of an oxide of vanadium, containing 42.0 g V and the rest, oxygen
    (d) a compound containing 67.35 g nickel, 43.46 g oxygen, and 23.69 g phosphorus

32. Determine the empirical formula for each of the following, using the given masses:
    (a) a compound containing 55.08 g carbon, 3.85 g hydrogen, and 61.07 g bromine
    (b) a 65.2-g sample of a compound containing 36.8 g silver, 12.1 g chlorine, and the rest, oxygen
    (c) a 25.25-g sample of a sulfide of vanadium, containing 12.99 g V, and the rest, sulfur
    (d) a compound containing 38.0 g zinc and 12.0 g phosphorus

33. A 15.267-g sample of a sulfide of gold was found to contain 12.272 g gold, and the rest, sulfur. Calculate the empirical formula of this sulfide of gold.

34. A 10.724-g sample of an oxide of titanium was found to contain 7.143 g titanium, and the rest, oxygen. Calculate the empirical formula of this oxide of titanium.

35. Lenthionine, a naturally occurring sulfur compound, gives shitake mushrooms their interesting flavor. This compound is composed of carbon, sulfur, and hydrogen. A 5.000-g sample of lenthionine contains 0.6375 g carbon and 0.1070 g hydrogen, and the remainder is sulfur. The molar mass of lenthionine is 188.4 g/mol. Determine the empirical formula for lenthionine.

36. A 5.276-g sample of an unknown compound was found to contain 3.989 g of mercury and the rest, chlorine. Calculate the empirical formula of this chloride of mercury.

37. Traumatic acid is a plant hormone that induces injured cells to begin to divide and repair the trauma they have experienced. Traumatic acid contains 63.13% carbon, 8.830% hydrogen, and 28.03% oxygen. Its molar mass is 228 g/mol. Determine the empirical and molecular formulas of traumatic acid.

38. Dixanthogen, an herbicide, is composed of 29.73% carbon, 4.16% hydrogen, 13.20% oxygen, and 52.91% sulfur. It has a molar mass of 242.4 g/mol. Determine the empirical and the molecular formulas.

39. Ethanedioic acid, a compound that is present in many vegetables, has a molar mass of 90.04 g/mol and a composition of 26.7% C, 2.2% H, and 71.1% O. What is the molecular formula for this substance?

40. Butyric acid is a compound that is present in butter. It has a molar mass of 88.11 g/mol and is composed of 54.5% C, 9.2% H, and 36.3% O. What is the molecular formula for this substance?

41. Calculate the percent composition and determine the molecular formula and the empirical formula for the nitrogen-oxygen compound that results when 12.04 g of nitrogen are reacted with enough oxygen to produce 39.54 g of product. The molar mass of the product is 92.02 g.

42. Calculate the percent composition and determine the molecular formula and the empirical formula for the carbon-hydrogen-oxygen compound that results when 30.21 g of carbon, 40.24 g of oxygen, and 5.08 g of hydrogen are reacted to produce a product with a molar mass of 180.18 g.

43. The compound XYZ_3 has a molar mass of 100.09 g and a percent composition (by mass) of 40.04% X, 12.00% Y, and 47.96% Z. What is the formula of the compound?

44. The compound $X_2(YZ_3)_3$ has a molar mass of 282.23 g and a percent composition (by mass) of 19.12% X, 29.86% Y, and 51.02% Z. What is the formula of the compound?

ADDITIONAL EXERCISES

45. White phosphorus is one of several forms of phosphorus and exists as a waxy solid consisting of P_4 molecules. How many atoms are present in 0.350 mol of P_4?

46. How many grams of sodium contain the same number of atoms as 10.0 g of potassium?

47. One molecule of an unknown compound is found to have a mass of 3.27×10^{-22} g. What is the molar mass of this compound?

48. How many molecules of sugar are in a 5-lb bag of sugar? The formula for table sugar or sucrose is $C_{12}H_{22}O_{11}$.

49. If a stack of 500 sheets of paper is 4.60 cm high, what will be the height, in meters, of a stack of Avogadro's number of sheets of paper?

50. There are about 7.0 billion (7.0×10^9) people on Earth. If exactly 1 mol of dollars were distributed equally among these people, how many dollars would each person receive?

51. If 20. drops of water equal 1.0 mL ($1.0 \, cm^3$),
    (a) how many drops of water are there in a cubic mile of water?
    (b) what would be the volume in cubic miles of a mole of drops of water?

52. Silver has a density of $10.5 \, g/cm^3$. If 1.00 mol of silver were shaped into a cube,
    (a) what would be the volume of the cube?
    (b) what would be the length of one side of the cube?

53. Given 1.00-g samples of each of the compounds CO_2, O_2, H_2O, and CH_3OH,
    (a) which sample will contain the largest number of molecules?
    (b) which sample will contain the largest number of atoms? Show proof for your answers.

54. How many grams of Fe_2S_3 will contain a total number of atoms equal to Avogadro's number?

55. How many grams of calcium must be combined with 1 g phosphorus to form the compound Ca_3P_2?

56. An iron ore contains 5% $FeSO_4$ by mass. How many grams of iron could be obtained from 1.0 ton of this ore?

57. How many grams of lithium will combine with 20.0 g of sulfur to form the compound Li_2S?

58. Calculate the percentage of
    (a) mercury in $HgCO_3$
    (b) oxygen in $Ca(ClO_3)_2$
    (c) nitrogen in $C_{10}H_{14}N_2$ (nicotine)
    (d) Mg in $C_{55}H_{72}MgN_4O_5$ (chlorophyll)

59. Zinc and sulfur react to form zinc sulfide, ZnS. If we mix 19.5 g of zinc and 9.40 g of sulfur, have we added sufficient sulfur to fully react all the zinc? Show evidence for your answer.

60. Vomitoxin is produced by some fungi that grow on wheat and barley. It derives its name from the fact that it causes pigs that eat contaminated wheat to vomit. The chemical formula for vomitoxin is $C_{15}H_{20}O_6$. What is the percent composition of this compound?

61. Diphenhydramine hydrochloride, a drug used commonly as an antihistamine, has the formula $C_{17}H_{21}NO \cdot HCl$. What is the percent composition of each element in this compound?

62. What is the percent composition of each element in sucrose, $C_{12}H_{22}O_{11}$?

63. Aspirin is well known as a pain reliever (analgesic) and as a fever reducer (antipyretic). It has a molar mass of 180.2 g/mol and a composition of 60.0% C, 4.48% H, and 35.5% O. Calculate the molecular formula of aspirin.

64. How many grams of oxygen are contained in 8.50 g of $Al_2(SO_4)_3$?

65. Gallium arsenide is one of the newer materials used to make semiconductor chips for use in supercomputers. Its composition is 48.2% Ga and 51.8% As. What is the empirical formula?

66. Calcium tartrate is used as a preservative for certain foods and as an antacid. It contains 25.5% C, 2.1% H, 21.3% Ca, and 51.0% O. What is the empirical formula for calcium tartrate?

67. The compositions of four different compounds of carbon and chlorine follow. Determine the empirical formula and the molecular formula for each compound.

	Percent C	Percent Cl	Molar mass (g)
(a) 7.79	92.21	153.8
(b) 10.13	89.87	236.7
(c) 25.26	74.74	284.8
(d) 11.25	88.75	319.6

68. How many years is a mole of seconds?

69. A normal penny has a mass of about 2.5 g. If we assume the penny to be pure copper (which means the penny is very old since newer pennies are a mixture of copper and zinc), how many atoms of copper does it contain?

70. What would be the mass (in grams) of one thousand trillion molecules of glycerin ($C_3H_8O_3$)?

71. If we assume that there are 7.0 billion people on the Earth, how many moles of people is this?

72. An experimental catalyst used to make polymers has the following composition: Co, 23.3%; Mo, 25.3%; and Cl, 51.4%. What is the empirical formula for this compound?

73. If a student weighs 18 g of aluminum and needs twice as many atoms of magnesium as she has of aluminum, how many grams of Mg does she need?

74. If 10.0 g of an unknown compound composed of carbon, hydrogen, and nitrogen contains 17.7% N and 3.8×10^{23} atoms of hydrogen, what is its empirical formula?

75. A substance whose formula is A_2O (A is a mystery element) is 60.0% A and 40.0% O. Identify the element A.

76. For the following compounds whose molecular formulas are given, indicate the empirical formula:
    (a) $C_6H_{12}O_6$ glucose
    (b) C_8H_{18} octane
    (c) $C_3H_6O_3$ lactic acid
    (d) $C_{25}H_{52}$ paraffin
    (e) $C_{12}H_4Cl_4O_2$ dioxin (a powerful poison)
77. Copper is often added to paint for ocean-going ships and boats to discourage the growth of marine organisms on their hulls. Unfortunately the copper dissolves into the water and is toxic to the marine life in harbors where these boats are docked. When copper(II) ions reach a concentration of 9.0 microgram/L, the growth of some marine life slows. How many copper ions are found in a liter of water containing 9.0 micrograms of Cu^{2+}/L?
78. Molecules of oxygen gas have been very difficult to find in space. Recently the European Space Agency's Herschel space observatory has found molecular oxygen in the Orion star-forming complex. It is present at very low concentrations, 1 molecule of oxygen per every million (1.0×10^6) molecules of hydrogen, but it does exist. How many molecules of oxygen would exist in a 3.0-g sample of hydrogen gas?
79. Scientists from the European Space Agency have been studying geysers located around the southern pole of one of Saturn's moons. These geysers send 250.0 kg of water into the atmosphere every second. Scientists trying to discover what happens to this water have found that it forms a very thin vapor ring around Saturn. How many moles of water are shot into the atmosphere in a Saturn day? (One Saturn day is equal to 10 hours and 45 minutes.)
80. Researchers from the University of Cape Town in South Africa have discovered that penguins are able to detect a chemical released by plankton as they are being consumed by schools of fish. By following this scent they are able to find these schools of fish and feast on them. The chemical they smell is composed of 38.65% carbon, 9.74% hydrogen, and 51.61% sulfur. Determine the empirical formula of this compound.

CHALLENGE EXERCISES

81. The compound $A(BC)_3$ has a molar mass of 78.01 g and a percent composition of 34.59% A, 61.53% B, and 3.88% C. Determine the identity of the elements A, B, and C. What is the percent composition by mass of the compound A_2B_3?
82. A 2.500-g sample of an unknown compound containing only C, H, and O was burned in O_2. The products were 4.776 g of CO_2 and 2.934 g of H_2O.
    (a) What is the percent composition of the original compound?
    (b) What is the empirical formula of the compound?
83. Researchers at Anna Gudmundsdottir's laboratory at the University of Cincinnati have been studying extremely reactive chemicals known as radicals. One of the interesting phenomena they have discovered is that these radicals can be chemically attached to fragrance molecules, effectively tethering them to a solution. When light strikes these tethered molecules, the fragrance is released. This property would allow us to produce perfumes, cleansers, and other consumer products that release fragrance only when exposed to light. If limonene, $C_{10}H_{16}$, the molecule that gives fruits their citrus scent, were able to be tethered to one of these radicals and every photon of light would release one molecule of limonene, calculate the time in seconds required to release 1.00 picogram of limonene if ambient light releases 2.64×10^{18} photons/sec.

ANSWERS TO PRACTICE EXERCISES

7.1   (a) 6.022×10^{23} atoms Fe
      (b) 1.204×10^{24} atoms H
      (c) 4.215×10^{24} atoms
7.2   10.0 g helium
7.3 1.5×10^{22} atoms
7.4   101.1 g KNO_3
7.5   21.3 g Na_2SO_4

7.6   8.326 mol and 5.014×10^{24} molecules $HC_2H_3O_2$
7.7   24.42% Ca; 17.07% N; 58.50% O
7.8   40.27% K; 26.78% Cr; 32.96% O
7.9   20.16% Al; 79.84% Cl
7.10 C_2H_6O
7.11 P_2O_5
7.12 The empirical formula is CH_3; the molecular formula is C_2H_6.

Flames and sparks result when aluminum foil is dropped into liquid bromine.

Charles D. Winters/Photo Researchers

CHAPTER **8**

CHEMICAL EQUATIONS

In the world today, we continually strive to express information in a concise, useful manner. From early childhood, we are taught to translate our ideas and desires into sentences. In mathematics, we learn to describe numerical relationships and situations through mathematical expressions and equations. Historians describe thousands of years of history in 500-page textbooks. Filmmakers translate entire events, such as the Olympics, into a few hours of entertainment.

Chemists use chemical equations to describe reactions they observe in the laboratory or in nature. Chemical equations provide us with the means to (1) summarize the reaction, (2) display the substances that are reacting, (3) show the products, and (4) indicate the amounts of all component substances in a reaction.

8.1 THE CHEMICAL EQUATION

LEARNING OBJECTIVE ● Describe the information present in a chemical equation.

KEY TERMS

reactants
products
chemical equation
law of conservation of mass

Charles D. Winters/Science Source Images

Molten iron falls from the reaction container during the thermite reaction.

Chemical reactions always involve change. Atoms, molecules, or ions rearrange to form different substances, sometimes in a spectacular manner. For example, the thermite reaction is a reaction between aluminum metal and iron(III) oxide, which produces molten iron and aluminum oxide. The substances entering the reaction are called the **reactants**, and the substances formed are called the **products**. In our example,

reactants	aluminum
	iron(III) oxide
products	iron
	aluminum oxide

During reactions, chemical bonds are broken and new bonds are formed. The reactants and products may be present as solids, liquids, gases, or in solution.

In a chemical reaction atoms are neither created nor destroyed. All atoms present in the reactants must also be present in the products.

A **chemical equation** is a shorthand expression for a chemical change or reaction. A chemical equation uses the chemical symbols and formulas of the reactants and products and other symbolic terms to represent a chemical reaction. The equations are written according to this general format:

1. Reactants are separated from products by an arrow ($\longrightarrow$) that indicates the direction of the reaction. The reactants are placed to the left and the products to the right of the arrow. A plus sign ($+$) is placed between reactants and between products when needed.

$$\underset{\text{reactants}}{Al + Fe_2O_3} \longrightarrow \underset{\text{products}}{Fe + Al_2O_3}$$

2. Coefficients (whole numbers) are placed in front of substances to balance the equation and to indicate the number of units (atoms, molecules, moles, ions) of each substance reacting or being produced. When no number is shown, it is understood that one unit of the substance is indicated.

$$2\,Al + Fe_2O_3 \longrightarrow 2\,Fe + Al_2O_3$$

3. Conditions required to carry out the reaction may, if desired, be placed above or below the arrow or equality sign. For example, a delta sign placed over the arrow ($\xrightarrow{\Delta}$) indicates that heat is supplied to the reaction.

$$2\,Al + Fe_2O_3 \xrightarrow{\Delta} 2\,Fe + Al_2O_3$$

4. The physical state of a substance is indicated by the following symbols: (s) for solid state; (l) for liquid state; (g) for gaseous state; and (aq) for substances in aqueous solution. States are not always given in chemical equations.

$$2\,Al(s) + Fe_2O_3(s) \xrightarrow{\Delta} Fe(l) + Al_2O_3(s)$$

Symbols commonly used in chemical equations are given in Table 8.1.

TABLE 8.1 Symbols Commonly Used in Chemical Equations

Symbol	Meaning
$+$	Plus or added to (placed between substances)
$\longrightarrow$	Yields; produces (points to products)
(s)	Solid state (written after a substance)
(l)	Liquid state (written after a substance)
(g)	Gaseous state (written after a substance)
(aq)	Aqueous solution (substance dissolved in water)
Δ	Heat is added (when written above or below arrow)

EXAMPLE 8.1

Classify each formula in the chemical reactions below as a reactant or a product.

(a) $MnO_2 + 4\,HCl \longrightarrow MnCl_2 + Cl_2 + 2\,H_2O$
(b) $Na_2SO_3 + H_2SO_4 \longrightarrow Na_2SO_4 + SO_2 + H_2O$

SOLUTION

(a) Reactants: MnO_2 and HCl
    Products: $MnCl_2$, Cl_2, and H_2O
(b) Reactants: Na_2SO_3, and H_2SO_4
    Products: Na_2SO_4, SO_2, and H_2O

PRACTICE 8.1

How is a substance in a chemical equation identified as a solid, a gas, or in a water solution?

Conservation of Mass

The **law of conservation of mass** states that no change is observed in the total mass of the substances involved in a chemical change. This law, tested by extensive laboratory experimentation, is the basis for the quantitative mass relationships among reactants and products.

The decomposition of water into hydrogen and oxygen illustrates this law. Thus, 100.0 g of water decompose into 11.2 g of hydrogen and 88.8 g of oxygen:

$$\text{water} \longrightarrow \text{hydrogen} + \text{oxygen}$$

100.0 g	11.2 g	88.8 g

$$100.0 \text{ g} \longrightarrow 100.0 \text{ g}$$

reactant   products

In a chemical reaction

mass of reactants = mass of products

Yuri Gripas/Reuters/Landov LLC

Combustion of gasoline is a chemical change.

8.2 WRITING AND BALANCING CHEMICAL EQUATIONS

Write and balance chemical equations.

● **LEARNING OBJECTIVE**

KEY TERM
balanced equation

To represent the quantitative relationships of a reaction, the chemical equation must be balanced. A **balanced equation** contains the same number of each kind of atom on each side of the equation. The balanced equation therefore obeys the law of conservation of mass.

Every chemistry student must learn to *balance* equations. Many equations are balanced by trial and error, but care and attention to detail are still required. The way to balance an equation is to adjust the number of atoms of each element so that they are the same on each side of the equation, but a correct formula is never changed in order to balance an equation. The general procedure for balancing equations is as follows:

Correct formulas are not changed to balance an equation.

PROBLEM-SOLVING STRATEGY: For Writing and Balancing a Chemical Equation

1. **Identify the reaction.** Write a description or word equation for the reaction. For example, let's consider mercury(II) oxide decomposing into mercury and oxygen.

$$\text{mercury(II) oxide} \xrightarrow{\Delta} \text{mercury} + \text{oxygen}$$

2. **Write the unbalanced (skeleton) equation.** Make sure that the formula for each substance is correct and that reactants are written to the left and products to the right of the arrow. For our example,

$$\text{HgO} \xrightarrow{\Delta} \text{Hg} + \text{O}_2$$

The correct formulas must be known or determined from the periodic table, lists of ions, or experimental data.

3. **Balance the equation.** Use the following process as necessary:

(a) Count and compare the number of atoms of each element on each side of the equation and determine those that must be balanced:

Hg is balanced   (1 on each side)

O needs to be balanced   (1 on reactant side, 2 on product side)

(b) Balance each element, one at a time, by placing whole numbers (coefficients) in front of the formulas containing the unbalanced element. It is usually best to balance metals first, then nonmetals, then hydrogen and oxygen. Select the smallest coefficients that will give the same number of atoms of the element on each side. A coefficient placed in front of a formula multiplies every atom in the formula by that number (e.g., 2 H_2SO_4

Study this procedure carefully and refer to it when you work examples.

Leave elements that are in two or more formulas (on the same side of the equation) unbalanced until just before balancing hydrogen and oxygen.

means two units of sulfuric acid and also means four H atoms, two S atoms, and eight O atoms). Place a 2 in front of HgO to balance O:

$$2\,HgO \xrightarrow{\Delta} Hg + O_2$$

(c) Check all other elements after each individual element is balanced to see whether, in balancing one element, other elements have become unbalanced. Make adjustments as needed. Now Hg is not balanced. To adjust this, we write a 2 in front of Hg:

$$2\,HgO \xrightarrow{\Delta} 2\,Hg + O_2 \qquad \text{(balanced)}$$

(d) Do a final check, making sure that each element and/or polyatomic ion is balanced and that the smallest possible set of whole-number coefficients has been used:

$$2\,HgO \xrightarrow{\Delta} 2\,Hg + O_2 \qquad \text{(correct form)}$$
$$4\,HgO \xrightarrow{\Delta} 4\,Hg + 2\,O_2 \qquad \text{(incorrect form)}$$

Not all chemical equations can be balanced by the simple method of inspection just described. The following examples show *stepwise* sequences leading to balanced equations. Study each one carefully.

EXAMPLE 8.2

Write the balanced equation for the reaction that takes place when magnesium metal is burned in air to produce magnesium oxide.

SOLUTION

Use the Problem-Solving Strategy for Writing and Balancing a Chemical Equation.

1. *Word equation:*

$$\text{magnesium} + \text{oxygen} \longrightarrow \text{magnesium oxide}$$
$$\text{reactants (R)} \qquad\qquad \text{product (P)}$$

2. *Skeleton equation:*

$$Mg + O_2 \longrightarrow MgO \qquad \text{(unbalanced)}$$

3. *Balance:*

(a) Mg is balanced.
  Oxygen is not balanced. Two O atoms appear on the left side and one on the right side.
(b) Place the coefficient 2 in front of MgO to balance oxygen:

$$Mg + O_2 \longrightarrow 2\,MgO \qquad \text{(unbalanced)}$$

(c) Now Mg is not balanced. One Mg atom appears on the left side and two on the right side. Place a 2 in front of Mg:

$$2\,Mg + O_2 \longrightarrow 2\,MgO \qquad \text{(balanced)}$$

(d) *Check:* Each side has two Mg and two O atoms.

Elements shown in color are balanced.

R = reactant
P = product

(a)	R	1 Mg	2 O
	P	1 Mg	1 O

(b)	R	1 Mg	2 O
	P	2 Mg	2 O

(c)	R	2 Mg	2 O
	P	2 Mg	2 O

EXAMPLE 8.3

When methane, CH_4, undergoes complete combustion, it reacts with oxygen to produce carbon dioxide and water. Write the balanced equation for this reaction.

SOLUTION

Use the Problem-Solving Strategy for Writing and Balancing a Chemical Equation.

1. *Word equation:*

$$\text{methane} + \text{oxygen} \longrightarrow \text{carbon dioxide} + \text{water}$$

2. *Skeleton equation:*

$$CH_4 + O_2 \longrightarrow CO_2 + H_2O \qquad \text{(unbalanced)}$$

3. *Balance:*

(a) Carbon is balanced.
  Hydrogen and oxygen are not balanced.

(a)	R	1 C	4 H	2 O
	P	1 C	2 H	3 O

(b) Balance H atoms by placing a 2 in front of H_2O:

$$CH_4 + O_2 \longrightarrow CO_2 + 2\,H_2O \quad \text{(unbalanced)}$$

Each side of the equation has four H atoms; oxygen is still not balanced. Place a 2 in front of O_2 to balance the oxygen atoms:

$$CH_4 + 2\,O_2 \longrightarrow CO_2 + 2\,H_2O \quad \text{(balanced)}$$

(c) The other atoms remain balanced.

(d) *Check:* The equation is correctly balanced; it has one C, four O, and four H atoms on each side.

(b)	R	1 C	4 H	2 O
	P	1 C	4 H	4 O

(c)	R	1 C	4 H	4 O
	P	1 C	4 H	4 O

EXAMPLE 8.4

Oxygen and potassium chloride are formed by heating potassium chlorate. Write a balanced equation for this reaction.

SOLUTION

Use the Problem-Solving Strategy for Writing and Balancing a Chemical Equation.

1. *Word equation:*

$$\text{potassium chlorate} \xrightarrow{\Delta} \text{potassium chloride} + \text{oxygen}$$

2. *Skeleton equation:*

$$KClO_3 \xrightarrow{\Delta} KCl + O_2 \quad \text{(unbalanced)}$$

3. *Balance:*

(a) Potassium and chlorine are balanced.
    Oxygen is unbalanced (three O atoms on the left and two on the right side).

(b) How many oxygen atoms are needed? The subscripts of oxygen (3 and 2) in $KClO_3$ and O_2 have a least common multiple of 6. Therefore, coefficients for $KClO_3$ and O_2 are needed to get six O atoms on each side. Place a 2 in front of $KClO_3$ and a 3 in front of O_2 to balance oxygen:

$$2\,KClO_3 \xrightarrow{\Delta} KCl + 3\,O_2 \quad \text{(unbalanced)}$$

(c) Now K and Cl are not balanced. Place a 2 in front of KCl, which balances both K and Cl at the same time:

$$2\,KClO_3 \xrightarrow{\Delta} 2\,KCl + 3\,O_2 \quad \text{(balanced)}$$

(d) *Check:* Each side now contains two K, two Cl, and six O atoms.

(a)	R	1 K	1 Cl	3 O
	P	1 K	1 Cl	2 O

(b)	R	2 K	2 Cl	6 O
	P	1 K	1 Cl	6 O

(c)	R	2 K	2 Cl	6 O
	P	2 K	2 Cl	6 O

EXAMPLE 8.5

Silver nitrate reacts with hydrogen sulfide to produce silver sulfide and nitric acid. Write a balanced equation for this reaction.

SOLUTION

Use the Problem-Solving Strategy for Writing and Balancing a Chemical Equation.

1. *Word equation:*

$$\text{silver nitrate} + \text{hydrogen sulfide} \longrightarrow \text{silver sulfide} + \text{nitric acid}$$

2. *Skeleton equation:*

$$AgNO_3 + H_2S \longrightarrow Ag_2S + HNO_3 \quad \text{(unbalanced)}$$

3. *Balance:*

(a) Ag and H are unbalanced.

(b) Place a 2 in front of $AgNO_3$ to balance Ag:

$$2\,AgNO_3 + H_2S \longrightarrow Ag_2S + HNO_3 \quad \text{(unbalanced)}$$

(c) H and NO_3^- are still unbalanced. Balance by placing a 2 in front of HNO_3:

$$2\,AgNO_3 + H_2S \longrightarrow Ag_2S + 2\,HNO_3 \quad \text{(balanced)}$$

In this example, N and O atoms are balanced by balancing the NO_3^- ion as a unit.

(d) The other atoms remain balanced.

(e) *Check:* Each side has two Ag, two H, and one S atom. Also, each side has two NO_3^- ions.

(a)	R	1 Ag	2 H	1 S	1 NO_3
	P	2 Ag	1 H	1 S	1 NO_3

(b)	R	2 Ag	2 H	1 S	2 NO_3
	P	2 Ag	1 H	1 S	1 NO_3

(c)	R	2 Ag	2 H	1 S	2 NO_3
	P	2 Ag	2 H	1 S	2 NO_3

EXAMPLE 8.6

When aluminum hydroxide is mixed with sulfuric acid, the products are aluminum sulfate and water. Write a balanced equation for this reaction.

SOLUTION

Use the Problem-Solving Strategy for Writing and Balancing a Chemical Equation.

1. *Word equation:*

$$\text{aluminum hydroxide} + \text{sulfuric acid} \longrightarrow \text{aluminum sulfate} + \text{water}$$

2. *Skeleton equation:*

$$Al(OH)_3 + H_2SO_4 \longrightarrow Al_2(SO_4)_3 + H_2O \qquad \text{(unbalanced)}$$

3. *Balance:*
   (a) All elements are unbalanced.
   (b) Balance Al by placing a 2 in front of $Al(OH)_3$. Treat the unbalanced SO_4^{2-} ion as a unit and balance by placing a 3 in front of H_2SO_4:

$$2\,Al(OH)_3 + 3\,H_2SO_4 \longrightarrow Al_2(SO_4)_3 + H_2O \qquad \text{(unbalanced)}$$

   Balance the unbalanced H and O by placing a 6 in front of H_2O:

$$2\,Al(OH)_3 + 3\,H_2SO_4 \longrightarrow Al_2(SO_4)_3 + 6\,H_2O \quad \text{(balanced)}$$

   (c) The other atoms remain balanced.
   (d) *Check:* Each side has 2 Al, 12 H, 3 S, and 18 O atoms.

	R	1 Al	1 SO₄	3 O	5 H
(a)	P	2 Al	3 SO₄	1 O	2 H
(b)	R	2 Al	3 SO₄	6 O	12 H
	P	2 Al	3 SO₄	1 O	2 H
(c)	R	2 Al	3 SO₄	6 O	12 H
	P	2 Al	3 SO₄	6 O	12 H

EXAMPLE 8.7

When the fuel in a butane gas stove undergoes complete combustion, it reacts with oxygen to form carbon dioxide and water. Write the balanced equation for this reaction.

SOLUTION

Use the Problem-Solving Strategy for Writing and Balancing a Chemical Equation.

1. *Word equation:*

$$\text{butane} + \text{oxygen} \longrightarrow \text{carbon dioxide} + \text{water}$$

2. *Skeleton equation:*

$$C_4H_{10} + O_2 \longrightarrow CO_2 + H_2O \qquad \text{(unbalanced)}$$

3. *Balance:*
   (a) All elements are unbalanced.
   (b) Balance C by placing a 4 in front of CO_2:

$$C_4H_{10} + O_2 \longrightarrow 4\,CO_2 + H_2O \qquad \text{(unbalanced)}$$

   Balance H by placing a 5 in front of H_2O:

$$C_4H_{10} + O_2 \longrightarrow 4\,CO_2 + 5\,H_2O \qquad \text{(unbalanced)}$$

   Oxygen remains unbalanced. The oxygen atoms on the right side are fixed because 4 CO_2 and 5 H_2O are derived from the single C_4H_{10} molecule on the left. When we try to balance the O atoms, we find that there is no whole number that can be placed in front of O_2 to bring about a balance, so we double the coefficients of each substance, and then balance the oxygen:

$$2\,C_4H_{10} + 13\,O_2 \longrightarrow 8\,CO_2 + 10\,H_2O \quad \text{(balanced)}$$

   (c) The other atoms remain balanced.
   (d) *Check:* Each side now has 8 C, 20 H, and 26 O atoms.

Butane
C_4H_{10}

	R	4 C	10 H	2 O
(a)	P	1 C	2 H	3 O
(b)	R	4 C	10 H	2 O
	P	4 C	10 H	13 O
(c)	R	8 C	20 H	26 O
	P	8 C	20 H	26 O

PRACTICE 8.2

Write a balanced formula equation for:

$$\text{aluminum} + \text{oxygen} \longrightarrow \text{aluminum oxide}$$

PRACTICE 8.3

Write a balanced formula equation for:

magnesium hydroxide + phosphoric acid ⟶ magnesium phosphate + water

Information in a Chemical Equation

Depending on the particular context in which it is used, a formula can have different meanings. A formula can refer to an individual chemical entity (atom, ion, molecule, or formula unit) or to a mole of that chemical entity. For example, the formula H_2O can mean any of the following:

- 2 H atoms and 1 O atom
- 1 molecule of water
- 1 *mol of water*
- 6.022×10^{23} molecules of water
- 18.02 g of water

Formulas used in equations can represent units of individual chemical entities or moles, the latter being more commonly used. For example, in the reaction of hydrogen and oxygen to form water,

$$2\ H_2 \quad + \quad O_2 \quad \longrightarrow \quad 2\ H_2O$$

| 2 molecules hydrogen | 1 molecule oxygen | 2 molecules water |
| 2 mol hydrogen | 1 mol oxygen | 2 mol water |

We generally use moles in equations because molecules are so small.

As indicated earlier, a chemical equation is a shorthand description of a chemical reaction. Interpretation of a balanced equation gives us the following information:

1. What the reactants are and what the products are
2. The formulas of the reactants and products
3. The number of molecules or formula units of reactants and products in the reaction
4. The number of atoms of each element involved in the reaction
5. The number of moles of each substance

Consider the reaction that occurs when propane gas (C_3H_8) is burned in air; the products are carbon dioxide (CO_2) and water (H_2O). The balanced equation and its interpretation are as follows:

Propane		Oxygen		Carbon dioxide		Water
$C_3H_8(g)$	+	$5\ O_2(g)$	⟶	$3\ CO_2(g)$	+	$4\ H_2O(g)$
1 molecule		5 molecules		3 molecules		4 molecules
3 atoms C 8 atoms H		10 atoms O		3 atoms C 6 atoms O		8 atoms H 4 atoms O
1 mol		5 mol		3 mol		4 mol
44.09 g		5(32.00 g) = (160.0 g)		3(44.01 g) = (132.0 g)		4(18.02 g) = (72.08 g)

PRACTICE 8.4

Consider the reaction that occurs when hydrogen gas reacts with chlorine gas to produce gaseous hydrogen chloride:

(a) Write a word equation for this reaction.

(b) Write a balanced formula equation including the state for each substance.

(c) Label each reactant and product to show the relative amounts of each substance.

    (1) number of molecules   (3) number of moles

    (2) number of atoms   (4) mass

(d) What mass of HCl would be produced if you reacted 2 mol hydrogen gas with 2 mol chlorine gas?

The quantities involved in chemical reactions are important when working in industry or the laboratory. We will study the relationship among quantities of reactants and products in the next chapter.

8.3 TYPES OF CHEMICAL EQUATIONS

LEARNING OBJECTIVE   ● Give examples of a combination reaction, decomposition reaction, single-displacement reaction, and double-displacement reaction.

KEY TERMS

combination reaction
decomposition reaction
single-displacement reaction
double-displacement reaction

Chemical equations represent chemical changes or reactions. Reactions are classified into types to assist in writing equations and in predicting other reactions. Many chemical reactions fit one or another of the four principal reaction types that we discuss in the following paragraphs. Reactions are also classified as oxidation–reduction. Special methods are used to balance complex oxidation–reduction equations. (See Chapter 17.)

Combination Reaction

In a **combination reaction**, two reactants combine to give one product. The general form of the equation is

$$A + B \longrightarrow AB$$

in which A and B are either elements or compounds and AB is a compound. The formula of the compound in many cases can be determined from knowledge of the ionic charges of the reactants in their combined states. Some reactions that fall into this category are given here:

1. metal + oxygen $\longrightarrow$ metal oxide:

$$2\,Mg(s) + O_2(g) \xrightarrow{\Delta} 2\,MgO(s)$$
$$4\,Al(s) + 3\,O_2(g) \xrightarrow{\Delta} 2\,Al_2O_3(s)$$

2. nonmetal + oxygen $\longrightarrow$ nonmetal oxide:

$$S(s) + O_2(g) \xrightarrow{\Delta} SO_2(g)$$
$$N_2(g) + O_2(g) \xrightarrow{\Delta} 2\,NO(g)$$

3. metal + nonmetal $\longrightarrow$ salt:

$$2\,Na(s) + Cl_2(g) \longrightarrow 2\,NaCl(s)$$
$$2\,Al(s) + 3\,Br_2(l) \longrightarrow 2\,AlBr_3(s)$$

4. metal oxide + water $\longrightarrow$ metal hydroxide:

$$Na_2O(s) + H_2O(l) \longrightarrow 2\,NaOH(aq)$$
$$CaO(s) + H_2O(l) \longrightarrow Ca(OH)_2(aq)$$

5. nonmetal oxide + water $\longrightarrow$ oxy-acid:

$$SO_3(g) + H_2O(l) \longrightarrow H_2SO_4(aq)$$
$$N_2O_5(s) + H_2O(l) \longrightarrow 2\,HNO_3(aq)$$

Charles D. Winters/Photo Researchers, Inc.

A strip of Mg burning in air produces MgO (left of the flame).

>CHEMISTRY *IN ACTION*

CO Poisoning—A Silent Killer

Carbon monoxide (CO) is one possible product when carbon-containing fuels such as coal, natural gas, propane, heating oil, and gasoline are burned. For example, when methane, the main component of natural gas, burns, the reaction is

$$CH_4(g) + 2\ O_2(g) \longrightarrow 2\ H_2O(g) + CO_2(g)$$

However, if not enough oxygen is available, carbon monoxide will be produced instead of carbon dioxide:

$$2\ CH_4(g) + 3\ O_2(g) \longrightarrow 4\ H_2O(g) + 2\ CO(g)$$

Carbon monoxide is colorless and has no flavor or smell. It often can poison several people at once, since it can build up undetected in enclosed spaces. The symptoms of carbon monoxide poisoning are so easily missed that people often don't realize that they have been poisoned. Common symptoms are headache, ringing in ears, nausea, dizziness, weakness, confusion, and drowsiness. A low concentration of CO in the air may go completely unnoticed while the toxicity level increases in the blood.

Carbon monoxide in the blood is poisonous because of its ability to bond to a hemoglobin molecule. Both CO and O_2 bond to the same place on the hemoglobin molecule. The CO bonds more tightly than O_2. We use hemoglobin to transport oxygen to the various tissues from the lungs. Unfortunately, CO also bonds to hemoglobin, forming a molecule called carboxyhemoglobin. In fact, hemoglobin prefers CO to O_2. Once a CO is bound to a hemoglobin molecule, it cannot carry an oxygen molecule. So, until the CO is released, that molecule of hemoglobin is lost as an O_2 carrier. If you breathe normal air (about 20% oxygen) containing 0.1% CO, in just one hour the CO bonds to 50% of the hemoglobin molecules. To keep CO from being a silent killer, there are three possible actions:

1. Immediate treatment of victims to restore the hemoglobin
2. Detection of CO levels before poisoning occurs
3. Conversion of CO to CO_2 to eliminate the threat

If a person already has CO poisoning, the treatment must focus on getting CO released from the hemoglobin. This can be done by giving the victim oxygen or by placing the victim in a hyperbaric chamber (at about 3 atm pressure). These treatments reduce the time required for carboxyhemoglobin to release CO from between 4 to 6 hours to 30 to 90 min. This treatment also supplies more oxygen to the system to help keep the victim's brain functioning.

A CO detector can sound an alarm before the CO level becomes toxic in a home. Current CO detectors sound an alarm when levels increase rapidly or when lower concentrations are present over a long time. Inside a CO detector is a beam of infrared light that shines on a chromophore (a substance that turns darker with increasing CO levels). If the infrared light passing through the chromophore is too low, the alarm sounds. Typically, these alarms ring when CO levels reach 70 ppm, or greater than 30 ppm for 30 days.

The final option is to convert CO to CO_2 before toxicity occurs. David Schreyer from NASA's Langley Research Center has devised a catalyst (tin hydroxide with small amounts of Pd) that speeds up the conversion of CO to CO_2 at room temperature. He and his colleagues have adapted their catalyst to home ventilation systems to eliminate even low levels of CO before it has a chance to build up. Using all of these approaches can help to eliminate 500–10,000 cases of CO poisoning each year.

People in a hyperbaric chamber.

Mark Harmel/Photo Researchers

Decomposition Reaction

In a **decomposition reaction**, a single substance is decomposed, or broken down, to give two or more different substances. This reaction may be considered the reverse of combination. The starting material must be a compound, and the products may be elements or compounds. The general form of the equation is

$$AB \longrightarrow A + B$$

Predicting the products of a decomposition reaction can be difficult and requires an understanding of each individual reaction. Heating oxygen-containing compounds often results in decomposition. The following reactions fall into this category.

Hydrogen peroxide decomposes to steam ($H_2O(g)$) and oxygen.

When pieces of zinc metal are placed in hydrochloric acid, hydrogen bubbles form immediately.

1. Some metal oxides decompose to yield the free metal plus oxygen; others give another oxide, and some are very stable, resisting decomposition by heating:

$$2\,HgO(s) \xrightarrow{\Delta} 2\,Hg(l) + O_2(g)$$
$$2\,PbO_2(s) \xrightarrow{\Delta} 2\,PbO(s) + O_2(g)$$

2. Carbonates and hydrogen carbonates decompose to yield CO_2 when heated:

$$CaCO_3(s) \xrightarrow{\Delta} CaO(s) + CO_2(g)$$
$$2\,NaHCO_3(s) \xrightarrow{\Delta} Na_2CO_3(s) + H_2O(g) + CO_2(g)$$

3. Miscellaneous reactions in this category:

$$2\,KClO_3(s) \xrightarrow{\Delta} 2\,KCl(s) + 3\,O_2(g)$$
$$2\,NaNO_3(s) \xrightarrow{\Delta} 2\,NaNO_2(s) + O_2(g)$$
$$2\,H_2O_2(l) \xrightarrow{\Delta} 2\,H_2O(l) + O_2(g)$$

Single-Displacement Reaction

In a **single-displacement reaction**, one element reacts with a compound to replace one of the elements of that compound, yielding a different element and a different compound. The general forms of the equation follow.

If A is a *metal*, A will replace B to form AC, provided that A is a more reactive metal than B.

$$A + BC \longrightarrow B + AC$$

If A is a *halogen*, it will replace C to form BA, provided that A is a more reactive halogen than C.

$$A + BC \longrightarrow C + BA$$

A brief activity series of selected metals (and hydrogen) and halogens is shown in Table 8.2. This series is listed in descending order of chemical activity, with the most active metals and halogens at the top. Many chemical reactions can be predicted from an activity series because the atoms of any element in the series will replace the atoms of those elements below it. For example, zinc metal will replace hydrogen from a hydrochloric acid solution. But copper metal, which is below hydrogen on the list and thus less reactive than hydrogen, will not replace hydrogen from a hydrochloric acid solution. Here are some reactions that fall into this category:

1. metal + acid ⟶ hydrogen + salt

$$Zn(s) + 2\,HCl(aq) \longrightarrow H_2(g) + ZnCl_2(aq)$$
$$2\,Al(s) + 3\,H_2SO_4(aq) \longrightarrow 3\,H_2(g) + Al_2(SO_4)_3(aq)$$

2. metal + water ⟶ hydrogen + metal hydroxide or metal oxide

$$2\,Na(s) + 2\,H_2O \longrightarrow H_2(g) + 2\,NaOH(aq)$$
$$Ca(s) + 2\,H_2O \longrightarrow H_2(g) + Ca(OH)_2(aq)$$
$$3\,Fe(s) + 4\,H_2O(g) \longrightarrow 4\,H_2(g) + Fe_3O_4(s)$$
$$\text{steam}$$

3. metal + salt ⟶ metal + salt

$$Fe(s) + CuSO_4(aq) \longrightarrow Cu(s) + FeSO_4(aq)$$
$$Cu(s) + 2\,AgNO_3(aq) \longrightarrow 2\,Ag(s) + Cu(NO_3)_2(aq)$$

4. halogen + halide salt ⟶ halogen + halide salt

$$Cl_2(g) + 2\,NaBr(aq) \longrightarrow Br_2(l) + 2\,NaCl(aq)$$
$$Cl_2(g) + 2\,KI(aq) \longrightarrow I_2(s) + 2\,KCl(aq)$$

A common chemical reaction is the displacement of hydrogen from water or acids (shown in 1 and 2 above). This reaction is a good illustration of the relative reactivity of metals and the use of the activity series. For example,

- K, Ca, and Na displace hydrogen from cold water, steam (H_2O), and acids.
- Mg, Al, Zn, and Fe displace hydrogen from steam and acids.
- Ni, Sn, and Pb displace hydrogen only from acids.
- Cu, Ag, Hg, and Au do not displace hydrogen.

TABLE 8.2	Activity Series
Metals	**Halogens**
K	F_2
Ca	Cl_2
Na	Br_2
Mg	I_2
Al	
Zn	
Fe	
Ni	
Sn	
Pb	
H	
Cu	
Ag	
Hg	
Au	

increasing activity

EXAMPLE 8.8

Will a reaction occur between (a) nickel metal and hydrochloric acid and (b) tin metal and a solution of aluminum chloride? Write balanced equations for the reactions.

SOLUTION

(a) Nickel is more reactive than hydrogen, so it will displace hydrogen from hydrochloric acid. The products are hydrogen gas and a salt of Ni^{2+} and Cl^- ions:

$$Ni(s) + 2\ HCl(aq) \longrightarrow H_2(g) + NiCl_2(aq)$$

(b) According to the activity series, tin is less reactive than aluminum, so no reaction will occur:

$$Sn(s) + AlCl_3(aq) \longrightarrow \text{no reaction}$$

PRACTICE 8.5

Write balanced equations for these reactions:

(a) iron metal and a solution of magnesium chloride
(b) zinc metal and a solution of lead(II) nitrate

Double-Displacement Reaction

In a **double-displacement reaction**, two compounds exchange partners with each other to produce two different compounds. The general form of the equation is

$$AB + CD \longrightarrow AD + CB$$

This reaction can be thought of as an exchange of positive and negative groups, in which A combines with D and C combines with B. In writing formulas for the products, we must account for the charges of the combining groups.

It's also possible to write an equation in the form of a double-displacement reaction when a reaction has not occurred. For example, when solutions of sodium chloride and potassium nitrate are mixed, the following equation can be written:

$$NaCl(aq) + KNO_3(aq) \longrightarrow NaNO_3(aq) + KCl(aq)$$

When the procedure is carried out, no physical changes are observed, indicating that no chemical reaction has taken place.

A double-displacement reaction is accompanied by evidence of reaction such as:

1. The evolution of heat
2. The formation of an insoluble precipitate
3. The production of gas bubbles

Let's look at some of these reactions more closely:

Neutralization of an acid and a base The production of a molecule of water from an H^+ and an OH^- ion is accompanied by a *release of heat*, which can be detected by touching the reaction container or by using a thermometer. For neutralization reactions, $H^+ + OH^- \longrightarrow H_2O$:

$$\text{acid} + \text{base} \longrightarrow \text{salt} + \text{water} + \text{heat}$$
$$HCl(aq) + NaOH(aq) \longrightarrow NaCl(aq) + H_2O(l) + \text{heat}$$
$$H_2SO_4(aq) + Ba(OH)_2(aq) \longrightarrow BaSO_4(s) + 2\ H_2O(l) + \text{heat}$$

Metal oxide + acid *Heat is released* by the production of a molecule of water.

$$\text{metal oxide} + \text{acid} \longrightarrow \text{salt} + \text{water} + \text{heat}$$
$$CuO(s) + 2\ HNO_3(aq) \longrightarrow Cu(NO_3)_2(aq) + H_2O(l) + \text{heat}$$
$$CaO(s) + 2\ HCl(aq) \longrightarrow CaCl_2(aq) + H_2O(l) + \text{heat}$$

A double-displacement reaction results from pouring a clear, colorless solution of $Pb(NO_3)_2$ into a clear, colorless solution of KI, forming a yellow precipitate of PbI_2.

$Pb(NO_3)_2 + 2KI \longrightarrow$
$\quad PbI_2 + 2KNO_3$.

Formation of an insoluble precipitate The solubilities of the products can be determined by consulting the solubility table in Appendix V to see whether one or both of the products are insoluble in water. An insoluble product (precipitate) is indicated by placing (s) after its formula in the equation.

$$BaCl_2(aq) + 2\,AgNO_3(aq) \longrightarrow 2\,AgCl(s) + Ba(NO_3)_2(aq)$$

$$Pb(NO_3)_2(aq) + 2\,KI(aq) \longrightarrow PbI_2(s) + 2\,KNO_3(aq)$$

Formation of a gas A gas such as HCl or H_2S may be produced directly, as in these two examples:

$$H_2SO_4(l) + NaCl(s) \longrightarrow NaHSO_4(s) + HCl(g)$$

$$2\,HCl(aq) + ZnS(s) \longrightarrow ZnCl_2(aq) + H_2S(g)$$

A gas can also be produced indirectly. Some unstable compounds formed in a double-displacement reaction, such as H_2CO_3, H_2SO_3, and NH_4OH, will decompose to form water and a gas:

$$2\,HCl(aq) + Na_2CO_3(aq) \longrightarrow 2\,NaCl(aq) + H_2CO_3(aq) \longrightarrow 2\,NaCl(aq) + H_2O(l) + CO_2(g)$$

$$2\,HNO_3(aq) + K_2SO_3(aq) \longrightarrow 2\,KNO_3(aq) + H_2SO_3(aq) \longrightarrow 2\,KNO_3(aq) + H_2O(l) + SO_2(g)$$

$$NH_4Cl(aq) + NaOH(aq) \longrightarrow NaCl(aq) + NH_4OH(aq) \longrightarrow NaCl(aq) + H_2O(l) + NH_3(g)$$

EXAMPLE 8.9

Write the equation for the reaction between aqueous solutions of hydrobromic acid and potassium hydroxide.

SOLUTION

First we write the formulas for the reactants. They are HBr and KOH. Then we classify the type of reaction that would occur between them. Because the reactants are compounds, one an acid and the other a base, the reaction will be of the neutralization type:

$$acid + base \longrightarrow salt + water$$

Now rewrite the equation using the formulas for the known substances:

$$HBr(aq) + KOH(aq) \longrightarrow salt + H_2O$$

In this reaction, which is a double-displacement type, the H^+ from the acid combines with the OH^- from the base to form water. The ionic compound must be composed of the other two ions, K^+ and Br^-. We determine the formula of the ionic compound to be KBr from the fact that K is a +1 cation and Br is a −1 anion. The final balanced equation is

$$HBr(aq) + KOH(aq) \longrightarrow KBr(aq) + H_2O(l)$$

EXAMPLE 8.10

Complete and balance the equation for the reaction between aqueous solutions of barium chloride and sodium sulfate.

SOLUTION

First determine the formulas for the reactants. They are $BaCl_2$ and Na_2SO_4. Then classify these substances as acids, bases, or ionic compounds. Both substances are ionic compounds. Since both substances are compounds, the reaction will be of the double-displacement type. Start writing the equation with the reactants:

$$BaCl_2(aq) + Na_2SO_4(aq) \longrightarrow$$

If the reaction is double-displacement, Ba^{2+} will be written combined with SO_4^{2-}, and Na^+ with Cl^- as the products. The balanced equation is

$$BaCl_2(aq) + Na_2SO_4(aq) \longrightarrow BaSO_4(s) + 2\,NaCl(aq)$$

When barium chloride is poured into a solution of sodium sulfate, a white precipitate of barium sulfate forms.

The final step is to determine the nature of the products, which controls whether or not the reaction will take place. If both products are soluble, we have a mixture of all the ions in solution. But if an insoluble precipitate is formed, the reaction will definitely occur. We know from experience that NaCl is fairly soluble in water, but what about $BaSO_4$? Consulting the solubility table in Appendix V, we see that $BaSO_4$ is insoluble in water, so it will be a precipitate in the reaction. Thus, the reaction will occur, forming a precipitate. The equation is

$$BaCl_2(aq) + Na_2SO_4(aq) \longrightarrow BaSO_4(s) + 2\ NaCl(aq)$$

PRACTICE 8.6

Complete and balance the equations for these reactions in water:
(a) potassium phosphate + barium chloride
(b) hydrochloric acid + nickel carbonate
(c) ammonium chloride + sodium nitrate

Some of the reactions you attempt may fail because the substances are not reactive or because the proper conditions for reaction are not present. For example, mercury(II) oxide does not decompose until it is heated; magnesium does not burn in air or oxygen until the temperature reaches a certain point. When silver is placed in a solution of copper(II) sulfate, no reaction occurs. When copper wire is placed in a solution of silver nitrate, a single-displacement reaction takes place because copper is a more reactive metal than silver. (See Figure 8.1.)

$$Cu(s) + 2\ AgNO_3(aq) \longrightarrow 2Ag(s) + Cu(NO_3)_2(aq)$$

Ag^+

NO_3^-

Cu^{2+}

A solution of silver nitrate contains Ag^+ ions and NO_3^- ions.

A copper wire is placed in a solution of silver nitrate. After 24 hours, crystals of silver are seen hanging on the copper wire and the solution has turned blue, indicating copper ions are present there.

The silver metal clings to the copper wire, and the blue solution contains Cu^{2+} and NO_3^- ions.

Figure 8.1
Reaction of a copper wire and silver nitrate solution.

The successful prediction of the products of a reaction is not always easy. The ability to predict products correctly comes with knowledge and experience. Although you may not be able to predict many reactions at this point, as you continue to experiment you will find that reactions can be categorized and that prediction of the products becomes easier, if not always certain.

8.4 HEAT IN CHEMICAL REACTIONS

LEARNING OBJECTIVE • Explain the following terms and how they relate to a chemical reaction: *exothermic reaction, endothermic reaction, heat of reaction,* and *activation energy.*

KEY TERMS

exothermic reactions
endothermic reactions
heat of reaction
hydrocarbons
activation energy

Energy changes always accompany chemical reactions. One reason reactions occur is that the products attain a lower, more stable energy state than the reactants. When the reaction leads to a more stable state, energy is released to the surroundings as heat and/or work. When a solution of a base is neutralized by the addition of an acid, the liberation of heat energy is signaled by an immediate rise in the temperature of the solution. When an automobile engine burns gasoline, heat is certainly liberated; at the same time, part of the liberated energy does the work of moving the automobile.

Reactions are either exothermic or endothermic. **Exothermic reactions** liberate heat; **endothermic reactions** absorb heat. In an exothermic reaction, heat is a product and may be written on the right side of the equation for the reaction. In an endothermic reaction, heat can be regarded as a reactant and is written on the left side of the equation. Here are two examples:

$$H_2(g) + Cl_2(g) \longrightarrow 2\,HCl(g) + 185\ kJ \quad \text{(exothermic)}$$
$$N_2(g) + O_2(g) + 181\ kJ \longrightarrow 2\,NO(g) \quad \text{(endothermic)}$$

The quantity of heat produced by a reaction is known as the **heat of reaction**. The units used can be kilojoules or kilocalories. Consider the reaction represented by this equation:

$$C(s) + O_2(g) \longrightarrow CO_2(g) + 393\ kJ$$

When the heat released is expressed as part of the equation, the substances are expressed in units of moles. Thus, when 1 mol (12.01 g) of C combines with 1 mol (32.00 g) of O_2, 1 mol (44.01 g) of CO_2 is formed and 393 kJ of heat are released. In this reaction, as in many others, the heat energy is more useful than the chemical products.

Aside from relatively small amounts of energy from nuclear processes, the sun is the major provider of energy for life on Earth. The sun maintains the temperature necessary for life and also supplies light energy for the endothermic photosynthetic reactions of green plants. In photosynthesis, carbon dioxide and water are converted to free oxygen and glucose:

$$6\,CO_2 + 6\,H_2O + 2519\ kJ \longrightarrow C_6H_{12}O_6 + 6\,O_2$$
$$\text{glucose}$$

Nearly all of the chemical energy used by living organisms is obtained from glucose or compounds derived from glucose.

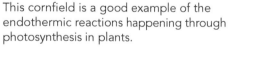

Glucose
$C_6H_{12}O_6$

= O
= C
= H

This cornfield is a good example of the endothermic reactions happening through photosynthesis in plants.

Paul Damien/National Geographic Society

The major source of energy for modern technology is fossil fuel—coal, petroleum, and natural gas. The energy is obtained from the combustion (burning) of these fuels, which are converted to carbon dioxide and water. Fossil fuels are mixtures of **hydrocarbons**, compounds containing only hydrogen and carbon.

Natural gas is primarily methane, CH_4. Petroleum is a mixture of hydrocarbons (compounds of carbon and hydrogen). Liquefied petroleum gas (LPG) is a mixture of propane (C_3H_8) and butane (C_4H_{10}).

Here are some examples:

$$CH_4(g) + 2\ O_2(g) \longrightarrow CO_2(g) + 2\ H_2O(g) + 890\ kJ$$

$$C_3H_8(g) + 5\ O_2(g) \longrightarrow 3\ CO_2(g) + 4\ H_2O(g) + 2200\ kJ$$

The combustion of these fuels releases a tremendous amount of energy, but reactions won't occur to a significant extent at ordinary temperatures. A spark or a flame must be present before methane will ignite. The amount of energy that must be supplied to start a chemical reaction is called the **activation energy**. In an exothermic reaction, once this activation energy is provided, enough energy is then generated to keep the reaction going.

Be careful not to confuse an exothermic reaction that requires heat (activation energy) to get it *started* with an endothermic process that requires energy to keep it going. The combustion of magnesium, for example, is highly exothermic, yet magnesium must be heated to a fairly high temperature in air before combustion begins. Once started, however, the combustion reaction goes very vigorously until either the magnesium or the available supply of oxygen is exhausted. The electrolytic decomposition of water to hydrogen and oxygen is highly endothermic. If the electric current is shut off when this process is going on, the reaction stops instantly. The relative energy levels of reactants and products in exothermic and endothermic processes are presented graphically in Figures 8.2 and 8.3.

Examples of endothermic and exothermic processes can be easily demonstrated. In Figure 8.2, the products are at a higher potential energy than the reactants. Energy has therefore been absorbed, and the reaction is endothermic. An endothermic reaction takes place when you apply a cold pack to an injury. When a cold pack is activated, ammonium chloride (NH_4Cl) dissolves in water. For example, temperature changes from 24.5°C to 18.1°C result when 10 g of NH_4Cl are added to 100 mL of water. Energy, in the form of heat, is taken from the immediate surroundings (water), causing the salt solution to become cooler.

Combustion of Mg inside a block of dry ice (CO_2) makes a glowing lantern.

Figure 8.2

An endothermic process occurs when a cold pack containing an ampule of solid NH_4Cl is broken, releasing the crystals into water in the pack. The dissolving of NH_4Cl in water is endothermic, producing a salt solution that is cooler than the surroundings. This process is represented graphically to show the energy changes between the reactants and the products.

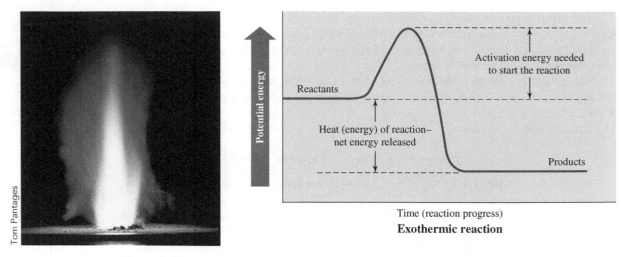

Tom Pantages

Figure 8.3

Exothermic reaction between $KClO_3$ and sugar. A sample of $KClO_3$ and sugar is well mixed and placed on a fireproof pad. Several drops of concentrated H_2SO_4 are used to ignite the mixture.

EXAMPLE 8.11

Label the graph in Figure 8.2 showing the specific reactants and products as well as the heat of reaction for the reaction.

SOLUTION

For Figure 8.2 the chemical equation is $NH_4Cl(s) + H_2O(l) \longrightarrow NH_4^+(aq) + Cl^-(aq) + H_2O(l)$. The reactants are $NH_4Cl(s) + H_2O(l)$ and the products are $NH_4^+(aq) + Cl^-(aq) + H_2O(l)$. The graph is labeled and shown here:

PRACTICE 8.7

For each of the following reactions, draw a reaction graph (like those in Figure 8.2 or 8.3) and label the parts of the graph with the information from the chemical equation.

(a) $2\,Na + Cl_2 \longrightarrow 2\,NaCl + 822\ kJ$

(b) $2\,BrF_3 + 300.8\ kJ/mol \longrightarrow Br_2 + 3\,F_2$

In Figure 8.3, the products are at a lower potential energy than the reactants. Energy (heat) is given off, producing an exothermic reaction. Here, potassium chlorate ($KClO_3$) and sugar are mixed and placed into a pile. A drop of concentrated sulfuric acid is added, creating a spectacular exothermic reaction.

8.5 GLOBAL WARMING: THE GREENHOUSE EFFECT

Discuss the possible causes and results of the greenhouse effect.   ● LEARNING OBJECTIVE

Fossil fuels, derived from coal and petroleum, provide the energy we use to power our industries, heat and light our homes and workplaces, and run our cars. As these fuels are burned, they produce carbon dioxide and water, releasing over 50 billion tons of carbon dioxide into our atmosphere each year.

The concentration of CO_2 has been monitored by scientists since 1958. Each week a scientist walks outdoors at a particular location and, carefully holding his breath, opens a basketball-sized glass sphere and collects 5 liters of the atmosphere. At these same remote sites all over the globe (and at dozens of others), instruments sniff the air adding more measurements of the atmosphere to the data. These data are summarized in Figure 8.4. Several trends have been discovered in these data.

1. In the Northern Hemisphere the concentration of CO_2 rises and falls 7 ppm over a year, peaking in May and dropping as plants use the CO_2 to produce growth till October, when a second peak occurs as a result of the fallen leaves decaying.

2. The 7-ppm annual variation is superimposed on an average increase in the concentration of CO_2. Our current average is more then 380 ppm, or an increase of more than 65 ppm over the last 50 years. It continues to rise about 2 ppm annually.

Carbon dioxide is a minor component in our atmosphere and is not usually considered to be a pollutant. The concern expressed by scientists arises from the dramatic increase occurring in the Earth's atmosphere. Without the influence of humans in the environment, the exchange of carbon dioxide between plants and animals would be relatively balanced. Our continued use of fossil fuels led to an increase of 7.4% in carbon dioxide between 1900 and 1970 and an additional 3.5% increase during the 1980s. Continued increases were observed in the 1990s.

Besides our growing consumption of fossil fuels, other factors contribute to increased carbon dioxide levels in the atmosphere: Rain forests are being destroyed by cutting and burning to make room for increased population and agricultural needs. Carbon dioxide is added to the atmosphere during the burning, and the loss of trees diminishes the uptake of carbon dioxide by plants.

About half of all the carbon dioxide released into our atmosphere each year remains there, thus increasing its concentration. The other half is absorbed by plants during photosynthesis or is dissolved in the ocean to form hydrogen carbonates and carbonates.

Figure 8.4

Concentration of CO_2 in the atmosphere.

Source: Data from the National Oceanic and Atmospheric Administration, http://www.esrl.noaa.gov/gmd/ccgg/trends/#mol-full, February 28, 2012.

>CHEMISTRY *IN ACTION*

Decreasing Carbon Footprints

In order to slow down global warming, we need to stop the increase of carbon dioxide (CO_2) in the air. We can, of course, continue to try to limit our dependence on fossil fuels. But scientists are also working to capture carbon dioxide emissions. Capturing CO_2 presents two challenges: how to remove the CO_2 from the air and what to do with it once it has been collected.

One way of capturing and storing carbon dioxide is to let nature work. Plants capture 505 million tons of carbon dioxide in North America through photosynthesis by storing it as carbon in woody plants and trees or as organic material in the soil and wetlands or sediments in rivers and lakes. The difficulty with this method is that as the decay process continues in an oxygen-rich environment, the carbon is returned to the atmosphere as CO_2. Ning Zing, from the University of Maryland, suggests that we could prevent the release of this CO_2 from forests by burying wood in an oxygen-poor environment. The carbon would then remain in the ground and not in the atmosphere. He notes that it is possible to accomplish this process at a cost of $14 per ton of wood, but that would mean collecting wood and burying it in trenches, which is not an environment-friendly method of capture and storage. Other scientists have suggested seeding the oceans to increase the algae and phytoplankton. This would also pull CO_2 from the atmosphere, but many scientists think that this method would not have much effect on climate since the oceans could only capture a small fraction of the CO_2 emitted by humans.

Coal and petroleum each account for about 40% of global CO_2 emissions. Coal is the resource that is the greatest threat to our climate since it produces more CO_2 per unit of energy than any other fossil fuel. Each year coal-fired power plants produce 8 billion tons of CO_2 (containing 2.2 billion tons of C). Future coal plants (planned in the next 25 years) will generate 660 billion tons of CO_2. This is 25% more than all the CO_2 that humans have produced by burning coal since 1751. How can we reduce these numbers? The current goal is to capture 90% of the CO_2 emissions from a power plant but only increase the cost of electricity by 20%. Scientists are developing materials that act as CO_2 sponges. These materials, called zeolites, are very porous and have large surface areas where CO_2 molecules can attach themselves.

The question here is that once the CO_2 is captured, how can it be stored? Many scientists propose to lock it underground or in deep ocean. Since CO_2 is a liquid at high pressure (as in ocean depths below 500 meters) and does not mix very well with water, it could be stored as large pool on the ocean floor. This storage method raises a number of environmental concerns. In some places there are saline aquifers underground. The water from these aquifers is not drinkable, and so some of them might be a suitable storage place for CO_2. Another possibility is using volcanic rock as a storage site. Tests indicate that liquid CO_2 will react with basalt to produce minerals such as calcium carbonate. These deposits contain many holes and cracks where the CO_2 might be injected. It is thought that in the United States these saline aquifers and geologic formations could store 150 years' worth of power plant emissions.

We are now looking seriously at ways to slow down the rise in atmospheric CO_2 and to decrease our carbon footprints without losing our fossil fuels as one of our energy sources.

Steven Raniszewski /Design Pics/Newscom

Zeolite (a basaltic volcanic rock) could be used as a storage place for carbon dioxide from power plants.

Methane is another important greenhouse gas. Its concentration in the atmosphere has also increased significantly since the 1850s, as shown in **Figure 8.5**. Methane is produced by cows, termites, agriculture, and anaerobic bacteria. Coal mining and oil wells also release methane into the atmosphere. The greenhouse effect of methane is 20 times more than that of CO_2, but there is less methane in the atmosphere.

Carbon dioxide and other greenhouse gases, such as methane and water, act to warm our atmosphere by trapping heat near the surface of the Earth. Solar radiation strikes the Earth and warms the surface. The warmed surface then reradiates this energy as heat. The greenhouse gases absorb some of this heat energy from the surface, which then warms our atmosphere. (See **Figure 8.6**.) A similar principle is illustrated in a greenhouse, where sunlight comes through the glass yet heat cannot escape. The air in the greenhouse warms, producing a climate considerably different than that in nature.

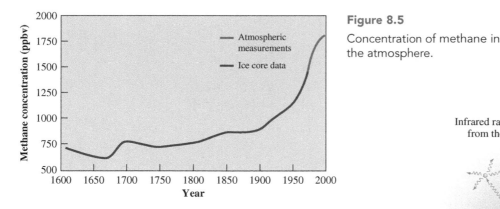

Figure 8.5

Concentration of methane in the atmosphere.

The long-term effects of global warming are still a matter of debate. One consideration is whether the polar ice caps will melt; this would cause a rise in sea level and lead to major flooding on the coasts of our continents. Further effects could include shifts in rainfall patterns, producing droughts and extreme seasonal change in such major agricultural regions as California. To reverse these trends will require major efforts in the following areas:

- The development of new energy sources to cut our dependence on fossil fuels
- An end to deforestation worldwide
- Intense efforts to improve conservation

On an individual basis each of us play a significant role. Recycling, switching to more fuel-efficient cars, and using energy-efficient appliances, heaters, and air conditioners all would result in decreased energy consumption.

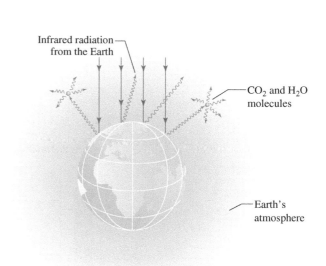

Figure 8.6

Visible light from the sun (red arrows) penetrates the atmosphere and strikes the Earth. Part of this light is changed to infrared radiation. Molecules of CO_2 and H_2O in the atmosphere absorb infrared radiation, acting like the glass of a greenhouse by trapping the energy.

CHAPTER **8 REVIEW**

8.1 THE CHEMICAL EQUATION

- A chemical equation is shorthand for expressing a chemical change or reaction.
- In a chemical reaction atoms are neither created nor destroyed.
- All atoms in the reactants must be present in the products.

KEY TERMS

reactants
products
chemical equation
law of conservation of mass

8.2 WRITING AND BALANCING CHEMICAL EQUATIONS

- To balance a chemical equation:
  - Identify the reaction.
  - Write the unbalanced (skeleton) equation.
  - Balance the equation:
    - Count the number of atoms of each element on each side and determine which need to be balanced.
    - Balance each element (one at a time) by placing whole numbers (coefficients) in front of the formulas containing the unbalanced element:
      - Begin with metals, then nonmetals, and then H and O.
    - Check the other elements to see if they have become unbalanced in the process of balancing the chosen element. If so, rebalance as needed.
    - Do a final check to make sure all elements are balanced.
- The following information can be found in a chemical equation:
  - Identity of reactants and products
  - Formulas for reactants and products
  - Number of formula units for reactants and products
  - Number of atoms of each element in the reaction
  - Number of moles of each substance

KEY TERM

balanced equation

8.3 TYPES OF CHEMICAL EQUATIONS

- Combination reactions $A + B \rightarrow AB$
- Decomposition reactions $AB \rightarrow A + B$
- Single-displacement reactions:
  - In which A is a metal $A + BC \rightarrow B + AC$
  - In which A is a halogen $A + BC \rightarrow C + BA$
- Double-displacement reactions $AB + CD \rightarrow AD + CB$
- Evidence for a chemical reaction:
  - Evolution of heat
  - Formation of an insoluble precipitate
  - Production of a gas

8.4 HEAT IN CHEMICAL REACTIONS

- Exothermic reactions release heat.

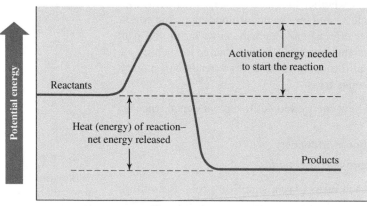

- Endothermic reactions absorb heat.

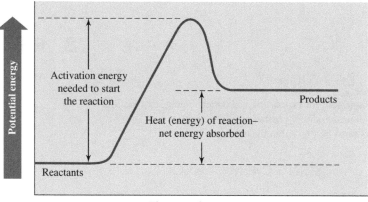

- The amount of heat released or absorbed in a chemical reaction is called the heat of reaction:
  - It can be written as a reactant or product in the chemical equation.
  - Units are joules (J) or kilojoules (kJ).
- The major source of energy for modern technology is hydrocarbon combustion.
- To initiate a chemical reaction, activation energy is required:
  - In exothermic reactions, this energy is returned and more is released, which allows the reaction to continue on its own.
  - In endothermic reactions, energy must be added to start and continue to be added to sustain the reaction.

8.5 GLOBAL WARMING: THE GREENHOUSE EFFECT

- Carbon dioxide levels are now increasing on our planet every year.
- Carbon dioxide and other greenhouse gases warm the atmosphere by trapping heat near the surface of the Earth.

REVIEW QUESTIONS

1. What is represented by the numbers (coefficients) that are placed in front of the formulas in a balanced equation?
2. What is meant by the physical state of a substance? What symbols are used to represent these physical states, and what does each symbol mean?
3. What is the purpose of balancing chemical equations?
4. In a balanced chemical equation:
   (a) Are atoms conserved?
   (b) Are molecules conserved?
   (c) Are moles conserved?
   Explain your answers briefly.
5. In Section 8.2, there are small charts in color along the margins. What information is represented in those charts?
6. Why is it incorrect to balance chemical reactions by changing the subscripts on the reactants and products?

7. What is a combustion reaction? How can you identify whether a reaction is a combustion reaction?
8. What information does the activity series shown in Table 8.2 give?
9. What major types of chemical reactions are studied in this chapter?
10. What three observations indicate a chemical reaction has taken place?
11. Explain how endothermic reactions differ from exothermic reactions.
12. Why does an exothermic reaction require heat to occur?
13. Name several greenhouse gases.
14. What factors are responsible for the annual rise and fall in carbon dioxide levels?

Most of the exercises in this chapter are available for assignment via the online homework management program, WileyPLUS (www.wileyplus.com). All exercises with blue numbers have answers in Appendix VI.

PAIRED EXERCISES

1. Classify the following as an endothermic or exothermic reaction:
   (a) freezing water
   (b) the reaction inside an ice pack
   (c) burning wood
   (d) combustion of Mg in dry ice
   (e) melting ice

2. Classify the following as an endothermic or exothermic reaction:
   (a) making popcorn in a microwave oven
   (b) a burning match
   (c) boiling water
   (d) burning rocket fuel
   (e) the reaction inside a heat pack

3. Balance each of the following equations. Classify each reaction as combination, decomposition, single-displacement, or double-displacement.
   (a) $H_2 + O_2 \longrightarrow H_2O$
   (b) $N_2H_4(l) \longrightarrow NH_3(g) + N_2(g)$
   (c) $H_2SO_4 + NaOH \longrightarrow H_2O + Na_2SO_4$
   (d) $Al_2(CO_3)_3 \xrightarrow{\Delta} Al_2O_3 + CO_2$
   (e) $NH_4I + Cl_2 \longrightarrow NH_4Cl + I_2$

4. Balance each of the following equations. Classify each reaction as combination, decomposition, single-displacement, or double-displacement.
   (a) $H_2 + Br_2 \longrightarrow HBr$
   (b) $BaO_2(s) + H_2SO_4(aq) \longrightarrow BaSO_4(s) + H_2O_2(aq)$
   (c) $Ba(ClO_3)_2 \xrightarrow{\Delta} BaCl_2 + O_2$
   (d) $CrCl_3 + AgNO_3 \longrightarrow Cr(NO_3)_3 + AgCl$
   (e) $H_2O_2 \longrightarrow H_2O + O_2$

5. What reactant(s) is (are) required to form an oxide product?

6. What reactant(s) is (are) required to form a salt?

7. Balance the following equations:
   (a) $MnO_2 + CO \longrightarrow Mn_2O_3 + CO_2$
   (b) $Cu_2O(s) + C(s) \longrightarrow Cu(s) + CO(g)$
   (c) $C_3H_5(NO_3)_3 \longrightarrow CO_2 + H_2O + N_2 + O_2$
   (d) $FeS + O_2 \longrightarrow Fe_2O_3 + SO_2$
   (e) $Cu(NO_3)_2 \longrightarrow CuO + NO_2 + O_2$
   (f) $NO_2 + H_2O \longrightarrow HNO_3 + NO$
   (g) $Fe(s) + S(l) \longrightarrow Fe_2S_3(s)$
   (h) $HCN + O_2 \longrightarrow N_2 + CO_2 + H_2O$
   (i) $B_5H_9 + O_2 \longrightarrow B_2O_3 + H_2O$

8. Balance the following equations:
   (a) $SO_2 + O_2 \longrightarrow SO_3$
   (b) $Li_2O(s) + H_2O(l) \longrightarrow LiOH(aq)$
   (c) $Na + H_2O \longrightarrow NaOH + H_2$
   (d) $AgNO_3 + Ni \longrightarrow Ni(NO_3)_2 + Ag$
   (e) $Bi_2S_3 + HCl \longrightarrow BiCl_3 + H_2S$
   (f) $PbO_2 \xrightarrow{\Delta} PbO + O_2$
   (g) $Hg_2(C_2H_3O_2)_2(aq) + KCl(aq) \longrightarrow Hg_2Cl_2(s) + KC_2H_3O_2(aq)$
   (h) $KI + Br_2 \longrightarrow KBr + I_2$
   (i) $K_3PO_4 + BaCl_2 \longrightarrow KCl + Ba_3(PO_4)_2$

9. Change these word equations into formula equations and balance them. Be sure to use the proper symbols to indicate the state of each substance, as given.
   (a) Magnesium metal is placed into hydrobromic acid solution, forming hydrogen gas and aqueous magnesium bromide.
   (b) When heated, solid calcium chlorate decomposes into calcium chloride solid, releasing oxygen gas.
   (c) Lithium metal reacts with oxygen gas to form solid lithium oxide.
   (d) Solutions of barium bromate and sodium phosphate combine to form solid barium phosphate and aqueous sodium bromate.
   (e) Solutions of acetic acid and sodium carbonate are mixed together, forming a solution of sodium acetate, along with carbon dioxide gas and liquid water.
   (f) Solutions of silver nitrate and aluminum iodide are mixed together, forming solid silver iodide and aqueous aluminum nitrate.

10. Change these word equations into formula equations and balance them. Be sure to use the proper symbols to indicate the state of each substance, as given.
   (a) Upon heating, solid magnesium carbonate decomposes into solid magnesium oxide and carbon dioxide gas.
   (b) Solid calcium hydroxide reacts with aqueous chloric acid to form a solution of calcium chlorate along with liquid water.
   (c) Solutions of iron(III) sulfate and sodium hydroxide are mixed together, forming solid iron(III) hydroxide and a solution of sodium sulfate.
   (d) Zinc metal is placed into a solution of acetic acid, producing hydrogen gas and aqueous zinc acetate.
   (e) Gaseous sulfur trioxide reacts with liquid water to form a solution of sulfuric acid.
   (f) Solutions of sodium carbonate and cobalt(II) chloride react to form solid cobalt(II) carbonate and a solution of sodium chloride.

11. For each of the following reactions, predict the products, converting each to a balanced formula equation:
   (a) Aqueous solutions of sulfuric acid and sodium hydroxide are mixed together. (Heat is released during the reaction.)
   (b) Aqueous solutions of lead(II) nitrate and potassium bromide are mixed together. (The solution turns cloudy white during the reaction.)
   (c) Aqueous solutions of ammonium chloride and silver nitrate are mixed together. (The solution turns cloudy white during the reaction.)
   (d) Solid calcium carbonate is mixed with acetic acid. (Bubbles of gas are formed during the reaction.)

12. For each of the following reactions, predict the products, converting each to a balanced formula equation:
   (a) Aqueous solutions of copper(II) sulfate and potassium hydroxide are mixed together. (The solution turns cloudy and light blue during the reaction.)
   (b) Aqueous solutions of phosphoric acid and sodium hydroxide are mixed together. (Heat is produced during the reaction.)
   (c) Solid sodium bicarbonate is mixed with phosphoric acid. (Bubbles of gas are formed during the reaction.)
   (d) Aqueous solutions of aluminum chloride and lead(II) nitrate are mixed together. (The solution turns cloudy white during the reaction.)

13. Use the activity series to predict which of the following reactions will occur. Complete and balance the equations. If no reactions occurs, write "no reaction" as the product.
   (a) $Ca(s) + H_2O(l) \rightarrow$
   (b) $Br_2(l) + KI(aq) \rightarrow$
   (c) $Cu(s) + HCl(aq) \rightarrow$
   (d) $Al(s) + H_2SO_4(aq) \rightarrow$

14. Use the activity series to predict which of the following reactions will occur. Complete and balance the equations. If no reaction occurs, write "no reaction" as the product.
   (a) $Cu(s) + NiCl_2(aq) \rightarrow$
   (b) $Rb(s) + H_2O(l) \rightarrow$
   (c) $I_2(s) + CaCl_2(aq) \rightarrow$
   (d) $Mg(s) + Al(NO_3)_3(aq) \rightarrow$

15. Complete and balance the equations for each of the following reactions. All yield products.
   (a) $Sr(s) + H_2O(l) \rightarrow$
   (b) $BaCl_2(aq) + AgNO_3(aq) \rightarrow$
   (c) $Mg(s) + ZnBr_2(aq) \rightarrow$
   (d) $K(s) + Cl_2(g) \rightarrow$

16. Complete and balance the equations for each of the following reactions. All yield products.
   (a) $Li_2O(s) + H_2O(l) \rightarrow$
   (b) $Na_2SO_4(aq) + Pb(NO_3)_2(aq) \rightarrow$
   (c) $Zn(s) + CuSO_4(aq) \rightarrow$
   (d) $Al(s) + O_2(g) \rightarrow$

17. Complete and balance the equations for these reactions. All reactions yield products.
   (a) $Ba + O_2 \longrightarrow$
   (b) $NaHCO_3 \xrightarrow{\Delta} Na_2CO_3 +$
   (c) $Ni + CuSO_4 \longrightarrow$
   (d) $MgO + HCl \longrightarrow$
   (e) $H_3PO_4 + KOH \longrightarrow$

18. Complete and balance the equations for these reactions. All reactions yield products.
   (a) $C + O_2 \longrightarrow$
   (b) $Al(ClO_3)_3 \xrightarrow{\Delta} O_2 +$
   (c) $CuBr_2 + Cl_2 \longrightarrow$
   (d) $SbCl_3 + (NH_4)_2S \longrightarrow$
   (e) $NaNO_3 \longrightarrow NaNO_2 +$

19. Interpret these chemical reactions in terms of the number of moles of each reactant and product:
   (a) $MgBr_2 + 2\,AgNO_3 \longrightarrow Mg(NO_3)_2 + 2\,AgBr$
   (b) $N_2 + 3\,H_2 \longrightarrow 2\,NH_3$
   (c) $2\,C_3H_7OH + 9\,O_2 \longrightarrow 6\,CO_2 + 8\,H_2O$

20. Interpret these equations in terms of the relative number of moles of each substance involved and indicate whether the reaction is exothermic or endothermic:
   (a) $2\,Na + Cl_2 \longrightarrow 2\,NaCl + 822\ kJ$
   (b) $PCl_5 + 92.9\ kJ \longrightarrow PCl_3 + Cl_2$
   (c) $S(s) + 2\,CO(g) \longrightarrow SO_2(g) + 2\,C(s) + 76\ kJ$

21. Write balanced equations for each of these reactions, including the heat term:
   (a) Solid mercury(II) oxide decomposes into liquid mercury and oxygen gas upon the absorption of 90.8 kJ for each mole of mercury(II) oxide decomposed.
   (b) Hydrogen gas reacts with oxygen gas to form liquid water. The reaction produces 285.8 kJ of heat for each mole of water formed

22. Write balanced equations for each of these reactions, including the heat term:
   (a) Calcium metal reacts with water to produce calcium hydroxide and hydrogen gas, releasing 635.1 kJ of heat for every mole of calcium that reacts.
   (b) Bromine trifluoride decomposes into bromine and fluorine upon the absorption of 300.8 kJ of heat for each mole of bromine trifluoride decomposed.

23. Determine what reactants would form the given products. Give a balanced equation for each and classify the reaction as a combination, decomposition, single-displacement, or double-displacement reaction.
   (a) $AgCl(s) + O_2(g)$
   (b) $H_2(g) + FeSO_4(aq)$
   (c) $ZnCl_2(s)$
   (d) $KBr(aq) + H_2O(l)$

24. Determine what reactants would form the given products. Give a balanced equation for each and classify the reaction as a combination, decomposition, single-displacement, or double-displacement reaction.
   (a) $Pb(s) + Ni(NO_3)_2(aq)$
   (b) $Mg(OH)_2(s)$
   (c) $Hg(l) + O_2(g)$
   (d) $PbCO_3(s) + NH_4Cl(aq)$

ADDITIONAL EXERCISES

25. An aqueous mixture of the nitrate salts of sodium, calcium, and silver is mixed with ammonium salts of chloride, sulfate, and carbonate. Write balanced equations for any combination that will form a precipitate.

26. Balance this equation, using the smallest possible whole numbers. Then determine how many atoms of oxygen appear on each side of the equation:

$$P_4O_{10} + HClO_4 \longrightarrow Cl_2O_7 + H_3PO_4$$

27. Suppose that in a balanced equation the term $5 \, Ni_3(PO_4)_2$ appears.
    (a) How many atoms of nickel are represented?
    (b) How many atoms of phosphorus are represented?
    (c) How many atoms of oxygen are represented?
    (d) How many atoms of all kinds are represented?

28. In a lab experiment, a student places a few stones, composed mainly of calcium carbonate, into a beaker and then adds some acetic acid. The student observes that effervescence occurs immediately. Explain this observation by writing a balanced formula equation.

29. Make a drawing to show the combustion reaction of one molecule of methane, CH_4.

30. A variety of iron-containing ores can be converted into iron and steel in a blast furnace. The reactions that take place are outlined below. Write balanced chemical equations for each reaction.
    (a) Pure carbon is reacted with oxygen gas to form carbon dioxide.
    (b) Carbon dioxide is reacted with more carbon to form monoxide.
    (c) Carbon monoxide reacts with the iron ore to form elemental iron and carbon dioxide. There are two main types of ore that may be used: hematite (Fe_2O_3) and magnetite (Fe_3O_4).

31. The box at the left represents the reactant atoms in blue (B) and molecules in green (G_2). After reacting, these reactants from the compound pictured in the box at the right. Write a balanced chemical reaction for this process.

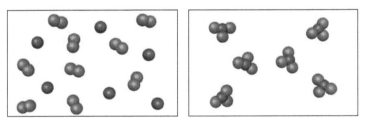

32. Students in a lab exercise were asked to choose among a sample of different metals to react with a solution of nickel(II) chloride. Which of the following metals should they choose? Write balanced equations for all that will react and explain why each will or will not react.
    (a) copper   (d) lead
    (b) zinc   (e) calcium
    (c) aluminum

33. A student does an experiment to determine where titanium metal should be placed on the activity series chart. He places newly cleaned pieces of titanium into solutions of nickel(II) nitrate, lead(II) nitrate, and magnesium nitrate. He finds that the titanium reacts with the nickel(II) nitrate and lead(II) nitrate solutions, but not with the magnesium nitrate solution. From this information, place titanium in the activity series in a position relative to these ions.

34. Predict the products of each of the following combination reactions in words. Then change each equation into a balanced formula equation.
    (a) Cesium reacts with oxygen.
    (b) Aluminum metal reacts with sulfur.
    (c) Sulfur trioxide reacts with water.
    (d) Sodium oxide reacts with water.

35. Automobile designers are currently working on cars that will run on hydrogen. Hydrogen-fueled cars have the advantage that they produce only water as a waste product. In these cars, hydrogen gas reacts with oxygen gas to form gaseous water.
    (a) Write a balanced chemical equation for this reaction.
    (b) There are many ways to generate hydrogen to fuel these cars. The most commonly used method of making hydrogen gas is to react methane gas (CH_4) with gaseous water at 1000°C to form gaseous carbon monoxide and hydrogen gas. The carbon monoxide gas can then be reacted with more gaseous water to produce more hydrogen gas and carbon dioxide gas. Write balanced chemical equations for these two reactions.
    (c) One of the products of burning fossil fuels to provide energy is carbon dioxide. This carbon dioxide may be increasing the temperature of the planet. Methane can also be used to provide energy by reacting it with oxygen gas to form carbon dioxide and water. Write the balanced chemical equation for this reaction.
    (d) Compare the number of molecules of carbon dioxide produced out of one molecule of methane by burning it directly to produce energy and by converting it to hydrogen gas and using this hydrogen gas to produce energy. Is there an advantage to using hydrogen gas as the fuel source? Explain.

36. Many paint pigments are composed of ionic compounds. For each of the pigments listed below, write a complete balanced equation to synthesize the pigment using the reagents listed in parentheses. Write the correct IUPAC name of each pigment.
    (a) chrome yellow, $PbCrO_4$ ($Pb(NO_3)_2(aq) + K_2CrO_4(aq)$)
    (b) cadmium yellow, CdS ($CdCl_2(aq) + Li_2S(aq)$)
    (c) white lead, $PbCO_3$ ($Pb(C_2H_3O_2)_2(aq) + H_2CO_3(aq)$)
    (d) vermillion, HgS ($Hg(NO_3)_2(aq) + Na_2S(aq)$)
    (e) titanium black, Ti_2O_3 ($Ti(s) + O_2(g)$)
    (f) iron oxide red, Fe_2O_3 ($Fe(s) + O_2(g)$)

37. Predict the products of each of the following decomposition reactions in words. Then change each equation into a balanced formula equation.
    (a) Zinc oxide decomposes upon heating strongly.
    (b) Tin(IV) oxide decomposes into two products when heated.
    (c) Sodium carbonate decomposes when heated.
    (d) Magnesium chlorate decomposes when heated.

38. Predict the products of each of the following single-displacement reactions in words. Then change each equation into a balanced formula equation. All reactions occur in aqueous solution.
    (a) Magnesium metal reacts with hydrochloric acid.
    (b) Sodium bromide reacts with chlorine.
    (c) Zinc metal reacts with iron(III) nitrate.
    (d) Aluminum reacts with copper(II) sulfate.

39. Predict the products of each of the following double-displacement reactions in words. Then change each equation into a balanced formula equation. All reactants are in aqueous solution.
    (a) Ammonium phosphate reacts with barium nitrate.
    (b) Sodium sulfide reacts with lead(II) acetate.
    (c) Copper(II) sulfate reacts with calcium chlorate.
    (d) Barium hydroxide reacts with oxalic acid.
    (e) Phosphoric acid reacts with potassium hydroxide.
    (f) Sulfuric acid reacts with sodium carbonate.

40. Predict which of the following double-displacement reactions will occur. For those that do, write a balanced formula equation. For any

reaction that does not occur, write "no reaction" as the product. All reactants are in aqueous solution.
   (a) potassium sulfate and barium acetate
   (b) sulfuric acid and lithium hydroxide
   (c) ammonium phosphate and sodium bromide
   (d) calcium iodide and silver nitrate
   (e) nitric acid and strontium hydroxide
   (f) cesium nitrate and calcium hydroxide
41. Write balanced equations for each of the following combustion reactions:

CHALLENGE EXERCISE

48. You are given a solution of the following cations in water: Ag^+, Co^{2+}, Ba^{2+}, Zn^{2+}, and Sn^{2+}. You want to separate the ions out *one at a time* by precipitation using the following reagents: NaF, NaI, Na_2SO_4, and NaCl.
   (a) In what order would you add the reagents to ensure that *only one cation* is precipitating out at a time? Use the solubility

42. Write balanced equations for the complete combustion of the following hydrocarbons:
   (a) CH_4 (b) C_3H_6 (c) $C_6H_5CH_3$
43. List the factors that contribute to an increase in carbon dioxide in our atmosphere.
44. List three gases considered to be greenhouse gases. Explain why they are given this name.
45. How can the effects of global warming be reduced?
46. What happens to carbon dioxide released into our atmosphere?
47. In the Northern Hemisphere, the concentration of CO_2 peaks twice a year. When do these peaks occur, and what causes them?

table in Appendix V to help you. (*Note:* A precipitate that is slightly soluble in water is still considered to precipitate out of the solution.)
   (b) Why are the anionic reagents listed above all sodium salts?

ANSWERS TO PRACTICE EXERCISES

8.1   To show that a substance is a solid, write (*s*) after the formula of the substance. When the substance is a gas, write (*g*) after the formula, and when the substance is in an aqueous solution write (*aq*) after the formula.

8.2 $4 Al + 3 O_2 \longrightarrow 2 Al_2O_3$

8.3 $3 Mg(OH)_2 + 2 H_3PO_4 \longrightarrow Mg_3(PO_4)_2 + 6 H_2O$

8.4   (a) hydrogen gas + chlorine gas $\longrightarrow$ hydrogen chloride gas
      (b) $H_2(g) + Cl_2(g) \longrightarrow 2 HCl(g)$
      (c)

$H_2(g)$	+	$Cl_2(g)$	$\longrightarrow$	$2 HCl(g)$
1 molecule		1 molecule		2 molecules
2 atoms H		2 atoms Cl		2 atoms H 2 atoms Cl
1 mol 2.016 g		1 mol 70.90 g		2 mol 2 (36.46 g) (72.92 g)

      (d) $2 mol H_2 + 2 mol Cl_2 \longrightarrow 4 mol HCl(145.8 g)$

8.5   (a) $Fe + MgCl_2 \longrightarrow$ no reaction
      (b) $Zn(s) + Pb(NO_3)_2(aq) \longrightarrow Pb(s) + Zn(NO_3)_2(aq)$

8.6   (a) $2 K_3PO_4(aq) + 3 BaCl_2(aq) \longrightarrow$
                          $Ba_3(PO_4)_2(s) + 6 KCl(aq)$
      (b) $2 HCl(aq) + NiCO_3(aq) \longrightarrow$
                          $NiCl_2(aq) + H_2O(l) + CO_2(g)$
      (c) $NH_4Cl(aq) + NaNO_3(aq) \longrightarrow$ no reaction

8.7   (a)

      (b)

Accurate calculations of dose and accurate measurement of chemicals are required in order for a pharmacist to dispense the correct dosage of medicine to her patients.

Corbis RF/Age Fotostock America, Inc.

CHAPTER **9**

CALCULATIONS FROM CHEMICAL EQUATIONS

The old adage "waste not, want not" is appropriate in our daily life and in the laboratory. Determining correct amounts comes into play in almost all professions. A seamstress determines the amount of material, lining, and trim necessary to produce a gown for her client by relying on a pattern or her own experience to guide the selection. A carpet layer determines the correct amount of carpet and padding necessary to recarpet a customer's house by calculating the floor area. The IRS determines the correct deduction for federal income taxes from your paycheck based on your expected annual income.

9.1 INTRODUCTION TO STOICHIOMETRY

LEARNING OBJECTIVE ● Define stoichiometry and describe the strategy required to solve problems based on chemical equations.

KEY TERMS

stoichiometry
molar mass
mole ratio

We often need to calculate the amount of a substance that is either produced from, or needed to react with, a given quantity of another substance. The area of chemistry that deals with quantitative relationships among reactants and products is known as **stoichiometry** (*stoy-key-ah-meh-tree*). Solving problems in stoichiometry requires the use of *moles* in the form of *mole ratios*.

The chemist also finds it necessary to calculate amounts of products or reactants by using a balanced chemical equation. With these calculations, the chemist can control the amount of product by scaling the reaction up or down to fit the needs of the laboratory and can thereby minimize waste or excess materials formed during the reaction.

A Short Review

Molar mass The sum of the atomic masses of all the atoms in an element or compound is called **molar mass**. The term *molar mass* also applies to the mass of a mole of any formula unit—atoms, molecules, or ions; it is the atomic mass of an atom or the sum of the atomic masses in a molecule or an ion (in grams).

Relationship between molecule and mole A molecule is the smallest unit of a molecular substance (e.g., Br_2), and a mole is Avogadro's number (6.022×10^{23}) of molecules of that substance. A mole of bromine (Br_2) has the same number of molecules as a mole of carbon dioxide, a mole of water, or a mole of any other molecular substance. When we relate molecules to molar mass, 1 molar mass is equivalent to 1 mol, or 6.022×10^{23} molecules.

The term *mole* also refers to any chemical species. It represents a quantity (6.022×10^{23} particles) and may be applied to atoms, ions, electrons, and formula units of nonmolecular substances. In other words,

$$1 \text{ mole} = \begin{cases} 6.022 \times 10^{23} \text{ molecules} \\ 6.022 \times 10^{23} \text{ formula units} \\ 6.022 \times 10^{23} \text{ atoms} \\ 6.022 \times 10^{23} \text{ ions} \end{cases}$$

A mole of water, salt, and any gas all have the same number of particles (6.022×10^{23}).

Other useful mole relationships are

$$\text{molar mass} = \frac{\text{grams of a substance}}{\text{number of moles of the substance}}$$

$$\text{molar mass} = \frac{\text{grams of a monatomic element}}{\text{number of moles of the element}}$$

$$\text{number of moles} = \frac{\text{number of molecules}}{6.022 \times 10^{23} \text{ molecules/mole}}$$

Balanced equations When using chemical equations for calculations of mole–mass–volume relationships between reactants and products, the equations must be balanced. *Remember:* The number in front of a formula in a balanced chemical equation represents the number of moles of that substance in the chemical reaction.

A **mole ratio** is a ratio between the number of moles of any two species involved in a chemical reaction. For example, in the reaction

$$2 \text{ H}_2 + \text{O}_2 \longrightarrow 2 \text{ H}_2\text{O}$$
$$\text{2 mol   1 mol} \qquad \text{2 mol}$$

six mole ratios can be written:

$$\frac{2 \text{ mol H}_2}{1 \text{ mol O}_2} \qquad \frac{2 \text{ mol H}_2}{2 \text{ mol H}_2\text{O}} \qquad \frac{1 \text{ mol O}_2}{2 \text{ mol H}_2\text{O}}$$

$$\frac{1 \text{ mol O}_2}{2 \text{ mol H}_2} \qquad \frac{2 \text{ mol H}_2\text{O}}{2 \text{ mol H}_2} \qquad \frac{2 \text{ mol H}_2\text{O}}{1 \text{ mol O}_2}$$

We use the mole ratio to convert the number of moles of one substance to the corresponding number of moles of another substance in a chemical reaction. For example, if we want to calculate the number of moles of H_2O that can be obtained from 4.0 mol of O_2, we use the mole ratio 2 mol H_2O/1 mol O_2:

$$(4.0 \text{ mol } O_2)\left(\frac{2 \text{ mol } H_2O}{1 \text{ mol } O_2}\right) = 8.0 \text{ mol } H_2O$$

EXAMPLE 9.1

Use the following equation $CO_2 + 4 H_2 \rightarrow CH_4 + 2 H_2O$ to write the mole ratio needed to calculate

(a) the number of moles of water that can be produced from 3 moles of CO_2.
(b) the number of moles of hydrogen required to make 3 moles of water.

SOLUTION

In order to write the mole ratio we need to determine the relationship between the desired substance and the starting substance.

(a) In this case the desired substance is water. The moles of water belong in the numerator of the mole ratio. The starting substance is CO_2. The moles of CO_2 then belong in the denominator of the mole ratio. In the mole ratio the coefficients of the balanced equation are used. Therefore, the mole ratio is $\dfrac{2 \text{ mol } H_2O}{1 \text{ mol } CO_2}$.

(b) In this case the desired substance is hydrogen. The moles of hydrogen belong in the numerator of the mole ratio. The starting substance is water. The moles of water then belong in the denominator of the mole ratio. In the mole ratio the coefficients of the balanced equation are used. Therefore, the mole ratio is $\dfrac{4 \text{ mol } H_2}{2 \text{ mol } H_2O}$.

PRACTICE 9.1

Use the equation $2 KClO_3 \rightarrow 2 KCl + 3 O_2$ to write the mole ratio needed to calculate

(a) moles of KCl produced from 3.5 moles of $KClO_3$.
(b) moles of KCl produced when 4.5 moles of O_2 are produced.

PROBLEM-SOLVING STRATEGY: For Stoichiometry Problems

1. Convert the quantity of starting substance to moles (if it is not given in moles).
2. Convert the moles of starting substance to moles of desired substance.
3. Convert the moles of desired substance to the units specified in the problem.

Write and balance the equation before you begin the problem.

Like balancing chemical equations, making stoichiometric calculations requires practice. Several worked examples follow. Study this material and practice on the problems at the end of this chapter.

PROBLEM-SOLVING STRATEGY: For Stoichiometry Problems

Use a balanced equation.

1. **Determine the number of moles of starting substance.** Identify the starting substance from the data given in the problem statement. Convert the quantity of the starting substance to moles, if it is not already done:

$$\text{moles} = (\text{grams})\left(\frac{1 \text{ mole}}{\text{molar mass}}\right)$$

189

As in all problems with units, the desired quantity is in the numerator, and the quantity to be eliminated is in the denominator.

2. **Determine the mole ratio of the desired substance to the starting substance.** The number of moles of each substance in the balanced equation is indicated by the coefficient in front of each substance. Use these coefficients to set up the mole ratio:

$$\text{mole ratio} = \frac{\text{moles of desired substance in the equation}}{\text{moles of starting substance in the equation}}$$

Multiply the number of moles of starting substance (from Step 1) by the mole ratio to obtain the number of moles of desired substance:

Units of moles of starting substance cancel in the numerator and denominator.

3. **Calculate the desired substance in the units specified in the problem.** If the answer is to be in moles, the calculation is complete. If units other than moles are wanted, multiply the moles of the desired substance (from Step 2) by the appropriate factor to convert moles to the units required. For example, if grams of the desired substance are wanted:

From Step 2

$$\text{grams} = (\text{moles}) \left(\frac{\text{molar mass}}{1 \text{ mol}} \right)$$

If moles ⟶ atoms, use $\dfrac{6.022 \times 10^{23} \text{ atoms}}{1 \text{ mol}}$

If moles ⟶ molecules, use $\dfrac{6.022 \times 10^{23} \text{ molecules}}{1 \text{ mol}}$

The steps for converting the mass of a starting substance A to either the mass, atoms, or molecules of desired substance B are summarized in Figure 9.1.

Figure 9.1

Steps for converting starting substance A to mass, atoms, or molecules of desired substance B.

9.2 MOLE–MOLE CALCULATIONS

LEARNING OBJECTIVE ● Solve problems in which the reactants and products are both in moles.

Let's solve stoichiometric problems for mole–mole calculations. The quantity of starting substance is given in moles, and the quantity of desired substance is requested in moles.

EXAMPLE 9.2

How many moles of carbon dioxide will be produced by the complete reaction of 2.0 mol of glucose ($C_6H_{12}O_6$) according to the following equation?

$$\underset{\text{1 mol}}{C_6H_{12}O_6} + \underset{\text{6 mol}}{6 \, O_2} \rightarrow \underset{\text{6 mol}}{6 \, CO_2} + \underset{\text{6 mol}}{6 \, H_2O}$$

SOLUTION

Read ● **Knowns:** 2.0 mol of glucose

$C_6H_{12}O_6 + 6 \, O_2 \rightarrow 6 \, CO_2 + 6 \, H_2O$

Solving for: moles of carbon dioxide

<table>
<tr><td>Plan •</td><td>The balanced equation states that 6 mol CO_2 will be produced from 1 mol $C_6H_{12}O_6$. Even though we can readily see that 12 mol CO_2 will be formed, let's use the Problem-Solving Strategy for Stoichiometry Problems.</td><td>The mole ratio is exact and does not affect the number of significant figures in the answer.</td></tr>
</table>

Solution map: moles of $C_6H_{12}O_6 \rightarrow$ moles of CO_2

The mole ratio from the balanced equation is $\dfrac{6 \text{ mol } CO_2}{1 \text{ mol } C_6H_{12}O_6}$.

Calculate • $(2.0 \text{ mol } C_6H_{12}O_6)\left(\dfrac{6 \text{ mol } CO_2}{1 \text{ mol } C_6H_{12}O_6}\right) = 12 \text{ mol } CO_2$

Check • Note that the moles $C_6H_{12}O_6$ cancel and that the answer agrees with our reasoned answer.

EXAMPLE 9.3

How many moles of ammonia can be produced from 8.00 mol of hydrogen reacting with nitrogen? The balanced equation is

$$3 H_2 + N_2 \rightarrow 2 NH_3$$

SOLUTION

Read •   Knowns: 8.00 mol of hydrogen
$$3 H_2 + N_2 \rightarrow 2 NH_3$$

Solving for: moles of ammonia

Plan •   The balanced equation states that we get 2 mol NH_3 for every 3 mol H_2 that react. Let's use the Problem-Solving Strategy for Stoichiometry Problems.

Solution map: moles of $H_2 \rightarrow$ moles of NH_3

The mole ratio from the balanced equation is $\dfrac{2 \text{ mol } NH_3}{3 \text{ mol } H_2}$.

Calculate • $(8.00 \text{ mol } H_2)\left(\dfrac{2 \text{ mol } NH_3}{3 \text{ mol } H_2}\right) = 5.33 \text{ mol } NH_3$

Check •   Note that the moles H_2 cancel and that the answer is less than the starting 8.00 mol, which makes sense since our mole ratio is 2:3.

Ammonia
NH_3

EXAMPLE 9.4

Given the balanced equation

$$\underset{\substack{1 \text{ mol}}}{K_2Cr_2O_7} + \underset{\substack{6 \text{ mol}}}{6 KI} + 7 H_2SO_4 \rightarrow Cr_2(SO_4)_3 + 4 K_2SO_4 + \underset{\substack{3 \text{ mol}}}{3 I_2} + 7 H_2O$$

Calculate (a) the number of moles of potassium dichromate ($K_2Cr_2O_7$) that will react with 2.0 mol of potassium iodide (KI) and (b) the number of moles of iodine (I_2) that will be produced from 2.0 mol of potassium iodide.

SOLUTION

Read •   Knowns:

$$K_2Cr_2O_7 + 6 KI + 7 H_2SO_4 \rightarrow Cr_2(SO_4)_3 + 4 K_2SO_4 + 3 I_2 + 7 H_2O$$

(a) 2.0 mol KI
(b) 2.0 mol KI

(a) **Solving for:** moles of $K_2Cr_2O_7$

Plan •   Use the Problem-Solving Strategy for Stoichiometry Problems.

Solution map: moles of KI → moles of $K_2Cr_2O_7$

The mole ratio from the balanced equation is $\dfrac{1\ mol\ K_2Cr_2O_7}{6\ mol\ KI}$.

Calculate • $(2.0\ \cancel{mol\ KI})\left(\dfrac{1\ mol\ K_2Cr_2O_7}{6\ \cancel{mol\ KI}}\right) = 0.33\ mol\ K_2Cr_2O_7$

Check •   Note that the moles KI cancel and that the answer is less than the starting 2.0 mol, which makes sense since our mole ratio is 1:6.

(b) **Solving for:** moles of I_2

Plan •   Use the Problem-Solving Strategy for Stoichiometry Problems.

Solution map: mole of KI → moles of I_2

The mole ratio from the balanced equation is $\dfrac{3\ mol\ I_2}{6\ mol\ KI}$.

Calculate • $(2.0\ \cancel{mol\ KI})\left(\dfrac{3\ mol\ I_2}{6\ \cancel{mol\ KI}}\right) = 1.0\ mol\ I_2$

Check •   Note that the moles KI cancel and that the answer is half the starting 2.0 mol, which makes sense since our mole ratio is 1:2.

EXAMPLE 9.5

How many molecules of water can be produced by reacting 0.010 mol of oxygen with hydrogen? The balanced equation is $2\ H_2 + O_2 \rightarrow 2\ H_2O$.

SOLUTION

Read •   **Knowns:**   0.010 mol O_2
$2\ H_2 + O_2 \rightarrow 2\ H_2O$

Solving for: molecules H_2O

Plan •   Use the Problem-Solving Strategy for Stoichiometry Problems.

Solution map: moles of O_2 → moles of H_2O → molecules of H_2O

The mole ratio from the balanced equation is $\dfrac{2\ mol\ H_2O}{1\ mol\ O_2}$.

Calculate • $(0.010\ \cancel{mol\ O_2})\left(\dfrac{2\ mol\ H_2O}{1\ \cancel{mol\ O_2}}\right) = 0.020\ mol\ H_2O$

Conversion factor for moles H_2O → molecules H_2O

$$\dfrac{6.022 \times 10^{23}\ molecules}{1\ mol}$$

$(0.020\ \cancel{mol\ H_2O})\left(\dfrac{6.022 \times 10^{23}\ molecules}{1\ \cancel{mol}}\right) = 1.2 \times 10^{22}\ molecules\ H_2O$

NOTE   Note that 0.020 mol is still quite a large number of water molecules.

PRACTICE 9.2

How many moles of aluminum oxide will be produced from 0.50 mol of oxygen?

$$4\ Al + 3\ O_2 \longrightarrow 2\ Al_2O_3$$

PRACTICE 9.3

How many moles of aluminum hydroxide are required to produce 22.0 mol of water?

$$2\ Al(OH)_3 + 3\ H_2SO_4 \longrightarrow Al_2(SO_4)_3 + 6\ H_2O$$

9.3 MOLE–MASS CALCULATIONS

Solve problems in which mass is given and the answer is to be determined in moles   ● **LEARNING OBJECTIVE**
or the moles are given and mass is to be determined.

The object of this type of problem is to calculate the mass of one substance that reacts with or is produced from a given number of moles of another substance in a chemical reaction. If the mass of the starting substance is given, we need to convert it to moles. We use the mole ratio to convert moles of starting substance to moles of desired substance. We can then change moles of desired substance to mass.

EXAMPLE 9.6

What mass of hydrogen can be produced by reacting 6.0 mol of aluminum with hydrochloric acid? The balanced equation is $2\ Al(s) + 6\ HCl(aq) \rightarrow 2\ AlCl_3(aq) + H_2(g)$.

SOLUTION

Read ●   **Knowns:**   6.0 mol Al
$$2\ Al(s) + 6\ HCl(aq) \rightarrow 2\ AlCl_3(aq) + 3\ H_2(g)$$

Solving for: mass H_2

Plan ●   Use the Problem-Solving Strategy for Stoichiometry Problems.

Solution map: moles of Al → moles of H_2 → grams H_2

The mole ratio from the balanced equation is $\dfrac{3\ mol\ H_2}{2\ mol\ Al}$.

Calculate ● $(6.0\ \cancel{mol\ Al}) \left(\dfrac{3\ mol\ H_2}{2\ \cancel{mol\ Al}} \right) = 9.0\ mol\ H_2$

Conversion factor for moles H_2 → grams H_2 $\dfrac{2.016\ g\ H_2}{1\ mol\ H_2}$

$(9.0\ \cancel{mol\ H_2}) \left(\dfrac{2.016\ g\ H_2}{1\ \cancel{mol\ H_2}} \right) = 18\ g\ H_2$

NOTE   You can keep the answer for the first calculation (9.0 mol H_2) on your calculator and continue the calculation to the answer of 18 g H_2 in one continuous calculation as shown below:

moles of Al → moles of H_2 → grams H_2

$(6.0\ \cancel{mol\ Al}) \left(\dfrac{3\ \cancel{mol\ H_2}}{2\ \cancel{mol\ Al}} \right) \left(\dfrac{2.016\ g\ H_2}{1\ \cancel{mol\ H_2}} \right) = 18\ g\ H_2$

EXAMPLE 9.7

How many moles of water can be produced by burning 325 g of octane (C_8H_{18})? The balanced equation is $2 C_8H_{18}(l) + 25 O_2(g) \rightarrow 16 CO_2(g) + 18 H_2O(g)$.

SOLUTION

Octane
C_8H_{18}

Read •   **Knowns:**   325 g C_8H_{18}

$$2 C_8H_{18}(l) + 25 O_2(g) \rightarrow 16 CO_2(g) + 18 H_2O(g)$$

Solving for: mol H_2O

Plan •   Use the Problem-Solving Strategy for Stoichiometry Problems.

Solution map: grams of $C_8H_{18} \rightarrow$ moles of $C_8H_{18} \rightarrow$ moles of H_2O

Conversion factor for grams $C_8H_{18} \rightarrow$ moles C_8H_{18} $\dfrac{1 \text{ mol } C_8H_{18}}{114.2 \text{ g } C_8H_{18}}$

The mole ratio from the balanced equation is $\dfrac{18 \text{ mol } H_2O}{2 \text{ mol } C_8H_{18}}$.

Calculate • $(325 \text{ g } C_8H_{18})\left(\dfrac{1 \text{ mol } C_8H_{18}}{114.2 \text{ g } C_8H_{18}}\right) = 2.85 \text{ mol } C_8H_{18}$

$(2.85 \text{ mol } C_8H_{18})\left(\dfrac{18 \text{ mol } H_2O}{2 \text{ mol } C_8H_{18}}\right) = 25.7 \text{ mol } H_2O$

Check •   On your calculator in continuous calculation you might get 25.6 mol H_2O for your answer. The difference in the last digit is due to rounding off at different points in the calculation. You should check with your instructor to find out the appropriate rules for your course. In our examples we round at the end of each step to show the proper number of significant figures for each calculation.

PRACTICE 9.4

How many moles of potassium chloride and oxygen can be produced from 100.0 g of potassium chlorate? The balanced equation is:

$$2 KClO_3 \longrightarrow 2 KCl + 3 O_2$$

PRACTICE 9.5

How many grams of silver nitrate are required to produce 0.25 mol of silver sulfide? The balanced equation is:

$$2 AgNO_3 + H_2S \longrightarrow Ag_2S + 2 HNO_3$$

9.4 MASS–MASS CALCULATIONS

LEARNING OBJECTIVE •   Solve problems in which mass is given and the answer is to be determined as mass.

Solving mass–mass stoichiometry problems requires all the steps of the mole-ratio method. The mass of starting substance is converted to moles. The mole ratio is then used to determine moles of desired substance, which, in turn, is converted to mass of desired substance.

EXAMPLE 9.8

What mass of carbon dioxide is produced by the complete combustion of 100. g of the hydrocarbon pentane, C_5H_{12}? The balanced equation is
$C_5H_{12}(l) + 8 O_2(g) \rightarrow 5 CO_2(g) + 6 H_2O(g)$.

SOLUTION

Pentane
C_5H_{12}

Read •   **Knowns:**   100. g C_5H_{12}

$$C_5H_{12}(l) + 8 O_2(g) \rightarrow 5 CO_2(g) + 6 H_2O(g)$$

Solving for: mass CO_2

Plan • Use the Problem-Solving Strategy for Stoichiometry Problems.

Solution map: grams of C_5H_{12} → moles of C_5H_{12} → moles CO_2 → g CO_2

Conversion factor for grams C_5H_{12} → moles C_5H_{12} $\dfrac{1 \text{ mol } C_5H_{12}}{72.15 \text{ g } C_5H_{12}}$

The mole ratio from the balanced equation is $\dfrac{5 \text{ mol } CO_2}{1 \text{ mol } C_5H_{12}}$.

Conversion factor for moles CO_2 → g CO_2 $\dfrac{44.01 \text{ g } CO_2}{1 \text{ mol } CO_2}$

Calculate • grams of C_5H_{12} → moles of C_5H_{12}

$$(100.\text{ g } C_5H_{12})\left(\frac{1 \text{ mol } C_5H_{12}}{72.15 \text{ g } C_5H_{12}}\right) = 1.39 \text{ mol } C_5H_{12}$$

moles of C_5H_{12} → moles CO_2

$$(1.39 \text{ mol } C_5H_{12})\left(\frac{5 \text{ mol } CO_2}{1 \text{ mol } C_5H_{12}}\right) = 6.95 \text{ mol } CO_2$$

moles of CO_2 → g CO_2

$$(6.95 \text{ mol } CO_2)\left(\frac{44.01 \text{ g } CO_2}{1 \text{ mol } CO_2}\right) = 306 \text{ g } CO_2$$

EXAMPLE 9.9

How many grams of nitric acid (HNO_3) are required to produce 8.75 g of dinitrogen monoxide (N_2O) according to the following equation?

$$4 \text{ Zn}(s) + 10 \text{ HNO}_3(aq) \rightarrow 4 \text{ Zn(NO}_3)_2(aq) + N_2O(g) + 5 \text{ H}_2O(l)$$

SOLUTION

Read • **Knowns:** 8.75 g N_2O

$$4 \text{ Zn}(s) + 10 \text{ HNO}_3(aq) \rightarrow 4 \text{ Zn(NO}_3)_2(aq) + N_2O(g) + 5 \text{ H}_2O(l)$$

Solving for: g HNO_3

Plan • Use the Problem-Solving Strategy for Stoichiometry Problems.

Solution map: grams of N_2O → moles N_2O → moles HNO_3 → g HNO_3

Conversion factor for grams N_2O → moles N_2O $\dfrac{1 \text{ mol } N_2O}{44.02 \text{ g } N_2O}$

The mole ratio from the balanced equation is $\dfrac{10 \text{ mol } HNO_3}{1 \text{ mol } N_2O}$.

Conversion factor for moles HNO_3 → g HNO_3 $\dfrac{63.02 \text{ g } HNO_3}{1 \text{ mol } HNO_3}$

Calculate • grams of N_2O → moles of N_2O

$$(8.75 \text{ g } N_2O)\left(\frac{1 \text{ mol } N_2O}{44.02 \text{ g } N_2O}\right) = 0.199 \text{ mol } N_2O$$

moles N_2O → moles HNO_3

$$(0.199 \text{ mol } N_2O)\left(\frac{10 \text{ mol } HNO_3}{1 \text{ mol } N_2O}\right) = 1.99 \text{ mol } HNO_3$$

moles HNO_3 → g HNO_3

$$(1.99 \text{ mol } HNO_3)\left(\frac{63.02 \text{ g } HNO_3}{1 \text{ mol } HNO_3}\right) = 125 \text{ g } HNO_3$$

PRACTICE 9.6

How many grams of chromium(III) chloride are required to produce 75.0 g of silver chloride? The balanced equation is:

$$CrCl_3 + 3\, AgNO_3 \longrightarrow Cr(NO_3)_3 + 3\, AgCl$$

PRACTICE 9.7

What mass of water is produced by the complete combustion of 225.0 g of butane (C_4H_{10})? The balanced equation is:

$$2\, C_4H_{10} + 13\, O_2 \longrightarrow 8\, CO_2 + 10\, H_2O$$

9.5 LIMITING REACTANT AND YIELD CALCULATIONS

LEARNING OBJECTIVE ● Solve problems involving limiting reactants and yield.

KEY TERMS

limiting reactant
theoretical yield
actual yield
percent yield

In many chemical processes, the quantities of the reactants used are such that one reactant is in excess. The amount of the product(s) formed in such a case depends on the reactant that is not in excess. This reactant is called the **limiting reactant**—it limits the amount of product that can be formed.

Consider the case illustrated in **Figure 9.2**. How many bicycles can be assembled from the parts shown? The limiting part in this case is the number of pedal assemblies; only three bicycles can be built because there are only three pedal assemblies. The wheels and frames are parts in excess.

Let's consider a chemical example at the molecular level in which seven molecules of H_2 are combined with four molecules of Cl_2 (**Figure 9.3** before reaction). How many molecules of HCl can be produced according to this reaction?

$$H_2 + Cl_2 \longrightarrow 2\, HCl$$

Figure 9.2

The number of bicycles that can be built from these parts is determined by the "limiting reactant" (the pedal assemblies).

8 wheels   4 frames

3 pedal assemblies

3 bicycles

>CHEMISTRY *IN ACTION*

A Shrinking Technology

The microchip has revolutionized the field of electronics. Engineers at Bell Laboratories, Massachusetts Institute of Technology, the University of California, and Stanford University are racing to produce parts for tiny machines and robots. New techniques now produce gears smaller than a grain of sand and motors lighter than a speck of dust.

To produce ever smaller computers, calculators, and even microbots (microsized robots), precise quantities of chemicals in exact proportions are required. The secret to producing minute circuits is to print the entire circuit or blueprint at one time. Computers are used to draw a chip. This image is then transferred onto a pattern, or mask, with details finer than a human hair. In a process similar to photography, light is then shined through the mask onto a silicon-coated surface. The areas created on the silicon exhibit high or low resistance to chemical etching. Chemicals then etch away the silicon.

Micromachinery is produced in the same way. First a thin layer of silicon dioxide is applied (sacrificial material); then a layer of polysilicon is carefully applied (structural material). Next, a mask is applied, and the whole structure is covered with plasma (excited gas). The plasma acts as a tiny sandblaster, removing everything the mask doesn't protect. This process is repeated as the entire machine is constructed. When the entire assembly is complete, the whole machine is placed in hydrofluoric acid, which dissolves all the sacrificial material and permits the various parts of the machine to move.

To turn these micromachines into true microbots, current research is focusing on locomotion and sensing imaging systems. Possible uses for these microbots include "smart" pills, which could contain sensors or drug reservoirs (currently used in birth control). Tiny pumps, once inside the body, will dispense the proper amount of medication at precisely the correct site. These microbots are currently in production for the treatment of diabetes (to release insulin).

© Michael Knight/iStockphoto

These nanorobots attach themselves to red blood cells.

If the molecules of H_2 and Cl_2 are taken apart and recombined as HCl (Figure 9.3 after reaction), we see that eight molecules of HCl can be formed before we run out of Cl_2. Therefore, the Cl_2 is the limiting reactant and H_2 is in excess—three molecules of H_2 remain unreacted.

Before reaction

After reaction

○ H
● Cl

Figure 9.3

Reaction of H_2 with Cl_2. Eight molecules of HCl are formed, and three molecules of H_2 remain. The limiting reactant is Cl_2.

When problem statements give the amounts of two reactants, one of them is usually a limiting reactant. We can identify the limiting reactant using the following method:

PROBLEM-SOLVING STRATEGY: For Limiting Reactant Problems

1. Calculate the amount of product (moles or grams, as needed) formed from each reactant.

2. Determine which reactant is limiting. (The reactant that gives the least amount of product is the limiting reactant; the other reactant is in excess.)

3. Once we know the limiting reactant, the amount of product formed can be determined. It is the amount determined by the limiting reactant.

4. If we need to know how much of the other reactant remains, we calculate the amount of the other reactant required to react with the limiting reactant, then subtract this amount from the starting quantity of the reactant. This gives the amount of that substance that remains unreacted.

EXAMPLE 9.10

How many moles of HCl can be produced by reacting 4.0 mol H_2 and 3.5 mol Cl_2? Which compound is the limiting reactant? The equation is $H_2(g) + Cl_2(g) \rightarrow 2\ HCl(g)$.

SOLUTION

Read •   **Knowns:**   4.0 mol H_2

                           3.5 mol Cl_2

                           $H_2(g) + Cl_2(g) \rightarrow 2\ HCl(g)$

           Solving for: mol HCl

Plan •   Use the Problem-Solving Strategy for Limiting Reactant Problems.

Calculate the mol HCl formed from each reactant.

The mole ratios from the balanced equation are

$$\frac{2\ mol\ HCl}{1\ mol\ H_2} \qquad \frac{2\ mol\ HCl}{1\ mol\ Cl_2}$$

Calculate • moles $H_2\ \rightarrow$ moles HCl

$$(4.0\ mol\ H_2)\left(\frac{2\ mol\ HCl}{1\ mol\ H_2}\right) = 8.0\ mol\ HCl$$

moles of $Cl_2\ \rightarrow$ moles HCl

$$(3.5\ mol\ Cl_2)\left(\frac{2\ mol\ HCl}{1\ mol\ Cl_2}\right) = 7.0\ mol\ HCl$$

Determine the limiting reactant. The limiting reactant is Cl_2 because it produces less HCl than H_2. The H_2 is in excess. The yield of HCl is 7.0 mol.

Check •   In this reaction we can decide on the limiting reactant by inspection. From the equation you can see that 1 mol H_2 reacts with 1 mol Cl_2. Therefore, when we react 4.0 mol H_2 with 3.5 mol Cl_2, Cl_2 is the reactant that limits the amount of HCl produced, since it is present in smaller amount.

EXAMPLE 9.11

How many moles of Fe_3O_4 can be obtained by reacting 16.8 g Fe with 10.0 g H_2O? Which substance is the limiting reactant? Which substance is in excess?

$$3\ Fe(s) + 4\ H_2O(g) \xrightarrow{\Delta} Fe_3O_4(s) + 4\ H_2(g)$$

SOLUTION

Read •   **Knowns:**   16.5 g Fe

                           10.0 g H_2O

                           $3\ Fe(s) + 4\ H_2O(g) \xrightarrow{\Delta} Fe_3O_4(s) + 4\ H_2(g)$

          Solving for: mol Fe_3O_4

Plan •   Use the Problem-Solving Strategy for Limiting Reactant Problems.

Calculate the mol Fe_3O_4 formed from each reactant:

g reactant $\rightarrow$ mol reactant $\rightarrow$ mol Fe_3O_4

Calculate • For Fe

$$(16.8\ g\ Fe)\left(\frac{1\ mol\ Fe}{55.85\ g\ Fe}\right)\left(\frac{1\ mol\ Fe_3O_4}{3\ mol\ Fe}\right) = 0.100\ mol\ Fe_3O_4$$

For H$_2$O

$$(10.0 \text{ g H}_2\text{O})\left(\frac{1 \text{ mol H}_2\text{O}}{18.02 \text{ g H}_2\text{O}}\right)\left(\frac{1 \text{ mol Fe}_3\text{O}_4}{4 \text{ mol H}_2\text{O}}\right) = 0.139 \text{ mol Fe}_3\text{O}_4$$

Determine the limiting reactant. The limiting reactant is Fe because it produces less Fe$_3$O$_4$ than H$_2$O. The H$_2$O is in excess. The yield of Fe$_3$O$_4$ is 0.100 mol.

EXAMPLE 9.12

How many grams of silver bromide (AgBr) can be formed when solutions containing 50.0 g of MgBr$_2$ and 100.0 g of AgNO$_3$ are mixed together? How many grams of excess reactant remain unreacted?

SOLUTION

Read •   **Knowns:**   50.0 g MgBr$_2$

100.0 g AgNO$_3$

MgBr$_2$(aq) + 2 AgNO$_3$(aq) → 2 AgBr(s) + Mg(NO$_3$)$_2$(aq)

Solving for: g AgBr

Plan •   Use the Problem-Solving Strategy for Limiting Reactant Problems.

Calculate the g AgBr formed from each reactant:

g reactant → mol reactant → mol AgBr → g AgBr

Calculate • For MgBr$_2$

$$(50.0 \text{ g MgBr}_2)\left(\frac{1 \text{ mol MgBr}_2}{184.1 \text{ g MgBr}_2}\right)\left(\frac{2 \text{ mol AgBr}}{1 \text{ mol MgBr}_2}\right)\left(\frac{187.8 \text{ g AgBr}}{1 \text{ mol AgBr}}\right)$$

$$= 102 \text{ g AgBr}$$

For AgNO$_3$

$$(100.0 \text{ g AgNO}_3)\left(\frac{1 \text{ mol AgNO}_3}{169.9 \text{ g AgNO}_3}\right)\left(\frac{2 \text{ mol AgBr}}{2 \text{ mol AgNO}_3}\right)\left(\frac{187.8 \text{ g AgBr}}{1 \text{ mol AgBr}}\right)$$

$$= 110.5 \text{ g AgBr}$$

Determine the limiting reactant. The limiting reactant is MgBr$_2$ because it produces less AgBr than AgNO$_3$. The AgNO$_3$ is in excess. The yield of AgBr is 102 g.

Calculate the mass of unreacted AgNO$_3$. We must first determine the g AgNO$_3$ that react with 50.0 g MgBr$_2$.

g MgBr$_2$ → mol MgBr$_2$ → mol AgNO$_3$ → g AgNO$_3$

$$(50.0 \text{ g MgBr}_2)\left(\frac{1 \text{ mol MgBr}_2}{184.1 \text{ g MgBr}_2}\right)\left(\frac{2 \text{ mol AgNO}_3}{1 \text{ mol MgBr}_2}\right)\left(\frac{169.9 \text{ g AgNO}_3}{1 \text{ mol AgNO}_3}\right)$$

$$= 92.3 \text{ g AgNO}_3$$

Unreacted AgNO$_3$ = 100.0 g AgNO$_3$ − 92.3 g AgNO$_3$ = 7.7 g AgNO$_3$

The final mixture will contain:

102 g AgBr(s)   7.7 g AgNO$_3$

PRACTICE 9.8

How many grams of hydrogen chloride can be produced from 0.490 g of hydrogen and 50.0 g of chlorine? The balanced equation is:

$$\text{H}_2(g) + \text{Cl}_2(g) \longrightarrow 2 \text{ HCl}(g)$$

PRACTICE 9.9

How many grams of barium sulfate will be formed from 200.0 g of barium nitrate and 100.0 g of sodium sulfate? The balanced equation is:

$$Ba(NO_3)_2(aq) + Na_2SO_4(aq) \longrightarrow BaSO_4(s) + 2\,NaNO_3(aq)$$

The quantities of the products we have been calculating from chemical equations represent the maximum yield (100%) of product according to the reaction represented by the equation. Many reactions, especially those involving organic substances, fail to give a 100% yield of product. The main reasons for this failure are the side reactions that give products other than the main product and the fact that many reactions are reversible. In addition, some product may be lost in handling and transferring from one vessel to another. The **theoretical yield** of a reaction is the calculated amount of product that can be obtained from a given amount of reactant, according to the chemical equation. The **actual yield** is the amount of product that we finally obtain.

The **percent yield** is the ratio of the actual yield to the theoretical yield multiplied by 100. Both the theoretical and the actual yields must have the same units to obtain a percent:

$$\frac{\text{actual yield}}{\text{theoretical yield}} \times 100 = \text{percent yield}$$

For example, if the theoretical yield calculated for a reaction is 14.8 g, and the amount of product obtained is 9.25 g, the percent yield is

Round off as appropriate for your particular course.

$$\text{percent yield} = \left(\frac{9.25\ \cancel{g}}{14.8\ \cancel{g}}\right)(100) = 62.5\%\ \text{yield}$$

EXAMPLE 9.13

Carbon tetrachloride (CCl_4) was prepared by reacting 100. g of carbon disulfide and 100. g of chlorine. Calculate the percent yield if 65.0 g of CCl_4 were obtained from the reaction $CS_2 + 3\,Cl_2 \rightarrow CCl_4 + S_2Cl_2$.

SOLUTION

Read •   **Knowns:**   100. g CS_2

100. g Cl_2

65.0 g CCl_4 obtained

$CS_2 + 3\,Cl_2 \rightarrow CCl_4 + S_2Cl_2$

Solving for: % yield of CCl_4

Plan •   Use the equation for percent yield

$$\frac{\text{actual yield}}{\text{theoretical yield}} \times 100 = \text{percent yield}$$

Determine the theoretical yield. Calculate the g CCl_4 formed from each reactant.

g reactant $\rightarrow$ mol reactant $\rightarrow$ mol CCl_4 $\rightarrow$ g CCl_4

Calculate • For CS_2

$$(100.\ \text{g CS}_2)\left(\frac{1\ \text{mol } \cancel{CS_2}}{76.15\ \text{g } \cancel{CS_2}}\right)\left(\frac{1\ \text{mol } \cancel{CCl_4}}{1\ \text{mol } \cancel{CS_2}}\right)\left(\frac{153.8\ \text{g CCl}_4}{1\ \text{mol } \cancel{CCl_4}}\right)$$

$$= 202\ \text{g CCl}_4$$

For Cl_2

$$(100. \text{ g } Cl_2)\left(\frac{1 \text{ mol } Cl_2}{70.90 \text{ g } Cl_2}\right)\left(\frac{1 \text{ mol } CCl_4}{3 \text{ mol } Cl_2}\right)\left(\frac{153.8 \text{ g } CCl_4}{1 \text{ mol } CCl_4}\right)$$

$$= 72.3 \text{ g } CCl_4$$

Determine the limiting reactant. The limiting reactant is Cl_2 because it produces less CCl_4 than CS_2. The CS_2 is in excess. The theoretical yield of CCl_4 is 72.3 g.

Calculate the percent yield

$$\frac{\text{actual yield}}{\text{theoretical yield}} \times 100 = \left(\frac{65.0 \text{ g}}{72.3 \text{ g}}\right)(100) = 89.9\% \text{ yield}$$

EXAMPLE 9.14

Silver bromide was prepared by reacting 200.0 g of magnesium bromide and an adequate amount of silver nitrate. Calculate the percent yield if 375.0 g of silver bromide were obtained from the reaction:

$$MgBr_2 + 2 AgNO_3 \rightarrow Mg(NO_3)_2 + 2 AgBr$$

SOLUTION

Read • **Knowns:**   200.0 g $MgBr_2$

375.0 g AgBr

$$MgBr_2 + 2 AgNO_3 \rightarrow Mg(NO_3)_2 + 2 AgBr$$

Solving for: % yield AgBr

Plan • Use the equation for percent yield

$$\frac{\text{actual yield}}{\text{theoretical yield}} \times 100 = \text{percent yield}$$

Determine the theoretical yield. Calculate the grams of AgBr formed:

$$\text{g } MgBr_2 \rightarrow \text{mol } MgBr_2 \rightarrow \text{mol AgBr} \rightarrow \text{g AgBr}$$

Calculate • $(200.0 \text{ g } MgBr_2)\left(\frac{1 \text{ mol } MgBr_2}{184.1 \text{ g } MgBr_2}\right)\left(\frac{2 \text{ mol AgBr}}{1 \text{ mol } MgBr_2}\right)\left(\frac{187.8 \text{ g AgBr}}{1 \text{ mol AgBr}}\right)$

$$= 408.0 \text{ g AgBr}$$

The theoretical yield is 408.0 g AgBr.

Calculate the percent yield.

$$\frac{\text{actual yield}}{\text{theoretical yield}} \times 100 = \left(\frac{375.0 \text{ g}}{408.0 \text{ g}}\right)(100) = 91.91\% \text{ yield}$$

PRACTICE 9.10

Aluminum oxide was prepared by heating 225 g of chromium(II) oxide with 125 g of aluminum. Calculate the percent yield if 100.0 g of aluminum oxide were obtained. The balanced equation is:

$$2 Al + 3 CrO \longrightarrow Al_2O_3 + 3 Cr$$

CHAPTER 9 REVIEW

KEY TERMS

stoichiometry
molar mass
mole ratio

9.1 INTRODUCTION TO STOICHIOMETRY

- Solving stoichiometry problems requires the use of moles and mole ratios.
- To solve a stoichiometry problem:
  - Convert the quantity of starting substance to moles.
  - Convert the moles of starting substance to moles of desired substance.
  - Convert the moles of desired substance to the appropriate unit.

KEY TERMS

stoichiometry
molar mass
mole ratio

```
Grams of A ──────────┐
                     ▼        Step 2
         Step 1   Moles of A ────────── Moles of B   Step 3
                     ▲       Mole ratio
Atoms or  ───────────┘
molecules of A

                              ┌──────────► Grams of B
                              │
                              └──────────► Atoms or
                                           molecules of B
```

9.2 MOLE–MOLE CALCULATIONS

- If the starting substance is given in moles and the unit specified for the answer is moles:
  - Convert the moles of starting substance to moles of desired substance.

9.3 MOLE–MASS CALCULATIONS

- If the starting substance is given in moles and the unit specified for the answer is grams:
  - Convert the moles of starting substance to moles of desired substance.
  - Convert the moles of desired substance to grams.

9.4 MASS–MASS CALCULATIONS

- If the starting substance is given in grams and the unit specified for the answer is grams:
  - Convert the quantity of starting substance to moles.
  - Convert the moles of starting substance to moles of desired substance.
  - Convert the moles of desired substance to grams.

9.5 LIMITING REACTANT AND YIELD CALCULATIONS

KEY TERMS

limiting reactant
theoretical yield
actual yield
percent yield

- To identify the limiting reactant in a reaction:
  - Calculate the amount of product formed from each reactant.
  - Determine the limiting reactant by selecting the one that gives the least amount of product.
- To determine the actual amount of product formed in a limiting reactant situation:
  - Use the result calculated that is the least amount of product.
- To determine the amount of the other reactants required to react with the limiting reactant:
  - Calculate the amount of the other reactant needed to react with the limiting reactant.
  - Subtract this amount from the original amount of the other reactant to find the amount of excess reactant (unreacted).
- The theoretical yield of a chemical reaction is the calculated amount of product from a given amount of reactant (the limiting reactant).
- The actual yield is the amount of product actually obtained experimentally.
- The percent yield is

$$\frac{\text{actual yield}}{\text{theoretical yield}} \times 100 = \text{percent yield}$$

REVIEW QUESTIONS

1. What is a mole ratio?
2. What piece of information is needed to convert grams of a compound to moles of the same compound?
3. Phosphine (PH_3) can be prepared by the reaction of calcium phosphide, Ca_3P_2:

$$Ca_3P_2 + 6\,H_2O \longrightarrow 3\,Ca(OH)_2 + 2\,PH_3$$

Based on this equation, which of the following statements are correct? Show evidence to support your answer.
   (a) One mole of Ca_3P_2 produces 2 mol of PH_3.
   (b) One gram of Ca_3P_2 produces 2 g of PH_3.
   (c) Three moles of $Ca(OH)_2$ are produced for each 2 mol of PH_3 produced.
   (d) The mole ratio between phosphine and calcium phosphide is

$$\frac{2 \text{ mol } PH_3}{1 \text{ mol } Ca_3P_2}$$

   (e) When 2.0 mol of Ca_3P_2 and 3.0 mol of H_2O react, 4.0 mol of PH_3 can be formed.
   (f) When 2.0 mol of Ca_3P_2 and 15.0 mol of H_2O react, 6.0 mol of $Ca(OH)_2$ can be formed.
   (g) When 200. g of Ca_3P_2 and 100. g of H_2O react, Ca_3P_2 is the limiting reactant.
   (h) When 200. g of Ca_3P_2 and 100. g of H_2O react, the theoretical yield of PH_3 is 57.4 g.

4. The equation representing the reaction used for the commercial preparation of hydrogen cyanide is

$$2\,CH_4 + 3\,O_2 + 2\,NH_3 \longrightarrow 2\,HCN + 6\,H_2O$$

Based on this equation, which of the following statements are correct? Rewrite incorrect statements to make them correct.
   (a) Three moles of O_2 are required for 2 mol of NH_3.
   (b) Twelve moles of HCN are produced for every 16 mol of O_2 that react.
   (c) The mole ratio between H_2O and CH_4 is

$$\frac{6 \text{ mol } H_2O}{2 \text{ mol } CH_4}$$

   (d) When 12 mol of HCN are produced, 4 mol of H_2O will be formed.
   (e) When 10 mol of CH_4, 10 mol of O_2, and 10 mol of NH_3 are mixed and reacted, O_2 is the limiting reactant.
   (f) When 3 mol each of CH_4, O_2, and NH_3 are mixed and reacted, 3 mol of HCN will be produced.
5. What information beyond the mole ratio is needed to convert from moles of reactant to grams of product?
6. Draw a flowchart showing the conversions necessary to determine grams of ammonia formed from 10 g of hydrogen gas.

$$3\,H_2 + 2\,N_2 \longrightarrow 2\,NH_3$$

7. What is the difference between the theoretical and the actual yield of a chemical reaction?
8. How is the percent yield of a reaction calculated?

Most of the exercises in this chapter are available for assignment via the online homework management program, WileyPLUS (www.wileyplus.com). All exercises with blue numbers have answers in Appendix VI.

PAIRED EXERCISES

1. Calculate the number of moles in these quantities:
   (a) 25.0 g KNO_3
   (b) 56 millimol NaOH
   (c) 5.4×10^2 g $(NH_4)_2C_2O_4$
   (d) 16.8 mL H_2SO_4 solution
       ($d = 1.727$ g/mL, 80.0% H_2SO_4 by mass)
3. Calculate the number of grams in these quantities:
   (a) 2.55 mol $Fe(OH)_3$
   (b) 125 kg $CaCO_3$
   (c) 10.5 mol NH_3
   (d) 72 millimol HCl
   (e) 500.0 mL of liquid Br_2 ($d = 3.119$ g/mL)

5. Which contains the larger number of molecules, 10.0 g H_2O or 10.0 g H_2O_2? Show evidence for your answer.

7. Balance the equation for the synthesis of sucrose

$$CO_2 + H_2O \longrightarrow C_{12}H_{22}O_{11} + O_2$$

   and set up the mole ratio of

   (a) CO_2 to H_2O (d) $C_{12}H_{22}O_{11}$ to CO_2
   (b) H_2O to $C_{12}H_{22}O_{11}$ (e) H_2O to O_2
   (c) O_2 to CO_2 (f) O_2 to $C_{12}H_{22}O_{11}$

2. Calculate the number of moles in these quantities:
   (a) 2.10 kg $NaHCO_3$
   (b) 525 mg $ZnCl_2$
   (c) 9.8×10^{24} molecules CO_2
   (d) 250 mL ethyl alcohol, C_2H_5OH ($d = 0.789$ g/mL)

4. Calculate the number of grams in these quantities:
   (a) 0.00844 mol $NiSO_4$
   (b) 0.0600 mol $HC_2H_3O_2$
   (c) 0.725 mol Bi_2S_3
   (d) 4.50×10^{21} molecules glucose, $C_6H_{12}O_6$
   (e) 75 mL K_2CrO_4 solution
       ($d = 1.175$ g/mL, 20.0% K_2CrO_4 by mass)

6. Which contains the larger numbers of molecules, 25.0 g HCl or 85.0 g $C_6H_{12}O_6$? Show evidence for your answer.

8. Balance the equation for the combustion of butanol

$$C_4H_9OH + O_2 \longrightarrow CO_2 + H_2O$$

   and set up the mole ratio of

   (a) O_2 to C_4H_9OH (d) C_4H_9OH to CO_2
   (b) H_2O to O_2 (e) H_2O to C_4H_9OH
   (c) CO_2 to H_2O (f) CO_2 to O_2

9. Given the unbalanced equation

$$CO_2 + H_2 \longrightarrow CH_4 + H_2O$$

(a) How many moles of water can be produced from 25 moles of carbon dioxide?
(b) How many moles of CH_4 will be produced along with 12 moles of water?

11. Given the equation

$$MnO_2(s) + HCl(aq) \longrightarrow Cl_2(g) + MnCl_2(aq) + H_2O(l)$$
$$\text{(unbalanced)}$$

(a) How many moles of HCl will react with 1.05 mol of MnO_2?
(b) How many moles of $MnCl_2$ will be produced when 1.25 mol of H_2O are formed?
(c) How many grams of Cl_2 will be produced when 3.28 mol of MnO_2 react with excess HCl?
(d) How many moles of HCl are required to produce 15.0 kg of $MnCl_2$?

13. Carbonates react with acids to form a salt, water, and carbon dioxide gas. When 50.0 g of calcium carbonate are reacted with sufficient hydrochloric acid, how many grams of calcium chloride will be produced? (Write a balanced equation first.)

15. In a blast furnace, iron(III) oxide reacts with coke (carbon) to produce molten iron and carbon monoxide:

$$Fe_2O_3 + 3\,C \xrightarrow{\Delta} 2\,Fe + 3\,CO$$

How many kilograms of iron would be formed from 125 kg of Fe_2O_3?

17. Polychlorinated biphenyls (PCBs), which were formerly used in the manufacture of electrical transformers, are environmental and health hazards. They break down very slowly in the environment. The decomposition of PCBs can be represented by the equation

$$2\,C_{12}H_4Cl_6 + 23\,O_2 + 2\,H_2O \longrightarrow 24\,CO_2 + 12\,HCl$$

(a) How many moles of water are needed to react 10.0 mol O_2?
(b) How many grams of HCl are produced when 15.2 mol H_2O react?
(c) How many moles of CO_2 are produced when 76.5 g HCl are produced?
(d) How many grams of $C_{12}H_4Cl_6$ are reacted when 100.25 g CO_2 are produced?
(e) How many grams of HCl are produced when 2.5 kg $C_{12}H_4Cl_6$ react?

19. Draw the molecules of product(s) formed for each of the following reactions; then determine which substance is the limiting reactant:

(a)

(b)

10. Given the unbalanced equation

$$H_2SO_4 + NaOH \longrightarrow Na_2SO_4 + H_2O$$

(a) How many moles of NaOH will react with 17 mol of H_2SO_4?
(b) How many moles of Na_2SO_4 will be produced when 21 mol of NaOH react?

12. Given the equation

$$Al_4C_3 + 12\,H_2O \longrightarrow 4\,Al(OH)_3 + 3\,CH_4$$

(a) How many moles of water are needed to react with 100. g of Al_4C_3?
(b) How many moles of $Al(OH)_3$ will be produced when 0.600 mol of CH_4 is formed?
(c) How many moles of CH_4 will be formed by the reaction of 275 grams of Al_4C_3 with excess water?
(d) How many grams of water are required to produce 4.22 moles of $Al(OH)_3$?

14. Certain metals can displace hydrogen from acids to produce hydrogen gas and a salt. When 25.2 g of aluminum metal are placed into hydrobromic acid, how many grams of aluminum bromide will be produced? (Write the balanced equation first.)

16. How many grams of steam and iron must react to produce 375 g of magnetic iron oxide, Fe_3O_4?

$$3\,Fe(s) + 4\,H_2O(g) \xrightarrow{\Delta} Fe_3O_4(s) + 4\,H_2(g)$$

18. Mercury can be isolated from its ore by the reaction

$$4\,HgS + 4\,CaO \longrightarrow 4\,Hg + 3\,CaS + CaSO_4$$

(a) How many moles of CaS are produced from 2.5 mol CaO?
(b) How many grams of Hg are produced along with 9.75 mol of $CaSO_4$?
(c) How many moles of CaO are required to react with 97.25 g of HgS?
(d) How many grams of Hg are produced from 87.6 g of HgS?
(e) How many grams of CaS are produced along with 9.25 kg of Hg?

20. Draw the molecules of product(s) formed for the following reactions; then determine which substance is the limiting reactant:

(a)

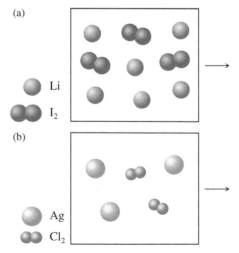

(b)

21. Draw pictures similar to those in Question 19 and determine which is the limiting reactant in the following reactions:
(a) Eight atoms of potassium react with five molecules of chlorine to produce potassium chloride.
(b) Ten atoms of aluminum react with three molecules of oxygen to produce aluminum oxide.

22. Draw pictures similar to those in Question 20 and determine which is the limiting reactant in the following reactions:
(a) Eight molecules of nitrogen react with six molecules of oxygen to produce nitrogen dioxide.
(b) Fifteen atoms of iron react with twelve molecules of water to produce magnetic iron oxide (Fe_3O_4) and hydrogen.

23. In the following equations, determine which reactant is the limiting reactant and which reactant is in excess. The amounts used are given below each reactant. Show evidence for your answers.
(a) $KOH + HNO_3 \longrightarrow KNO_3 + H_2O$
    16.0 g   12.0 g
(b) $2\,NaOH + H_2SO_4 \longrightarrow Na_2SO_4 + H_2O$
    10.0 g   10.0 g

25. Aluminum sulfate has many uses in industry. It can be prepared by reacting aluminum hydroxide and sulfuric acid:

$$2\,Al(OH)_3 + 3\,H_2SO_4 \longrightarrow Al_2(SO_4)_3 + 6\,H_2O$$

(a) When 35.0 g of $Al(OH)_3$ and 35.0 g of H_2SO_4 are reacted, how many moles of $Al_2(SO_4)_3$ can be produced? Which substance is the limiting reactant?
(b) When 45.0 g of H_2SO_4 and 25.0 g of $Al(OH)_3$ are reacted, how many grams of $Al_2(SO_4)_3$ are produced? Which reactant is in excess?
(c) In a reaction vessel, 2.5 mol of $Al(OH)_3$ and 5.5 mol of H_2SO_4 react. Determine which substances will be present in the container when the reaction goes to completion and how many moles of each.

27. When a certain nonmetal whose formula is X_8 burns in air, XO_3 forms. Write a balanced equation for this reaction. If 120.0 g of oxygen gas are consumed completely, along with 80.0 g of X_8, identify the element X.

29. Elemental silicon can be produced by the reduction of silicon dioxide, or sand, with carbon:

$$SiO_2 + 2\,C \longrightarrow Si + 2\,CO$$

When 35.0 kg of SiO_2 reacts with 25.3 kg of carbon, and 14.4 kg of silicon is recovered, what is the percent yield for the reaction?

31. In a laboratory experiment, 27.5 g of Cu were reacted with 125 g of HNO_3:

$$3\,Cu + 8\,HNO_3 \longrightarrow 3\,Cu(NO_3)_2 + 4\,H_2O + 2\,NO$$

(a) How many grams of $Cu(NO_3)_2$ can be theoretically produced?
(b) How many grams of the excess reactant remain?
(c) If the percent yield of $Cu(NO_3)_2$ is 87.3%, what is the actual yield in grams?

24. In the following equations, determine which reactant is the limiting reactant and which reactant is in excess. The amounts used are given below each reactant. Show evidence for your answers.
(a) $2\,Bi(NO_3)_3 + 3\,H_2S \longrightarrow Bi_2S_3 + 6\,HNO_3$
    50.0 g   6.00 g
(b) $3\,Fe + 4\,H_2O \longrightarrow Fe_3O_4 + 4\,H_2$
    40.0 g 16.0 g

26. Phosphorous trichloride, a precursor for the manufacture of certain pesticides and herbicides, can be produced by the reaction of phosphorous and chlorine:

$$P_4 + 6\,Cl_2 \longrightarrow 4\,PCl_3$$

(a) When 20.5 g of P_4 and 20.5 g of Cl_2 are reacted, how many moles of PCl_3 can be produced?
(b) When 55 g of Cl_2 are reacted with 25 g of P_4, how many grams of PCl_3 can be produced? Which reactant is in excess?
(c) In a reaction vessel, 15 mol of P_4 and 35 mol of Cl_2 react. Determine which substances will be present in the container after the reaction goes to completion and how many moles of each substance is present.

28. When a particular metal X reacts with HCl, the resulting products are XCl_2 and H_2. Write and balance the equation. When 78.5 g of the metal react completely, 2.42 g of hydrogen gas result. Identify the element X.

30. Chromium metal can be produced by the reduction of Cr_2O_3 with elemental silicon:

$$2\,Cr_2O_3 + 3\,Si \longrightarrow 4\,Cr + 3\,SiO_2$$

If 350.0 grams of Cr_2O_3 are reacted with 235.0 grams of elemental silicon and 213.2 grams of chromium metal are recovered, what is the percent yield?

32. In aqueous solution, metal oxides can react with acids to form a salt and water:

$$Fe_2O_3(s) + 6\,HCl(aq) \longrightarrow 2\,FeCl_3(aq) + 3\,H_2O(l)$$

(a) How many moles of each product will be formed when 35 g of Fe_2O_3 react with 35 g of HCl?
(b) From part (a), how many grams of the excess reactant remain?
(c) If the percent yield of $FeCl_3$ is 92.5%, what is the actual yield in grams?

ADDITIONAL EXERCISES

33. A tool set contains 6 wrenches, 4 screwdrivers, and 2 pliers. The manufacturer has 1000 pliers, 2000 screwdrivers, and 3000 wrenches in stock. Can an order for 600 tool sets be filled? Explain briefly.

34. Write a balanced equation for the fermentation of glucose, $C_6H_{12}O_6$, into ethyl alcohol, C_2H_5OH and CO_2. Determine how many liters of ethyl alcohol ($d = 0.789$ g/mL) can be produced from 575 lb of glucose.

35. For mass–mass calculation, why is it necessary to convert the grams of starting material to moles of starting material, then determine the moles of product from the moles of starting material, and convert the moles of product to grams of product? Why can't you calculate the grams of product directly from the grams of starting material?

36. Oxygen masks for producing O_2 in emergency situations contain potassium superoxide (KO_2). It reacts according to this equation:

$$4\,KO_2 + 2\,H_2O + 4\,CO_2 \longrightarrow 4\,KHCO_3 + 3\,O_2$$

(a) If a person wearing such a mask exhales 0.85 g of CO_2 every minute, how many moles of KO_2 are consumed in 10.0 minutes?
(b) How many grams of oxygen are produced in 1.0 hour?

37. In the presence of concentrated H_2SO_4, sucrose, $C_{12}H_{22}O_{11}$, undergoes dehydration, forming carbon and water:

$$C_{12}H_{22}O_{11} \xrightarrow{H_2SO_4} 12\,C + 11\,H_2O$$

(a) How many grams of carbon and how many grams of water can be produced from 2.0 lb of sucrose?
(b) If 25.2 g sucrose are dehydrated, how many grams of liquid water with a density of 0.994 g/mL can be collected?

38. Alfred Nobel extended Sobrero's work on nitroglycerin and discovered that when mixed with diatomaceous earth it would form a stable mixture. This mixture is now known as dynamite. The reaction of nitroglycerin is

$$4\,C_3H_5(NO_3)_3(l) \longrightarrow 12\,CO_2(g) + 10\,H_2O(g) + 6\,N_2(g) + O_2(g)$$

(a) Calculate the number of grams of each product that are produced by the decomposition of 45.0 g of nitroglycerin.
(b) Calculate the total number of moles of gas produced.

39. The methyl alcohol (CH_3OH) used in alcohol burners combines with oxygen gas to form carbon dioxide and water. How many grams of oxygen are required to burn 60.0 mL of methyl alcohol ($d = 0.787$ g/mL)?

40. Hydrazine (N_2H_4) and hydrogen peroxide (H_2O_2) have been used as rocket propellants. They react according to the following equation:

$$7\ H_2O_2 + N_2H_4 \longrightarrow 2\ HNO_3 + 8\ H_2O$$

(a) When 75 kg of hydrazine react, how many grams of nitric acid can be formed?
(b) When 250 L of hydrogen peroxide ($d = 1.41$ g/mL) react, how many grams of water can be formed?
(c) How many grams of hydrazine will be required to react with 725 g hydrogen peroxide?
(d) How many grams of water can be produced when 750 g hydrazine combine with 125 g hydrogen peroxide?
(e) How many grams of the excess reactant in part (d) are left unreacted?

41. Chlorine gas can be prepared according to the reaction

$$16\ HCl + 2\ KMnO_4 \longrightarrow 5\ Cl_2 + 2\ KCl + 2\ MnCl_2 + 8\ H_2O$$

(a) How many moles of $MnCl_2$ can be produced when 25 g $KMnO_4$ are mixed with 85 g HCl?
(b) How many grams of water will be produced when 75 g KCl are produced?
(c) What is the percent yield of Cl_2 if 150 g HCl are reacted, producing 75 g of Cl_2?
(d) When 25 g HCl react with 25 g $KMnO_4$, how many grams of Cl_2 can be produced?
(e) How many grams of the excess reactant in part (d) are left unreacted?

42. Silver tarnishes in the presence of hydrogen sulfide (which smells like rotten eggs) and oxygen because of the reaction

$$4\ Ag + 2\ H_2S + O_2 \longrightarrow 2\ Ag_2S + 2\ H_2O$$

(a) How many grams of silver sulfide can be formed from a mixture of 1.1 g Ag, 0.14 g H_2S, and 0.080 g O_2?
(b) How many more grams of H_2S would be needed to completely react all of the Ag?

43. Humans long ago discovered that they could make soap by cooking fat with ashes from a fire. This happens because the ash contains potassium hydroxide that reacts with the triglycerides in the fat to form soap. The chemical reaction for this process is

$$C_3H_5(C_{15}H_{31}CO_2)_3 + 3\ KOH \longrightarrow C_3H_5(OH)_3 + 3\ C_{15}H_{31}CO_2K$$
$$\text{(triglyceride)} \qquad\qquad\qquad\qquad \text{(soap)}$$

If 500.0 g of this triglyceride are mixed with 500.0 g of potassium hydroxide and 361.7 g of soap are produced, what is the percent yield for the reaction?

44. Group 2A metal oxides react with water to produce hydroxides. When 35.55 g of CaO are placed into 125 mL water ($d = 1.000$ g/mL), how many grams of $Ca(OH)_2$ can be produced?

45. When a solution of lead(II) nitrate is mixed with a solution of sodium chromate, a yellow precipitate forms.
(a) Write the balanced equation for the reaction, including the states of all the substances.
(b) When 26.41 g of lead(II) nitrate are mixed with 18.33 g of sodium chromate, what is the percent yield of the solid if 21.23 g are recovered?

46. Ethyl alcohol burns, producing carbon dioxide and water:

$$C_2H_5OH + 3\ O_2 \longrightarrow 2\ CO_2 + 3\ H_2O$$

(a) If 2.5 mol of C_2H_5OH react with 7.5 mol of O_2 in a closed container, what substances and how many moles of each will be present in the container when the reaction has gone to completion?
(b) When 225 g of C_2H_5OH are burned, how many grams of CO_2 and how many grams of H_2O will be produced?

47. After 180.0 g of zinc were dropped into a beaker of hydrochloric acid and the reaction ceased, 35 g of unreacted zinc remained in the beaker:

$$Zn + HCl \longrightarrow ZnCl_2 + H_2$$

(a) How many grams of hydrogen gas were produced?
(b) How many grams of HCl were reacted?
(c) How many more grams of HCl would be required to completely react with the original sample of zinc?

48. Use this equation to answer (a) and (b):

$$Fe(s) + CuSO_4(aq) \longrightarrow Cu(s) + FeSO_4(aq)$$

(a) When 2.0 mol of Fe and 3.0 mol of $CuSO_4$ are reacted, what substances will be present when the reaction is over? How many moles of each substance are present?
(b) When 20.0 g of Fe and 40.0 g of $CuSO_4$ are reacted, what substances will be present when the reaction is over? How many grams of each substance are present?

49. Methyl alcohol (CH_3OH) is made by reacting carbon monoxide and hydrogen in the presence of certain metal oxide catalysts. How much alcohol can be obtained by reacting 40.0 g of CO and 10.0 g of H_2? How many grams of excess reactant remain unreacted?

$$CO(g) + 2\ H_2(g) \longrightarrow CH_3OH(l)$$

50. Ethyl alcohol (C_2H_5OH), also called grain alcohol, can be made by the fermentation of glucose:

$$C_6H_{12}O_6 \longrightarrow 2\ C_2H_5OH + 2\ CO_2$$
$$\text{glucose} \qquad\quad \text{ethyl alcohol}$$

If an 84.6% yield of ethyl alcohol is obtained,
(a) what mass of ethyl alcohol will be produced from 750 g of glucose?
(b) what mass of glucose should be used to produce 475 g of C_2H_5OH?

51. Both $CaCl_2$ and $MgCl_2$ react with $AgNO_3$ to precipitate AgCl. When solutions containing equal masses of $CaCl_2$ and $MgCl_2$ are reacted with $AgNO_3$, which salt solution will produce the larger amount of AgCl? Show proof.

52. An astronaut excretes about 2500 g of water a day. If lithium oxide (Li_2O) is used in the spaceship to absorb this water, how many kilograms of Li_2O must be carried for a 30-day space trip for three astronauts?

$$Li_2O + H_2O \longrightarrow 2\ LiOH$$

53. Much commercial hydrochloric acid is prepared by the reaction of concentrated sulfuric acid with sodium chloride:

$$H_2SO_4 + 2\ NaCl \longrightarrow Na_2SO_4 + 2\ HCl$$

How many kilograms of concentrated H_2SO_4, 96% H_2SO_4 by mass, are required to produce 20.0 L of concentrated hydrochloric acid ($d = 1.20$ g/mL, 42.0% HCl by mass)?

54. Silicon carbide or carborundum is a widely used ceramic material in car brakes and bullet-proof vests because of its hardness. Carborundum is found naturally in the mineral moissanite, but the demand for it exceeds the supply. For this reason it is generally synthesized in the laboratory. The reaction is

$$SiO_2 + 3\ C \longrightarrow SiC + 2\ CO$$

How many kg of silicon carbide can be formed by the reaction of 250.0 kg of sand (SiO_2) with excess carbon?

55. Three chemical reactions that lead to the formation of sulfuric acid are

$$S + O_2 \longrightarrow SO_2$$
$$2\,SO_2 + O_2 \longrightarrow 2\,SO_3$$
$$SO_3 + H_2O \longrightarrow H_2SO_4$$

Starting with 100.0 g of sulfur, how many grams of sulfuric acid will be formed, assuming a 10% loss in each step? What is the percent yield of H_2SO_4?

56. A 10.00-g mixture of $NaHCO_3$ and Na_2CO_3 was heated and yielded 0.0357 mol H_2O and 0.1091 mol CO_2. Calculate the percent composition of the mixture:

$$NaHCO_3 \longrightarrow Na_2O + CO_2 + H_2O$$
$$Na_2CO_3 \longrightarrow Na_2O + CO_2$$

57. Draw a picture showing the reaction of 2 molecules CH_4 with 3 molecules of O_2 to form water and carbon dioxide gas. Also show any unreacted CH_4 and O_2. Does one of the reactants limit the amount of products formed? If so, which one?

CHALLENGE EXERCISES

58. When 12.82 g of a mixture of $KClO_3$ and $NaCl$ are heated strongly, the $KClO_3$ reacts according to this equation:

$$2\,KClO_3(s) \longrightarrow 2\,KCl(s) + 3\,O_2(g)$$

The NaCl does not undergo any reaction. After the heating, the mass of the residue (KCl and NaCl) is 9.45 g. Assuming that all the loss of mass represents loss of oxygen gas, calculate the percent of $KClO_3$ in the original mixture.

59. Gastric juice contains about 3.0 g HCl per liter. If a person produces about 2.5 L of gastric juice per day, how many antacid tablets, each containing 400 mg of $Al(OH)_3$, are needed to neutralize all the HCl produced in one day?

$$Al(OH)_3(s) + 3\,HCl(aq) \longrightarrow AlCl_3(aq) + 3\,H_2O(l)$$

60. Phosphoric acid, H_3PO_4, can be synthesized from phosphorus, oxygen, and water according to these two reactions:

$$4\,P + 5\,O_2 \longrightarrow P_4O_{10}$$
$$P_4O_{10} + 6\,H_2O \longrightarrow 4\,H_3PO_4$$

Starting with 20.0 g P, 30.0 g O_2, and 15.0 g H_2O, what is the mass of phosphoric acid that can be formed?

61. You have just finished your first year of college in South Carolina and decide to take a cross-country trip to visit California. You begin your drive west, but upon arriving in Kansas you discover to your dismay that your funds have dwindled. You meet up with the manager of a feed mill who has just lost his formulations chemist and needs help determining how many bags of feed supplement he can produce with the oats, molasses, alfalfa, and apples that are arriving on Monday. Luckily you just finished your chemistry class and remember learning about limiting reactants. If you can use these ideas to solve the following problem your money worries may be over! Here is the problem: A new customer just ordered a new formulation of supplement containing 25.0 lb of oats, 17.5 lb of molasses, 30.0 lb of alfalfa, and 28.5 lb of apples per bag. If four train cars of materials are due in the plant on Monday containing the components listed below, how much money will you make for the remainder of your trip if you earn $2.25 for every bag of supplement produced?

Raw materials

1 boxcar of oats containing 4.20 tons of oats

1 tanker of molasses containing 2490 gallons of molasses (molasses has a density of 1.46 g/mL)

250.0 crates of apples, each containing 12.5 kg of apples

350.0 bales of alfalfa, each weighing 62.8 kg

ANSWERS TO PRACTICE EXERCISES

9.1 (a) $\dfrac{2\ mol\ KCl}{2\ mol\ KClO_3}$ (b) $\dfrac{2\ mol\ KCl}{3\ mol\ O_2}$

9.2 0.33 mol Al_2O_3

9.3 7.33 mol $Al(OH)_3$

9.4 0.8157 mol KCl, 1.223 mol O_2

9.5 85 g $AgNO_3$

9.6 27.6 g $CrCl_3$

9.7 348.6 g H_2O

9.8 17.7 g HCl

9.9 164.3 g $BaSO_4$

9.10 89.1% yield

Multiple Choice

Choose the correct answer to each of the following.

1. 4.0 g of oxygen contain
   (a) 1.5×10^{23} atoms of oxygen
   (b) 4.0 molar masses of oxygen
   (c) 0.50 mol of oxygen
   (d) 6.022×10^{23} atoms of oxygen

2. One mole of hydrogen atoms contains
   (a) 2.016 g of hydrogen
   (b) 6.022×10^{23} atoms of hydrogen
   (c) 1 atom of hydrogen
   (d) 12 g of carbon-12

3. The mass of one atom of magnesium is
   (a) 24.31 g   (c) 12.00 g
   (b) 54.94 g   (d) 4.037×10^{-23} g

4. Avogadro's number of magnesium atoms
   (a) has a mass of 1.0 g
   (b) has the same mass as Avogadro's number of sulfur atoms
   (c) has a mass of 12.0 g
   (d) is 1 mol of magnesium atoms

5. Which of the following contains the largest number of moles?
   (a) 1.0 g Li   (c) 1.0 g Al
   (b) 1.0 g Na   (d) 1.0 g Ag

6. The number of moles in 112 g of acetylsalicylic acid (aspirin), $C_9H_8O_4$, is
   (a) 1.61   (c) 112
   (b) 0.622   (d) 0.161

7. How many moles of aluminum hydroxide are in one antacid tablet containing 400 mg of $Al(OH)_3$?
   (a) 5.13×10^{-3} (c) 5.13
   (b) 0.400   (d) 9.09×10^{-3}

8. How many grams of Au_2S can be obtained from 1.17 mol of Au?
   (a) 182 g   (c) 364 g
   (b) 249 g   (d) 499 g

9. The molar mass of $Ba(NO_3)_2$ is
   (a) 199.3   (c) 247.3
   (b) 261.3   (d) 167.3

10. A 16-g sample of oxygen
    (a) is 1 mol of O_2
    (b) contains 6.022×10^{23} molecules of O_2
    (c) is 0.50 molecule of O_2
    (d) is 0.50 molar mass of O_2

11. What is the percent composition for a compound formed from 8.15 g of zinc and 2.00 g of oxygen?
    (a) 80.3% Zn, 19.7% O   (c) 70.3% Zn, 29.7% O
    (b) 80.3% O, 19.7% Zn   (d) 65.3% Zn, 34.7% O

12. Which of these compounds contains the largest percentage of oxygen?
    (a) SO_2 (c) N_2O_3
    (b) SO_3 (d) N_2O_5

13. 2.00 mol of CO_2
    (a) have a mass of 56.0 g
    (b) contain 1.20×10^{24} molecules
    (c) have a mass of 44.0 g
    (d) contain 6.00 molar masses of CO_2

14. In Ag_2CO_3, the percent by mass of
    (a) carbon is 43.5%   (c) oxygen is 17.4%
    (b) silver is 64.2%   (d) oxygen is 21.9%

15. The empirical formula of the compound containing 31.0% Ti and 69.0% Cl is
    (a) TiCl   (c) $TiCl_3$
    (b) $TiCl_2$ (d) $TiCl_4$

16. A compound contains 54.3% C, 5.6% H, and 40.1% Cl. The empirical formula is
    (a) CH_3Cl (c) $C_2H_4Cl_2$
    (b) C_2H_5Cl (d) C_4H_5Cl

17. A compound contains 40.0% C, 6.7% H, and 53.3% O. The molar mass is 60.0 g/mol. The molecular formula is
    (a) $C_2H_3O_2$ (c) C_2HO
    (b) C_3H_8O (d) $C_2H_4O_2$

18. How many chlorine atoms are in 4.0 mol of PCl_3?
    (a) 3   (c) 12
    (b) 7.2×10^{24} (d) 2.4×10^{24}

19. What is the mass of 4.53 mol of Na_2SO_4?
    (a) 142.1 g   (c) 31.4 g
    (b) 644 g   (d) 3.19×10^{-2} g

20. The percent composition of Mg_3N_2 is
    (a) 72.2% Mg, 27.8% N   (c) 83.9% Mg, 16.1% N
    (b) 63.4% Mg, 36.6% N   (d) no correct answer given

21. How many grams of oxygen are contained in 0.500 mol of Na_2SO_4?
    (a) 16.0 g   (c) 64.0 g
    (b) 32.0 g   (d) no correct answer given

22. The empirical formula of a compound is CH. If the molar mass of this compound is 78.11, then the molecular formula is
    (a) C_2H_2 (c) C_6H_6
    (b) C_5H_{18} (d) no correct answer given

23. The reaction

    $$BaCl_2 + (NH_4)_2CO_3 \longrightarrow BaCO_3 + 2\ NH_4Cl$$

    is an example of
    (a) combination   (c) single displacement
    (b) decomposition   (d) double displacement

188

24. When the equation

$$Al + O_2 \longrightarrow Al_2O_3$$

is properly balanced, which of the following terms appears?
(a) 2 Al   (b) 2 Al_2O_3 (c) 3 Al   (d) 2 O_2

25. Which equation is *incorrectly* balanced?

(a) 2 $KNO_3 \xrightarrow{\Delta}$ 2 $KNO_2 + O_2$
(b) $H_2O_2 \longrightarrow H_2O + O_2$
(c) 2 Na_2O_2 + 2 $H_2O \longrightarrow$ 4 NaOH + O_2
(d) 2 $H_2O \xrightarrow[H_2SO_4]{electrical\ energy}$ 2 $H_2 + O_2$

26. The reaction

$$2\ Al + 3\ Br_2 \longrightarrow 2\ AlBr_3$$

is an example of
(a) combination   (c) decomposition
(b) single displacement (d) double displacement

27. When the equation

$$PbO_2 \xrightarrow{\Delta} PbO + O_2$$

is balanced, one term in the balanced equation is
(a) PbO_2 (c) 3 PbO
(b) 3 O_2 (d) O_2

28. When the equation

$$Cr_2S_3 + HCl \longrightarrow CrCl_3 + H_2S$$

is balanced, one term in the balanced equation is
(a) 3 HCl   (c) 3 H_2S
(b) $CrCl_3$ (d) 2 Cr_2S_3

29. When the equation

$$F_2 + H_2O \longrightarrow HF + O_2$$

is balanced, one term in the balanced equation is
(a) 2 HF   (c) 4 HF
(b) 3 O_2 (d) 4 H_2O

30. When the equation

$$NH_4OH + H_2SO_4 \longrightarrow$$

is completed and balanced, one term in the balanced equation is
(a) NH_4SO_4 (c) H_2OH
(b) 2 H_2O (d) 2 $(NH_4)_2SO_4$

31. When the equation

$$H_2 + V_2O_5 \longrightarrow V +$$

is completed and balanced, one term in the balanced equation is
(a) 2 V_2O_5 (c) 2 V
(b) 3 H_2O (d) 8 H_2

32. When the equation

$$Al(OH)_3 + H_2SO_4 \longrightarrow Al_2(SO_4)_3 + H_2O$$

is balanced, the sum of the coefficients will be
(a) 9   (c) 12
(b) 11   (d) 15

33. When the equation

$$H_3PO_4 + Ca(OH)_2 \longrightarrow H_2O + Ca_3(PO_4)_2$$

is balanced, the proper sequence of coefficients is
(a) 3, 2, 1, 6   (c) 2, 3, 1, 6
(b) 2, 3, 6, 1   (d) 2, 3, 3, 1

34. When the equation

$$Fe_2(SO_4)_3 + Ba(OH)_2 \longrightarrow$$

is completed and balanced, one term in the balanced equation is
(a) $Ba_2(SO_4)_3$ (c) 2 $Fe_2(SO_4)_3$
(b) 2 $Fe(OH)_2$ (d) 2 $Fe(OH)_3$

35. For the reaction

$$2\ H_2 + O_2 \longrightarrow 2\ H_2O + 572.4\ kJ$$

which of the following is not true?
(a) The reaction is exothermic.
(b) 572.4 kJ of heat are liberated for each mole of water formed.
(c) 2 mol of hydrogen react with 1 mol of oxygen.
(d) 572.4 kJ of heat are liberated for each 2 mol of hydrogen reacted.

36. How many moles are 20.0 g of Na_2CO_3?
(a) 1.89 mol   (c) 212 mol
(b) 2.12 $\times$ 10^3 mol   (d) 0.189 mol

37. What is the mass in grams of 0.30 mol of $BaSO_4$?
(a) 7.0 $\times$ 10^3 g   (c) 70. g
(b) 0.13 g   (d) 700.2 g

38. How many molecules are in 5.8 g of acetone, C_3H_6O?
(a) 0.10 molecule
(b) 6.0 $\times$ 10^{22} molecules
(c) 3.5 $\times$ 10^{24} molecules
(d) 6.0 $\times$ 10^{23} molecules

Problems 39–45 refer to the reaction

$$2\ C_2H_4 + 6\ O_2 \longrightarrow 4\ CO_2 + 4\ H_2O$$

39. If 6.0 mol of CO_2 are produced, how many moles of O_2 were reacted?
(a) 4.0 mol   (c) 9.0 mol
(b) 7.5 mol   (d) 15.0 mol

40. How many moles of O_2 are required for the complete combustion of 45 g of C_2H_4?
(a) 1.3 $\times$ 10^2 mol   (c) 112.5 mol
(b) 0.64 mol   (d) 4.8 mol

41. If 18.0 g of CO_2 are produced, how many grams of H_2O are produced?
(a) 7.37 g   (c) 9.00 g
(b) 3.68 g   (d) 14.7 g

42. How many moles of CO_2 can be produced by the reaction of 5.0 mol of C_2H_4 and 12.0 mol of O_2?
(a) 4.0 mol   (c) 8.0 mol
(b) 5.0 mol   (d) 10. mol

43. How many moles of CO_2 can be produced by the reaction of 0.480 mol of C_2H_4 and 1.08 mol of O_2?
(a) 0.240 mol   (c) 0.720 mol
(b) 0.960 mol   (d) 0.864 mol

44. How many grams of CO_2 can be produced from 2.0 g of C_2H_4 and 5.0 g of O_2?
(a) 5.5 g   (c) 7.6 g
(b) 4.6 g   (d) 6.3 g

45. If 14.0 g of C_2H_4 are reacted and the actual yield of H_2O is 7.84 g, the percent yield in the reaction is
(a) 0.56%   (c) 87.1%
(b) 43.6%   (d) 56.0%

Problems 46–48 refer to the equation

$$H_3PO_4 + MgCO_3 \longrightarrow Mg_3(PO_4)_2 + CO_2 + H_2O$$

46. The sequence of coefficients for the balanced equation is
(a) 2, 3, 1, 3, 3   (c) 2, 2, 1, 2, 3
(b) 3, 1, 3, 2, 3   (d) 2, 3, 1, 3, 2

47. If 20.0 g of carbon dioxide are produced, the number of moles of magnesium carbonate used is
(a) 0.228 mol   (c) 0.910 mol
(b) 1.37 mol   (d) 0.454 mol

48. If 50.0 g of magnesium carbonate react completely with H_3PO_4, the number of grams of carbon dioxide produced is
(a) 52.2 g   (c) 13.1 g
(b) 26.1 g   (d) 50.0 g

49. When 10.0 g of $MgCl_2$ and 10.0 g of Na_2CO_3 are reacted in

$$MgCl_2 + Na_2CO_3 \longrightarrow MgCO_3 + 2\,NaCl$$

the limiting reactant is
(a) $MgCl_2$ (c) $MgCO_3$
(b) Na_2CO_3 (d) NaCl

50. When 50.0 g of copper are reacted with silver nitrate solution

$$Cu + 2\,AgNO_3 \longrightarrow Cu(NO_3)_2 + 2\,Ag$$

148 g of silver are obtained. What is the percent yield of silver obtained?
(a) 87.1%   (c) 55.2%
(b) 84.9%   (d) no correct answer given

Free Response Questions

Answer each of the following. Be sure to include your work and explanations in a clear, logical form.

1. Compound X requires 104 g of O_2 to produce 2 moles of CO_2 and 2.5 moles of H_2O.
   (a) What is the empirical formula for X?
   (b) What additional information would you need to determine the molecular formula for X?

2. Consider the reaction of sulfur dioxide with oxygen to form sulfur trioxide taking place in a closed container.

   (a) Draw what you would expect to see in the box at the completion of the reaction.
   (b) If you begin with 25 g of SO_2 and 5 g of oxygen gas, which is the limiting reagent?
   (c) Is the following statement true or false? "When SO_2 is converted into SO_3, the percent composition of S in the compounds changes from 33% to 25%." Explain.

3. The percent composition of compound Z is 63.16% C and 8.77% H. When compound Z burns in air, the only products are carbon dioxide and water. The molar mass for Z is 114.
   (a) What is the molecular formula for compound Z?
   (b) What is the balanced reaction for Z burning in air?

4. 16% of the U.S. RDA for Ca is 162 mg.
   (a) What mass of calcium phosphate, $Ca_3(PO_4)_2$, provides 162 mg of calcium?

(b) Is $Ca_3(PO_4)_2$ an element, a mixture, or a compound?
(c) Milk is a good source of calcium in the diet. If 120 mL of skim milk provide 13% of the U.S. RDA for Ca, how many cups of milk should you drink per day if that is your only source of calcium?

5. Compound A decomposes at room temperature in an exothermic reaction, while compound B requires heating before it will decompose in an endothermic reaction.
   (a) Draw reaction profiles (potential energy vs. reaction progress) for both reactions.
   (b) The decomposition of 0.500 mol of $NaHCO_3$ to form sodium carbonate, water, and carbon dioxide requires 85.5 kJ of heat. How many grams of water could be collected, and how many kJ of heat are absorbed when 24.0 g of CO_2 are produced?
   (c) Could $NaHCO_3$ be compound A or compound B? Explain your reasoning.

6. Aqueous ammonium hydroxide reacts with aqueous cobalt(II) sulfate to produce aqueous ammonium sulfate and solid cobalt(II) hydroxide. When 38.0 g of one of the reactants is fully reacted with enough of the other reactant, 8.09 g of ammonium sulfate is obtained, which corresponded to a 25.0% yield.
   (a) What type of reaction took place?
   (b) Write the balanced chemical equation.
   (c) What is the theoretical yield of ammonium sulfate?
   (d) Which reactant was the limiting reagent?

7. $C_6H_{12}O_6 \longrightarrow 2\,C_2H_5OH + 2\,CO_2(g)$
   (a) If 25.0 g of $C_6H_{12}O_6$ were used, and only 11.2 g of C_2H_5OH were produced, how much reactant was left over and what volume of gas was produced? (*Note:* One mole of gas occupies 24.0 L of space at room temperature.)
   (b) What was the yield of the reaction?
   (c) What type of reaction took place?

8. When solutions containing 25 g each of lead(II) nitrate and potassium iodide were mixed, a yellow precipitate resulted.
   (a) What type of reaction occurred?
   (b) What are the name and formula for the solid product?
   (c) If after filtration and drying, the solid product weighed 7.66 g, what was the percent yield for the reaction?

9. Consider the following unbalanced reaction:

$$XNO_3 + CaCl_2 \longrightarrow XCl + Ca(NO_3)_2$$

   (a) If 30.8 g of $CaCl_2$ produced 79.6 g of XCl, what is X?
   (b) Would X be able to displace hydrogen from an acid?

10. Consider the following reaction: $H_2O_2 \longrightarrow H_2O + O_2$
   (a) If at the end of the reaction there are eight water molecules and eight oxygen molecules, what was in the flask at the start of the reaction?
   (b) Does the following reaction profile indicate the reaction is exothermic or endothermic?

Reaction progress

   (c) What type of reaction is given above?
   (d) What is the empirical formula for hydrogen peroxide?

The amazing colors in these fireworks explosions are the result of electrons transferring between energy levels in atoms.

© Hannu Viitanen/iStockphoto

CHAPTER **10**

MODERN ATOMIC THEORY AND THE PERIODIC TABLE

How do we go about studying an object that is too small to see? Think back to that birthday present you could look at but not yet open. Judging from the wrapping and size of the box was not very useful, but shaking, turning, and lifting the package all gave indirect clues to its contents. After all your experiments were done, you could make a fairly good guess about the contents. But was your guess correct? The only way to know for sure would be to open the package.

Chemists have the same dilemma when they study the atom. Atoms are so very small that it isn't possible to use the normal senses to describe them. We are essentially working in the dark with this package we call the atom. However, our improvements in instruments (X-ray machines and scanning tunneling microscopes) and measuring devices (spectrophotometers and magnetic resonance imaging, MRI) as well as in our mathematical skills are bringing us closer to revealing the secrets of the atom.

10.1 ELECTROMAGNETIC RADIATION

LEARNING OBJECTIVE ● List the three basic characteristics of electromagnetic radiation.

KEY TERMS
wavelength
frequency
speed
photons

In the last 200 years, vast amounts of data have been accumulated to support the atomic theory. When atoms were originally suggested by the early Greeks, no physical evidence existed to support their ideas. Early chemists did a variety of experiments, which culminated in Dalton's model of the atom. Because of the limitations of Dalton's model, modifications were proposed first by Thomson and then by Rutherford, which eventually led to our modern concept of the nuclear atom. These early models of the atom work reasonably well—in fact, we continue to use them to visualize a variety of chemical concepts. There remain questions that these models cannot answer, including an explanation of how atomic structure relates to the periodic table. In this chapter, we will present our modern model of the atom; we will see how it varies from and improves upon the earlier atomic models.

Electromagnetic Radiation

Scientists have studied energy and light for centuries, and several models have been proposed to explain how energy is transferred from place to place. One way energy travels through space is by *electromagnetic radiation*. Examples of electromagnetic radiation include light from the sun, X-rays in your dentist's office, microwaves from your microwave oven, radio and television waves, and radiant heat from your fireplace. While these examples seem quite different, they are all similar in some important ways. Each shows wavelike behavior, and all travel at the same speed in a vacuum (3.00×10^8 m/s).

The study of wave behavior is a topic for another course, but we need some basic terminology to understand atoms. Waves have three basic characteristics: wavelength, frequency, and speed. **Wavelength** (lambda, λ) is the distance between consecutive peaks (or troughs) in a wave, as shown in **Figure 10.1**. **Frequency** (nu, ν) tells how many waves pass a particular point per second. **Speed** (ν) tells how fast a wave moves through space.

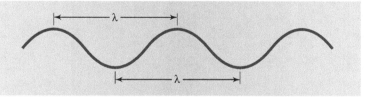

Figure 10.1
The wavelength of this wave is shown by λ. It can be measured from peak to peak or trough to trough.

Surfers judge the wavelength, frequency, and speed of waves to get the best ride.

Light is one form of electromagnetic radiation and is usually classified by its wavelength, as shown in **Figure 10.2**. Visible light, as you can see, is only a tiny part of the electromagnetic spectrum. Some examples of electromagnetic radiation involved in energy transfer outside the visible region are hot coals in your backyard grill, which transfer infrared radiation to cook your food, and microwaves, which transfer energy to water molecules in the food, causing them to move more quickly and thus raise the temperature of the food.

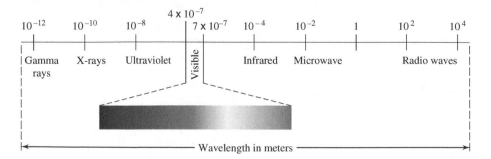

Figure 10.2
The electromagnetic spectrum.

>CHEMISTRY *IN ACTION*

You Light Up My Life

Birds in the parrot family have an unusual way to attract their mates—their feathers glow in the dark! This phenomenon is called fluorescence. It results from the absorption of ultraviolet (UV) light, which is then reemitted at longer wavelengths that both birds and people can see. In everyday life this happens in a fluorescent bulb or in the many glow-in-the-dark products such as light sticks.

Kathleen Arnold from the University of Glasgow, Scotland, discovered that the feathers of parrots that fluoresced were only those used in display or those shown off during courtship. She decided to experiment using budgerigars with their natural colors. The researchers offered birds a choice of two companion birds, which were smeared with petroleum jelly. One of the potential companions also had a UV blocker in the petroleum jelly. The birds clearly preferred companions without the UV blocker, leading the researchers to conclude that the parrots prefer to court radiant partners. The researchers also tested same-sex companions and discovered they did not prefer radiant companions.

Perhaps we may find that the glow of candlelight really does add to the radiance of romance. Ultraviolet light certainly does for parrots!

Courtesy of NJ Marshall, University of Queensland

Budgerigars under normal light and under UV light showing the glow used to attract mates.

We have evidence for the wavelike nature of light. We also know that a beam of light behaves like a stream of tiny packets of energy called **photons**. So what is light exactly? Is it a particle? Is it a wave? Scientists have agreed to explain the properties of electromagnetic radiation by using both wave and particle properties. Neither explanation is ideal, but currently these are our best models.

EXAMPLE 10.1

What is a wavelength?

SOLUTION

A wavelength is the distance between consecutive peaks or troughs of a wave. The symbol used for wavelength is lambda (λ).

PRACTICE 10.1

Draw a wave function and indicate the distance of two wavelengths (2 lambda).

10.2 THE BOHR ATOM

Explain the relationship between the line spectrum and the quantized energy levels of an electron in an atom.

● LEARNING OBJECTIVE

As scientists struggled to understand the properties of electromagnetic radiation, evidence began to accumulate that atoms could radiate light. At high temperatures, or when subjected to high voltages, elements in the gaseous state give off colored light. Brightly colored neon signs illustrate this property of matter very well. When the light emitted by a gas is passed through a prism or diffraction grating, a set of brightly colored lines called

KEY TERMS

line spectrum
quanta
ground state
orbital

410   434   486   656

(in nanometers)

Figure 10.3

Line spectrum of hydrogen. Each line corresponds to the wavelength of the energy emitted when the electron of a hydrogen atom, which has absorbed energy, falls back to a lower principal energy level.

a **line spectrum** results (Figure 10.3). These colored lines indicate that the light is being emitted only at certain wavelengths, or frequencies, that correspond to specific colors. Each element possesses a unique set of these spectral lines that is different from the sets of all the other elements.

In 1912–1913, while studying the line spectrum of hydrogen, Niels Bohr (1885–1962), a Danish physicist, made a significant contribution to the rapidly growing knowledge of atomic structure. His research led him to believe that electrons exist in specific regions at various distances from the nucleus. He also visualized the electrons as revolving in orbits around the nucleus, like planets rotating around the sun, as shown in Figure 10.4.

Bohr's first paper in this field dealt with the hydrogen atom, which he described as a single electron revolving in an orbit about a relatively heavy nucleus. He applied the concept of energy quanta, proposed in 1900 by the German physicist Max Planck (1858–1947), to the observed line spectrum of hydrogen. Planck stated that energy is never emitted in a continuous stream but only in small, discrete packets called **quanta** (Latin, *quantus*, "how much"). From this, Bohr theorized that electrons have several possible energies corresponding to several possible orbits at different distances from the nucleus. Therefore, an electron has to be in one specific energy level; it cannot exist between energy levels. In other words, the energy of the electron is said to be quantized. Bohr also stated that when a hydrogen atom absorbed one or more quanta of energy, its electron would "jump" to a higher energy level.

Bohr was able to account for spectral lines of hydrogen this way. A number of energy levels are available, the lowest of which is called the **ground state**. When an electron falls from a high energy level to a lower one (say, from the fourth to the second), a quantum of energy is emitted as light at a specific frequency, or wavelength (Figure 10.5). This light corresponds to one of the lines visible in the hydrogen spectrum (Figure 10.3). Several lines are visible in this spectrum, each one corresponding to a specific electron energy-level shift within the hydrogen atom.

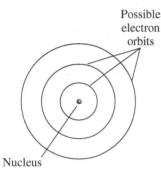

Possible electron orbits

Nucleus

Figure 10.4

The Bohr model of the hydrogen atom described the electron revolving in certain allowed circular orbits around the nucleus.

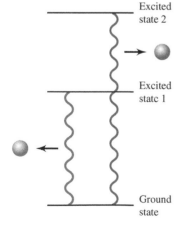

Excited state 2

Excited state 1

Ground state

Figure 10.5

When an excited electron returns to the ground state, energy emitted as a photon is released. The color (wavelength) of the light is determined by the difference in energy between the two states (excited and ground).

EXAMPLE 10.2

What does the line spectrum of a hydrogen atom illustrate?

SOLUTION

Each line shows the frequency of light energy emitted when an electron that has absorbed energy falls from a higher energy level to a lower energy level.

PRACTICE 10.2

What is a photon?

The chemical properties of an element and its position in the periodic table depend on electron behavior within the atoms. In turn, much of our knowledge of the behavior of electrons within atoms is based on spectroscopy. Niels Bohr contributed a great deal to our knowledge of atomic structure by (1) suggesting quantized energy levels for electrons and (2) showing that spectral lines result from the radiation of small increments of energy (Planck's quanta) when electrons shift from one energy level to another. Bohr's calculations succeeded very well in correlating the experimentally observed spectral lines with electron energy levels for the hydrogen atom. However, Bohr's methods of calculation did not succeed for heavier atoms. More theoretical work on atomic structure was needed.

In 1924, the French physicist Louis de Broglie (1892–1957) suggested a surprising hypothesis: All objects have wave properties. Louis de Broglie used sophisticated mathematics to show that the wave properties for an object of ordinary size, such as a baseball, are too small to be observed. But for smaller objects, such as an electron, the wave properties become significant. Other scientists confirmed de Broglie's hypothesis, showing that electrons do exhibit wave properties. In 1926, Erwin Schrödinger (1887–1961), an Austrian physicist, created a mathematical model that described electrons as waves. Using Schrödinger's wave mechanics, we can determine the *probability* of finding an electron in a certain region around the nucleus of the atom.

This treatment of the atom led to a new branch of physics called *wave mechanics* or *quantum mechanics*, which forms the basis for our modern understanding of atomic structure. Although the wave-mechanical description of the atom is mathematical, it can be translated, at least in part, into a visual model. It is important to recognize that we cannot locate an electron precisely within an atom; however, it is clear that electrons are not revolving around the nucleus in orbits as Bohr postulated. The electrons are instead found in *orbitals*. An **orbital** is pictured in Figure 10.6 as a region in space around the nucleus where there is a high probability of finding a given electron.

Figure 10.6
An orbital for a hydrogen atom. The intensity of the dots shows that the electron spends more time closer to the nucleus.

10.3 ENERGY LEVELS OF ELECTRONS

Describe the principal energy levels, sublevels, and orbitals of an atom.

● LEARNING OBJECTIVE

KEY TERMS
principal energy levels
sublevels
spin
Pauli exclusion principle

One of the ideas Bohr contributed to the modern concept of the atom was that the energy of the electron is quantized—that is, the electron is restricted to only certain allowed energies. The wave-mechanical model of the atom also predicts discrete **principal energy levels** within the atom. These energy levels are designated by the letter n, where n is a positive integer (Figure 10.7). The lowest principal energy level corresponds to $n = 1$, the next to $n = 2$, and so on. As n increases, the energy of the electron increases, and the electron is found on average farther from the nucleus.

Each principal energy level is divided into **sublevels**, which are illustrated in Figure 10.8. The first principal energy level has one sublevel. The second principal energy level has two sublevels, the third energy level has three sublevels, and so on. Each of these sublevels contains spaces for electrons called orbitals.

In each sublevel the electrons are found within specified orbitals (s, p, d, f). Let's consider each principal energy level in turn. The first principal energy level ($n = 1$) has one

Figure 10.7
The first four principal energy levels in the hydrogen atom. Each level is assigned a principal quantum number n.

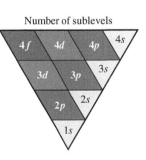

Figure 10.8
The types of orbitals on each of the first four principal energy levels.

Figure 10.9

Perspective representation of the p_x, p_y, and p_z atomic orbitals.

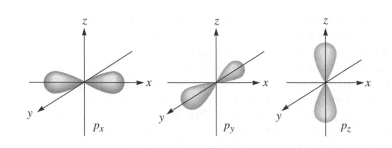

sublevel or type of orbital. It is spherical in shape and is designated as 1s. It is important to understand what the spherical shape of the 1s orbital means. The electron does *not* move around on the surface of the sphere, but rather the surface encloses a space where there is a 90% probability where the electron may be found. It might help to consider these orbital shapes in the same way we consider the atmosphere. There is no distinct dividing line between the atmosphere and "space." The boundary is quite fuzzy. The same is true for atomic orbitals. Each has a region of highest density roughly corresponding to its shape. The probability of finding the electron outside this region drops rapidly but never quite reaches zero. Scientists often speak of orbitals as electron "clouds" to emphasize the fuzzy nature of their boundaries.

How many electrons can fit into a 1s orbital? To answer this question, we need to consider one more property of electrons. This property is called **spin**. Each electron appears to be spinning on an axis, like a globe. It can only spin in two directions. We represent this spin with an arrow: ↑ *or* ↓. In order to occupy the same orbital, electrons must have *opposite* spins. That is, two electrons with the same spin cannot occupy the same orbital. This gives us the answer to our question: An atomic orbital can hold a maximum of two electrons, which must have opposite spins. This rule is called the **Pauli exclusion principle**. The first principal energy level contains one type of orbital (1s) that holds a maximum of two electrons.

What happens with the second principal energy level ($n = 2$)? Here we find two sublevels, 2s and 2p. Like 1s in the first principal energy level, the 2s orbital is spherical in shape but is larger in size and higher in energy. It also holds a maximum of two electrons. The second type of orbital is designated by 2p. The 2p sublevel consists of three orbitals: $2p_x$, $2p_y$, and $2p_z$. The shape of p orbitals is quite different from the s orbitals, as shown in Figure 10.9.

Each p orbital has two "lobes." Remember, the space enclosed by these surfaces represents the regions of probability for finding the electrons 90% of the time. There are three separate p orbitals, each oriented in a different direction, and each p orbital can hold a maximum of two electrons. Thus the total number of electrons that can reside in all three p orbitals is six. To summarize our model, the first principal energy level of an atom has a 1s orbital. The second principal energy level has a 2s and three 2p orbitals labeled $2p_x$, $2p_y$, and $2p_z$, as shown in Figure 10.10.

Notice that there is a correspondence between the energy level and number of sublevels.

The third principal energy level has three sublevels labeled 3s, 3p, and 3d. The 3s orbital is spherical and larger than the 1s and 2s orbitals. The $3p_x$, $3p_y$, and $3p_z$ orbitals are shaped

Figure 10.10

Orbitals on the second principal energy level are one 2s and three 2p orbitals.

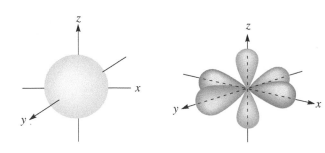

s orbital   p orbitals

>CHEMISTRY *IN ACTION*

Atomic Clocks

Imagine a clock that keeps time to within 1 second over a million years. The National Institute of Standards and Technology in Boulder, Colorado, has an atomic clock that does just that—a little better than your average alarm, grandfather, or cuckoo clock! This atomic clock serves as the international standard for time and frequency. How does it work?

Within the case are several layers of magnetic shielding. In the heart of the clock is a small oven that heats cesium metal to release cesium atoms, which are collected into a narrow beam (1 mm wide). The beam of atoms passes down a long evacuated tube while being excited by a laser until all the cesium atoms are in the same electron state.

The atoms then enter another chamber filled with reflecting microwaves. The frequency of the microwaves (9,192,631,770 cycles per second) is exactly the same frequency required to excite a cesium atom from its ground state to the next higher energy level. These excited cesium atoms then release electromagnetic radiation in a process known as fluorescence. Electronic circuits maintain the microwave frequency at precisely the right level to keep the cesium atoms moving from one level to the next. One second is equal to 9,192,631,770 of these vibrations. The clock is set to this frequency and can keep accurate time for over a million years.

This clock automatically updates itself by comparing time with an atomic clock by radio signal.

like those of the second level, only larger. The five $3d$ orbitals have the shapes shown in Figure 10.11. You don't need to memorize these shapes, but notice that they look different from the s or p orbitals.

Each time a new principal energy level is added, we also add a new sublevel. This makes sense because each energy level corresponds to a larger average distance from the nucleus, which provides more room on each level for new sublevels containing more orbitals.

The pattern continues with the fourth principal energy level. It has $4s$, $4p$, $4d$, and $4f$ orbitals. There are one $4s$, three $4p$, five $4d$, and seven $4f$ orbitals. The shapes of the s, p, and d orbitals are the same as those for lower levels, only larger. We will not consider the shapes of the f orbitals. Remember that for all s, p, d, and f orbitals, the maximum number of electrons per orbital is two. We summarize each principal energy level:

$n = 1$	$1s$			
$n = 2$	$2s$	$2p$ $2p$ $2p$		
$n = 3$	$3s$	$3p$ $3p$ $3p$	$3d$ $3d$ $3d$ $3d$ $3d$	
$n = 4$	$4s$	$4p$ $4p$ $4p$	$4d$ $4d$ $4d$ $4d$ $4d$	$4f$ $4f$ $4f$ $4f$ $4f$ $4f$ $4f$

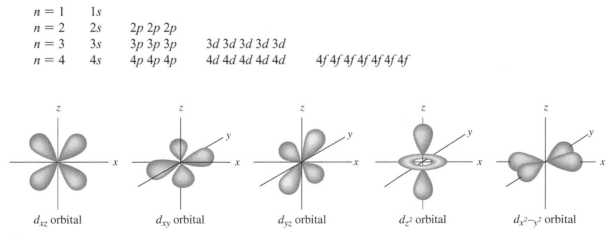

d_{xz} orbital d_{xy} orbital d_{yz} orbital d_{z^2} orbital $d_{x^2-y^2}$ orbital

Figure 10.11

The five d orbitals are found in the third principal energy level along with one $3s$ orbital and three $3p$ orbitals.

EXAMPLE 10.3

Energy levels of the atoms are designated as principal energy levels and energy sublevels.

(a) What labels are used for these energy levels?
(b) How many of each of these labels are there?

SOLUTION

(a) The letter n is used to designate the principal energy levels. The letters s, p, d, and f are used to designate the energy sublevels.
(b) According to the periodic table, there are seven (7) principal energy levels and $2s$, $6p$, $10d$, and $14f$ energy sublevels.

PRACTICE 10.3

(a) How many electrons can occupy a single subenergy level?
(b) What is the maximum number of electrons that can occupy the third principal energy level? List them.

Figure 10.12

The modern concept of a hydrogen atom consists of a proton and an electron in an s orbital. The shaded area represents a region where the electron may be found with 90% probability.

The hydrogen atom consists of a nucleus (containing one proton) and one electron occupying a region outside of the nucleus. In its ground state, the electron occupies a $1s$ orbital, but by absorbing energy the electron can become *excited* and move to a higher energy level.

The hydrogen atom can be represented as shown in **Figure 10.12**. The diameter of the nucleus is about 10^{-13} cm, and the diameter of the electron orbital is about 10^{-8} cm. The diameter of the electron cloud of a hydrogen atom is about 100,000 times greater than the diameter of the nucleus.

10.4 ATOMIC STRUCTURES OF THE FIRST 18 ELEMENTS

LEARNING OBJECTIVE • Use the guidelines to write electron configurations.

KEY TERMS

electron configuration
orbital diagram
valence electrons

We have seen that hydrogen has one electron that can occupy a variety of orbitals in different principal energy levels. Now let's consider the structure of atoms with more than one electron. Because all atoms contain orbitals similar to those found in hydrogen, we can describe the structures of atoms beyond hydrogen by systematically placing electrons in these hydrogen-like orbitals. We use the following guidelines:

1. No more than two electrons can occupy one orbital.

2. Electrons occupy the lowest energy orbitals available. They enter a higher energy orbital only when the lower orbitals are filled. For the atoms beyond hydrogen, orbital energies vary as $s < p < d < f$ for a given value of n.

3. Each orbital in a sublevel is occupied by a single electron before a second electron enters. For example, all three p orbitals must contain one electron before a second electron enters a p orbital.

We can use several methods to represent the atomic structures of atoms, depending on what we are trying to illustrate. When we want to show both the nuclear makeup and the electron structure of each principal energy level (without orbital detail), we can use a diagram such as **Figure 10.13**.

Figure 10.13

Atomic structure diagrams of fluorine, sodium, and magnesium atoms. The number of protons and neutrons is shown in the nucleus. The number of electrons is shown in each principal energy level outside the nucleus.

Fluorine atom

Sodium atom   Magnesium atom

Often we are interested in showing the arrangement of the electrons in an atom in their orbitals. There are two ways to do this. The first method is called the **electron configuration**. In this method, we list each type of orbital, showing the number of electrons in it as an exponent. An electron configuration is read as follows:

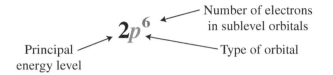

We can also represent this configuration with an **orbital diagram** in which boxes represent the orbitals (containing small arrows indicating the electrons). When the orbital contains one electron, an arrow, pointing upward ($\uparrow$), is placed in the box. A second arrow, pointing downward ($\downarrow$), indicates the second electron in that orbital.

Let's consider each of the first 18 elements on the periodic table in turn. The order of filling for the orbitals in these elements is $1s$, $2s$, $2p$, $3s$, $3p$, and $4s$. Hydrogen, the first element, has only one electron. The electron will be in the $1s$ orbital because this is the most favorable position (where it will have the greatest attraction for the nucleus). Both representations are shown here:

H $\boxed{\uparrow}$ $1s^1$

Orbital   Electron
diagram configuration

Helium, with two electrons, can be shown as

He $\boxed{\uparrow\downarrow}$ $1s^2$

Orbital   Electron
diagram configuration

The first energy level, which can hold a maximum of two electrons, is now full. An atom with three electrons will have its third electron in the second principal energy level. Thus, in lithium (atomic number 3), the first two electrons are in the $1s$ orbital, and the third electron is in the $2s$ orbital of the second energy level.

Lithium has the following structure:

Li $\boxed{\uparrow\downarrow}$ $\boxed{\uparrow}$ $1s^2 2s^1$
    $1s$ $2s$

All four electrons of beryllium are s electrons:

Be $\boxed{\uparrow\downarrow}$ $\boxed{\uparrow\downarrow}$ $1s^2 2s^2$
    $1s$ $2s$

The next six elements illustrate the filling of the p orbitals. Boron has the first p electron. Because p orbitals all have the same energy, it doesn't matter which of these orbitals fills first:

B $\boxed{\uparrow\downarrow}$ $\boxed{\uparrow\downarrow}$ $\boxed{\uparrow||}$ $1s^2 2s^2 2p^1$
   $1s$ $2s$ $2p$

Carbon is the sixth element. It has two electrons in the $1s$ orbital, two electrons in the $2s$ orbital, and two electrons to place in the $2p$ orbitals. Because it is more difficult for the p electrons to pair up than to occupy a second p orbital, the second p electron is located in a different p orbital. We could show this by writing $2p_x^1 2p_y^1$, but we usually write it as $2p^2$; it is *understood* that the electrons are in different p orbitals. The spins on these electrons are alike, for reasons we will not explain here.

C $\boxed{\uparrow\downarrow}$ $\boxed{\uparrow\downarrow}$ $\boxed{\uparrow|\uparrow|}$ $1s^2 2s^2 2p^2$
   $1s$ $2s$ $2p$

Nitrogen has seven electrons. They occupy the $1s$, $2s$, and $2p$ orbitals. The third p electron in nitrogen is still unpaired and is found in the $2p_z$ orbital:

Oxygen is the eighth element. It has two electrons in both the $1s$ and $2s$ orbitals and four electrons in the $2p$ orbitals. One of the $2p$ orbitals is now occupied by a second electron, which has a spin opposite the electron already in that orbital:

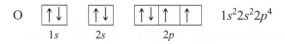

The next two elements are fluorine with nine electrons and neon with ten electrons:

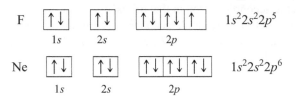

With neon, the first and second energy levels are filled as shown in Table 10.1. The second energy level can hold a maximum of eight electrons, $2s^2 2p^6$.

Sodium, element 11, has two electrons in the first energy level and eight electrons in the second energy level, with the remaining electron occupying the $3s$ orbital in the third energy level:

TABLE 10.1   Orbital Filling for the First Ten Elements*

Atomic number	Element	Orbitals			Electron configuration
		$1s$	$2s$	$2p$	
1	H	↑			$1s^1$
2	He	↑↓			$1s^2$
3	Li	↑↓	↑		$1s^2 2s^1$
4	Be	↑↓	↑↓		$1s^2 2s^2$
5	B	↑↓	↑↓	↑	$1s^2 2s^2 2p^1$
6	C	↑↓	↑↓	↑ ↑	$1s^2 2s^2 2p^2$
7	N	↑↓	↑↓	↑ ↑ ↑	$1s^2 2s^2 2p^3$
8	O	↑↓	↑↓	↑↓ ↑ ↑	$1s^2 2s^2 2p^4$
9	F	↑↓	↑↓	↑↓ ↑↓ ↑	$1s^2 2s^2 2p^5$
10	Ne	↑↓	↑↓	↑↓ ↑↓ ↑↓	$1s^2 2s^2 2p^6$

*Boxes represent the orbitals grouped by sublevel. Electrons are shown by arrows.

TABLE 10.2 Orbital Diagrams and Electron Configurations for Elements 11–18

Atomic number	Element	Orbitals					Electron configuration
		1s	2s	2p	3s	3p	
11	Na	↑↓	↑↓	↑↓ ↑↓ ↑↓	↑		$1s^22s^22p^63s^1$
12	Mg	↑↓	↑↓	↑↓ ↑↓ ↑↓	↑↓		$1s^22s^22p^63s^2$
13	Al	↑↓	↑↓	↑↓ ↑↓ ↑↓	↑↓	↑	$1s^22s^22p^63s^23p^1$
14	Si	↑↓	↑↓	↑↓ ↑↓ ↑↓	↑↓	↑ ↑	$1s^22s^22p^63s^23p^2$
15	P	↑↓	↑↓	↑↓ ↑↓ ↑↓	↑↓	↑ ↑ ↑	$1s^22s^22p^63s^23p^3$
16	S	↑↓	↑↓	↑↓ ↑↓ ↑↓	↑↓	↑↓ ↑ ↑	$1s^22s^22p^63s^23p^4$
17	Cl	↑↓	↑↓	↑↓ ↑↓ ↑↓	↑↓	↑↓ ↑↓ ↑	$1s^22s^22p^63s^23p^5$
18	Ar	↑↓	↑↓	↑↓ ↑↓ ↑↓	↑↓	↑↓ ↑↓ ↑↓	$1s^22s^22p^63s^23p^6$

Magnesium (12), aluminum (13), silicon (14), phosphorus (15), sulfur (16), chlorine (17), and argon (18) follow in order. Table 10.2 summarizes the filling of the orbitals for elements 11–18.

The electrons in the outermost (highest) energy level of an atom are called the **valence electrons**. For example, oxygen, which has the electron configuration of $1s^22s^22p^4$, has electrons in the first and second energy levels. Therefore, the second principal energy level is the valence level for oxygen. The $2s$ and $2p$ electrons are the valence electrons. Valence electrons are involved in bonding atoms together to form compounds and are of particular interest to chemists, as we will see in Chapter 11.

The number of the column in 1A–7A of the periodic table gives the number of valence electrons of the element in those columns.

EXAMPLE 10.4

What is the electron configuration for the valence electrons in magnesium?

SOLUTION

Magnesium has the electron configuration of $1s^22s^22p^63s^2$. The electrons are in the first, second, and third energy levels. This means the valence electrons are in the third energy level. The $3s$ electrons are the valence electrons for magnesium. The electron configuration for the valence electrons in $3s^2$.

PRACTICE 10.4

Give the electron configuration for the valence electrons in these elements.

(a) B   (b) N   (c) Na   (d) Cl

10.5 ELECTRON STRUCTURES AND THE PERIODIC TABLE

Describe how the electron configurations of the atoms relate to their position on the periodic table and write electron configurations for elements based on their position on the periodic table.

● **LEARNING OBJECTIVE**

KEY TERMS

period
groups or families (of elements)
representative elements
transition elements

We have seen how the electrons are assigned for the atoms of elements 1–18. How do the electron structures of these atoms relate to their position on the periodic table? To answer this question, we need to look at the periodic table more closely.

>CHEMISTRY *IN ACTION*
Collecting the Elements

Theodore Gray loves collecting samples of elements. He had an idea several years ago to design a conference table for his company, Wolfram Research in Champaign, Illinois. He built the table in the shape of the periodic table and made little boxes below each element to house a sample of the element. As he was collecting the element samples, he began to realize that he needed to keep track of where each sample had come from before he forgot. So he began to keep notes on each element sample, where he obtained it, what it was, and why it was there. Gray says, "Once I had collected three or four dozen such descriptions, I thought, "'Well I had better put this on a website, because that's what you do when you have anything these days—you put it on your own website." His element collection is ever expanding and contains more than 1400 samples.

Theodore Gray's websites, http://www.theodoregray.com/PeriodicTable and periodictable.com, both include elemental data and many stories that are both entertaining and very distracting. Gray also has created video for each element from all angles in stunning high-resolution photography, formed into video loops. He used to take all the photos himself, but the project has grown so big he now has an assistant and utilizes Mathematica, a computer program from Wolfram Research, to help him. He has also created a beautiful periodic table poster from the element images.

Take a couple of minutes and spend some time with Gray on his websites enjoying the photos and stories of the elements. He has some truly amazing examples of the elements.

Theodore Gray and his periodic table conference table containing samples of each element.

The periodic table represents the efforts of chemists to organize the elements logically. Chemists of the early nineteenth century had sufficient knowledge of the properties of elements to recognize similarities among groups of elements. In 1869, Dimitri Mendeleev (1834–1907) of Russia and Lothar Meyer (1830–1895) of Germany independently published periodic arrangements of the elements based on increasing atomic masses. Mendeleev's arrangement is the precursor to the modern periodic table, and his name is associated with it. The modern periodic table is shown on the inside front cover of this book.

Each horizontal row in the periodic table is called a **period**, as shown in Figure 10.14. There are seven periods of elements. The number of each period corresponds to the outermost

Figure 10.14

The periodic table of the elements.

Figure 10.15

Valence electron configurations for the first 18 elements.

							Noble gases
1A							

1 **H** $1s^1$	2A	3A	4A	5A	6A	7A	2 **He** $1s^2$
3 **Li** $2s^1$	4 **Be** $2s^2$	5 **B** $2s^22p^1$	6 **C** $2s^22p^2$	7 **N** $2s^22p^3$	8 **O** $2s^22p^4$	9 **F** $2s^22p^5$	10 **Ne** $2s^22p^6$
11 **Na** $3s^1$	12 **Mg** $3s^2$	13 **Al** $3s^23p^1$	14 **Si** $3s^23p^2$	15 **P** $3s^23p^3$	16 **S** $3s^23p^4$	17 **Cl** $3s^23p^5$	18 **Ar** $3s^23p^6$

energy level that contains electrons for elements in that period. Those in Period 1 contain electrons only in energy level 1, while those in Period 2 contain electrons in levels 1 and 2. In Period 3, electrons are found in levels 1, 2, 3, and so on.

Elements that behave in a similar manner are found in **groups** or **families**. These form the vertical columns on the periodic table. Two systems exist for numbering the groups. In one system, the columns are numbered from left to right using the numbers 1–18. However, we use a system that numbers the columns with numbers and the letters A and B, as shown in Figure 10.14. The A groups are known as the **representative elements**. The B groups are called the **transition elements**. In this book we will focus on the representative elements. The groups (columns) of the periodic table often have family names. For example, the group on the far right side of the periodic table (He, Ne, Ar, Kr, Xe, and Rn) is called the *noble gases*. Group 1A is called the *alkali metals*, Group 2A the *alkaline earth metals*, and Group 7A the *halogens*.

How is the structure of the periodic table related to the atomic structures of the elements? We've just seen that the periods of the periodic table are associated with the energy level of the outermost electrons of the atoms in that period. Look at the valence electron configurations of the elements we have just examined (**Figure 10.15**). Do you see a pattern? The valence electron configuration for the elements in each column is the same. The chemical behavior and properties of elements in a particular family must therefore be associated with the electron configuration of the elements. The number for the principal energy level is different. This is expected since each new period is associated with a different energy level for the valence electrons.

The electron configurations for elements beyond these first 18 become long and tedious to write. We often abbreviate the electron configuration using the following notation:

Na   [Ne]$3s^1$

Look carefully at Figure 10.15 and you will see that the p orbitals are full at the noble gases. By placing the symbol for the noble gas in square brackets, we can abbreviate the complete electron configuration and focus our attention on the valence electrons (the electrons we will be interested in when we discuss bonding in Chapter 11). To write the abbreviated electron configuration for any element, go back to the previous noble gas and place its symbol in square brackets. Then list the valence electrons. Here are some examples:

B $1s^22s^22p^1$ [He] $2s^22p^1$

Cl $1s^22s^22p^63s^23p^5$ [Ne] $3s^23p^5$

Na $1s^22s^22p^63s^1$ [Ne] $3s^1$

The sequence for filling the orbitals is exactly as we would expect up through the $3p$ orbitals. The third energy level might be expected to fill with $3d$ electrons before electrons enter the $4s$ orbital, but this is not the case. The behavior and properties of the next two elements, potassium (19) and calcium (20), are very similar to the elements in Groups 1A and 2A, respectively. They clearly belong in these groups. The other elements in Group 1A and Group 2A have electron configurations that indicate valence electrons in the s orbitals. For example, since the electron configuration is connected to the element's properties,

Both numbering systems are shown in the periodic table on the inside front cover.

we should place the last electrons for potassium and calcium in the $4s$ orbital. Their electron configurations are

K $1s^2 2s^2 2p^6 3s^2 3p^6 4s^1$ or $[Ar]\,4s^1$

Ca $1s^2 2s^2 2p^6 3s^2 3p^6 4s^2$ or $[Ar]\,4s^2$

PRACTICE 10.5

Write the abbreviated electron configuration for the following elements:
(a) Br   (b) Sr   (c) Ba   (d) Te

Elements 21–30 belong to the elements known as *transition elements*. Electrons are placed in the $3d$ orbitals for each of these elements. When the $3d$ orbitals are full, the electrons fill the $4p$ orbitals to complete the fourth period. Let's consider the overall relationship between orbital filling and the periodic table. **Figure 10.16** illustrates the type of orbital filling and its location on the periodic table. The tall columns on the table (labeled 1A–7A, and noble gases) are often called the *representative elements*. Valence electrons in these elements occupy s and p orbitals. The period number corresponds to the energy level of the valence electrons. The elements in the center of the periodic table (shown in ▉) are the transition elements where the d orbitals are being filled. Notice that the number for the d orbitals is one less than the period number. The two rows shown at the bottom of the table in Figure 10.16 are called the *inner transition elements* or the *lanthanide* and *actinide series*. The last electrons in these elements are placed in the f orbitals. The number for the f orbitals is always two less than that of the s and p orbitals. A periodic table is almost always available to you, so if you understand the relationship between the orbitals and the periodic table, you can write the electron configuration for any element. There are several minor variations to these rules, but we won't concern ourselves with them in this course.

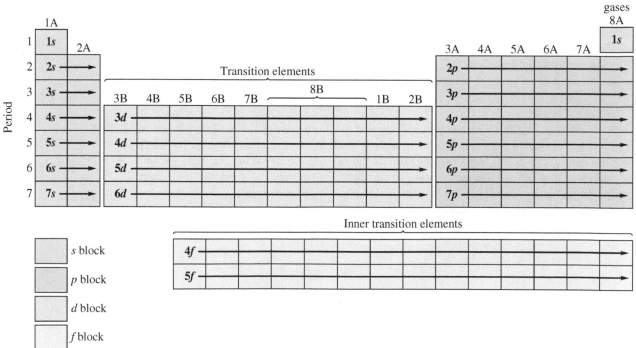

Figure 10.16

Arrangement of elements according to the electron sublevel being filled.

EXAMPLE 10.5

Use the periodic table to write the electron configuration for phosphorus and tin.

SOLUTION

Phosphorus is element 15 and is located in Period 3, Group 5A. The electron configuration must have a full first and second energy level:

P $1s^2 2s^2 2p^6 3s^2 3p^3$ or $[Ne]3s^2 3p^3$

You can determine the electron configuration by looking across the period and counting the element blocks.

Tin is element 50 in Period 5, Group 4A, two places after the transition metals. It must have two electrons in the $5p$ series. Its electron configuration is

Sn $1s^2 2s^2 2p^6 3s^2 3p^6 4s^2 3d^{10} 4p^6 5s^2 4d^{10} 5p^2$ or $[Kr]5s^2 4d^{10} 5p^2$

Notice that the d series of electrons always has a principal energy level number one less than its period.

PRACTICE 10.6

Use the periodic table to write the complete electron configuration for (a) O, (b) Ca, and (c) Ti.

The early chemists classified the elements based only on their observed properties, but modern atomic theory gives us an explanation for why the properties of elements vary periodically. For example, as we "build" atoms by filling orbitals with electrons, the same orbitals occur on each energy level. This means that the same electron configuration reappears regularly for each level. Groups of elements show similar chemical properties because of the similarity of these outermost electron configurations.

In Figure 10.17, only the electron configuration of the outermost electrons is given. This periodic table illustrates these important points:

1. The number of the period corresponds with the highest energy level occupied by electrons in that period.

Figure 10.17
Outermost electron configurations.

2. The group numbers for the representative elements are equal to the total number of outermost electrons in the atoms of the group. For example, elements in Group 7A always have the electron configuration ns^2np^5. The d and f electrons are always in a lower energy level than the highest principal energy level and so are not considered as outermost (valence) electrons.

3. The elements of a family have the same outermost electron configuration except that the electrons are in different principal energy levels.

4. The elements within each of the s, p, d, f blocks are filling the s, p, d, f orbitals, as shown in Figure 10.16.

5. Within the transition elements, some discrepancies in the order of filling occur. (Explanation of these discrepancies and similar ones in the inner transition elements is beyond the scope of this book.)

EXAMPLE 10.6

Write the complete electron configuration of a zinc atom and a rubidium atom.

SOLUTION

The atomic number of zinc is 30; it therefore has 30 protons and 30 electrons in a neutral atom. Using Figure 10.14, we see that the electron configuration of a zinc atom is $1s^2 2s^2 2p^6 3s^2 3p^6 4s^2 3d^{10}$. Check by adding the superscripts, which should equal 30.

The atomic number of rubidium is 37; therefore, it has 37 protons and 37 electrons in a neutral atom. With a little practice using a periodic table, you can write the electron configuration directly. The electron configuration of a rubidium atom is $1s^2 2s^2 2p^6 3s^2 3p^6 4s^2 3d^{10} 4p^6 5s^1$. Check by adding the superscripts, which should equal 37.

PRACTICE 10.7

Write the complete electron configuration for a gallium atom and a lead atom.

CHAPTER **10 REVIEW**

10.1 ELECTROMAGNETIC RADIATION

• Atomic theory has changed over the past 200 years:
  • Early Greek ideas
  • Dalton's model
  • Thomson's model
  • Rutherford's model
  • Modern atomic theory
• Basic wave characteristics include
  • Wavelength (λ)
  • Frequency (ν)
  • Speed (v)
• Light is a form of electromagnetic radiation.
• Light can also be considered to be composed of energy packets called photons, which behave like particles.

10.2 THE BOHR ATOM

• The study of atomic spectra led Bohr to propose that
  • Electrons are found in quantized energy levels in an atom.
  • Spectral lines result from the radiation of quanta of energy when the electron moves from a higher level to a lower level.
• The chemical properties of an element and its position on the periodic table depend on electrons.
• Louis de Broglie suggested that all objects have wave properties.
• Schrödinger created a mathematical model to describe electrons as waves.
  • Electrons are located in orbitals, or regions of probability, around the nucleus of an atom.

10.3 ENERGY LEVELS OF ELECTRONS

- Modern atomic theory predicts that
  - Electrons are found in discrete principal energy levels ($n = 1, 2, 3 \ldots$):
    - Energy levels contain sublevels.

Number of sublevels

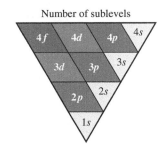

  - Two electrons fit into each orbital but must have opposite spin to do so.

KEY TERMS

principal energy levels
sublevels
spin
Pauli exclusion principle

10.4 ATOMIC STRUCTURES OF THE FIRST 18 ELEMENTS

- Guidelines for writing electron configurations:
  - Not more than two electrons per orbital
  - Electrons fill lowest energy levels first:
    - $s < p < d < f$ for a given value of n
  - Orbitals on a given sublevel are each filled with a single electron before pairing of electrons begins to occur
- For the representative elements, only electrons in the outermost energy level (valence electrons) are involved in bonding.

KEY TERMS

electron configuration
orbital diagram
valence electrons

10.5 ELECTRON STRUCTURES AND THE PERIODIC TABLE

- Elements in horizontal rows on the periodic table contain elements whose valence electrons (s and p) are generally on the same energy level as the number of the row.
- Elements that are chemically similar are arranged in columns (groups) on the periodic table.
- The valence electron configurations of elements in a group or family are the same, but they are located in different principal energy levels.

KEY TERMS

period
groups or families (of elements)
representative elements
transition elements

REVIEW QUESTIONS

1. Define the terms *wavelength* and *frequency*. What symbols do chemists generally use to represent these quantities?
2. What is the wavelength range for visible light? Which has a longer wavelength, red light or blue light?
3. What is the name given to a packet of energy?
4. What is an orbital?
5. What is meant when we say the electron structure of an atom is in its ground state?
6. What is the major difference between an orbital and a Bohr orbit?
7. Explain how and why Bohr's model of the atom was modified to include the cloud model of the atom.
8. How do $1s$ and $2s$ orbitals differ? How are they alike?
9. What letters are used to designate the types of orbitals?
10. List the following orbitals in order of increasing energy: $2s$, $2p$, $4s$, $1s$, $3d$, $3p$, $4p$, $3s$.
11. How many s electrons, p electrons, and d electrons are possible in any energy level?
12. Sketch the s, p_x, p_y, and p_z orbitals.
13. Under what conditions can a second electron enter an orbital already containing one electron?
14. What is a valence shell?
15. What are valence electrons, and why are they important?

16. A lanthanide element has the designation $4f^3$ in its electron structure. What is the significance of the 4, the f, and the 3?
17. Of the elements Ir, Pb, Xe, Zr, and Ag, which ones are not contained in the groups of representative elements?
18. From the standpoint of electron structure, what do the elements in the p block have in common?
19. Write symbols for the elements with atomic numbers 6, 7, 8, 15, and 33. Which of those elements have something in common? Explain.
20. Write the symbols of the first three elements that have six electrons in their outermost energy level.
21. What is the greatest number of elements to be found in any period? Which periods have this number?
22. From the standpoint of energy level, how does the placement of the last electron in the Group A elements differ from that of the Group B elements?
23. Find the places in the periodic table where elements are not in proper sequence according to atomic mass. (See inside of front cover for periodic table.)
24. What are the names of the two scientists who independently published results that have led to the establishment of the periodic table?
25. Which scientist is credited with being the author of the modern periodic table?

Most of the exercises in this chapter are available for assignment via the online homework management program, WileyPLUS (www.wileyplus.com). All exercises with blue numbers have answers in Appendix VI.

PAIRED EXERCISES

1. How many total and how many valence electrons are in each of the following neutral atoms?
   (a) lithium   (c) calcium
   (b) magnesium   (d) fluorine

2. How many total and how many valence electrons are in each of the following neutral atoms?
   (a) sodium   (c) phosphorus
   (b) arsenic   (d) aluminum

3. Write the complete electron configuration for each of the following elements:
   (a) scandium   (c) bromine
   (b) rubidium   (d) sulfur

4. Write the complete electron configuration for each of the following elements:
   (a) manganese   (c) gallium
   (b) krypton   (d) boron

5. Explain how the spectral lines of hydrogen occur.

6. Explain how Bohr used the data from the hydrogen spectrum to support his model of the atom.

7. How many orbitals exist in the fourth principal energy level? What are they, and in what periods can they be found?

8. How many total electrons can be present in the third principal energy level? In what orbitals are they found?

9. Write orbital diagrams for these elements:
   (a) N   (b) Cl   (c) Zn   (d) Zr   (e) I

10. Write orbital diagrams for these elements:
    (a) Si   (b) S   (c) Ar   (d) V   (e) P

11. For each of the orbital diagrams given, write out the corresponding electron configurations.

(a) O   [↑↓] [↑↓] [↑↓|↑|↑]

(b) Ca [↑↓] [↑↓] [↑↓|↑↓|↑↓] [↑↓] [↑↓|↑↓|↑↓] [↑↓]

(c) Ar [↑↓] [↑↓] [↑↓|↑↓|↑↓] [↑↓] [↑↓|↑↓|↑↓]

(d) Br [↑↓] [↑↓] [↑↓|↑↓|↑↓] [↑↓] [↑↓|↑↓|↑↓] [↑↓] [↑↓|↑↓|↑↓|↑↓|↑↓] [↑↓|↑↓|↑]

(e) Fe [↑↓] [↑↓] [↑↓|↑↓|↑↓] [↑↓] [↑↓|↑↓|↑↓] [↑↓] [↑↓|↑|↑|↑|↑]

12. For each of the orbital diagrams given, write out the corresponding electron configurations.

(a) Li [↑↓] [↑]

(b) P   [↑↓] [↑↓] [↑↓|↑↓|↑↓] [↑↓] [↑|↑|↑]

(c) Zn [↑↓] [↑↓] [↑↓|↑↓|↑↓] [↑↓] [↑↓|↑↓|↑↓] [↑↓] [↑↓|↑↓|↑↓|↑↓|↑↓]

(d) Na [↑↓] [↑↓] [↑↓|↑↓|↑↓] [↑]

(e) K   [↑↓] [↑↓] [↑↓|↑↓|↑↓] [↑↓] [↑↓|↑↓|↑↓] [↑]

13. Identify the correct orbital diagrams below. For the incorrect diagrams redraw the correct orbital diagram.

| | 1s | 2s | 2p | 3s | 3p | 4s | 3d | 4p |

(a) [↑↓] [↑↓] [↑↓|↑↓|↑] [↑]

(b) [↑↓] [↑↓] [↑↓|↑↓|↑↓] [↑↓] [↑|↑|↑]

(c) [↑↓] [↑↓] [↑↓|↑↓|↑↓] [↑↓] [↑↓|↑↓|↑↓] [↑↓] [↑↓|↑↓|↑↓|↑↓|↑↓] [↑| |]

(d) [↑↓] [↑↓] [↑↓|↑↓|↑↓] [↑↓] [↑↓|↑↓|↑↓] [↑↓] [↑↓|↑↓|↑| |]

14. Identify the correct orbital diagrams below. For the incorrect diagrams redraw the correct orbital diagram.

| | 1s | 2s | 2p | 3s | 3p | 4s | 4p | 3d |

(a) [↑↓] [↑↓] [↑|↑|↑]

(b) [↑↓] [↑↓] [↑↓|↑↓|↑↓] [↑↓] [↑↓|↑↓|↑↓] [↑↓] [↑↓|↑↓|↑↓] [↑|↑| | |]

(c) [↑↓] [↑↓] [↑↓|↑↓|↑↓] [↑↓] [↑↓|↑↓|↑↓] [↑↑]

(d) [↑↓] [↑↓] [↑↓|↑↓|↑↓] [↑↓] [↑↓|↑|↑]

15. Identify the element represented by each of the orbital diagrams in Problem 13.

16. Identify the element represented by each of the orbital diagrams in Problem 14.

17. Which elements have these electron configurations? Give both the symbol and the name:
    (a) $1s^2 2s^2 2p^5$
    (b) $1s^2 2s^2 2p^6 3s^1$
    (c) [Ne]$3s^2 3p^4$
    (d) [Ar]$4s^2 3d^8$

18. Which of the elements have these electron configurations? Give both the symbol and the name:
    (a) $1s^2 2s^2 2p^1$
    (b) $1s^2 2s^2 2p^6 3s^2 3p^2$
    (c) [Xe]$6s^2 4f^{14} 5d^{10} 6p^2$
    (d) [Kr]$5s^2 4d^{10} 5p^4$

19. Identify the element and draw orbital diagrams for elements with these atomic numbers:
    (a) 22 (b) 18 (c) 33 (d) 35 (e) 25

20. Identify the element and draw orbital diagrams for elements with these atomic numbers:
    (a) 15 (b) 30 (c) 20 (d) 34 (e) 19

21. For each of the electron configurations given, write the corresponding orbital diagrams.
    (a) F $1s^2 2s^2 2p^5$
    (b) S $1s^2 2s^2 2p^6 3s^2 3p^4$
    (c) Co $1s^2 2s^2 2p^6 3s^2 3p^6 4s^2 3d^7$
    (d) Kr $1s^2 2s^2 2p^6 3s^2 3p^6 4s^2 3d^{10} 4p^6$
    (e) Ru $1s^2 2s^2 2p^6 3s^2 3p^6 4s^2 3d^{10} 4p^6 5s^2 4d^6$

22. For each of the electron configuration given, write the corresponding orbital diagrams.
    (a) Cl $1s^2 2s^2 2p^6 3s^2 3p^5$
    (b) Mg $1s^2 2s^2 2p^6 3s^2$
    (c) Ni $1s^2 2s^2 2p^6 3s^2 3p^6 4s^2 3d^8$
    (d) Cu $1s^2 2s^2 2p^6 3s^2 3p^6 4s^2 3d^9$
    (e) Ba $1s^2 2s^2 2p^6 3s^2 3p^6 4s^2 3d^{10} 4p^6 5s^2 4d^{10} 5p^6 6s^2$

23. Identify these elements from their atomic structure diagrams:
    (a) (16p 16n) $2e^-$ $8e^-$ $6e^-$
    (b) (28p 32n) $2e^-$ $8e^-$ $16e^-$ $2e^-$

24. Diagram the atomic structures (as you see in Exercise 23) for these elements:
    (a) $^{27}_{13}$Al
    (b) $^{48}_{22}$Ti

25. Why is the eleventh electron of the sodium atom located in the third energy level rather than in the second energy level?

26. Why is the last electron in potassium located in the fourth energy level rather than in the third energy level?

27. What electron structure do the noble gases have in common?

28. What is the unique about the noble gases from an electron point of view?

29. How are elements in a period related to one another?

30. How are elements in a group related to one another?

31. How many valence electrons do each of the following elements have?
    (a) C   (b) S   (c) K   (d) I   (e) B

32. How many valence electrons do each of the following elements have?
    (a) N   (b) P   (c) O   (d) Ba   (e) Al

33. What do the electron structures of the alkali metals have in common?

34. Why would you expect elements zinc, cadmium, and mercury to be in the same chemical family?

35. Pick the electron structures that represent elements in the same chemical family:
    (a) $1s^2 2s^1$
    (b) $1s^2 2s^2 2p^4$
    (c) $1s^2 2s^2 2p^2$
    (d) $1s^2 2s^2 2p^6 3s^2 3p^4$
    (e) $1s^2 2s^2 2p^6 3s^2 3p^6$
    (f) $1s^2 2s^2 2p^6 3s^2 3p^6 4s^2$
    (g) $1s^2 2s^2 2p^6 3s^2 3p^6 4s^1$
    (h) $1s^2 2s^2 2p^6 3s^2 3p^6 4s^2 3d^1$

36. Pick the electron structures that represent elements in the same chemical family:
    (a) [He]$2s^2 2p^6$
    (b) [Ne]$3s^1$
    (c) [Ne]$3s^2$
    (d) [Ne]$3s^2 3p^3$
    (e) [Ar]$4s^2 3d^{10}$
    (f) [Ar]$4s^2 3d^{10} 4p^6$
    (g) [Ar]$4s^2 3d^5$
    (h) [Kr]$5s^2 4d^{10}$

37. In the periodic table, calcium, element 20, is surrounded by elements 12, 19, 21, and 38. Which of these have physical and chemical properties most resembling calcium?

38. In the periodic table, phosphorus, element 15, is surrounded by elements 14, 7, 16, and 33. Which of these have physical and chemical properties most resembling phosphorus?

39. Classify the following elements as metals, nonmetals, or metalloids (review Chapter 3 if you need help):
    (a) potassium   (c) sulfur
    (b) plutonium   (d) antimony

40. Classify the following elements as metals, nonmetals, or metalloids (review Chapter 3 if you need help):
    (a) iodine   (c) molybdenum
    (b) tungsten   (d) germanium

41. In which period and group does an electron first appear in an f orbital?

42. In which period and group does an electron first appear in a d orbital?

43. How many electrons occur in the valence level of Group 7A and 7B elements? Why are they different?

44. How many electrons occur in the valence level of Group 3A and 3B elements? Why are they different?

45. Determine the identity of the element that contains exactly
    (a) three $4p$ electrons in the ground state
    (b) seven $3d$ electrons in the ground state
    (c) one $2s$ electrons in the ground state
    (d) five $3p$ electrons in the ground state

46. Determine the identity of the element that contains exactly
    (a) two $6p$ electrons in the ground state
    (b) five $4f$ electrons in the ground state
    (c) one $4p$ electrons in the ground state
    (d) seven $5d$ electrons in the ground state

ADDITIONAL EXERCISES

47. Using only the periodic table, explain how the valence energy level and the number of valence electrons could be determined.

48. Using only a periodic table, write the full electron configuration for each of the following elements. Circle the valence electrons.
(a) Mg   (b) P   (c) K   (d) F   (e) Se   (f) N

49. Which of the following would have the same number of valence electrons?
(a) Na^+ (b) O   (c) Li   (d) F^- (e) Ne

50. Name the group in which each of the following elements appear:
(a) $1s^2 2s^2 2p^5$
(b) $1s^2 2s^2 2p^6 3s^2 3p^6 4s^2$
(c) $1s^2 2s^2 2p^6 3s^1$
(d) $1s^2 2s^2 2p^6 3s^2 3p^6 4s^2 3d^{10} 4p^6$
(e) $1s^2$
(f) $1s^2 2s^2 2p^6 3s^2 3p^6 4s^2 3d^{10} 4p^6 5s^1$

51. Chromium is a lustrous silver-colored metal that has been used to prevent corrosion for centuries. Bronze swords and other weapons discovered in burial pits from the Qin Dynasty were coated with chromium and had not corroded at all since their entombing. Today many items are coated with a layer of chromium as a decorative and protective covering.

O. Louis Mazzatenta/NG Image Collection

(a) Sometimes the actual electron configurations of the elements differ from those predicted by the periodic table. The experimentally determined electron configuration for chromium is $1s^2 2s^2 2p^6 3s^2 3p^6 4s^1 3d^5$. Is this the electronic configuration you would predict based on the periodic table? If not, what is the configuration predicted by the periodic table for chromium?
(b) Chromium has a density of 7.19 g/cm^3. How many atoms of chromium are contained in a 5.00-cm^3 sample of chromium?
(c) If the radius of a chromium atom is 1.40×10^{-8} cm, what is the volume $\left(V = \dfrac{4}{3} \pi r^3 \right)$ of a single chromium atom?
(d) How many chromium atoms occupy a volume of 5.00 cm^3?

52. Anyone watching fireworks enjoys the beautiful colors produced. The colors are produced by adding different elements to the mix of fuels in the fireworks. Red is produced by adding calcium, yellow by adding sodium, and blue by adding copper. Explain why adding different elements might give fireworks their characteristic colors.

53. There has long been speculation that Wolfgang Amadeus Mozart may have been poisoned by a rival. There is some evidence that he may have been poisoned by an antimony compound. This compound would have been prescribed by his doctor, however, suggesting that there was no foul play. What is the electronic configuration of antimony.

54. A dog is suspected of attacking a runner in the park. This runner was wearing a pearlescent lip gloss containing bismuth hypochlorite, a compound often used in cosmetics to give this pearlescent effect. Upon analyzing a residue on the dog's fur, this compound is detected giving additional support to the victim's claim. Write the complete and shorthand electronic configurations for bismuth.

55. Write the electron configuration of each of the following neutral atoms. (You may need to refer to Figure 3.2.)
(a) the four most abundant elements in the Earth's crust, seawater, and air
(b) the five most abundant elements in the human body

56. Give the maximum number of electrons that can reside in the following:
(a) a p orbital
(b) a d sublevel
(c) the third principal energy level
(d) an s orbital
(e) an f sublevel

57. Give the names of each of the following elements based on the information given:
(a) the second element in Period 3
(b) $[Ne]3s^2 3p^3$
(c)

$\uparrow\downarrow$	$\uparrow\downarrow$	$\uparrow\downarrow$ $\uparrow\downarrow$ $\uparrow\downarrow$	$\uparrow\downarrow$	$\uparrow\downarrow$ $\uparrow$ $\uparrow$ $\uparrow\downarrow$
$1s$	$2s$	$2p$	$3s$	$3p$

58. Why does the emission spectrum for nitrogen reveal many more spectral lines than that for hydrogen?

59. List the first element on the periodic table that satisfies each of these conditions:
(a) a completed set of p orbitals
(b) two $4p$ electrons
(c) seven valence electrons
(d) three unpaired electrons

60. In Group 7A, the first two elements are gases, the next one is a liquid, and the fourth one is a solid. What do they have in common that causes them to be in the same group?

61. In which groups are the transition elements located?

62. How do the electron structures of the transition elements differ from those of the representative elements?

63. The atomic numbers of the noble gases are 2, 10, 18, 36, 54 and 86. Without looking at a periodic table, determine the atomic numbers for the elements that have five electrons in their valence shell.

64. What is the family name for
(a) Group 1A?   (c) Group 7A?
(b) Group 2A?

65. What sublevel is being filled in
(a) Period 3, Group 3A to 7A?
(b) Period 5, transition elements?
(c) the lanthanide series?

66. Classify each of the following as a noble gas, a representative element, or a transition metal. Also indicate whether the element is a metal, nonmetal, or metalloid.
   (a) Na   (d) Ra
   (b) N   (e) As
   (c) Mo   (f) Ne

67. If element 36 is a noble gas, in which groups would you expect elements 35 and 37 to occur?

68. Write a paragraph describing the general features of the periodic table.

69. What is the relationship between two elements if
   (a) one of them has 10 electrons, 10 protons, and 10 neutrons and the other has 10 electrons, 10 protons, and 12 neutrons?
   (b) one of them has 23 electrons, 23 protons, and 27 neutrons and the other has 24 electrons, 24 protons, and 26 neutrons?

70. Is there any pattern for the location of gases on the periodic table? for the location of liquids? for the location of solids?

CHALLENGE EXERCISES

71. A valence electron in an atom of sulfur is excited by heating a sample. The electron jumps from the s orbital to the p orbital. What is the electron configuration of the excited sulfur atom, and what would the orbital diagram look like?

72. Element 87 is in Group 1A, Period 7. In how many principal energy levels are electrons located? Describe its outermost energy level.

73. Use the periodic table to explain why metals tend to lose electrons and nonmetals tend to gain electrons.

74. Show how the periodic table helps determine the expected electron configuration for any element.

ANSWERS TO PRACTICE EXERCISES

10.1
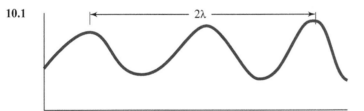

10.2   A photon is a little packet of electromagnetic radiation energy and has the property of both a particle and a wave. It travels at the speed of light, 3.00×10^8 meters per second.

10.3   (a) Two electrons. Wolfgang Pauli's exclusion principle.
   (b) $1s^2 2s^2 2p^6 3s^2 3p^6$ for a total of 18 electrons.

10.4   (a) $2s^2 2p^1$ (c) $3s^1$
   (b) $2s^2 2p^3$ (d) $3s^2 3p^5$

10.5   (a) $[Ar]4s^2 4p^5$ (c) $[Xe]6s^2$
   (b) $[Kr]5s^2$ (d) $[Kr]5s^2 5p^4$

10.6   (a) O $1s^2 2s^2 2p^4$
   (b) Ca $1s^2 2s^2 2p^6 3s^2 3p^6 4s^2$
   (c) Ti $1s^2 2s^2 2p^6 3s^2 3p^6 4s^2 3d^2$

10.7   Ga, $1s^2 2s^2 2p^6 3s^2 3p^6 4s^2 3d^{10} 4p^1$
   Pb, $1s^2 2s^2 2p^6 3s^2 3p^6 4s^2 3d^{10} 4p^6 5s^2 4d^{10} 5p^6 6s^2 4f^{14} 5d^{10} 6p^2$

The atoms in tartaric acid bond together in a very specific orientation to form the shape of the molecule. The molecules collect together to form a crystal, photographed here in a polarized light micrograph. Tartaric acid is used in baking powder and as a food additive.

Pasieka/Photo Researchers, Inc.

CHAPTER **11**

CHEMICAL BONDS: THE FORMATION OF COMPOUNDS FROM ATOMS

For centuries we've been aware that certain metals cling to a magnet. We've seen balloons sticking to walls. Why? High-speed levitation trains are heralded to be the wave of the future. How do they function? In each case, forces of attraction and repulsion are at work.

Human interactions also suggest that "opposites attract" and "likes repel." Attractions draw us into friendships and significant relationships, whereas repulsive forces may produce debate and antagonism. We form and break apart interpersonal bonds throughout our lives.

In chemistry, we also see this phenomenon. Substances form chemical bonds as a result of electrical attractions. These bonds provide the tremendous diversity of compounds found in nature. This chapter is one of the most significant and useful chapters in the book—chemical bonding between atoms. This is what chemistry is really all about. Study it carefully.

11.1 PERIODIC TRENDS IN ATOMIC PROPERTIES

Discuss the atomic trends for metals and nonmetals, atomic radius, and ionization energy.

LEARNING OBJECTIVE

KEY TERM
ionization energy

Although atomic theory and electron configuration help us understand the arrangement and behavior of the elements, it's important to remember that the design of the periodic table is based on observing properties of the elements. Before we use the concept of atomic structure to explain how and why atoms combine to form compounds, we need to understand the characteristic properties of the elements and the trends that occur in these properties on the periodic table. These trends allow us to use the periodic table to accurately predict properties and reactions of a wide variety of substances.

Metals and Nonmetals

In Section 3.5, we classified elements as metals, nonmetals, or metalloids. The heavy stair-step line beginning at boron and running diagonally down the periodic table separates the elements into metals and nonmetals. Metals are usually lustrous, malleable, and good conductors of heat and electricity. Nonmetals are just the opposite—nonlustrous, brittle, and poor conductors. Metalloids are found bordering the heavy diagonal line and may have properties of both metals and nonmetals.

Most elements are classified as metals (see Figure 11.1). Metals are found on the left side of the stair-step line, while the nonmetals are located toward the upper right of the table. Note that hydrogen does not fit into the division of metals and nonmetals. It displays nonmetallic properties under normal conditions, even though it has only one outermost electron like the alkali metals. Hydrogen is considered to be a unique element.

It is the chemical properties of metals and nonmetals that interest us most. Metals tend to lose electrons and form positive ions, while nonmetals tend to gain electrons and form negative ions. When a metal reacts with a nonmetal, electrons are often transferred from the metal to the nonmetal.

Figure 11.1

The elements are classified as metals, nonmetals, and metalloids.

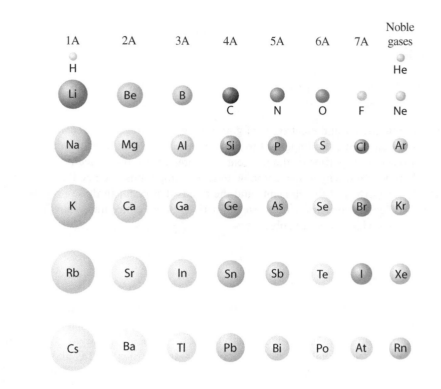

Figure 11.2

Relative atomic radii for the representative elements. Atomic radius decreases across a period and increases down a group in the periodic table.

Atomic Radius

The relative radii of the representative elements are shown in **Figure 11.2**. Notice that the radii of the atoms tend to increase down each group and that they tend to decrease from left to right across a period.

The increase in radius down a group can be understood if we consider the electron structure of the atoms. For each step down a group, an additional energy level is added to the atom. The average distance from the nucleus to the outside edge of the atom must increase as each new energy level is added. The atoms get bigger as electrons are placed in these new higher-energy levels.

Understanding the decrease in atomic radius across a period requires more thought, however. As we move from left to right across a period, electrons within the same block are being added to the same principal energy level. Within a given energy level, we expect the orbitals to have about the same size. We would then expect the atoms to be about the same size across the period. But each time an electron is added, a proton is added to the nucleus as well. The increase in positive charge (in the nucleus) pulls the electrons closer to the nucleus, which results in a gradual decrease in atomic radius across a period.

Ionization Energy

The **ionization energy** of an atom is the energy required to remove an electron from the atom. For example,

$$\text{Na} + \text{ionization energy} \longrightarrow \text{Na}^+ + \text{e}^-$$

The first ionization energy is the amount of energy required to remove the first electron from an atom, the second is the amount required to remove the second electron from that atom, and so on.

Table 11.1 gives the ionization energies for the removal of one to five electrons from several elements. The table shows that even higher amounts of energy are needed to remove the second, third, fourth, and fifth electrons. This makes sense because removing electrons leaves fewer electrons attracted to the same positive charge in the nucleus. The data in Table 11.1 also show that an extra-large ionization energy (blue) is needed when an electron is removed

TABLE 11.1   Ionization Energies for Selected Elements*

Element	Required amounts of energy (kJ/mol)				
	1st e⁻	2nd e⁻	3rd e⁻	4th e⁻	5th e⁻
H	1,314				
He	2,372	5,247			
Li	520	7,297	11,810		
Be	900	1,757	14,845	21,000	
B	800	2,430	3,659	25,020	32,810
C	1,088	2,352	4,619	6,222	37,800
Ne	2,080	3,962	6,276	9,376	12,190
Na	496	4,565	6,912	9,540	13,355

*Values are expressed in kilojoules per mole, showing energies required to remove 1 to 5 electrons per atom.
Blue type indicates the energy needed to remove an electron from a noble gas electron structure.

from a noble gas-like structure, clearly showing the stability of the electron structure of the noble gases.

First ionization energies have been experimentally determined for most elements. Figure 11.3 plots these energies for representative elements in the first four periods. Note these important points:

1. Ionization energy in Group A elements decreases from top to bottom in a group. For example, in Group 1A the ionization energy changes from 520 kJ/mol for Li to 419 kJ/mol for K.

2. Ionization energy gradually increases from left to right across a period. Noble gases have a relatively high value, confirming the nonreactive nature of these elements.

Metals don't behave in exactly the same manner. Some metals give up electrons much more easily than others. In the alkali metal family, cesium gives up its 6s electron much more easily than the metal lithium gives up its 2s electron. This makes sense when we consider that the size of the atoms increases down the group. The distance between the nucleus and the outer electrons increases and the ionization energy decreases. The most chemically active metals are located at the lower left of the periodic table.

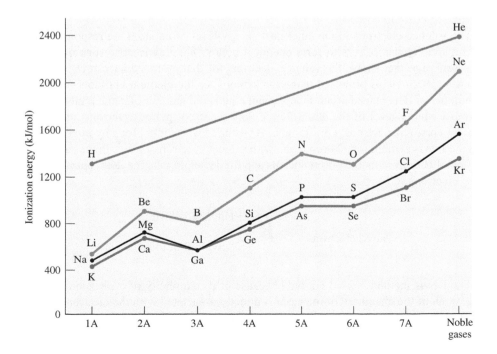

Figure 11.3

Periodic relationship of the first ionization energy for representative elements in the first four periods.

Nonmetals have relatively large ionization energies compared to metals. Nonmetals tend to gain electrons and form anions. Since the nonmetals are located at the right side of the periodic table, it is not surprising that ionization energies tend to increase from left to right across a period. The most active nonmetals are found in the *upper* right corner of the periodic table (excluding the noble gases).

EXAMPLE 11.1

Why is there such a large increase in the ionization energy to remove the fifth electron from a carbon atom? (See Table 11.1.)

SOLUTION

Two main factors apply here. (1) The remaining carbon atom has six protons attracting only two electrons and (2) these two electrons constitute the stable noble gas helium. Both factors make it much more difficult to withdraw the fifth electron.

PRACTICE 11.1

(a) What are the trends in the first ionization energy for the groups of elements and for the periods of elements in the periodic table?
(b) Consider your answer to part (a) and state why this is the case for the groups of elements.

11.2 LEWIS STRUCTURES OF ATOMS

LEARNING OBJECTIVE • Draw the Lewis structure for a given atom.

KEY TERM

Lewis structure

Metals tend to form cations (positively charged ions) and nonmetals form anions (negatively charged ions) in order to attain a stable valence electron structure. For many elements this stable valence level contains eight electrons (two s and six p), identical to the valence electron configuration of the noble gases. Atoms undergo rearrangements of electron structure to lower their chemical potential energy (or to become more stable). These rearrangements are accomplished by losing, gaining, or sharing electrons with other atoms. For example, a hydrogen atom could accept a second electron and attain an electron structure the same as the noble gas helium. A fluorine atom could gain an electron and attain an electron structure like neon. A sodium atom could lose one electron to attain an electron structure like neon.

The valence electrons in the outermost energy level of an atom are responsible for the electron activity that occurs to form chemical bonds. The **Lewis structure** of an atom is a representation that shows the valence electrons for that atom. American chemist Gilbert N. Lewis (1875–1946) proposed using the symbol for the element and dots for electrons. The number of dots placed around the symbol equals the number of s and p electrons in the outermost energy level of the atom. Paired dots represent paired electrons; unpaired dots represent unpaired electrons. For example, $\mathbf{H} \cdot$ is the Lewis symbol for a hydrogen atom, $1s^1$; $:\mathbf{B}$ is the Lewis symbol for a boron atom, with valence electrons $2s^2 2p^1$. In the case of boron, the symbol B represents the boron nucleus and the $1s^2$ electrons; the dots represent only the $2s^2 2p^1$ electrons.

The Lewis method is used not only because of its simplicity of expression but also because much of the chemistry of the atom is directly associated with the electrons in the outermost energy level. **Figure 11.4** shows Lewis structures for the elements hydrogen through calcium.

	1A	2A	3A	4A	5A	6A	7A	Noble gases
	H·							He:
	Li·	Be:	:B	:C·	:N·	·O:	:F:	:Ne:
	Na·	Mg:	:Al	:Si·	:P·	·S:	:Cl:	:Ar:
	K·	Ca:						

Figure 11.4

Lewis structures of the first 20 elements. Dots represent electrons in the outermost s and p energy levels only.

EXAMPLE 11.2

Write the Lewis structure for a phosphorus atom.

SOLUTION

First establish the electron structure for a phosphorus atom, which is $1s^2 2s^2 2p^6 3s^2 3p^3$. Note that there are five electrons in the outermost energy level; they are $3s^2 3p^3$. Write the symbol for phosphorus and place the five electrons as dots around it.

$$:\overset{\displaystyle .}{P}\cdot$$

The $3s^2$ electrons are paired and are represented by the paired dots. The $3p^3$ electrons, which are unpaired, are represented by the single dots.

A quick way to determine the correct number of dots (electrons) for a Lewis structure is to use the group number. For the A groups on the periodic table, the group number is the same as the number of electrons in the Lewis structure.

PRACTICE 11.2

Write the Lewis structure for the following elements:
(a) N   (b) Al   (c) Sr   (d) Br

11.3 THE IONIC BOND: TRANSFER OF ELECTRONS FROM ONE ATOM TO ANOTHER

Discuss the formation of an ionic bond and the chemical change that results from the bond.

LEARNING OBJECTIVE

KEY TERM
ionic bond

The chemistry of many elements, especially the representative ones, is to attain an outer electron structure like that of the chemically stable noble gases. With the exception of helium, this stable structure consists of eight electrons in the outermost energy level (see Table 11.2).

Let's look at the electron structures of sodium and chlorine to see how each element can attain a structure of 8 electrons in its outermost energy level. A sodium atom has 11 electrons:

TABLE 11.2   Arrangement of Electrons in the Noble Gases*

Noble gas	Symbol	Electron structure					
		$n = 1$	2	3	4	5	6
Helium	He	$1s^2$					
Neon	Ne	$1s^2$	$2s^2 2p^6$				
Argon	Ar	$1s^2$	$2s^2 2p^6$	$3s^2 3p^6$			
Krypton	Kr	$1s^2$	$2s^2 2p^6$	$3s^2 3p^6 3d^{10}$	$4s^2 4p^6$		
Xenon	Xe	$1s^2$	$2s^2 2p^6$	$3s^2 3p^6 3d^{10}$	$4s^2 4p^6 4d^{10}$	$5s^2 5p^6$	
Radon	Rn	$1s^2$	$2s^2 2p^6$	$3s^2 3p^6 3d^{10}$	$4s^2 4p^6 4d^{10} 4f^{14}$	$5s^2 5p^6 5d^{10}$	$6s^2 6p^6$

*Each gas except helium has eight electrons in its outermost energy level.

2 in the first energy level, 8 in the second energy level, and 1 in the third energy level. A chlorine atom has 17 electrons: 2 in the first energy level, 8 in the second energy level, and 7 in the third energy level. If a sodium atom transfers or loses its $3s$ electron, its third energy level becomes vacant, and it becomes a sodium ion with an electron configuration identical to that of the noble gas neon. This process requires energy:

An atom that has lost or gained electrons will have a positive or negative charge, depending on which particles (protons or electrons) are in excess. Remember that a charged particle or group of particles is called an *ion*.

By losing a negatively charged electron, the sodium atom becomes a positively charged particle known as a sodium ion. The charge, $+1$, results because the nucleus still contains 11 positively charged protons, and the electron orbitals contain only 10 negatively charged electrons. The charge is indicated by a plus sign ($+$) and is written as a superscript after the symbol of the element (Na^+).

A chlorine atom with seven electrons in the third energy level needs one electron to pair up with its one unpaired $3p$ electron to attain the stable outer electron structure of argon. By gaining one electron, the chlorine atom becomes a chloride ion (Cl^-), a negatively charged particle containing 17 protons and 18 electrons. This process releases energy:

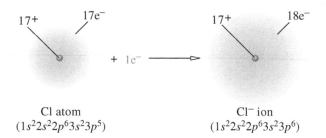

Consider sodium and chlorine atoms reacting with each other. The $3s$ electron from the sodium atom transfers to the half-filled $3p$ orbital in the chlorine atom to form a positive sodium ion and a negative chloride ion. The compound sodium chloride results because the Na^+ and Cl^- ions are strongly attracted to each other by their opposite electrostatic charges. The force holding the oppositely charged ions together is called an ionic bond:

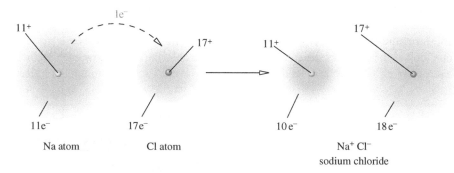

The Lewis representation of sodium chloride formation is

$$Na\cdot + \cdot\ddot{\underset{\cdot\cdot}{Cl}}: \longrightarrow [Na]^+ \left[:\ddot{\underset{\cdot\cdot}{Cl}}:\right]^-$$

The chemical reaction between sodium and chlorine is a very vigorous one, producing considerable heat in addition to the salt formed. When energy is released in a chemical reaction, the products are more stable than the reactants. Note that in NaCl both atoms attain a noble gas electron structure.

These tiny NaCl crystals show the cubic structure illustrated in Figure 11.5.

Figure 11.5

Sodium chloride crystal. Diagram represents a small fragment of sodium chloride, which forms cubic crystals. Each sodium ion is surrounded by six chloride ions, and each chloride ion is surrounded by six sodium ions. The tiny NaCl crystals show the cubic crystal structure of salt.

Sodium chloride is made up of cubic crystals in which each sodium ion is surrounded by six chloride ions and each chloride ion by six sodium ions, except at the crystal surface. A visible crystal is a regularly arranged aggregate of millions of these ions, but the ratio of sodium to chloride ions is 1:1, hence the formula NaCl. The cubic crystalline lattice arrangement of sodium chloride is shown in Figure 11.5.

Figure 11.6 contrasts the relative sizes of sodium and chlorine atoms with those of their ions. The sodium ion is smaller than the atom due primarily to two factors: (1) The sodium atom has lost its outermost electron, thereby reducing its size; and (2) the 10 remaining electrons are now attracted by 11 protons and are thus drawn closer to the nucleus. Conversely, the chloride ion is larger than the atom because (1) it has 18 electrons but only 17 protons and (2) the nuclear attraction on each electron is thereby decreased, allowing the chlorine atom to expand as it forms an ion.

We've seen that when sodium reacts with chlorine, each atom becomes an ion. Sodium chloride, like all ionic substances, is held together by the attraction existing between positive and negative charges. An **ionic bond** is the attraction between oppositely charged ions.

Ionic bonds are formed whenever one or more electrons are transferred from one atom to another. Metals, which have relatively little attraction for their valence electrons, tend to form ionic bonds when they combine with nonmetals.

It's important to recognize that substances with ionic bonds do not exist as molecules. In sodium chloride, for example, the bond does not exist solely between a single sodium ion and a single chloride ion. Each sodium ion in the crystal attracts six near-neighbor negative chloride ions; in turn, each negative chloride ion attracts six near-neighbor positive sodium ions (see Figure 11.5).

A metal will usually have one, two, or three electrons in its outer energy level. In reacting, metal atoms characteristically lose these electrons, attain the electron structure of a noble gas, and become positive ions. A nonmetal, on the other hand, is only a few electrons short of having a noble gas electron structure in its outer energy level and thus has a tendency to gain electrons. In reacting with metals, nonmetal atoms characteristically gain one to four electrons; attain the electron structure of a noble gas; and become negative ions. The ions

Remember: A cation is always smaller than its parent atom, whereas an anion is always larger than its parent atom.

Figure 11.6

Relative radii of sodium and chlorine atoms and their ions.

TABLE 11.3   Change in Atomic Radii (nm) of Selected Metals and Nonmetals*

Atomic radius		Ionic radius		Atomic radius		Ionic radius	
Li	0.152	Li$^+$	0.060	F	0.071	F$^-$	0.136
Na	0.186	Na$^+$	0.095	Cl	0.099	Cl$^-$	0.181
K	0.227	K$^+$	0.133	Br	0.114	Br$^-$	0.195
Mg	0.160	Mg^{2+}	0.065	O	0.074	O^{2-}	0.140
Al	0.143	Al^{3+}	0.050	S	0.103	S^{2-}	0.184

*The metals shown lose electrons to become positive ions. The nonmetals gain electrons to become negative ions.

formed by loss of electrons are much smaller than the corresponding metal atoms; the ions formed by gaining electrons are larger than the corresponding nonmetal atoms. The dimensions of the atomic and ionic radii of several metals and nonmetals are given in Table 11.3.

PRACTICE 11.3

What noble gas structure is formed when an atom of each of these metals loses all its valence electrons? Write the formula for the metal ion formed.

(a) K   (b) Mg   (c) Al   (d) Ba

Study the following examples. Note the loss and gain of electrons between atoms; also note that the ions in each compound have a noble gas electron structure.

EXAMPLE 11.3

Explain how magnesium and chlorine combine to form magnesium chloride, $MgCl_2$.

SOLUTION

A magnesium atom of electron structure $1s^2 2s^2 2p^6 3s^2$ must lose two electrons or gain six to reach a stable electron structure. If magnesium reacts with chlorine and each chlorine atom can accept only one electron, two chlorine atoms will be needed for the two electrons from each magnesium atom. The compound formed will contain one magnesium ion and two chloride ions. The magnesium atom, having lost two electrons, becomes a magnesium ion with a +2 charge. Each chloride ion will have a −1 charge. The transfer of electrons from a magnesium atom to two chlorine atoms is shown in the following illustration:

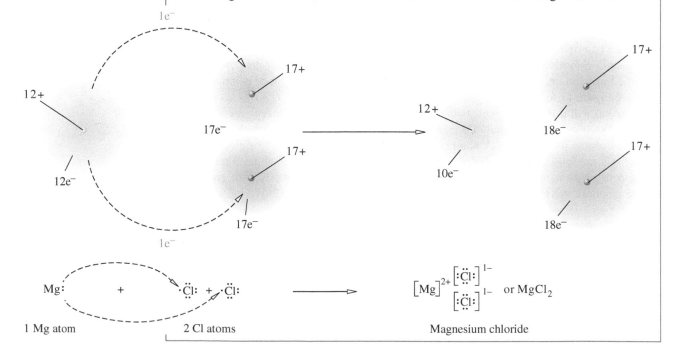

EXAMPLE 11.4

Explain the formation of sodium fluoride (NaF) from its elements.

SOLUTION

The fluorine atom, with seven electrons in its outer energy level, behaves similarly to the chlorine atom.

EXAMPLE 11.5

Explain the formation of aluminum fluoride (AlF_3) from its elements.

SOLUTION

Each fluorine atom can accept only one electron. Therefore, three fluorine atoms are needed to combine with the three valence electrons of one aluminum atom. The aluminum atom has lost three electrons to become an aluminum ion (Al^{3+}) with a +3 charge.

EXAMPLE 11.6

Explain the formation of magnesium oxide (MgO) from its elements.

SOLUTION

The magnesium atom, with two electrons in the outer energy level, exactly fills the need of one oxygen atom for two electrons. The resulting compound has a ratio of one magnesium atom to one oxygen atom. The oxygen (oxide) ion has a -2 charge, having gained two electrons. In combining with oxygen, magnesium behaves the same way as when it combines with chlorine—it loses two electrons.

EXAMPLE 11.7

Explain the formation of sodium sulfide (Na_2S) from its elements.

SOLUTION

2 Na atoms   1 S atom   Sodium sulfide

Two sodium atoms supply the electrons that one sulfur atom needs to make eight in its outer energy level.

EXAMPLE 11.8

Explain the formation of aluminum oxide (Al_2O_3) from its elements.

SOLUTION

2 Al atoms   3 O atoms   Aluminium oxide

One oxygen atom, needing two electrons, cannot accommodate the three electrons from one aluminum atom. One aluminum atom falls one electron short of the four electrons needed by two oxygen atoms. A ratio of two atoms of aluminum to three atoms of oxygen, involving the transfer of six electrons (two to each oxygen atom), gives each atom a stable electron configuration.

Note that in each of these examples, outer energy levels containing eight electrons were formed in all the negative ions. This formation resulted from the pairing of all the s and p electrons in these outer energy levels.

11.4 PREDICTING FORMULAS OF IONIC COMPOUNDS

LEARNING OBJECTIVE • Predict the formulas of ionic compounds from their position on the periodic table.

In previous examples, we learned that when a metal and a nonmetal react to form an ionic compound, the metal loses one or more electrons to the nonmetal. In Chapter 6, where we learned to name compounds and write formulas, we saw that Group 1A metals always form $+1$ cations, whereas Group 2A elements form $+2$ cations. Group 7A elements form -1 anions and Group 6A elements form -2 anions.

It stands to reason, then, that this pattern is directly related to the stability of the noble gas configuration. Metals lose electrons to attain the electron configuration of a noble gas (the previous one on the periodic table). A nonmetal forms an ion by gaining enough electrons to achieve the electron configuration of the noble gas following it on the periodic table. These observations lead us to an important chemical principle:

In almost all stable chemical compounds of representative elements, each atom attains a noble gas electron configuration. This concept forms the basis for our understanding of chemical bonding.

We can apply this principle in predicting the formulas of ionic compounds. To predict the formula of an ionic compound, we must recognize that chemical compounds are always electrically neutral. In addition, the metal will lose electrons to achieve noble gas configuration and the nonmetal will gain electrons to achieve noble gas configuration. Consider the compound formed between barium and sulfur. Barium has two valence electrons, whereas sulfur has six valence electrons:

$$\text{Ba} \quad [\text{Xe}]6s^2 \quad \text{S} \quad [\text{Ne}]3s^23p^4$$

If barium loses two electrons, it will achieve the configuration of xenon. By gaining two electrons, sulfur achieves the configuration of argon. Consequently, a pair of electrons is transferred between atoms. Now we have Ba^{2+} and S^{2-}. Since compounds are electrically neutral, there must be a ratio of one Ba to one S, giving the formula BaS.

The same principle works for many other cases. Since the key lies in the electron configuration, the periodic table can be used to extend the prediction even further. Because of similar electron structures, the elements in a family generally form compounds with the same atomic ratios. In general, if we know the atomic ratio of a particular compound—say, NaCl—we can predict the atomic ratios and formulas of the other alkali metal chlorides. These formulas are LiCl, KCl, RbCl, CsCl, and FrCl (see Table 11.4).

Similarly, if we know that the formula of the oxide of hydrogen is H_2O, we can predict that the formula of the sulfide will be H_2S, because sulfur has the same valence electron structure as oxygen. Recognize, however, that these are only predictions; it doesn't necessarily follow that every element in a group will behave like the others or even that a predicted compound will actually exist. For example, knowing the formulas for potassium chlorate, bromate, and iodate to be $KClO_3$, $KBrO_3$, and KIO_3, we can correctly predict the corresponding sodium compounds to have the formulas $NaClO_3$, $NaBrO_3$, and $NaIO_3$. Fluorine belongs to the same family of elements (Group 7A) as chlorine, bromine, and iodine, so it would appear that fluorine should combine with potassium and sodium to give fluorates with the formulas KFO_3 and $NaFO_3$. However, potassium and sodium fluorates are not known to exist.

In the discussion in this section, we refer only to representative metals (Groups 1A, 2A, and 3A). The transition metals (Group B) show more complicated behavior (they form multiple ions), and their formulas are not as easily predicted.

TABLE 11.4   Formulas of Compounds Formed by Alkali Metals

Lewis structure	Oxides	Chlorides	Bromides	Sulfates
Li·	Li_2O	LiCl	LiBr	Li_2SO_4
Na·	Na_2O	NaCl	NaBr	Na_2SO_4
K·	K_2O	KCl	KBr	K_2SO_4
Rb·	Rb_2O	RbCl	RbBr	Rb_2SO_4
Cs·	Cs_2O	CsCl	CsBr	Cs_2SO_4

> ### EXAMPLE 11.9
>
> The formula for calcium sulfide is CaS and that for lithium phosphide is Li₃P. Predict formulas for (a) magnesium sulfide, (b) potassium phosphide, and (c) magnesium selenide.
>
> **SOLUTION**
>
> (a) Look up calcium and magnesium in the periodic table; they are both in Group 2A. The formula for calcium sulfide is CaS, so it's reasonable to predict that the formula for magnesium sulfide is MgS.
>
> (b) Find lithium and potassium in the periodic table; they are in Group 1A. Since the formula for lithium phosphide is Li_3P, it's reasonable to predict that K_3P is the formula for potassium phosphide.
>
> (c) Find selenium in the periodic table; it is in Group 6A just below sulfur. Therefore, it's reasonable to assume that selenium forms selenide in the same way that sulfur forms sulfide. Since MgS was the predicted formula for magnesium sulfide in part (a), we can reasonably assume that the formula for magnesium selenide is MgSe.

PRACTICE 11.4

The formula for sodium oxide is Na_2O. Predict the formula for

(a) sodium sulfide   (b) rubidium oxide

PRACTICE 11.5

The formula for barium phosphide is Ba_3P_2. Predict the formula for

(a) magnesium nitride   (b) barium arsenide

11.5 THE COVALENT BOND: SHARING ELECTRONS

LEARNING OBJECTIVE ● Draw the electron structure of a covalent bond.

KEY TERMS

covalent bond
polar covalent bond

Some atoms do not transfer electrons from one atom to another to form ions. Instead they form a chemical bond by sharing pairs of electrons between them. A **covalent bond** consists of a pair of electrons shared between two atoms. This bonding concept was introduced in 1916 by G. N. Lewis. In the millions of known compounds, the covalent bond is the predominant chemical bond.

True molecules exist in substances in which the atoms are covalently bonded. It is proper to refer to molecules of such substances as hydrogen, chlorine, hydrogen chloride, carbon dioxide, water, or sugar (Figure 11.7). These substances contain only covalent bonds and exist as aggregates of molecules. We don't use the term *molecule* when talking about ionically bonded compounds, such as sodium chloride, because such substances exist as large aggregates of positive and negative ions, not as molecules (Figure 11.7).

A study of the hydrogen molecule gives us an insight into the nature of the covalent bond and its formation. The formation of a hydrogen molecule (H_2) involves the overlapping and pairing of 1s electron orbitals from two hydrogen atoms, shown in Figure 11.8. Each atom contributes one electron of the pair that is shared jointly by two hydrogen nuclei. The orbital of the electrons now includes both hydrogen nuclei, but probability factors show that the most

O   C   Dry ice

Na⁺   Cl⁻
Sodium chloride

Figure 11.7

Solid carbon dioxide (dry ice) is composed of individual covalently bonded molecules of CO_2 closely packed together. Table salt is a large aggregate of Na⁺ and Cl⁻ ions instead of molecules.

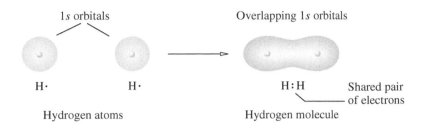

Figure 11.8

The formation of a hydrogen molecule from two hydrogen atoms. The two 1s orbitals overlap, forming the H_2 molecule. In this molecule the two electrons are shared between the atoms, forming a covalent bond.

likely place to find the electrons (the point of highest electron density) is between the two nuclei. The two nuclei are shielded from each other by the pair of electrons, allowing the two nuclei to be drawn very close to each other.

The formula for chlorine gas is Cl_2. When the two atoms of chlorine combine to form this molecule, the electrons must interact in a manner similar to that shown in the hydrogen example. Each chlorine atom would be more stable with eight electrons in its outer energy level. But chlorine atoms are identical, and neither is able to pull an electron away from the other. What happens is this: The unpaired 3p electron orbital of one chlorine atom overlaps the unpaired 3p electron orbital of the other atom, resulting in a pair of electrons that is mutually shared between the two atoms. Each atom furnishes one of the pair of shared electrons. Thus, each atom attains a stable structure of eight electrons by sharing an electron pair with the other atom. The pairing of the p electrons and the formation of a chlorine molecule are illustrated in Figure 11.9. Neither chlorine atom has a positive or negative charge because both contain the same number of protons and have equal attraction for the pair of electrons being shared. Other examples of molecules in which electrons are equally shared between two atoms are hydrogen (H_2), oxygen (O_2), nitrogen (N_2), fluorine (F_2), bromine (Br_2), and iodine (I_2). Note that more than one pair of electrons may be shared between atoms:

H:H	:F̈:F̈:	:B̈r:B̈r:	:Ï:Ï:	:Ö::Ö:	:N⋮⋮⋮N:
hydrogen	fluorine	bromine	iodine	oxygen	nitrogen

The Lewis structure given for oxygen does not adequately account for all the properties of the oxygen molecule. Other theories explaining the bonding in oxygen molecules have been advanced, but they are complex and beyond the scope of this book.

In writing structures, we commonly replace the pair of dots used to represent a shared pair of electrons with a dash (—). One dash represents a single bond; two dashes, a double bond; and three dashes, a triple bond. The six structures just shown may be written thus:

$$H—H \qquad :F̈—F̈: \qquad :B̈r—B̈r: \qquad :Ï—Ï: \qquad :Ö=Ö: \qquad :N≡N:$$

The ionic bond and the covalent bond represent two extremes. In ionic bonding the atoms are so different that electrons are transferred between them, forming a charged pair of ions. In covalent bonding, two identical atoms share electrons equally. The bond is the mutual attraction of the two nuclei for the shared electrons. Between these extremes lie many cases in which the atoms are not different enough for a transfer of electrons but are different enough that the electron pair cannot be shared equally. This unequal sharing of electrons results in the formation of a **polar covalent bond**.

Tom Pantages

Molecular models for F_2 (green, single bond), O_2 (black, double bond), and N_2 (blue, triple bond).

Remember: A dash represents a shared pair of electrons.

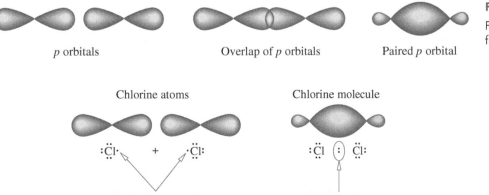

Figure 11.9

Pairing of p electrons in the formation of a chlorine molecule.

EXAMPLE 11.10

What is the basic concept of a covalent bond?

SOLUTION

The basic concept of a covalent bond is the sharing of one or more pairs of electrons between two atoms to form a covalent bond between the two atoms.

PRACTICE 11.6

The atoms in the two molecules HBr and C_2H_6 are bonded by covalent bonds. Draw Lewis structures showing these covalent bonds.

11.6 ELECTRONEGATIVITY

LEARNING OBJECTIVE • Explain how electronegativities of component atoms in a molecule determine the polarity of the molecule.

KEY TERMS

electronegativity
nonpolar covalent bond
dipole

When two *different* kinds of atoms share a pair of electrons, a bond forms in which electrons are shared unequally. One atom assumes a partial positive charge and the other a partial negative charge with respect to each other. This difference in charge occurs because the two atoms exert unequal attraction for the pair of shared electrons. The attractive force that an atom of an element has for shared electrons in a molecule or polyatomic ion is known as its **electronegativity**. Elements differ in their electronegativities. For example, both hydrogen and chlorine need one electron to form stable electron configurations. They share a pair of electrons in hydrogen chloride (HCl). Chlorine is more electronegative and therefore has a greater attraction for the shared electrons than does hydrogen. As a result, the pair of electrons is displaced toward the chlorine atom, giving it a partial negative charge and leaving the hydrogen atom with a partial positive charge. Note that the electron is not transferred entirely to the chlorine atom (as in the case of sodium chloride) and that no ions are formed. The entire molecule, HCl, is electrically neutral. A partial charge is usually indicated by the Greek letter delta, δ. Thus, a partial positive charge is represented by $\delta+$ and a partial negative charge by $\delta-$.

Hydrogen chloride

The pair of shared electrons in HCl is closer to the more electronegative chlorine atom than to the hydrogen atom, giving chlorine a partial negative charge with respect to the hydrogen atom.

A scale of relative electronegativities, in which the most electronegative element, fluorine, is assigned a value of 4.0, was developed by the Nobel Laureate (1954 and 1962) Linus Pauling (1901–1994). Table 11.5 shows that the relative electronegativity of the nonmetals is high and that of the metals is low. These electronegativities indicate that atoms of metals have a greater tendency to lose electrons than do atoms of nonmetals and that nonmetals have a greater tendency to gain electrons than do metals. The higher the electronegativity value, the greater the attraction for electrons. Note that electronegativity generally increases from left to right across a period and decreases down a group for the representative elements. The highest electronegativity is 4.0 for fluorine, and the lowest is 0.7 for francium and cesium. It's important to remember that the higher the electronegativity, the more strongly an atom attracts electrons.

EXAMPLE 11.11

What are the electronegativity trends for the groups of representative elements and the periods of representative elements in the periodic table?

SOLUTION

In general, electronegativity decreases from top to bottom for a group of representative elements and increases from left to right across a period of representative elements.

TABLE 11.5 Three-Dimensional Representation of Electronegativity

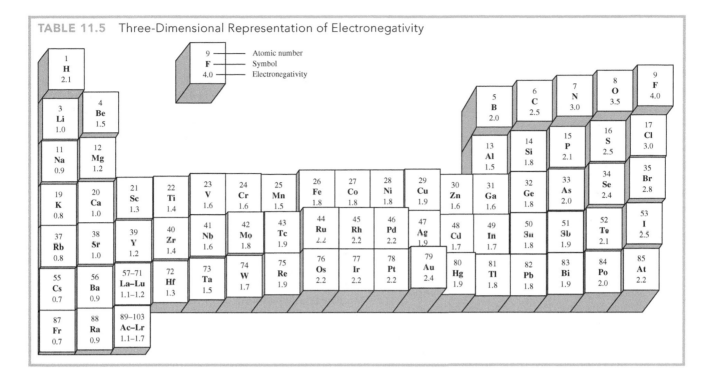

PRACTICE 11.7

Explain the term *electronegativity* and how it relates to the elements in the periodic table.

The polarity of a bond is determined by the difference in electronegativity values of the atoms forming the bond (see **Figure 11.10**). If the electronegativities are the same, the bond is **nonpolar covalent** and the electrons are shared equally. If the atoms have greatly different electronegativities, the bond is very *polar*. At the extreme, one or more electrons are actually transferred and an ionic bond results.

A **dipole** is a molecule that is electrically asymmetrical, causing it to be oppositely charged at two points. A dipole is often written as ⊕ ⊖. A hydrogen chloride molecule is polar and behaves as a small dipole. The HCl dipole may be written as H+⟶Cl. The arrow points toward the negative end of the dipole. Molecules of H_2O, HBr, and ICl are polar:

$$H\!+\!\longrightarrow\!Cl \qquad H\!+\!\longrightarrow\!Br \qquad I\!+\!\longrightarrow\!Cl \qquad H\overset{O}{\diagup\diagdown}H$$

How do we know whether a bond between two atoms is ionic or covalent? The difference in electronegativity between the two atoms determines the character of the bond formed between them. As the difference in electronegativity increases, the polarity of the bond (or percent ionic character) increases.

In general, if the electronegativity difference between two bonded atoms is greater than 1.7–1.9, the bond will be more ionic than covalent.

If the electronegativity difference is greater than 2.0, the bond is strongly ionic. If the electronegativity difference is less than 1.5, the bond is strongly covalent.

H_2 Cl_2

Nonpolar
molecules

HCl

Polar covalent
molecule

NaCl

Ionic
compound

Figure 11.10

Nonpolar, polar covalent, and ionic compounds.

>CHEMISTRY *IN ACTION*

Trans-forming Fats

Trans fats are virtually everywhere in the American diet. These fats remain when vegetable oils are converted into solid substances that are used in many processed foods. In fact, beginning January 1, 2006, manufacturers were required to label products to show their *trans* fat content. So just what is a *trans* fat?

Different categories of fat can be identified from the pattern of bonds and hydrogen atoms in the molecule. Fatty acids are one component of fats and contain long chains of carbon atoms with hydrogen atoms bonded to some or all of the carbon atoms. Unsaturated fats (such as corn or soybean oil) contain double bonds between some of the carbon atoms in the chains. A carbon that is doubly bonded to another carbon usually also bonds to a hydrogen atom. If the fatty acid has only one double bond, it is monounsaturated (such as olive oil). If the fatty acid contains more than one double bond, it is polyunsaturated. All fat with no double bonds is saturated—all the carbon atoms have the maximum possible hydrogen atoms bonded to them.

Trans fats contain a particular kind of unsaturated fatty acid. When there is a double bond between carbon atoms, the molecule bends in one of two ways: the *cis* or the *trans* direction. In cis configuration, the carbon chain on both sides of the double bond bends in to the same side of the double bond (see structure). In the *trans* configuration, the chain on either side of the double bond bends toward opposite sides of the double bond (see structure). Most *trans* fats come from processing oils for prepared foods and from solid fats such as margarine.

When an oil is converted into a solid fat, some of the double bonds are converted to single bonds by adding hydrogen (hydrogenation). This process is easier at *cis* double bonds and, therefore, the remaining double bonds are mainly in the *trans* configuration. These *trans* fatty acids tend to stack together, making a solid easier than the *cis* forms. Studies have linked diets high in *trans* fats to poor health, high cholesterol, heart disease, and diabetes. Food producers are working on ways to lower the *trans* fat content of foods. Gary List at USDA in Peoria, Illinois, has used high-pressure hydrogen gas on soybean oil at 140°–170°C to hydrogenate the oil, producing a soft margarine containing 5%–6% *trans* fat instead of the ~40% from the standard hydrogenation techniques. This could lead to a product that qualifies for a label of 0 g *trans* fat. Look for lots of new products and labels in your grocery stores as manufacturers *trans*-form products into ones with less *trans* fat.

cis fatty acid

trans fatty acid

PRACTICE 11.8

Which of these compounds would you predict to be ionic and which would be covalent?
(a) $SrCl_2$ (d) RbBr
(b) PCl_3 (e) LiCl
(c) NH_3 (f) CS_2

Spacefilling molecular model CCl_4 (top) and methane (CH_4).

Care must be taken to distinguish between polar bonds and polar molecules. A covalent bond between different kinds of atoms is always polar. But a molecule containing different kinds of atoms may or may not be polar, depending on its shape or geometry. Molecules of HF, HCl, HBr, HI, and ICl are all polar because each contains a single polar bond. However, CO_2, CH_4, and CCl_4 are nonpolar molecules despite the fact that all three contain polar bonds. The carbon dioxide molecule $O{=}C{=}O$ is nonpolar because the carbon–oxygen dipoles cancel each other by acting in opposite directions.

$$O{=}C{=}O$$

dipoles in equal and opposite directions

Carbon tetrachloride (CCl_4) is nonpolar because the four C—Cl polar bonds are identical, and since these bonds emanate from the center to the corners of a tetrahedron in the molecule, their polarities cancel one another. Methane has the same molecular structure and is also nonpolar. We will discuss the shapes of molecules later in this chapter.

Bond type

Electronegativity difference

Figure 11.11
Relating bond type to electronegativity difference between atoms.

We have said that water is a polar molecule. If the atoms in water were linear like those in carbon dioxide, the two O—H dipoles would cancel each other, and the molecule would be nonpolar. However, water is definitely polar and has a nonlinear (bent) structure with an angle of 105° between the two O—H bonds.

The relationships among types of bonds are summarized in Figure 11.11. It is important to realize that bonding is a continuum, that is, the difference between ionic and covalent is a gradual change.

11.7 LEWIS STRUCTURES OF COMPOUNDS

Draw the Lewis structure of a covalent compound.   ● LEARNING OBJECTIVE

As we have seen, Lewis structures are a convenient way of showing the covalent bonds in many molecules or ions of the representative elements. In writing Lewis structures, the most important consideration for forming a stable compound is that the atoms attain a noble gas configuration.

The most difficult part of writing Lewis structures is determining the arrangement of the atoms in a molecule or an ion. In simple molecules with more than two atoms, one atom will be the central atom surrounded by the other atoms. Thus, Cl_2O has two possible arrangements, Cl—Cl—O or Cl—O—Cl. Usually, but not always, the single atom in the formula (except H) will be the central atom.

Although Lewis structures for many molecules and ions can be written by inspection, the following procedure is helpful for learning to write them:

PROBLEM-SOLVING STRATEGY: Writing a Lewis Structure

1. Obtain the total number of valence electrons to be used in the structure by adding the number of valence electrons in all the atoms in the molecule or ion. If you are writing the structure of an ion, add one electron for each negative charge or subtract one electron for each positive charge on the ion.

2. Write the skeletal arrangement of the atoms and connect them with a single covalent bond (two dots or one dash). Hydrogen, which contains only one bonding electron, can form only one covalent bond. Oxygen atoms are not normally bonded to each other, except in compounds known to be peroxides. Oxygen atoms normally have a maximum of two covalent bonds (two single bonds or one double bond).

3. Subtract two electrons for each single bond you used in Step 2 from the total number of electrons calculated in Step 1. This gives you the net number of electrons available for completing the structure.

4. Distribute pairs of electrons (pairs of dots) around each atom (except hydrogen) to give each atom a noble gas structure.

5. If there are not enough electrons to give these atoms eight electrons, change single bonds between atoms to double or triple bonds by shifting unbonded pairs of electrons as needed. Check to see that each atom has a noble gas electron structure (two electrons for hydrogen and eight for the others). A double bond counts as four electrons for each atom to which it is bonded.

Remember: The number of valence electrons of Group A elements is the same as their group number in the periodic table.

EXAMPLE 11.12

How many valence electrons are in each of these atoms: Cl, H, C, O, N, S, P, I?

SOLUTION

You can look at the periodic table to determine the electron structure, or, if the element is in Group A of the periodic table, the number of valence electrons is equal to the group number:

Atom	Group	Valence electrons
Cl	7A	7
H	1A	1
C	4A	4
O	6A	6
N	5A	5
S	6A	6
P	5A	5
I	7A	7

EXAMPLE 11.13

Use the Writing a Lewis Structure Problem-Solving Strategy for water (H_2O).

SOLUTION

1. The total number of valence electrons is eight, two from the two hydrogen atoms and six from the oxygen atom.

2. The two hydrogen atoms are connected to the oxygen atom. Write the skeletal structure:

H O   or   H O H
 H

Place two dots between the hydrogen and oxygen atoms to form the covalent bonds:

H:O   or   H:O:H
 Ḧ

3. Subtract the four electrons used in Step 2 from eight to obtain four electrons yet to be used.

4. Distribute the four electrons in pairs around the oxygen atom. Hydrogen atoms cannot accommodate any more electrons:

H—Ö: or   H—Ö—H
 |
 H

These arrangements are Lewis structures because each atom has a noble gas electron structure. Note that the shape of the molecule is not shown by the Lewis structure.

EXAMPLE 11.14

Use the Writing a Lewis Structure Problem-Solving Strategy for a molecule of methane (CH_4).

SOLUTION

1. The total number of valence electrons is eight, one from each hydrogen atom and four from the carbon atom.

2. The skeletal structure contains four H atoms around a central C atom. Place two electrons between the C and each H.

　　H　　　　　H
H C H　　H:C:H
　　H　　　　　Ḧ

3. Subtract the eight electrons used in Step 2 from eight (obtained in Step 1) to obtain zero electrons yet to be placed. Therefore, the Lewis structure must be as written in Step 2:

$$
\begin{array}{ccc}
& & \text{H} \\
\text{H} & & | \\
\text{H:C:H} & \text{or} & \text{H—C—H} \\
\text{H} & & | \\
& & \text{H}
\end{array}
$$

EXAMPLE 11.15

Use the Writing a Lewis Structure Problem-Solving Strategy for a molecule of carbon tetrachloride (CCl_4).

SOLUTION

1. The total number of valence electrons to be used is 32, 4 from the carbon atom and 7 from each of the four chlorine atoms.

2. The skeletal structure contains the four Cl atoms around a central C atom. Place 2 electrons between the C and each Cl:

$$
\begin{array}{cc}
\text{Cl} & \text{Cl} \\
\text{Cl C Cl} \qquad & \text{Cl:C:Cl} \\
\text{Cl} & \text{Cl}
\end{array}
$$

3. Subtract the 8 electrons used in Step 2 from 32 (obtained in Step 1) to obtain 24 electrons yet to be placed.

4. Distribute the 24 electrons (12 pairs) around the Cl atoms so that each Cl atom has 8 electrons around it:

$$
\begin{array}{ccc}
& & :\ddot{C}l: \\
:\ddot{C}l: & & | \\
:\ddot{C}l:\ddot{C}:\ddot{C}l: & \text{or} & :\ddot{C}l—C—\ddot{C}l: \\
:\ddot{C}l: & & | \\
& & :\ddot{C}l:
\end{array}
$$

This arrangement is the Lewis structure; CCl_4 contains four covalent bonds.

EXAMPLE 11.16

Use the Writing a Lewis Structure Problem-Solving Strategy for CO_2.

SOLUTION

1. The total number of valence electrons is 16, 4 from the C atom and 6 from each O atom.

2. The two O atoms are bonded to a central C atom. Write the skeletal structure and place 2 electrons between the C and each O atom.

O : C : O

3. Subtract the 4 electrons used in Step 2 from 16 (found in Step 1) to obtain 12 electrons yet to be placed.

4. Distribute the 12 electrons (six pairs) around the C and O atoms. Several possibilities exist:

$$
\underset{\text{I}}{:\ddot{O}:C:\ddot{O}:} \qquad \underset{\text{II}}{:\ddot{O}:\underset{\cdot\cdot}{C}:\ddot{O}:} \qquad \underset{\text{III}}{:\ddot{O}:\overset{\cdot\cdot}{C}:\underset{\cdot\cdot}{O}:}
$$

5. Not all the atoms have 8 electrons around them (noble gas structure). Remove one pair of unbonded electrons from each O atom in structure I and place one pair between each O and the C atom, forming two double bonds:

$$
:\ddot{O}::C::\ddot{O}: \qquad \text{or} \qquad :\ddot{O}=C=\ddot{O}:
$$

Each atom now has 8 electrons around it. The carbon is sharing four pairs of electrons, and each oxygen is sharing two pairs. These bonds are known as double bonds because each involves sharing two pairs of electrons.

>CHEMISTRY *IN ACTION*

Strong Enough to Stop a Bullet?

What do color-changing pens, bullet-resistant vests, and calculators have in common? The chemicals that make each of them work are liquid crystals. These chemicals find numerous applications; you are probably most familiar with liquid crystal displays (LCDs) and color-changing products, but these chemicals are also used to make superstrong synthetic fibers.

Molecules in a normal crystal remain in an orderly arrangement, but in a liquid crystal the molecules can flow *and* maintain an orderly arrangement at the same time. Liquid crystal molecules are linear and polar. Since the atoms tend to lie in a relatively straight line, the molecules are generally much longer than they are wide. These polar molecules are attracted to each other and are able to line up in an orderly fashion without solidifying.

Liquid crystals with twisted arrangements of molecules give us novelty color-changing products. In these liquid crystals the molecules lie side by side in a nearly flat layer. The next layer is similar but at an angle to the one below. The closely packed flat layers have a special effect on light. As the light strikes the surface, some of it is reflected from the top layer and some from lower layers. When the same wavelength is reflected from many layers, we see a color. (This is similar to the rainbow of colors formed by oil in a puddle on the street or the film of a soap bubble.) As the temperature is increased, the molecules move faster, causing a change in the angle and the space between the layers. This results in a color change in the reflected light. Different compounds change color within different temperature ranges, allowing a variety of practical and amusing applications.

Liquid crystal (nematic) molecules that lie parallel to one another are used to manufacture very strong synthetic fibers. Perhaps the best example of these liquid crystals is Kevlar, a synthetic fiber used in bullet-resistant vests, canoes, and parts of the space shuttle. Kevlar is a synthetic polymer, like nylon or polyester, that gains strength by passing through a liquid crystal state during its manufacture.

In a typical polymer, the long molecular chains are jumbled together, somewhat like spaghetti. The strength of the material is limited by the disorderly arrangement. The trick is to get the molecules to line up parallel to each other. Once the giant molecules have been synthesized, they are dissolved in sulfuric acid. At the proper concentration the molecules align, and the solution is forced through tiny holes in a nozzle and further aligned. The sulfuric acid is removed in a water bath, thereby forming solid fibers in near-perfect alignment. One strand of Kevlar is stronger than an equal-sized strand of steel. It has a much lower density as well, making it a material of choice in bullet-resistant vests.

© Haku Nellies/iStockphoto

Kevlar is used to make protective vests for police.

PRACTICE 11.9

Write the Lewis structures for the following:
(a) PBr_3 (b) $CHCl_3$ (c) HF   (d) H_2CO (e) N_2

Although many compounds attain a noble gas structure in covalent bonding, there are numerous exceptions. Sometimes it's impossible to write a structure in which each atom has 8 electrons around it. For example, in BF_3 the boron atom has only 6 electrons around it, and in SF_6 the sulfur atom has 12 electrons around it.

Although there are exceptions, many molecules can be described using Lewis structures where each atom has a noble gas electron configuration. This is a useful model for understanding chemistry.

11.8 COMPLEX LEWIS STRUCTURES

LEARNING OBJECTIVE ● Draw the resonance structures for a polyatomic ion.

KEY TERM
resonance structure

Most Lewis structures give bonding pictures that are consistent with experimental information on bond strength and length. There are some molecules and polyatomic ions for which no single Lewis structure consistent with all characteristics and bonding information can be written. For example, consider the nitrate ion, NO_3^-. To write a Lewis structure for this polyatomic ion, we use the following steps.

1. The total number of valence electrons is 24, 5 from the nitrogen atom, 6 from each oxygen atom, and 1 from the −1 charge.

2. The three O atoms are bonded to a central N atom. Write the skeletal structure and place two electrons between each pair of atoms. Since we have an extra electron in this ion, resulting in a −1 charge, we enclose the group of atoms in square brackets and add a − charge as shown.

$$\left[\begin{array}{c} O \\ O\!:\!\ddot{N}\!:\!O \end{array} \right]^{-}$$

3. Subtract the 6 electrons used in Step 2 from 24 (found in Step 1) to obtain 18 electrons yet to be placed.

4. Distribute the 18 electrons around the N and O atoms:

$$:\!\ddot{O} \longleftarrow \text{electron deficient}$$
$$:\!\ddot{O}\!:\!\ddot{N}\!:\!\ddot{O}\!:$$

5. One pair of electrons is still needed to give all the N and O atoms a noble gas structure. Move the unbonded pair of electrons from the N atom and place it between the N and the electron-deficient O atom, making a double bond.

$$\left[:\!\ddot{O}\!-\!N\overset{\ddot{O}}{\underset{\|}{}}\!-\!\ddot{O}\!: \right]^{-} \text{ or } \left[:\!\ddot{O}\!-\!N\!=\!\ddot{O}\!: \right]^{-} \text{ or } \left[\ddot{O}\!=\!N\!-\!\ddot{O}\!: \right]^{-}$$

Are these all valid Lewis structures? Yes, so there really are three possible Lewis structures for NO_3^-.

A molecule or ion that has multiple correct Lewis structures shows *resonance*. Each of these Lewis structures is called a **resonance structure**. In this book, however, we will not be concerned with how to choose the correct resonance structure for a molecule or ion. Therefore, any of the possible resonance structures may be used to represent the ion or molecule.

EXAMPLE 11.17

Write the Lewis structure for a carbonate ion (CO_3^{2-}).

SOLUTION

1. These four atoms have 22 valence electrons plus 2 electrons from the −2 charge, which makes 24 electrons to be placed.

2. In the carbonate ion, the carbon is the central atom surrounded by the three oxygen atoms. Write the skeletal structure and place 2 electrons (or a single line) between each C and O:

$$\begin{array}{c} O \\ | \\ C\!-\!O \\ | \\ O \end{array}$$

3. Subtract the 6 electrons used in Step 2 from 24 (from Step 1) to give 18 electrons yet to be placed.

4. Distribute the 18 electrons around the three oxygen atoms and indicate that the carbonate ion has a −2 charge:

$$\left[\begin{array}{c} :\!\ddot{O}\!: \\ | \\ C \\ :\!\ddot{O} \quad \ddot{O}\!: \end{array} \right]^{2-}$$

The difficulty with this structure is that the carbon atom has only six electrons around it instead of a noble gas octet.

5. Move one of the nonbonding pairs of electrons from one of the oxygens and place them between the carbon and the oxygen. Three Lewis structures are possible:

PRACTICE 11.10

Write the Lewis structure for each of the following:
(a) NH_3 (b) H_3O^+ (c) NH_4^+ (d) HCO_3^-

11.9 COMPOUNDS CONTAINING POLYATOMIC IONS

LEARNING OBJECTIVE   ● Describe a compound that contains both ionic and covalent bonds.

A polyatomic ion is a stable group of atoms that has either a positive or a negative charge and behaves as a single unit in many chemical reactions. Sodium carbonate, Na_2CO_3, contains two sodium ions and a carbonate ion. The carbonate ion (CO_3^{2-}) is a polyatomic ion composed of one carbon atom and three oxygen atoms and has a charge of -2. One carbon and three oxygen atoms have a total of 22 electrons in their outer energy levels. The carbonate ion contains 24 outer electrons and therefore has a charge of -2. In this case, the 2 additional electrons come from the two sodium atoms, which are now sodium ions:

Sodium carbonate   Carbonate ion

Sodium carbonate has both ionic and covalent bonds. Ionic bonds exist between each of the sodium ions and the carbonate ion. Covalent bonds are present between the carbon and oxygen atoms within the carbonate ion. One important difference between the ionic and covalent bonds in this compound can be demonstrated by dissolving sodium carbonate in water. It dissolves in water, forming three charged particles—two sodium ions and one carbonate ion—per formula unit of Na_2CO_3:

$$Na_2CO_3(s) \xrightarrow{\text{water}} 2\,Na^+(aq) + CO_3^{2-}(aq)$$

sodium carbonate   sodium ions   carbonate ion

The CO_3^{2-} ion remains as a unit, held together by covalent bonds; but where the bonds are ionic, dissociation of the ions takes place. Do not think, however, that polyatomic ions are so stable that they cannot be altered. Chemical reactions by which polyatomic ions can be changed to other substances do exist.

PRACTICE 11.11

Write Lewis structures for the calcium compounds of the following anions: nitrate and sulfate.

11.10 MOLECULAR SHAPE

Determine the shape of a compound by using VSEPR method.

● **LEARNING OBJECTIVE**

KEY TERMS
linear structure
trigonal planar structure
tetrahedral structure
bent structure

So far in our discussion of bonding we have used Lewis structures to represent valence electrons in molecules and ions, but they don't indicate anything regarding the molecular or geometric shape of a molecule. The three-dimensional arrangement of the atoms within a molecule is a significant feature in understanding molecular interactions. Let's consider several examples illustrated in **Figure 11.12**.

Water is known to have the geometric shape known as "bent" or "V-shaped." Carbon dioxide exhibits a linear shape. BF_3 forms a third molecular shape called *trigonal planar* since all the atoms lie in one plane in a triangular arrangement. One of the more common molecular shapes is the tetrahedron, illustrated by the molecule methane (CH_4).

How do we predict the geometric shape of a molecule? We will now study a model developed to assist in making predictions from the Lewis structure.

The Valence Shell Electron Pair Repulsion (VSEPR) Model

The chemical properties of a substance are closely related to the structure of its molecules. A change in a single site on a large biomolecule can make a difference in whether or not a particular reaction occurs.

Figure 11.12
Geometric shapes of common molecules. Each molecule is shown as a ball-and-stick model (showing the bonds) and as a spacefilling model (showing the shape).

Water
H_2O
(V-shaped)

Carbon dioxide
CO_2
(linear shape)

Boron trifluoride
BF_3
(trigonal planar)

Methane
CH_4
(tetrahedral)

Instrumental analysis can be used to determine exact spatial arrangements of atoms. Quite often, though, we only need to be able to predict the approximate structure of a molecule. A relatively simple model has been developed to allow us to make predictions of shape from Lewis structures.

The VSEPR model is based on the idea that electron pairs will repel each other electrically and will seek to minimize this repulsion. To accomplish this minimization, the electron pairs will be arranged around a central atom as far apart as possible. Consider $BeCl_2$, a molecule with only two pairs of electrons surrounding the central atom. These electrons are arranged 180° apart for maximum separation:

> Nonbonding pairs of electrons are not shown here, so you can focus your attention on the shapes, not electron arrangement.

$$Cl \overset{180°}{-\!\!\!-\!\!\!-} Be \overset{}{-\!\!\!-\!\!\!-} Cl$$

This molecular structure can now be labeled as a **linear structure**. When only two pairs of electrons surround a central atom, they should be placed 180° apart to give a linear structure.

What occurs when there are only three pairs of electrons around the central atom? Consider the BF_3 molecule. The greatest separation of electron pairs occurs when the angles between atoms are 120°:

This arrangement of atoms is flat (planar) and, as noted earlier, is called **trigonal planar structure**. When three pairs of electrons surround an atom, they should be placed 120° apart to show the trigonal planar structure.

Now consider the most common situation (CH_4), with four pairs of electrons on the central carbon atom. In this case the central atom exhibits a noble gas electron structure. What arrangement best minimizes the electron pair repulsions? At first, it seems that an obvious choice is a 90° angle with all the atoms in a single plane:

$$\begin{array}{c} H \\ {}^{90°} + {}^{90°} \\ H + C + H \\ {}_{90°} + {}_{90°} \\ H \end{array}$$

However, we must consider that molecules are three-dimensional. This concept results in a structure in which the electron pairs are actually 109.5° apart:

$$\begin{array}{c} H \underset{}{\overset{109.5°}{\diagdown}} H \\ C \\ H \swarrow \quad \diagdown H \end{array}$$

In this diagram the wedged line seems to protrude from the page, whereas the dashed line recedes. Two representations of this arrangement, known as **tetrahedral structure**, are illustrated in Figure 11.13. When four pairs of electrons surround a central atom, they should be placed 109.5° apart to give them a tetrahedral structure.

Figure 11.13

Ball-and-stick models of methane and carbon tetrachloride. Methane and carbon tetrachloride are nonpolar molecules because their polar bonds cancel each other in the tetrahedral arrangement of their atoms. The carbon atoms are located in the centers of the tetrahedrons.

Methane, CH_4

CH_4

Carbon tetrachloride, CCl_4

CCl_4

Figure 11.14
(a) The tetrahedral arrangement of electron pairs around the N atom in the NH_3 molecule. (b) Three pairs are shared and one is unshared. (c) The NH_3 molecule is pyramidal.

(a)   (b)   (c)

The VSEPR model is based on the premise that we are counting electron pairs. It's quite possible that one or more of these electron pairs may be nonbonding (lone) pairs. What happens to the molecular structure in these cases?

Consider the ammonia molecule. First we draw the Lewis structure to determine the number of electron pairs around the central atom:

$$H:\overset{\cdot\cdot}{N}:H$$
$$\overset{|}{H}$$

Since there are four pairs of electrons, the arrangement of electrons around the central atom will be tetrahedral (Figure 11.14a). However, only three of the pairs are bonded to another atom, so the molecule itself is pyramidal. It is important to understand that the placement of the electron pairs determines the shape but the name for the molecule is determined by the position of the atoms themselves. Therefore, ammonia is pyramidal. See Figure 11.14c.

Now consider the effect of two unbonded pairs of electrons in the water molecule. The Lewis structure for water is

$$H-\overset{\cdot\cdot}{O}:$$
$$\overset{|}{H}$$

The four electron pairs indicate that a tetrahedral electron arrangement is necessary (see Figure 11.15a). The molecule is not called tetrahedral because two of the electron pairs are unbonded pairs. The water molecule displays a **bent structure**.

Let's summarize the VSEPR model.

The arrangement of electron pairs around an atom determines its shape, but we name the shape of molecules by the position of the atoms.

PROBLEM-SOLVING STRATEGY: Determining Molecular Shape Using VSEPR

1. Draw the Lewis structure for the molecule.

2. Count the electron pairs around the central atom and arrange them to minimize repulsions (as far apart as possible). This determines the electron pair arrangement.

3. Determine the positions of the atoms.

4. Name the molecular structure from the position of the atoms.

It is important to recognize that the placement of the electron pairs determines the structure but the name of the molecular structure is determined by the position of the atoms. Table 11.6 shows the results of this process. Note that when the number of electron pairs is the same as the number of atoms, the electron pair arrangement and the molecular structure are the same. But when the number of atoms and the number of electron pairs are not the same, the molecular structure is different from the electron pair arrangement. This is illustrated when the number of electron pairs is four (a tetrahedral arrangement) in Table 11.6.

(a)   (b)   (c)

Figure 11.15
(a) The tetrahedral arrangement of the four electron pairs around oxygen in the H_2O molecule. (b) Two of the pairs are shared and two are unshared. (c) The H_2O molecule is bent.

TABLE 11.6   Arrangement of Electron Pairs and Molecular Structure

Number of electron pairs	Electron pair arrangement	Ball-and-stick model	Bonds	Molecular structure	Molecular structure model
2	Linear	180°	2	Linear	
3	Trigonal planar	120°	3	Trigonal planar	
4	Tetrahedral	109.5°	4	Tetrahedral	
4	Tetrahedral	109.5°	3	Pyramidal	
4	Tetrahedral	109.5°	2	Bent	

EXAMPLE 11.18

Predict the molecular shape for these molecules: H_2S, CCl_4, $AlCl_3$.

SOLUTION

1. Draw the Lewis structure.
2. Count the electron pairs around the central atom and determine the electron arrangement that will minimize repulsions.
3. Determine the positions of the atoms and name the shape of the molecule.

Molecule	Lewis structure	Number of electron pairs	Electron pair arrangement	Molecular shape
H_2S	H:S̈:H	4	tetrahedral	bent
CCl_4	:C̈l:C:C̈l: with :C̈l: above and :C̈l: below	4	tetrahedral	tetrahedral
$AlCl_3$	:C̈l: above, :C̈l:Al:C̈l:	3	trigonal planar	trigonal planar

PRACTICE 11.12

Predict the shape for CF_4, NF_3, and BeI_2.

CHAPTER **11 REVIEW**

11.1 PERIODIC TRENDS IN ATOMIC PROPERTIES

- Metals and nonmetals
- Atomic radius:
  - Increases down a group
  - Decreases across a row
- Ionization energy:
  - Energy required to remove an electron from an atom
  - Decreases down a group
  - Increases across a row

KEY TERM

ionization energy

11.2 LEWIS STRUCTURES OF ATOMS

- A Lewis structure is a representation of the atom where the symbol represents the element and dots around the symbol represent the valence electrons.
- To determine a Lewis structure for representative elements, use the group number as the number of electrons to place around the symbol for the element.

KEY TERM

Lewis structure

11.3 THE IONIC BOND: TRANSFER OF ELECTRONS FROM ONE ATOM TO ANOTHER

- The goal of bonding is to achieve stability:
  - For representative elements, this stability can be achieved by attaining a valence electron structure of a noble gas.
- In an ionic bond stability is attained by transferring an electron from one atom to another:
  - The atom that loses an electron becomes a cation:
    - Positive ions are smaller than their parent atoms.
    - Metals tend to form cations.
  - The atom gaining an electron becomes an anion:
    - Negative ions are larger than their parent atoms.
    - Nonmetals tend to form anions.
  - Ionic compounds do not exist as molecules:
    - Ions are attracted by multiple ions of the opposite charge to form a crystalline structure.

KEY TERM

ionic bond

11.4 PREDICTING FORMULAS OF IONIC COMPOUNDS

- Chemical compounds are always electrically neutral.
- Metals lose electrons and nonmetals gain electrons to form compounds.
- Stability is achieved (for representative elements) by attaining a noble gas electron configuration.

11.5 THE COVALENT BOND: SHARING ELECTRONS

- Covalent bonds are formed when two atoms share a pair of electrons between them:
  - This is the predominant type of bonding in compounds.
  - True molecules exist in covalent compounds.
  - Overlap of orbitals forms a covalent bond.
- Unequal sharing of electrons results in a polar covalent bond.

KEY TERMS

covalent bond
polar covalent bond

11.6 ELECTRONEGATIVITY

- Electronegativity is the attractive force an atom has for shared electrons in a molecule or polyatomic ion.
- Electrons spend more time closer to the more electronegative atom in a bond forming a polar bond.
- The polarity of a bond is determined by the electronegativity difference between the atoms involved in the bond:
  - The greater the difference, the more polar the bond is.
  - At the extremes:
    - Large differences result in ionic bonds.
    - Tiny differences (or no difference) result(s) in a nonpolar covalent bond.

KEY TERMS

electronegativity
nonpolar covalent bond
dipole

• A molecule that is electrically asymmetrical has a dipole, resulting in charged areas within the molecule.

hydrogen chloride

• If the electronegativity difference between two bonded atoms is greater than 1.7–1.9, the bond will be more ionic than covalent.
• Polar bonds do not always result in polar molecules.

11.7 LEWIS STRUCTURES OF COMPOUNDS

PROBLEM-SOLVING STRATEGY: Writing a Lewis Structure

1. Obtain the total number of valence electrons to be used in the structure by adding the number of valence electrons in all the atoms in the molecule or ion. If you are writing the structure of an ion, add one electron for each negative charge or subtract one electron for each positive charge on the ion.

2. Write the skeletal arrangement of the atoms and connect them with a single covalent bond (two dots or one dash). Hydrogen, which contains only one bonding electron, can form only one covalent bond. Oxygen atoms are not normally bonded to each other, except in compounds known to be peroxides. Oxygen atoms normally have a maximum of two covalent bonds (two single bonds or one double bond).

3. Subtract two electrons for each single bond you used in Step 2 from the total number of electrons calculated in Step 1. This gives you the net number of electrons available for completing the structure.

4. Distribute pairs of electrons (pairs of dots) around each atom (except hydrogen) to give each atom a noble gas structure.

5. If there are not enough electrons to give these atoms eight electrons, change single bonds between atoms to double or triple bonds by shifting unbonded pairs of electrons as needed. Check to see that each atom has a noble gas electron structure (two electrons for hydrogen and eight for the others). A double bond counts as four electrons for each atom to which it is bonded.

11.8 COMPLEX LEWIS STRUCTURES

KEY TERM

resonance structure

• When a single unique Lewis structure cannot be drawn for a molecule, resonance structures (multiple Lewis structures) are used to represent the molecule.

11.9 COMPOUNDS CONTAINING POLYATOMIC IONS

• Polyatomic ions behave like a single unit in many chemical reactions.
• The bonds within a polyatomic ion are covalent.

11.10 MOLECULAR SHAPE

KEY TERMS

linear structure
trigonal planar structure
tetrahedral structure
bent structure

• Lewis structures do not indicate the shape of a molecule.

PROBLEM-SOLVING STRATEGY: Determining Molecular Shape Using VSEPR

1. Draw the Lewis structure for the molecule.

2. Count the electron pairs around the central atom and arrange them to minimize repulsions (as far apart as possible). This determines the electron pair arrangement.

3. Determine the positions of the atoms.

4. Name the molecular structure from the position of the atoms.

REVIEW QUESTIONS

1. Rank these elements according to the radii of their atoms, from smallest to largest: Na, Mg, Cl, K, and Rb. (Figure 11.2)
2. Explain why much more ionization energy is required to remove the first electron from neon than from sodium. (Table 11.1)

3. Explain the large increase in ionization energy needed to remove the third electron from beryllium compared with that needed for the second electron. (Table 11.1)

4. Does the first ionization energy increase or decrease from top to bottom in the periodic table for the alkali metal family? Explain. (Figure 11.3)

5. Does the first ionization energy increase or decrease from top to bottom in the periodic table for the noble gas family? Explain. (Figure 11.3)

6. Explain the reason that an atom of helium has a much higher first ionization energy than does an atom of hydrogen. (Table 11.1)

7. Why is there such a large increase in the energy required to remove a second electron from an atom of lithium? (Table 11.1)

8. Which element has the larger radius?
  (a) Li or Be   (d) F or Cl
  (b) K or Rb   (e) O or Se
  (c) Al or P   (f) As or Kr

9. In Groups 1A–7A, which element in each group has the smallest atomic radius? (Figure 11.2)

10. Why does the atomic size increase in going down any family of the periodic table?

11. Explain why potassium usually forms a K^+ ion but not a K^{2+} ion.

12. Why does an aluminum ion have a $+3$ charge?

13. Why are only valence electrons represented in a Lewis structure?

14. All the atoms within each Group A family of elements can be represented by the same Lewis structure. Complete the following table, expressing the Lewis structure for each group. (Use E to represent the elements.) (Figure 11.4)

Group	1A	2A	3A	4A	5A	6A	7A
	E·						

15. Draw the Lewis structure for Cs, Ba, Tl, Pb, Po, At, and Rn. How do these structures correlate with the group in which each element occurs?

16. What are valence electrons?

17. Why do metals tend to lose electrons and nonmetals tend to gain electrons when forming ionic bonds?

18. State whether the elements in each group gain or lose electrons in order to achieve a noble gas configuration. Explain.
  (a) Group 1A   (c) Group 6A
  (b) Group 2A   (d) Group 7A

19. What is the overall charge on an ionic compound?

20. Which family of elements tends to form ionic compounds with a 1 : 1 ratio of cation to anion with sulfur?

21. If the formula for calcium phosphate is $Ca_3(PO_4)_2$, predict the formulas of magnesium phosphate, beryllium phosphate, strontium phosphate, and barium phosphate.

22. Explain why magnesium tends to lose two electrons when forming an ionic compound.

23. Why is the term *molecule* used to describe covalent compounds but not ionic compounds?

24. How many shared electrons make up a single covalent bond? What is the maximum number of covalent bonds that can be formed between any two atoms?

25. Explain in simple terms how a chemist describes the formation of a covalent bond.

26. What does the dash between atoms represent in a Lewis electron dot structure?

27. Are all molecules that contain polar bonds polar molecules? Explain.

28. In a polar covalent bond, how do you determine which atom has a partial negative charge ($\delta-$) and which has a partial positive charge ($\delta+$)?

29. In which general areas of the periodic table are the elements with (a) the highest and (b) the lowest electronegativities located?

30. What is the purpose of a Lewis structure?

31. In a Lewis structure, what do the dots represent and what do the lines represent?

32. Can there be more than one correct Lewis structure for a compound? Explain.

33. If a molecule has more than one correct Lewis structure, what is the term used to describe these structures?

34. When drawing a Lewis structure for an ion, how is the charge represented?

35. Write two examples of molecules that have both ionic and covalent bonds.

36. What is the difference between electron pair arrangement and molecular shape?

Most of the exercises in this chapter are available for assignment via the online homework management program, WileyPLUS (www.wileyplus.com). All exercises with blue numbers have answers in Appendix VI.

PAIRED EXERCISES

1. An atom of potassium and a K^+ ion are drawn below. Identify each and explain your choice.

2. An atom of chlorine and a Cl^- ion are drawn below. Identify each and explain your choice.

3. Which one in each pair has the larger radius? Explain.
  (a) a calcium atom or a calcium ion
  (b) a chlorine atom or a chloride ion
  (c) a magnesium ion or an aluminum ion
  (d) a sodium atom or a silicon atom
  (e) a potassium ion or a bromide ion

4. Which one in each pair has the larger radius? Explain.
  (a) Fe^{2+} or Fe^{3+}
  (b) a potassium atom or a potassium ion
  (c) a sodium ion or a chloride ion
  (d) a strontium atom or an iodine atom
  (e) a rubidium ion or a strontium ion

5. Using the table of electronegativity values (Table 11.5), indicate which element is more positive and which is more negative in these compounds:
   (a) H_2O (d) PbS
   (b) RbCl   (e) PF_3
   (c) NH_3 (f) CH_4

6. Using the table of electronegativity values (Table 11.5), indicate which element is more positive and which is more negative in these compounds:
   (a) HCl   (d) IBr
   (b) SO_2 (e) CsI
   (c) CCl_4 (f) OF_2

7. Classify the bond between these pairs of elements as principally ionic or principally covalent (use Table 11.5):
   (a) sulfur and oxygen
   (b) barium and nitrogen
   (c) potassium and bromine
   (d) carbon and chlorine

8. Classify the bond between these pairs of elements as principally ionic or principally covalent (use Table 11.5):
   (a) sodium and oxygen
   (b) nitrogen and hydrogen
   (c) oxygen and hydrogen
   (d) phosphorus and chlorine

9. Write an equation representing each of the following:
   (a) the change of a magnesium atom to a magnesium ion
   (b) the change of a bromine atom to a bromide ion

10. Write an equation representing each of the following:
    (a) the change of a potassium atom to a potassium ion
    (b) the change of a sulfur atom to a sulfide ion

11. Use Lewis structures to show the electron transfer that enables these ionic compounds to form:
    (a) Li_2O (b) K_3N

12. Use Lewis structures to show the electron transfer that enables these ionic compounds to form:
    (a) K_2S (b) Ca_3N_2

13. State the number of valence electrons in an atom of each of the following elements:
    (a) selenium   (d) magnesium
    (b) phosphorus   (e) helium
    (c) bromine   (f) arsenic

14. State the number of valence electrons in an atom of each of the following elements:
    (a) lead   (d) cesium
    (b) lithium   (e) gallium
    (c) oxygen   (f) argon

15. How many electrons must be gained or lost for the following to achieve a noble gas electron configuration?
    (a) a potassium atom   (c) a bromine atom
    (b) an aluminum ion   (d) a selenium atom

16. How many electrons must be gained or lost for the following to achieve a noble gas electron structure?
    (a) a sulfur atom   (c) a nitrogen atom
    (b) a calcium atom   (d) an iodide ion

17. Determine whether the following atoms will form an ionic compound or a molecular compound, and give the formula of the compound.
    (a) sodium and chlorine
    (b) carbon and 4 hydrogen
    (c) magnesium and bromine
    (d) 2 bromine
    (e) carbon and 2 oxygen

18. Determine whether each of the following atoms will form a nonpolar covalent compound or a polar covalent compound, and give the formula of the compound.
    (a) 2 oxygen
    (b) hydrogen and bromine
    (c) oxygen and 2 hydrogen
    (d) 2 iodine

19. Let E be any representative element. Following the pattern in the table, write formulas for the hydrogen and oxygen compounds of the following:
    (a) Na   (c) Al
    (b) Ca   (d) Sn

Group						
1A	2A	3A	4A	5A	6A	7A
EH	EH_2	EH_3	EH_4	EH_3	H_2E	HE
E_2O	EO	E_2O_3	EO_2	E_2O_5	EO_3	E_2O_7

20. Let E be any representative element. Following the pattern in the table, write formulas for the hydrogen and oxygen compounds of the following:
    (a) Sb   (c) Cl
    (b) Se   (d) C

Group						
1A	2A	3A	4A	5A	6A	7A
EH	EH_2	EH_3	EH_4	EH_3	H_2E	HE
E_2O	EO	E_2O_3	EO_2	E_2O_5	EO_3	E_2O_7

21. The formula for sodium sulfate is Na_2SO_4. Write the names and formulas for the other alkali metal sulfates.

22. The formula for calcium bromide is $CaBr_2$. Write the names and formulas for the other alkaline earth metal bromides.

23. Write Lewis structures for the following:
    (a) Na   (b) Br^- (c) O^{2-}

24. Write Lewis structures for the following:
    (a) Ga   (b) Ga^{3+} (c) Ca^{2+}

25. Classify the bonding in each compound as ionic or covalent:
    (a) H_2O (c) MgO
    (b) NaCl   (d) Br_2

26. Classify the bonding in each compound as ionic or covalent:
    (a) HCl   (c) NH_3
    (b) $BaCl_2$ (d) SO_2

27. Predict the type of bond that would be formed between the following pairs of atoms:
    (a) P and I   (b) N and S   (c) Br and I

28. Predict the type of bond that would be formed between the following pairs of atoms:
    (a) H and Si   (b) O and F   (c) Si and Br

29. Draw Lewis structures for the following:
    (a) H_2
    (b) N_2
    (c) Cl_2

30. Draw Lewis structures for the following:
    (a) O_2
    (b) Br_2
    (c) I_2

31. Draw Lewis structures for the following:
    (a) NCl_3
    (c) C_2H_6
    (b) H_2CO_3
    (d) $NaNO_3$

32. Draw Lewis structures for the following:
    (a) H_2S
    (c) NH_3
    (b) CS_2
    (d) NH_4Cl

33. Draw Lewis structures for the following:
    (a) Ba^{2+}
    (d) CN^-
    (b) Al^{3+}
    (e) HCO_3^-
    (c) SO_3^{2-}

34. Draw Lewis structures for the following:
    (a) I^-
    (d) ClO_3^-
    (b) S^{2-}
    (e) NO_3^-
    (c) CO_3^{2-}

35. Classify each of the following molecules as polar or nonpolar:
    (a) CH_3Cl
    (c) OF_2
    (b) Cl_2
    (d) PBr_3

36. Classify each of the following molecules as polar or nonpolar:
    (a) H_2
    (c) CH_3OH
    (b) NI_3
    (d) CS_2

37. Give the number and arrangement of the electron pairs around the central atom:
    (a) C in CCl_4
    (c) Al in AlH_3
    (b) S in H_2S

38. Give the number and arrangement of the electron pairs around the central atom:
    (a) Ga in $GaCl_3$
    (c) Cl in ClO_3^-
    (b) N in NF_3

39. Use VSEPR theory to predict the structure of these polyatomic ions:
    (a) sulfate ion
    (c) periodate ion
    (b) chlorate ion

40. Use VSEPR theory to predict the structure of these polyatomic ions:
    (a) ammonium ion
    (c) phosphate ion
    (b) sulfite ion

41. Use VSEPR theory to predict the shape of these molecules:
    (a) SiH_4
    (b) PH_3
    (c) SeF_2

42. Use VSEPR theory to predict the shape of these molecules:
    (a) SiF_4
    (b) OF_2
    (c) Cl_2O

43. Element X reacts with sodium to form the compound Na_2X and is in the second period on the periodic table. Identify this element.

44. Element Y reacts with oxygen to form the compound Y_2O and has the lowest ionization energy of any Period 4 element on the periodic table. Identify this element.

ADDITIONAL EXERCISES

45. Atoms of sodium, cesium, and argon are drawn below. Identify each and explain your choice.

    1   2   3

46. Spheres representing Br^-, Se^{2-}, Rb^+, Sr^{2+}, and Kr are drawn below. Identify each and explain your choice.

  1   2   3   4   5

47. Write Lewis structures for hydrazine (N_2H_4) and hydrazoic acid (HN_3).

48. Draw Lewis structures and give the shape of each of the following compounds:
    (a) NO_2^-
    (c) $SOCl_2$
    (b) SO_4^{2-}
    (d) Cl_2O

49. Draw Lewis structures for each of the following compounds:
    (a) ethane (C_2H_6)
    (b) ethylene (C_2H_4)
    (c) acetylene (C_2H_2)

50. Using the periodic table, identify each element given the description:
    (a) the most electronegative element of the alkaline earth metals
    (b) the noble gas with the highest first ionization energy
    (c) the element in Period 4 with the lowest first ionization energy

(d) the element with the highest electronegativity
(e) the alkali metal with the largest radius
(f) the element in Period 2 with the smallest radius

51. Choose the element that fits each description:
    (a) the higher electronegativity   Cl or Br
    (b) the higher first ionization energy   O or S
    (c) the lower electronegativity   Ca or C

52. Why do you think there are no electronegativity values given for the noble gases in Table 11.5?

53. When one electron is removed from an atom of Li, it has two left. Helium atoms also have two electrons. Why is more energy required to remove the second electron from Li than to remove the first from He?

54. Group 1B elements (see the periodic table on the inside cover of your book) have one electron in their outer energy level, as do Group 1A elements. Would you expect them to form compounds such as CuCl, AgCl, and AuCl? Explain.

55. The formula for lead(II) bromide is $PbBr_2$. Predict formulas for tin(II) and germanium(II) bromides.

56. Why is it not proper to speak of sodium chloride molecules?

57. What is a covalent bond? How does it differ from an ionic bond?

58. Briefly comment on the structure $Na \colon \ddot{O} \colon Na$ for the compound Na_2O.

59. What are the four most electronegative elements?

60. Rank these elements from highest electronegativity to lowest: Mg, S, F, H, O, Cs.

61. Is it possible for a molecule to be nonpolar even though it contains polar covalent bonds? Explain.

62. Why is CO_2 a nonpolar molecule, whereas CO is a polar molecule?

63. Rank the following bonds in order of increasing polarity:
    (a) NaO, CO, NO
    (b) CO, SiO, GeO
    (c) BO, BS, BSe
64. Estimate the bond angle between atoms in these molecules:
    (a) H_2S
    (b) NH_3
    (c) NH_4^+
    (d) $SiCl_4$
65. Consider the two molecules BF_3 and NF_3. Compare and contrast them in terms of the following:
    (a) valence-level orbitals on the central atom that are used for bonding
    (b) shape of the molecule
    (c) number of lone electron pairs on the central atom
    (d) type and number of bonds found in the molecule
66. With respect to electronegativity, why is fluorine such an important atom? What combination of atoms on the periodic table results in the most ionic bond?
67. Why does the Lewis structure of each element in a given group of representative elements on the periodic table have the same number of dots?
68. A sample of an air pollutant composed of sulfur and oxygen was found to contain 1.40 g sulfur and 2.10 g oxygen. What is the empirical formula for this compound? Draw a Lewis structure to represent it.
69. A dry-cleaning fluid composed of carbon and chlorine was found to have the composition 14.5% carbon and 85.5% chlorine. Its known molar mass is 166 g/mol. Draw a Lewis structure to represent the compound.

70. Identify each of the following drawings as representing ionic compounds, covalent compounds, or compounds composed of both ionic and covalent portions.
    (a)

    (b)

    (c)

    (d)

71. Identify each of the following compounds as ionic, covalent, or both. Give the correct IUPAC name for each compound.
    (a) Na_3P (c) SO_2 (e) $Cu(NO_3)_2$
    (b) NH_4I (d) H_2S (f) MgO

CHALLENGE EXERCISES

72. Draw the following Lewis structures, showing any full charges where they exist on ions:
    (a) H_2SO_4 (d) HCN
    (b) $NaNO_3$ (e) $Al_2(SO_4)_3$
    (c) K_2CO_3 (f) CH_3COOH
73. The first ionization energy for lithium is 520 kJ/mol. How much energy would be required to change 25 g of lithium atoms to lithium ions? (Refer to Table 11.1.)
74. What is the total amount of energy required to remove the first two electrons from 15 moles of sodium atoms? (Refer to Table 11.1.)
75. Sulfur trioxide gas reacts with water to form sulfuric acid. Draw the Lewis structures of each substance to represent the reaction.
76. Compounds found in garlic have been shown to have significant biological effects including immune system enhancement, anti-cancer activity, and cardiovascular activity. Garlic clearly seems to have more value than as just a great tasting addition to spaghetti!

Some of the compounds in garlic that are currently being studied are shown in the following figures.

Alliin

Allicin (gives garlic its characteristic aroma)

Redraw these molecules adding in dots to represent any lone pairs present on atoms. Draw a circle around atoms with tetrahedral geometry, draw a square around atoms with trigonal planar geometry, draw a pentagon around atoms with a trigonal pyramidal geometry, and draw a hexagon around atoms with a bent geometry. Draw a triangle around any atoms that have an unexpected number of bonds.

77. Two of the most complex organic compounds found outside of our solar system have been detected in a massive star-forming region near the heart of the Milky Way known as Sagittarius B2. The skeleton structures of these two compounds, ethyl formate (the compound that gives raspberries their flavor) and *n*-propyl cyanide, are drawn below. Draw the complete Lewis electron dot structures for these two compounds, identify the electron pair and molecular geometry around each atom, and predict the bond angles.

Ethyl formate   *n*-propyl cyanide

ANSWERS TO PRACTICE EXERCISES

11.1 (a) Ionization energy decreases from top to bottom for a group of elements and increases from left to right across a period of elements.
  (b) For a group of elements the outer shell of electrons is increasingly further away from the nucleus as you go from top to bottom of the group. Thus, they are not held as strongly by the positive nucleus and are easier to ionize.

11.2 (a) :N·
  (b) :Al
  (c) Sr:
  (d) :Br·

11.3 (a) Ar;   K⁺
  (b) Ne;   Mg²⁺
  (c) Ne;   Al³⁺
  (d) Xe;   Ba²⁺

11.4 (a) Na₂S
  (b) Rb₂O

11.5 (a) Mg₃N₂
  (b) Ba₃As₂

11.6 H:Br: or   H—Br

  H H   H H
  H:C:C:H   or   H—C—C—H
  H H   H H

11.7 Electronegativity of an atom gives information about the strength that the atom has for attracting a pair of shared electrons in a covalent bond. The higher the electronegativity value,

the greater the attraction for a pair of shared electrons. Consequently, when two different atoms with different electronegativities share a pair of electrons, one atom becomes partially negative and the other atom becomes partially positive due to the attractive forces for the pair of electrons. The bond formed is said to be polar covalent.

11.8 ionic: (a), (d), (e)
  covalent: (b), (c), (f)

11.9 (a) :Br: (c) H:F: (e) :N⫶⫶N:
       :P:Br:
       :Br:

  (b) :Cl:C:Cl: (d) O:
          H   H:C:H
       :Cl:

11.10 (a) H:N:H   (c) [H:N:H]⁺
            H   H

  (b) [H:O:H]⁺   (d) [H:O:C⫶O:]⁻
          H   :O:

11.11

  [Ca]²⁺ [:O:]²⁻   [:O:]⁻   [Ca]²⁺ [:O:]⁻
         [O=S=O]   [N   ]   [‖   ]
         [:O:]   [:O: :O:]   [N   ]
                                         [:O: :O:]

11.12 CF₄, tetrahedral; NF₃, pyramidal; BeI₂, linear

PUTTING IT TOGETHER:
Review for Chapters 10–11

Answers for Putting It Together Reviews are found in Appendix VII.

Multiple Choice

Choose the correct answer to each of the following.

1. The concept of electrons existing in specific orbits around the nucleus was the contribution of
   (a) Thomson
   (b) Rutherford
   (c) Bohr
   (d) Schrödinger

2. The correct electron structure for a fluorine atom (F) is
   (a) $1s^2 2s^2 2p^5$
   (b) $1s^2 2s^2 2p^3 3s^2 3p^1$
   (c) $1s^2 2s^2 2p^4 3s^1$
   (d) $1s^2 2s^2 2p^3$

3. The correct electron structure for $_{48}$Cd is
   (a) $1s^2 2s^2 2p^6 3s^2 3p^6 4s^2 3d^{10}$
   (b) $1s^2 2s^2 2p^6 3s^2 3p^6 4s^2 3d^{10} 4p^6 5s^2 4d^{10}$
   (c) $1s^2 2s^2 2p^6 3s^2 3p^6 4s^2 3d^{10} 4p^6 4d^4$
   (d) $1s^2 2s^2 2p^6 3s^2 3p^6 4s^2 4p^6 4d^{10} 5s^2 5d^{10}$

4. The correct electron structure of $_{23}$V is
   (a) $[Ar]4s^2 3d^3$
   (b) $[Ar]4s^2 4p^3$
   (c) $[Ar]4s^2 4d^3$
   (d) $[Kr]4s^2 3d^3$

5. Which of the following is the correct atomic structure for $_{22}^{48}$Ti?

6. The number of orbitals in a d sublevel is
   (a) 3
   (b) 5
   (c) 7
   (d) no correct answer given

7. The number of electrons in the third principal energy level in an atom having the electron structure $1s^2 2s^2 2p^6 3s^2 3p^2$ is
   (a) 2
   (b) 4
   (c) 6
   (d) 8

8. The total number of orbitals that contain at least one electron in an atom having the structure $1s^2 2s^2 2p^6 3s^2 3p^2$ is
   (a) 5
   (b) 8
   (c) 14
   (d) no correct answer given

9. Which of these elements has two s and six p electrons in its outer energy level?
   (a) He
   (b) O
   (c) Ar
   (d) no correct answer given

10. Which element is not a noble gas?
    (a) Ra
    (b) Xe
    (c) He
    (d) Ar

11. Which element has the largest number of unpaired electrons?
    (a) F
    (b) S
    (c) Cu
    (d) N

12. How many unpaired electrons are in the electron structure of $_{24}$Cr, $[Ar]4s^1 3d^5$?
    (a) 2
    (b) 4
    (c) 5
    (d) 6

13. Groups 3A–7A plus the noble gases form the area of the periodic table where the electron sublevels being filled are
    (a) p sublevels
    (b) s and p sublevels
    (c) d sublevels
    (d) f sublevels

14. In moving down an A group on the periodic table, the number of electrons in the outermost energy level
    (a) increases regularly
    (b) remains constant
    (c) decreases regularly
    (d) changes in an unpredictable manner

15. Which of the following is an incorrect formula?
    (a) NaCl
    (b) K_2O
    (c) AlO
    (d) BaO

16. Elements of the noble gas family
    (a) form no compounds at all
    (b) have no valence electrons
    (c) have an outer electron structure of $ns^2 np^6$ (helium excepted), where n is the period number
    (d) no correct answer given

17. The lanthanide and actinide series of elements are
    (a) representative elements
    (b) transition elements
    (c) filling in d-level electrons
    (d) no correct answer given

18. The element having the structure $1s^2 2s^2 2p^6 3s^2 3p^2$ is in Group
    (a) 2A
    (b) 2B
    (c) 4A
    (d) 4B

19. In Group 5A, the element having the smallest atomic radius is
    (a) Bi
    (b) P
    (c) As
    (d) N

20. In Group 4A, the most metallic element is
    (a) C
    (b) Si
    (c) Ge
    (d) Sn

21. Which group in the periodic table contains the least reactive elements?
    (a) 1A
    (b) 2A
    (c) 3A
    (d) noble gases

22. Which group in the periodic table contains the alkali metals?
    (a) 1A
    (b) 2A
    (c) 3A
    (d) 4A

23. An atom of fluorine is smaller than an atom of oxygen. One possible explanation is that, compared to oxygen, fluorine has
    (a) a larger mass number
    (b) a smaller atomic number
    (c) a greater nuclear charge
    (d) more unpaired electrons

24. If the size of the fluorine atom is compared to the size of the fluoride ion,
    (a) they would both be the same size
    (b) the atom is larger than the ion
    (c) the ion is larger than the atom
    (d) the size difference depends on the reaction

246

25. Sodium is a very active metal because
    (a) it has a low ionization energy
    (b) it has only one outermost electron
    (c) it has a relatively small atomic mass
    (d) all of the above

26. Which of the following formulas is not correct?
    (a) Na^+ (b) S^- (c) Al^{3+} (d) F^-

27. Which of the following molecules does not have a polar covalent bond?
    (a) CH_4 (b) H_2O (c) CH_3OH (d) Cl_2

28. Which of the following molecules is a dipole?
    (a) HBr   (b) CH_4 (c) H_2 (d) CO_2

29. Which of the following has bonding that is ionic?
    (a) H_2 (b) MgF_2 (c) H_2O (d) CH_4

30. Which of the following is a correct Lewis structure?
    (a) :Ö:C:Ö: (c) C̈l::C̈l

        :C̈l:
    (b) :C̈l:C:C̈l: (d) :N̈:N̈:
        :C̈l:

31. Which of the following is an incorrect Lewis structure?
                   H
    (a) H:N̈:H   (c) H:C̈:H
                   H
    (b) :Ö:H   (d) :N:::N:
       Ḧ

32. The correct Lewis structure for SO_2 is
    (a) :Ö:S̈:Ö: (c) :Ö::S::Ö:
    (b) :Ö:S::Ö: (d) :Ö:S̈:Ö:

33. Carbon dioxide (CO_2) is a nonpolar molecule because
    (a) oxygen is more electronegative than carbon
    (b) the two oxygen atoms are bonded to the carbon atom
    (c) the molecule has a linear structure with the carbon atom in the middle
    (d) the carbon–oxygen bonds are polar covalent

34. When a magnesium atom participates in a chemical reaction, it is most likely to
    (a) lose 1 electron   (c) lose 2 electrons
    (b) gain 1 electron   (d) gain 2 electrons

35. If X represents an element of Group 3A, what is the general formula for its oxide?
    (a) X_3O_4 (b) X_3O_2 (c) XO   (d) X_2O_3

36. Which of the following has the same electron structure as an argon atom?
    (a) Ca^{2+} (b) Cl^0 (c) Na^+ (d) K^0

37. As the difference in electronegativity between two elements decreases, the tendency for the elements to form a covalent bond
    (a) increases
    (b) decreases
    (c) remains the same
    (d) sometimes increases and sometimes decreases

38. Which compound forms a tetrahedral molecule?
    (a) NaCl   (b) CO_2 (c) CH_4 (d) $MgCl_2$

39. Which compound has a bent (V-shaped) molecular structure?
    (a) NaCl   (b) CO_2 (c) CH_4 (d) H_2O

40. Which compound has double bonds within its molecular structure?
    (a) NaCl   (b) CO_2 (c) CH_4 (d) H_2O

41. The total number of valence electrons in a nitrate ion, NO_3^-, is
    (a) 12   (b) 18   (c) 23   (d) 24

42. The number of electrons in a triple bond is
    (a) 3   (b) 4   (c) 6   (d) 8

43. The number of unbonded pairs of electrons in H_2O is
    (a) 0   (b) 1   (c) 2   (d) 4

44. Which of the following does not have a noble gas electron structure?
    (a) Na   (b) Sc^{3+} (c) Ar   (d) O^{2-}

Free Response Questions

Answer each of the following. Be sure to include your work and explanations in a clear, logical form.

1. An alkaline earth metal, M, combines with a halide, X. Will the resulting compound be ionic or covalent? Why? What is the Lewis structure for the compound?

2. "All electrons in atoms with even atomic numbers are paired." Is this statement true or false? Explain your answer using an example.

3. Discuss whether the following statement is true or false: "All nonmetals have two valence electrons in an *s* sublevel with the exception of the noble gases, which have at least one unpaired electron in a *p* sublevel."

4. The first ionization energy (IE) of potassium is lower than the first IE for calcium, but the second IE of calcium is lower than the second IE of potassium. Use an electron configuration or size argument to explain this trend in ionization energies.

5. Chlorine has a very large first ionization energy, yet it forms a chloride ion relatively easily. Explain.

6. Three particles have the same electron configuration. One is a cation of an alkali metal, one is an anion of the halide in the third period, and the third particle is an atom of a noble gas. What are the identities of the three particles (including charges)? Which particle should have the smallest atomic/ionic radius, which should have the largest, and why?

7. Why is the Lewis structure of AlF_3 not written as

What is the correct Lewis structure, and which electrons are shown in a Lewis structure?

8. Why does carbon have a maximum of four covalent bonds?

9. Both NCl_3 and BF_3 have a central atom bonded to three other atoms, yet one is pyramidal and the other is trigonal planar. Explain.

10. Draw the Lewis structure of the atom whose electron configuration is $1s^2 2s^2 2p^6 3s^2 3p^6 4s^2 3d^{10} 4p^5$. Would you expect this atom to form an ionic, nonpolar covalent, or polar covalent bond with sulfur?

Mathematical Review

Multiplication

Multiplication is a process of adding any given number or quantity to itself a certain number of times. Thus, 4 times 2 means 4 added two times, or 2 added together four times, to give the product 8. Various ways of expressing multiplication are

$$ab \quad a \times b \quad a \cdot b \quad a(b) \quad (a)(b)$$

Each of these expressions means a times b, or a multiplied by b, or b times a.

When $a = 16$ and $b = 24$, we have $16 \times 24 = 384$.

The expression $\text{°F} = (1.8 \times \text{°C}) + 32$ means that we are to multiply 1.8 times the Celsius degrees and add 32 to the product. When °C equals 50,

$$\text{°F} = (1.8 \times 50) + 32 = 90 + 32 = 122\text{°F}$$

The result of multiplying two or more numbers together is known as the *product.*

Division

The word *division* has several meanings. As a mathematical expression, it is the process of finding how many times one number or quantity is contained in another. Various ways of expressing division are

$$a \div b \quad \frac{a}{b} \quad a/b$$

Each of these expressions means a divided by b.

When $a = 15$ and $b = 3$, $\dfrac{15}{3} = 5$.

The number above the line is called the *numerator;* the number below the line is the *denominator.* Both the horizontal and the slanted (/) division signs also mean "per." For example, in the expression for density, we determine the mass per unit volume:

$$\text{density} = \text{mass}/\text{volume} = \frac{\text{mass}}{\text{volume}} = \text{g/mL}$$

The diagonal line still refers to a division of grams by the number of milliliters occupied by that mass. The result of dividing one number into another is called the *quotient.*

Fractions and Decimals

A fraction is an expression of division, showing that the numerator is divided by the denominator. A *proper fraction* is one in which the numerator is smaller than the denominator. In an *improper fraction,* the numerator is the larger number. A decimal or a decimal fraction is a proper fraction in which the denominator is some power of 10. The decimal fraction is determined by carrying out the division of the proper fraction. Examples of proper fractions and their decimal fraction equivalents are shown in the accompanying table.

Proper fraction		Decimal fraction		Proper fraction
$\dfrac{1}{8}$	=	0.125	=	$\dfrac{125}{1000}$
$\dfrac{1}{10}$	=	0.1	=	$\dfrac{1}{10}$
$\dfrac{3}{4}$	=	0.75	=	$\dfrac{75}{100}$
$\dfrac{1}{100}$	=	0.01	=	$\dfrac{1}{100}$
$\dfrac{1}{4}$	=	0.25	=	$\dfrac{25}{100}$

A-1

Addition of Numbers with Decimals

To add numbers with decimals, we use the same procedure as that used when adding whole numbers, but we always line up the decimal points in the same column. For example, add $8.21 + 143.1 + 0.325$:

$$
\begin{array}{r}
8.21 \\
+143.1 \\
+\ \ \ 0.325 \\
\hline
151.635
\end{array}
$$

When adding numbers that express units of measurement, we must be certain that the numbers added together all have the same units. For example, what is the total length of three pieces of glass tubing: 10.0 cm, 125 mm, and 8.4 cm? If we simply add the numbers, we obtain a value of 143.4, but we are not certain what the unit of measurement is. To add these lengths correctly, first change 125 mm to 12.5 cm. Now all the lengths are expressed in the same units and can be added:

$$
\begin{array}{r}
10.0 \text{ cm} \\
12.5 \text{ cm} \\
8.4 \text{ cm} \\
\hline
30.9 \text{ cm}
\end{array}
$$

Subtraction of Numbers with Decimals

To subtract numbers containing decimals, we use the same procedure as for subtracting whole numbers, but we always line up the decimal points in the same column. For example, subtract 20.60 from 182.49:

$$
\begin{array}{r}
182.49 \\
-\ \ 20.60 \\
\hline
161.89
\end{array}
$$

When subtracting numbers that are measurements, be certain that the measurements are in the same units. For example, subtract 22 cm from 0.62 m. First change m to cm, then do the subtraction.

$$
(0.62 \text{ m})\left(\frac{100 \text{ cm}}{\text{m}}\right) = 62 \text{ cm} \qquad
\begin{array}{r}
62\ \ \text{cm} \\
-22\ \ \text{cm} \\
\hline
40.\ \text{cm}
\end{array}
$$

Multiplication of Numbers with Decimals

To multiply two or more numbers together that contain decimals, we first multiply as if they were whole numbers. Then, to locate the decimal point in the product, we add together the number of digits to the right of the decimal in all the numbers multiplied together. The product should have this same number of digits to the right of the decimal point.

Multiply $2.05 \times 2.05 = 4.2025$ (total of four digits to the right of the decimal).

If a number is a measurement, the answer must be adjusted to the correct number of significant figures.

Here are more examples:

$14.25 \times 6.01 \times 0.75 = 64.231875$ (six digits to the right of the decimal)
$39.26 \times 60 = 2355.60$ (two digits to the right of the decimal)

Division of Numbers with Decimals

To divide numbers containing decimals, we first relocate the decimal points of the numerator and denominator by moving them to the right as many places as needed to make the denominator a whole number. (Move the decimal of both the numerator and the denominator the same amount and in the same direction.) For example,

$$
\frac{136.94}{4.1} = \frac{1369.4}{41}
$$

The decimal point adjustment in this example is equivalent to multiplying both numerator and denominator by 10. Now we carry out the division normally, locating the decimal point immediately above its position in the dividend:

$$\frac{33.4}{41\overline{)1269.4}} \qquad \frac{0.441}{26.25} = \frac{44.1}{2625} = \frac{0.0168}{2625\overline{)44.1000}}$$

These examples are guides to the principles used in performing the various mathematical operations illustrated. Every student of chemistry should learn to use a calculator for solving mathematical problems (see Appendix II). The use of a calculator will save many hours of doing tedious calculations. After solving a problem, the student should check for errors and evaluate the answer to see if it is logical and consistent with the data given.

Algebraic Equations

Many mathematical problems that are encountered in chemistry fall into the following algebraic forms. Solutions to these problems are simplified by first isolating the desired term on one side of the equation. This rearrangement is accomplished by treating both sides of the equation in an identical manner until the desired term is isolated.

(a) $a = \dfrac{b}{c}$

To solve for b, multiply both sides of the equation by c:

$$a \times c = \frac{b}{\cancel{c}} \times \cancel{c}$$

$$b = a \times c$$

To solve for c, multiply both sides of the equation by $\dfrac{c}{a}$:

$$\cancel{a} \times \frac{c}{\cancel{a}} = \frac{b}{\cancel{c}} \times \frac{\cancel{c}}{a}$$

$$c = \frac{b}{a}$$

(b) $\dfrac{a}{b} = \dfrac{c}{d}$

To solve for a, multiply both sides of the equation by b:

$$\frac{a}{\cancel{b}} \times \cancel{b} = \frac{c}{d} \times b$$

$$a = \frac{c \times b}{d}$$

To solve for b, multiply both sides of the equation by $\dfrac{b \times d}{c}$:

$$\frac{a}{\cancel{b}} \times \frac{\cancel{b} \times d}{c} = \frac{\cancel{c}}{\cancel{d}} \times \frac{b \times \cancel{d}}{\cancel{c}}$$

$$\frac{a \times d}{c} = b$$

(c) $a \times b = c \times d$

To solve for a, divide both sides of the equation by b:

$$\frac{a \times \cancel{b}}{\cancel{b}} = \frac{c \times d}{b}$$

$$a = \frac{c \times d}{b}$$

(d) $\dfrac{b - c}{a} = d$

To solve for b, first multiply both sides of the equation by a:

$$\frac{\cancel{a}(b - c)}{\cancel{a}} = d \times a$$

$$b - c = d \times a$$

Then add c to both sides of the equation:

$b - \cancel{c} + \cancel{c} = d \times a + c$

$b = (d \times a) + c$

When $a = 1.8, c = 32$, and $d = 35$,

$b = (35 \times 1.8) + 32 = 63 + 32 = 95$

Expression of Large and Small Numbers

scientific, or exponential, notation
exponent

In scientific measurement and calculations, we often encounter very large and very small numbers—for example, 0.00000384 and 602,000,000,000,000,000,000,000. These numbers are troublesome to write and awkward to work with, especially in calculations. A convenient method of expressing these large and small numbers in a simplified form is by means of exponents, or powers, of 10. This method of expressing numbers is known as **scientific, or exponential, notation**.

An **exponent** is a number written as a superscript following another number. Exponents are often called *powers* of numbers. The term *power* indicates how many times the number is used as a factor. In the number 10^2, 2 is the exponent, and the number means 10 squared, or 10 to the second power, or $10 \times 10 = 100$. Three other examples are

$$3^2 = 3 \times 3 = 9$$

$$3^4 = 3 \times 3 \times 3 \times 3 = 81$$

$$10^3 = 10 \times 10 \times 10 = 1000$$

For ease of handling, large and small numbers are expressed in powers of 10. Powers of 10 are used because multiplying or dividing by 10 coincides with moving the decimal point in a number by one place. Thus, a number multiplied by 10^1 would move the decimal point one place to the right; 10^2, two places to the right; 10^{-2}, two places to the left. To express a number in powers of 10, we move the decimal point in the original number to a new position, placing it so that the number is a value between 1 and 10. This new decimal number is multiplied by 10 raised to the proper power. For example, to write the number 42,389 in exponential form, the decimal point is placed between the 4 and the 2 (4.2389), and the number is multiplied by 10^4; thus, the number is 4.2389×10^4:

$$42{,}389 = 4.2389 \times 10^4$$
$$\underset{4\,3\,2\,1}{}$$

The exponent of 10 (4) tells us the number of places that the decimal point has been moved from its original position. If the decimal point is moved to the left, the exponent is a positive number; if it is moved to the right, the exponent is a negative number. To express the number 0.00248 in exponential notation (as a power of 10), the decimal point is moved three places to the right; the exponent of 10 is -3, and the number is 2.48×10^{-3}.

$$0.00248 = 2.48 \times 10^{-3}$$
$$\underset{1\,2\,3}{}$$

Study the following examples of changing a number to scientific notation.

$$1237 = 1.237 \times 10^3$$

$$988 = 9.88 \times 10^2$$

$$147.2 = 1.472 \times 10^2$$

$$2{,}200{,}000 = 2.2 \times 10^6$$

$$0.0123 = 1.23 \times 10^{-2}$$

$$0.00005 = 5 \times 10^{-5}$$

$$0.000368 = 3.68 \times 10^{-4}$$

Exponents in multiplication and division The use of powers of 10 in multiplication and division greatly simplifies locating the decimal point in the answer. In multiplication, first change all numbers to powers of 10, then multiply the numerical portion in the usual manner, and finally add the exponents of 10 algebraically, expressing them as a power of 10 in the product. In multiplication, the exponents (powers of 10) are added algebraically.

$$10^2 \times 10^3 = 10^{(2+3)} = 10^5$$
$$10^2 \times 10^2 \times 10^{-1} = 10^{(2+2-1)} = 10^3$$

Multiply:	$(40{,}000)(4200)$
Change to powers of 10:	$(4 \times 10^4)(4.2 \times 10^3)$
Rearrange:	$(4 \times 4.2)(10^4 \times 10^3)$
	$16.8 \times 10^{(4+3)}$
	16.8×10^7 or 1.68×10^8 (Answer)

Multiply: $(380)(0.00020)$

$(3.80 \times 10^2)(2.0 \times 10^{-4})$

$(3.80 \times 2.0)(10^2 \times 10^{-4})$

$7.6 \times 10^{(2-4)}$

7.6×10^{-2} or 0.076 (Answer)

Multiply: $(125)(284)(0.150)$

$(1.25 \times 10^2)(2.84 \times 10^2)(1.50 \times 10^{-1})$

$(1.25)(2.84)(1.50)(10^2 \times 10^2 \times 10^{-1})$

$5.325 \times 10^{(2+2-1)}$

5.33×10^3 (Answer)

In division, after changing the numbers to powers of 10, move the 10 and its exponent from the denominator to the numerator, changing the sign of the exponent. Carry out the division in the usual manner, and evaluate the power of 10. Change the sign(s) of the exponent(s) of 10 in the denominator, and move the 10 and its exponent(s) to the numerator. Then add all the exponents of 10 together. For example,

$$\frac{10^5}{10^3} = 10^5 \times 10^{-3} = 10^{(5-3)} = 10^2$$

$$\frac{10^3 \times 10^4}{10^{-2}} = 10^3 \times 10^4 \times 10^2 = 10^{(3+4+2)} = 10^9$$

Significant Figures in Calculations

The result of a calculation based on experimental measurements cannot be more precise than the measurement that has the greatest uncertainty. (See Section 2.4 for additional discussion.)

Addition and subtraction The result of an addition or subtraction should contain no more digits to the right of the decimal point than are contained in the quantity that has the least number of digits to the right of the decimal point.

Perform the operation indicated and then round off the number to the proper number of significant figures:

(a) 142.8   g
    18.843 g
    36.42 g
  198.063 g
  198.1   g   (Answer)

(b)   93.45 mL
  −18.0 mL
  75.45 mL
  75.5 mL   (Answer)

(a) The answer contains only one digit after the decimal point since 142.8 contains only one digit after the decimal point.

(b) The answer contains only one digit after the decimal point since 18.0 contains one digit after the decimal point.

Multiplication and division In calculations involving multiplication or division, the answer should contain the same number of significant figures as the measurement that has the least number of significant figures. In multiplication or division, the position of the decimal point has nothing to do with the number of significant figures in the answer. Study the following examples:

Round off to

$(2.05)(2.05) = 4.2025$	4.20
$(18.48)(5.2) = 96.096$	96
$(0.0126)(0.020) = 0.000252$ or	
$(1.26 \times 10^{-2})(2.0 \times 10^{-2}) = 2.520 \times 10^{-4}$	2.5×10^{-4}
$\dfrac{1369.4}{41} = 33.4$	33
$\dfrac{2268}{4.20} = 540.$	540.

Dimensional Analysis

Many problems of chemistry can be readily solved by dimensional analysis using the factor-label or conversion-factor method. Dimensional analysis involves the use of proper units of dimensions for all factors that are multiplied, divided, added, or subtracted in setting up and solving a problem. Dimensions are physical quantities such as length, mass, and time, which are expressed in such units as centimeters, grams, and seconds, respectively. In solving a problem, we treat these units mathematically just as though they were numbers, which gives us an answer that contains the correct dimensional units.

A measurement or quantity given in one kind of unit can be converted to any other kind of unit having the same dimension. To convert from one kind of unit to another, the original quantity or measurement is multiplied or divided by a conversion factor. The key to success lies in choosing the correct conversion factor. This general method of calculation is illustrated in the following examples.

Suppose we want to change 24 ft to inches. We need to multiply 24 ft by a conversion factor containing feet and inches. Two such conversion factors can be written relating inches to feet:

$$\frac{12 \text{ in.}}{1 \text{ ft}} \quad \text{or} \quad \frac{1 \text{ ft}}{12 \text{ in.}}$$

We choose the factor that will mathematically cancel feet and leave the answer in inches. Note that the units are treated in the same way we treat numbers, multiplying or dividing as required. Two possibilities then arise to change 24 ft to inches:

$$(24 \text{ ft})\left(\frac{12 \text{ in.}}{1 \text{ ft}}\right) \quad \text{or} \quad (24 \text{ ft})\left(\frac{1 \text{ ft}}{12 \text{ in.}}\right)$$

In the first case (the correct method), feet in the numerator and the denominator cancel, giving us an answer of 288 in. In the second case, the units of the answer are $\text{ft}^2/\text{in.}$, the answer being $2.0 \text{ ft}^2/\text{in.}$ In the first case, the answer is reasonable because it is expressed in units having the proper dimensions. That is, the dimension of length expressed in feet has been converted to length in inches according to the mathematical expression

$$\text{ft} \times \frac{\text{in.}}{\text{ft}} = \text{in.}$$

In the second case, the answer is not reasonable because the units ($\text{ft}^2/\text{in.}$) do not correspond to units of length. The answer is therefore incorrect. The units are the guiding factor for the proper conversion.

The reason we can multiply 24 ft times 12 in./ft and not change the value of the measurement is that the conversion factor is derived from two equivalent quantities. Therefore, the conversion factor 12 in./ft is equal to unity. When you multiply any factor by 1, it does not change the value:

$$12 \text{ in.} = 1 \text{ ft} \quad \text{and} \quad \frac{12 \text{ in.}}{1 \text{ ft}} = 1$$

Convert 16 kg to milligrams. In this problem it is best to proceed in this fashion:

$$kg \longrightarrow g \longrightarrow mg$$

The possible conversion factors are

$$\frac{1000\ g}{1\ kg} \quad \text{or} \quad \frac{1\ kg}{1000\ g} \qquad \frac{1000\ mg}{1\ g} \quad \text{or} \quad \frac{1\ g}{1000\ mg}$$

We use the conversion factor that leaves the proper unit at each step for the next conversion. The calculation is

$$(16\ \cancel{kg})\left(\frac{1000\ \cancel{g}}{1\ \cancel{kg}}\right)\left(\frac{1000\ mg}{1\ \cancel{g}}\right) = 1.6 \times 10^7\ mg$$

Regardless of application, the basis of dimensional analysis is the use of conversion factors to organize a series of steps in the quest for a specific quantity with a specific unit.

Graphical Representation of Data

A graph is often the most convenient way to present or display a set of data. Various kinds of graphs have been devised, but the most common type uses a set of horizontal and vertical coordinates to show the relationship of two variables. It is called an x–y graph because the data of one variable are represented on the horizontal or x-axis (abscissa) and the data of the other variable are represented on the vertical or y-axis (ordinate). See Figure I.1.

As a specific example of a simple graph, let us graph the relationship between Celsius and Fahrenheit temperature scales. Assume that initially we have only the information in the table next to Figure I.2.

On a set of horizontal and vertical coordinates (graph paper), scale off at least 100 Celsius degrees on the x-axis and at least 212 Fahrenheit degrees on the y-axis. Locate and mark the three points corresponding to the three temperatures given and draw a line connecting these points (see Figure I.2).

Here is how a point is located on the graph: Using the (50°C, 122°F) data, trace a vertical line up from 50°C on the x-axis and a horizontal line across from 122°F on the y-axis and mark

Figure I.1

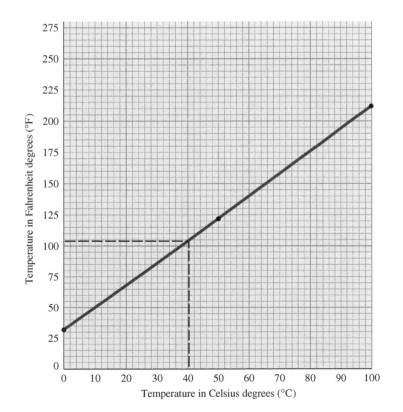

Temperature in Celsius degrees (°C)

Figure I.2

°C	°F
0	32
50	122
100	212

the point where the two lines intersect. This process is called *plotting*. The other two points are plotted on the graph in the same way. (*Note:* The number of degrees per scale division was chosen to give a graph of convenient size. In this case, there are 5 Fahrenheit degrees per scale division and 2 Celsius degrees per scale division.)

The graph in Figure I.2 shows that the relationship between Celsius and Fahrenheit temperature is that of a straight line. The Fahrenheit temperature corresponding to any given Celsius temperature between 0 and 100° can be determined from the graph. For example, to find the Fahrenheit temperature corresponding to 40°C, trace a perpendicular line from 40°C on the *x*-axis to the line plotted on the graph. Now trace a horizontal line from this point on the plotted line to the *y*-axis and read the corresponding Fahrenheit temperature (104°F). See the dashed lines in Figure I.2. In turn, the Celsius temperature corresponding to any Fahrenheit temperature between 32° and 212° can be determined from the graph by tracing a horizontal line from the Fahrenheit temperature to the plotted line and reading the corresponding temperature on the Celsius scale directly below the point of intersection.

The mathematical relationship of Fahrenheit and Celsius temperatures is expressed by the equation $°F = (1.8 \times °C) + 32$. Figure I.2 is a graph of this equation. Because the graph is a straight line, it can be extended indefinitely at either end. Any desired Celsius temperature can be plotted against the corresponding Fahrenheit temperature by extending the scales along both axes as necessary.

Figure I.3 is a graph showing the solubility of potassium chlorate in water at various temperatures. The solubility curve on this graph was plotted from the data in the table next to the graph.

In contrast to the Celsius–Fahrenheit temperature relationship, there is no simple mathematical equation that describes the exact relationship between temperature and the solubility of potassium chlorate. The graph in Figure I.3 was constructed from experimentally determined solubilities at the six temperatures shown. These experimentally determined solubilities are all located on the smooth curve traced by the unbroken-line portion of the graph. We are therefore confident that the unbroken line represents a very good approximation of the solubility data for potassium chlorate over the temperature range from 10 to 80°C. All points on the plotted

Temperature (°C)	Solubility (g $KClO_3$/ 100 g water)
10	5.0
20	7.4
30	10.5
50	19.3
60	24.5
80	38.5

Figure I.3

curve represent the composition of saturated solutions. Any point below the curve represents an unsaturated solution.

The dashed-line portions of the curve are *extrapolations;* that is, they extend the curve above and below the temperature range actually covered by the plotted solubility data. Curves such as this one are often extrapolated a short distance beyond the range of the known data, although the extrapolated portions may not be highly accurate. Extrapolation is justified only in the absence of more reliable information.

The graph in Figure I.3 can be used with confidence to obtain the solubility of $KClO_3$ at any temperature between 10° and 80°C, but the solubilities between 0° and 10°C and between 80° and 100°C are less reliable. For example, what is the solubility of $KClO_3$ at 55°C, at 40°C, and at 100°C?

First draw a perpendicular line from each temperature to the plotted solubility curve. Now trace a horizontal line to the solubility axis from each point on the curve and read the corresponding solubilities. The values that we read from the graph are

40°C	14.2 g $KClO_3$/100 g water
55°C	22.0 g $KClO_3$/100 g water
100°C	59 g $KClO_3$/100 g water

Of these solubilities, the one at 55°C is probably the most reliable because experimental points are plotted at 50° and at 60°C. The 40°C solubility value is a bit less reliable because the nearest plotted points are at 30° and 50°C. The 100°C solubility is the least reliable of the three values because it was taken from the extrapolated part of the curve, and the nearest plotted point is 80°C. Actual handbook solubility values are 14.0 and 57.0 g of $KClO_3$/100 g water at 40°C and 100°C, respectively.

The graph in Figure I.3 can also be used to determine whether a solution is saturated or unsaturated. For example, a solution contains 15 g of $KClO_3$/100 g of water and is at a temperature of 55°C. Is the solution saturated or unsaturated? *Answer:* The solution is unsaturated because the point corresponding to 15 g and 55°C on the graph is below the solubility curve; all points below the curve represent unsaturated solutions.

Using a Scientific Calculator

A calculator is useful for most calculations in this book. You should obtain a scientific calculator, that is, one that has at least the following function keys on its keyboard.

Addition $\boxed{+}$ Second function $\boxed{F}$, $\boxed{INV}$, $\boxed{Shift}$

Subtraction $\boxed{-}$ Change sign $\boxed{+/-}$

Multiplication $\boxed{\times}$ Exponential number $\boxed{Exp}$

Division $\boxed{\div}$ Logarithm $\boxed{Log}$

Equals $\boxed{=}$ Antilogarithm $\boxed{10^x}$

Not all calculators use the same symbolism for these function keys, nor do all calculators work in the same way. The following discussion may not pertain to your particular calculator. Refer to your instruction manual for variations from the function symbols shown above and for the use of other function keys.

The second function key may have a different designation on your calculator.

Some keys have two functions, upper and lower. In order to use the upper (second) function, the second function key $\boxed{F}$ must be pressed in order to activate the desired upper function after entering the number.

The display area of the calculator shows the numbers entered and often shows more digits in the answer than should be used. Therefore, the final answer should be rounded to reflect the proper number of significant figures of the calculations.

Addition and Subtraction

To add numbers using your calculator,

1. Enter the first number to be added followed by the plus key $\boxed{+}$.

2. Enter the second number to be added followed by the plus key $\boxed{+}$.

3. Repeat Step 2 for each additional number to be added, except the last number.

4. After the last number is entered, press the equal key $\boxed{=}$. You should now have the answer in the display area.

5. When a number is to be subtracted, use the minus key $\boxed{-}$ instead of the plus key.

As an example, to add 16.0 + 1.223 + 8.45, enter 16.0 followed by the $\boxed{+}$ key; then enter 1.223 followed by the $\boxed{+}$ key; then enter 8.45 followed by the $\boxed{=}$ key. The display shows 25.673, which is rounded to the answer 25.7.

Examples of Addition and Subtraction			
Calculation	Enter in sequence	Display	Rounded answer
a. 12.0 + 16.2 + 122.3	12.0 $\boxed{+}$ 16.2 $\boxed{+}$ 122.3 $\boxed{=}$	150.5	150.5
b. 132 − 62 + 141	132 $\boxed{-}$ 62 $\boxed{+}$ 141 $\boxed{=}$	211	211
c. 46.23 + 13.2	46.23 $\boxed{+}$ 13.2 $\boxed{=}$	59.43	59.4
d. 129.06 + 49.1 − 18.3	129.06 $\boxed{+}$ 49.1 $\boxed{-}$ 18.3 $\boxed{=}$	159.86	159.9

A-10

Multiplication

To multiply numbers using your calculator,

1. Enter the first number to be multiplied followed by the multiplication key $\boxed{\times}$.
2. Enter the second number to be multiplied followed by the multiplication key $\boxed{\times}$.
3. Repeat Step 2 for all other numbers to be multiplied except the last number.
4. Enter the last number to be multiplied followed by the equal key $\boxed{=}$. You now have the answer in the display area.

   Round off to the proper number of significant figures.
   As an example, to calculate (3.25)(4.184)(22.2), enter 3.25 followed by the $\boxed{\times}$ key; then enter 4.184 followed by the $\boxed{\times}$ key; then enter 22.2 followed by the $\boxed{=}$ key. The display shows 301.8756, which is rounded to the answer 302.

Examples of Multiplication			
Calculation	Enter in sequence	Display	Rounded answer
a. $12 \times 14 \times 18$	$12\boxed{\times}14\boxed{\times}18\boxed{=}$	3024	3.0×10^3
b. $122 \times 3.4 \times 60.$	$122\boxed{\times}3.4\boxed{\times}60.\boxed{=}$	24888	2.5×10^4
c. $0.522 \times 49.4 \times 6.33$	$0.522\boxed{\times}49.4\boxed{\times}6.33\boxed{=}$	163.23044	163

Division

To divide numbers using your calculator,

1. Enter the numerator followed by the division key $\boxed{\div}$.
2. Enter the denominator followed by the equal key to give the answer.
3. If there is more than one denominator, enter each denominator followed by the division key except for the last number, which is followed by the equal key.

As an example, to calculate $\dfrac{126}{12}$, enter 126 followed by the $\boxed{\div}$ key; then enter 12 followed by the $\boxed{=}$ key. The display shows 10.5, which is rounded to the answer 11.

Examples of Division			
Calculation	Enter in sequence	Display	Rounded answer
a. $\dfrac{142}{25}$	$142\boxed{\div}25\boxed{=}$	5.68	5.7
b. $\dfrac{0.422}{5.00}$	$0.422\boxed{\div}5.00\boxed{=}$	0.0844	0.0844
c. $\dfrac{124}{0.022 \times 3.00}$	$124\boxed{\div}0.022\boxed{\div}3.00\boxed{=}$	1878.7878	1.9×10^3

Exponents

In scientific measurements and calculations, we often encounter very large and very small numbers. To express these large and small numbers conveniently, we use exponents, or powers, of 10. A number in exponential form is treated like any other number; that is, it can be added, subtracted, multiplied, or divided.

To enter an exponential number into your calculator, first enter the nonexponential part of the number and then press the exponent key $\boxed{\text{Exp}}$, followed by the exponent. For example, to enter 4.9×10^3, enter 4.94, then press $\boxed{\text{Exp}}$, and then press 3. When the exponent of 10 is a negative number, press the Change of Sign key $\boxed{+/-}$ after entering the exponent. For example, to enter 4.94×10^{-3}, enter in sequence 4.94 [Exp] 3 [+/−]. In most calculators, the exponent will appear in the display a couple of spaces after the nonexponent part of the number—for example, 4.94   03 or 4.94   −03.

Examples Using Exponential Numbers			
Calculation	Enter in sequence	Display	Rounded answer
a. $(4.94 \times 10^3)(21.4)$	4.94 [Exp] 3 [×] 21.4 [=]	105716	1.06×10^5
b. $(1.42 \times 10^4)(2.88 \times 10^{-5})$	1.42 [Exp] 4 [×] 2.88 [Exp] 5 [+/−] [=]	0.40896	0.409
c. $\dfrac{8.22 \times 10^{-5}}{5.00 \times 10^7}$	8.22 [Exp] 5 [+/−] [÷] 5.00 [Exp] 7 [=]	1.644 −12	1.64×10^{-12}

Logarithms

The logarithm of a number is the power (exponent) to which some base number must be raised to give the original number. The most commonly used base number is 10. The base number that we use is 10. For example, the log of 100 is 2.0 (log 100 = $10^{2.0}$). The log of 200 is 2.3 (log 200 = $10^{2.3}$). Logarithms are used in chemistry to calculate the pH of an aqueous acidic solution. The answer (log) should contain the same number of significant figures to the right of the decimal as is in the original number. Thus, log 100 = 2.0, but log 100. is 2.000.

The log key on most calculators is a function key. To determine the log using your calculator, enter the number and then press the log function key. For example, to determine the log of 125, enter 125 and then the [Log] key. The answer is 2.097.

Examples Using Logarithms Determine the log of the following:			
	Enter in sequence	Display	Rounded answer
a. 42	42 [Log]	1.6232492	1.62
b. 1.62×10^5	1.62 [Exp] 5 [Log]	5.209515	5.210
c. 6.4×10^{-6}	6.4 [Exp] 6 [+/−] [Log]	−5.19382	−5.19

Antilogarithms (Inverse Logarithms)

An antilogarithm is the number from which the logarithm has been calculated. It is calculated using the [10ˣ] key on your calculator. For example, to determine the antilogarithm of 2.891, enter 2.891 into your calculator and then press the second function key followed by the [10ˣ] key: 2.891 [F] [10ˣ].

The display shows 778.03655, which rounds to the answer 778.

Examples Using Antilogarithms Determine the antilogarithm of the following:			
	Enter in sequence	Display	Rounded answer
a. 1.628	1.628 [F] [10ˣ]	42.461956	42.5
b. 7.086	7.086 [F] [10ˣ]	12189896	1.22×10^7
c. −6.33	6.33 [+/−] [F] [10ˣ]	4.6773514 −07	4.7×10^{-7}
d. 6.33	6.33 [F] [10ˣ]	2137962	2.1×10^6

Additional Practice Problems*		
Problem	Display	Rounded answer
1. $143.5 + 14.02 + 1.202$	158.722	158.7
2. $72.06 - 26.92 - 49.66$	−4.52	−4.52
3. $2.168 + 4.288 - 1.62$	4.836	4.84
4. $(12.3)(22.8)(1.235)$	346.3434	346
5. $(2.42 \times 10^6)(6.08 \times 10^{-4})(0.623)$	916.65728	917
6. $\dfrac{(46.0)(82.3)}{19.2}$	197.17708	197
7. $\dfrac{0.0298}{243}$	1.2263374 −04	1.23×10^{-4}
8. $\dfrac{(5.4)(298)(760)}{(273)(1042)}$	4.2992554	4.3
9. $(6.22 \times 10^6)(1.45 \times 10^3)(9.00)$	8.1171 10	8.12×10^{10}
10. $\dfrac{(1.49 \times 10^6)(1.88 \times 10^6)}{6.02 \times 10^{23}}$	4.6531561 −12	4.65×10^{-12}
11. log 245	2.389166	2.389
12. $\log 6.5 \times 10^{-6}$	−5.1870866	−5.19
13. $\log 24 \times \log 34$	2.1137644	2.11
14. antilog 6.34	2187761.6	2.2×10^6
15. antilog −6.34	4.5708818 −07	4.6×10^{-7}

*Only the problem, the display, and the rounded answer are given.

Units of Measurement

Physical Constants		
Constant	**Symbol**	**Value**
Atomic mass unit	amu	1.6606×10^{-27} kg
Avogadro's number	N	6.022×10^{23} particles/mol
Gas constant	R (at STP)	0.08205 L atm/K mol
Mass of an electron	m_e	9.109×10^{-28} g
		5.486×10^{-4} amu
Mass of a neutron	m_n	1.675×10^{-27} kg
		1.00866 amu
Mass of a proton	m_p	1.673×10^{-27} kg
		1.00728 amu
Speed of light	c	2.997925×10^8 m/s

SI Units and Conversion Factors

Length

SI unit: meter (m)

1 meter	=	1.0936 yards
	=	100 centimeters
	=	1000 millimeters
1 centimeter	=	0.3937 inch
1 inch	=	2.54 centimeters (exactly)
1 kilometer	=	0.62137 mile
1 mile	=	5280 feet
	=	1.609 kilometers
1 angstrom	=	10^{-10} meter

Mass

SI unit: kilogram (kg)

1 kilogram	=	1000 grams
	=	2.20 pounds
1 gram	=	1000 milligrams
1 pound	=	453.59 grams
	=	0.45359 kilogram
	=	16 ounces
1 ton	=	2000 pounds
	=	907.185 kilograms
1 ounce	=	28.3 grams
1 atomic mass unit	=	1.6606×10^{-27} kilogram

Volume

SI unit: cubic meter (m^3)

1 liter	=	10^{-3} m^3
	=	1 dm^3
	=	1.0567 quarts
	=	1000 milliliters
1 gallon	=	4 quarts
	=	8 pints
	=	3.785 liters
1 quart	=	32 fluid ounces
	=	0.946 liter
1 fluid ounce	=	29.6 milliliters

Temperature

SI unit: kelvin (K)

$$0 \text{ K} = -273.15 °C$$
$$= -459.67 °F$$
$$K = °C + 273.15$$
$$°C = \frac{°F - 32}{1.8}$$
$$°F = 1.8(°C) + 32$$
$$°C = \frac{5}{9}(°F - 32)$$

Energy

SI unit: joule (J)

1 joule	=	1 kg m^2/s^2
	=	0.23901 calorie
1 calorie	=	4.184 joules

Pressure

SI unit: pascal (Pa)

1 pascal	=	1 kg/m s^2
1 atmosphere	=	101.325 kilopascals
	=	760 torr (mm Hg)
	=	14.70 pounds per square inch (psi)

A-14

Vapor Pressure of Water at Various Temperatures

Temperature (°C)	Vapor pressure (torr)	Temperature (°C)	Vapor pressure (torr)
0	4.6	26	25.2
5	6.5	27	26.7
10	9.2	28	28.3
15	12.8	29	30.0
16	13.6	30	31.8
17	14.5	40	55.3
18	15.5	50	92.5
19	16.5	60	149.4
20	17.5	70	233.7
21	18.6	80	355.1
22	19.8	90	525.8
23	21.2	100	760.0
24	22.4	110	1074.6
25	23.8		

Solubility Table

	F^-	Cl^-	Br^-	I^-	O^{2-}	S^{2-}	OH^-	NO_3^-	CO_3^{2-}	SO_4^{2-}	$C_2H_3O_2^-$
H^+	aq	aq	aq	aq	aq	sl.aq	aq	aq	sl.aq	aq	aq
Na^+	aq	aq	aq	aq	aq	aq	aq	aq	aq	aq	aq
K^+	aq	aq	aq	aq	aq	aq	aq	aq	aq	aq	aq
NH_4^+	aq	aq	aq	aq	—	aq	aq	aq	aq	aq	aq
Ag^+	aq	I	I	I	I	I	—	aq	I	I	I
Mg^{2+}	I	aq	aq	aq	I	d	I	aq	I	aq	aq
Ca^{2+}	I	aq	aq	aq	I	d	I	aq	I	I	aq
Ba^{2+}	I	aq	aq	aq	sl.aq	d	sl.aq	aq	I	I	aq
Fe^{2+}	sl.aq	aq	aq	aq	I	I	I	aq	sl.aq	aq	aq
Fe^{3+}	I	aq	aq	—	I	I	I	aq	I	aq	I
Co^{2+}	aq	aq	aq	aq	I	I	I	aq	I	aq	aq
Ni^{2+}	sl.aq	aq	aq	aq	I	I	I	aq	I	aq	aq
Cu^{2+}	sl.aq	aq	aq	—	I	I	I	aq	I	aq	aq
Zn^{2+}	sl.aq	aq	aq	aq	I	I	I	aq	I	aq	aq
Hg^{2+}	d	aq	I	I	I	I	I	aq	I	d	aq
Cd^{2+}	sl.aq	aq	aq	aq	I	I	I	aq	I	aq	aq
Sn^{2+}	aq	aq	aq	sl.aq	I	I	I	aq	I	aq	aq
Pb^{2+}	I	I	I	I	I	I	I	aq	I	I	aq
Mn^{2+}	sl.aq	aq	aq	aq	I	I	I	aq	I	aq	aq
Al^{3+}	I	aq	aq	aq	I	d	I	aq	—	aq	aq

Key: *aq* = soluble in water

     sl.aq = slightly soluble in water

       I = insoluble in water (less than 1 g/100 g H_2O)

       d = decomposes in water

A-16

APPENDIX VI

Answers to Selected Exercises

CHAPTER 1

Exercises

2. Two states are present; solid and liquid.

4. The maple leaf represents a heterogeneous mixture.

6. (a) homogeneous
   (b) homogeneous
   (c) heterogeneous
   (d) heterogeneous

9. (a) water, a pure substance
   (c) salt, a pure substance

12. (a) two phases, solid and gas
    (c) two phases, solid and liquid

CHAPTER 2

Exercises

2. (a) 1000 meters = 1 kilometer
   (c) 0.000001 liter = 1 microliter
   (e) 0.001 liter = 1 milliliter

4. (a) mg   (e) Å
   (c) m

6. (a) not significant   (e) significant
   (c) significant

8. (a) 40.0 (3 sig fig)
   (b) 0.081 (2 sig fig)
   (c) 129,042 (6 sig fig)
   (d) 4.090×10^{-3} (4 sig fig)

10. (a) 8.87   (c) 130. (1.30×10^2)
    (b) 21.3   (d) 2.00×10^6

12. (a) 4.56×10^{-2} (c) 4.030×10^1
    (b) 4.0822×10^3 (d) 1.2×10^7

14. (a) 28.1   (e) 2.49×10^{-4}
    (c) 4.0×10^1

16. (a) $\frac{1}{4}$ (c) $1\frac{2}{3}$ or $\frac{5}{3}$
    (b) $\frac{5}{8}$ (d) $\frac{8}{9}$

18. (a) 1.0×10^2 (c) 22
    (b) 4.6 mL

20. (a) 4.5×10^8 Å   (e) 6.5×10^5 mg
    (c) 8.0×10^6 mm   (g) 468 mL

22. (a) 117 ft
    (c) 7.4×10^4 mm^3
    (e) 75.7 L

24. 12 mi/hr

26. 8.33 gr

28. 3.54 days

30. 2.54×10^{-3} lb

32. 5.94×10^3 cm/s

34. (a) 50 ft/min
    (b) 3×10^{-4} km/s

36. 4.03×10^6 tilapia

38. 160 L

40. 4×10^5 m^2

42. 6 gal

44. 113°F Summer!

46. (a) 90.°F   (c) 546 K
    (b) −22.6°C   (d) −300°F

48. −11.4°C = 11.4°F

50. −153°C

52. 0.810 g/mL

54. 7.2 g/mL

56. 63 mL

59. A graduated cylinder would be the best choice for adding 100 mL of solvent to a reaction. While the volumetric flask is also labeled 100 mL, volumetric flasks are typically used for doing dilutions. The other three pieces of glassware could also be used, but they hold smaller volumes, so it would take a longer time to measure out 100 mL. Also, because you would have to repeat the measurement many times using the other glassware, there is a greater chance for error.

60. 14.5 mL

61. 26 mL

63. 3.43 vials potion

64. 10.1 lb sequins

65. Yes, 120 L additional solution

67. (a) −252.88°C
    (b) −423.18°F

68. 97°F − 100°F, similar to mammals

72. 5.1×10^3 L

75. 0.506 km^2

77. 0.965 g/mL

79. ethyl alcohol, because it has the lower density

81. 54.3 mL

82. 18.6 mg NHP

87. 76.9 g

A-17

CHAPTER 3

Exercises

2. (d) HI (f) Cl_2 (g) CO

4. (a) magnesium, bromine

(c) hydrogen, nitrogen, oxygen

(e) aluminum, phosphorus, oxygen

6. (a) $AlBr_3$ (c) $PbCrO_4$

8. (a) $C_{55}H_{66}O_{24}$ (b) $Cl_{15}H_{14}O_6$ (c) $Cl_{30}H_{48}O_3$

10. (a) hydrogen, 4 atoms; carbon, 2 atoms; oxygen, 2 atoms

(c) magnesium, 1 atom; hydrogen, 2 atoms; sulfur 2 atoms; oxygen, 6 atoms

(e) nickel, 1 atom; carbon, 1 atom; oxygen, 3 atoms

(g) carbon, 4 atoms; hydrogen, 10 atoms

12. (a) 9 atoms (c) 12 atoms

(b) 12 atoms (d) 12 atoms

14. (a) 6 atoms O (c) 6 atoms O

(b) 4 atoms O (d) 21 atoms O

16. (a) mixture (e) mixture

(c) pure substance

18. (c) element (d) compound

20. (a) compound (c) mixture

(b) compound

22. No. The only common liquid elements (at room temperature) are mercury and bromine.

24. 72% solids

26. The formula for hydrogen peroxide is H_2O_2. There are two atoms of oxygen for every two atoms of hydrogen. The molar mass of oxygen is 16.00 g, and the molar mass of hydrogen is 1.008 g. For hydrogen peroxide, the total mass of hydrogen is 2.016 g and the total mass of oxygen is 32.00 g, for a ratio of hydrogen to oxygen of approximately $2:32$. or $1:16$. Therefore, there is 1 gram of hydrogen for every 16 grams of oxygen.

29. (a) 1 carbon atom and 1 oxygen atom; total number of atoms $= 2$

(c) 1 hydrogen atom, 1 nitrogen atom, and 3 oxygen atoms; total number of atoms $= 5$

(e) 1 calcium atom, 2 nitrogen atoms, and 6 oxygen atoms; total number of atoms $= 9$

32. 40 atoms H

34. (a) magnesium, manganese, molybdenum, mendelevium, mercury, meitnerium

(c) sodium, potassium, iron, silver, tin, antimony

36. 420 atoms

39. (a) NaCl (g) $C_6H_{12}O_6$

(c) K_2O (i) $Cr(NO_3)_3$

(e) K_3PO_4

41. (a) 12C, 22H, 11O (e) 12C, 19H, 8O, 3Cl

(c) 14C, 18H, 5O, 2N

CHAPTER 4

Exercises

2. (a) physical (e) physical

(c) chemical (g) chemical

4. The copper wire, like the platinum wire, changed to a glowing red color when heated. Upon cooling, a new substance, black copper(II) oxide, had appeared.

6. Reactant: water

Products: hydrogen, oxygen

8. (a) physical (e) chemical

(c) chemical

10. (a) kinetic (e) kinetic

(c) potential

12. the transformation of kinetic energy to thermal energy

14. (a) + (b) − (c) + (d) − (e) −

16. 6.4×10^2 J

18. 5.58×10^3 J

20. 0.128 J/g°C

22. 31.7°C

27. 0.525 lb gold

30. 1.0×10^2 g Cu

32. 654°C

39. 8 g fat

40. (a) 1.12 kJ

(b) Glove made of wool felt

(c) wool felt 23.9°C, paper or cotton 24.8°C, rubber 9.04°C, silicon 22.6°C

43. A chemical change has occurred. Hydrogen molecules and oxygen molecules have combined to form water molecules.

CHAPTER 5

Exercises

2. Mg^{2+}, Cr^{3+}, Ba^{2+}, Ca^{2+}, and Y^{3+}.

4. (a) The nucleus of the atom contains most of the mass.

(c) The atom is mostly empty space.

6. The nucleus of an atom contains nearly all of its mass.

8. Electrons:

Dalton—Electrons are not part of his model.

Thomson—Electrons are scattered throughout the positive mass of matter in the atom.

Rutherford—Electrons are located out in space away from the central positive mass.

Positive matter:

Dalton—No positive matter in his model.

Thomson—Positive matter is distributed throughout the atom.

Rutherford—Positive matter is concentrated in a small central nucleus.

10. Yes. The mass of the isotope $^{12}_{6}C$, 12, is an exact number. The masses of other isotopes are not exact numbers.

12. Three isotopes of hydrogen have the same number of protons and electrons but differ in the number of neutrons.

14. All five isotopes have nuclei that contain 30 protons and 30 electrons. The numbers of neutrons are:

Isotope mass number	Neutrons
64	34
66	36
67	37
68	38
70	40

16. (a) $^{109}_{47}Ag$ (c) $^{57}_{26}Fe$

18. (a) 26 protons, 26 electrons, and 28 neutrons
    (c) 35 protons, 35 electrons, and 44 neutrons

20. (a) 56   (c) 79   (e) $^{135}_{56}Ba$

22. 50. amu

24. 35.46 amu; chlorine (Cl)

26. $1.5 \times 10^5 : 1.0$

28. (a) and (c) are isotopes of phosphorus

29. 9.2×10^8 atoms silicon

31. ^{160}Gd, ^{156}Dy, ^{163}Ho, ^{162}Er. This order differs from that on the periodic table.

33. (a) 197 amu   (b) gold (Au)

36.
C^+	6 protons, 5 electrons
O^I	8 protons, 7 electrons
O^{2+}	8 protons, 6 electrons

42. (a) 0.02644% electrons   (c) 0.02356% electrons

44. The electron region is the area around the nucleus where electrons are most likely to be located.

CHAPTER 6

Exercises

2. (a) Al_2S_3 (d) SrO
   (c) K_3N (f) $AlCl_3$

4. (a) F^- (i) $Cr_2O_7^{2-}$
   (c) I^- (k) PO_4^{3-}
   (e) S^{2-} (m) N^{3-}
   (g) P^{3-}

6. (a) sodium thiosulfate   (d) sodium chloride
   (b) dinitrogen oxide   (e) magnesium hydroxide
   (c) aluminum oxide   (f) lead (II) sulfide

8.

Ion	SO_4^{2-}	OH^-	AsO_4^{3-}	$C_2H_3O_2^-$	CrO_4^{2-}
NH_4^+	$(NH_4)_2SO_4$	NH_4OH	$(NH_4)_3AsO_4$	$NH_4C_2H_3O_2$	$(NH_4)_2CrO_4$
Ca^{2+}	$CaSO_4$	$Ca(OH)_2$	$Ca_3(AsO_4)_2$	$Ca(C_2H_3O_2)_2$	$CaCrO_4$
Fe^{3+}	$Fe_2(SO_4)_3$	$Fe(OH)_3$	$FeAsO_4$	$Fe(C_2H_3O_2)_3$	$Fe_2(CrO_4)_3$
Ag^+	Ag_2SO_4	$AgOH$	Ag_3AsO_4	$AgC_2H_3O_2$	Ag_2CrO_4
Cu^{2+}	$CuSO_4$	$Cu(OH)_2$	$Cu_3(AsO_4)_2$	$Cu(C_2H_3O_2)_2$	$CuCrO_4$

10. NH_4^+ compounds: ammonium sulfate, ammonium hydroxide, ammonium arsenate, ammonium acetate, ammonium chromate.

    Ca^{2+} compounds: calcium sulfate, calcium hydroxide, calcium arsenate, calcium acetate, calcium chromate.

    Fe^{3+} compounds: iron(III) sulfate, iron(III) hydroxide, iron(III) arsenate, iron(III) acetate, iron(III) chromate.

    Ag^+ compounds: silver sulfate, silver hydroxide, silver arsenate, silver acetate, silver chromate.

    Cu^{2+} compounds: copper(II) sulfate, copper(II) hydroxide, copper(II) arsenate, copper(II) acetate, copper(II) chromate.

12. (a) K_3N (e) Ca_3N_2
    (c) FeO (g) MnI_3

14. (a) phosphorus pentabromide
    (c) dinitrogen pentasulfide

(e) silicon tetrachloride
(g) tetraphosphorus heptasulfide

16. (a) $SnBr_4$ (d) $Hg(NO_2)_2$
    (c) $Ni(BO_3)_2$ (f) $Fe(C_2H_3O_2)_2$

18. (a) $HC_2H_3O_2$ (d) H_3BO_3
    (c) H_2S (f) $HClO$

20. (a) phosphoric acid   (f) nitric acid
    (c) iodic acid   (g) hydroiodic acid
    (d) hydrochloric acid   (i) sulfurous acid

22. (a) Na_2CrO_4 (i) $NaClO$
    (c) $Ni(C_2H_3O_2)_2$ (k) $Cr_2(SO_3)_3$
    (e) $Mg(BrO_3)_2$ (m) $Na_2C_2O_4$
    (g) $Mn(OH)_2$

24. (a) calcium hydrogen sulfate
    (c) tin(II) nitrite
    (e) potassium hydrogen carbonate
    (f) bismuth(III) arsenate
    (h) ammonium monohydrogen phosphate
    (j) potassium permanganate

26. (a) C_2H_5OH (e) HCl
    (c) $CaSO_4 \cdot 2H_2O$ (g) $NaOH$

28. (a) sulfate   (d) chlorate
    (c) nitrate   (f) carbonate

30. (a) K_2SO_4 (e) $KClO_3$
    (c) KNO_3 (f) K_2CO_3

32. Formula: KCl   Name: potassium chloride

34. (a) $CaCO_3$, no concern   (c) H_2O, no concern
    (b) $HC_2H_3O_2$, no concern

37. $Li_3Fe(CN)_6$
    $AlFe(CN)_6$
    $Zn_3[Fe(CN)_6]_2$

CHAPTER 7

Exercises

2. Molar masses
   (a) $NaOH$ 40.00
   (c) Cr_2O_3 152.0
   (e) $Mg(HCO_3)_2$ 146.3
   (g) $C_6H_{12}O_6$ 180.2
   (i) $BaCl_2 \cdot 2H_2O$ 244.2

4. (a) 0.625 mol $NaOH$
   (c) 7.18×10^{-3} mol $MgCl_2$
   (e) 2.03×10^{-2} mol Na_2SO_4

6. (a) 0.0417 g H_2SO_4 (c) 0.122 g Ti
   (b) 11 g CCl_4 (d) 8.0×10^{-7}g S

8. (a) 5.8×10^{24} molecules C_2H_4

(c) 4.36×10^{23} molecules CH_3OH

10. (a) 16 atoms

(c) 4.5×10^{25} atoms

(e) 1.3×10^{24} atoms

12. (a) 2.180×10^{-22} g Xe

(c) 8.975×10^{-22} g CH_3COOH

14. (a) 4.57×10^{-22} mol W

(c) 1.277×10^{-21} g SO_2

16. (a) 0.492 mol S_2F_{10}

(c) 3.56×10^{24} total atoms

(e) 2.96×10^{24} atoms F

18. (a) 138 atoms H

(b) 1.3×10^{25} atoms H

(c) 2.2×10^{24} atoms H

20. (a) 1.27 g Cl   (c) 0.274 g H

(b) 9.07 g H

22. (a) 47.98% Zn   (e) 23.09% Fe

52.02% Cl   17.37% N

(c) 12.26% Mg   59.53% O

31.24% P

56.48% O

24. (a) KCl   47.55% Cl   (c) $SiCl_4$ 83.46% Cl

(b) $BaCl_2$ 34.05% Cl   (d) LiCl   83.63% Cl

highest % Cl is LiCl

lowest % Cl is $BaCl_2$

26. 41.1% S, 6.02% H, 6.82% O, 46.0% C

28. (a) $KClO_3$ lower % Cl

(b) $KHSO_4$ higher % S

(c) Na_2CrO_4 lower % Cr

30. (a) CuCl   (e) $BaCr_2O_7$

(c) Cr_2S_3

32. (a) C_6H_5Br

(c) V_2S_3

34. Ti_2O_3

36. $HgCl_2$

38. Empirical formula is $C_3H_5OS_2$, molecular formula is $C_6H_{10}O_2S_4$.

40. The molecular formula is $C_4H_8O_2$.

42. 40.0% C, 6.73% H, 53.3% O. Empirical formula is CH_2O, molecular formula is $C_6H_{12}O_6$.

44. $Al_2(SiO_3)_3$

45. 8.43×10^{23} atoms P

47. 197 g/mol

49. 5.54×10^{19} m

50. 8.6×10^{13} dollars/person

52. (a) 10.3 cm^3 (b) 2.18 cm

54. 41.58 g Fe_2S_3

56. 1.0 ton of iron ore contains 2×10^4 g Fe

58. (a) 76.98% Hg   (c) 17.27% N

62. 42.10% C

6.480% H

51.42% O

64. 4.77 g O in 8.50 g $Al_2(SO_4)_3$

66. The empirical formula is $C_4H_4CaO_6$

68. 1.910×10^{16} years

70. 1.529×10^{-7} g $C_3H_8O_3$

72. $Co_3Mo_2Cl_{11}$

74. The empirical formula is C_5H_5N.

76. (a) CH_2O (c) CH_2O (e) $C_6H_2Cl_2O$

78. 9.0×10^{17} molecules O_2

CHAPTER 8

Exercises

2. (a) endothermic   (e) exothermic

(c) endothermic

4. (a) $H_2 + Br_2 \longrightarrow 2\,HBr$ combination

(c) $Ba(ClO_3)_2 \longrightarrow BaCl_2 + 3\,O_2$ decomposition

(e) $2\,H_2O_2 \longrightarrow 2\,H_2O + O_2$ decomposition

6. A metal and a nonmetal can react to form a salt; also an acid plus a base.

8. (a) $2\,SO_2 + O_2 \longrightarrow 2\,SO_3$

(c) $2\,Na + 2\,H_2O \longrightarrow 2\,NaOH + H_2$

(e) $Bi_2S_3 + 6\,HCl \longrightarrow 2\,BiCl_3 + 3\,H_2S$

(g) $Hg_2(C_2H_3O_2)_2(aq) + 2\,KCl(aq) \longrightarrow$
$\qquad\qquad Hg_2Cl_2(s) + 2\,KC_2H_3O_2(aq)$

(i) $2\,K_3PO_4 + 3\,BaCl_2 \longrightarrow 6\,KCl + Ba_3(PO_4)_2$

10. (a) $MgCO_3(s) \xrightarrow{\Delta} MgO(s) + CO_2(g)$

(c) $Fe_2(SO_4)_3(aq) + 6\,NaOH(aq) \longrightarrow$
$\qquad\qquad 2\,Fe(OH)_3(s) + 3\,Na_2SO_4(aq)$

(e) $SO_3(g) + H_2O(l) \longrightarrow H_2SO_4(aq)$

12. (a) $CuSO_4(aq) + 2\,KOH(aq) \longrightarrow Cu(OH)_2(s) + K_2SO_4(aq)$

(c) $3\,NaHCO_3(s) + H_3PO_4(aq) \longrightarrow$
$\qquad\qquad Na_3PO_4(aq) + 3\,H_2O(l) + 3\,CO_2(g)$

14. (a) $Cu(s) + NiCl_2(aq) \longrightarrow$ no reaction

(c) $I_2(s) + CaCl_2(aq) \longrightarrow$ no reaction

16. (a) $Li_2O(s) + H_2O(l) \longrightarrow 2\,LiOH(aq)$

(c) $Zn(s) + CuSO_4(aq) \longrightarrow Cu(s) + ZnSO_4(aq)$

18. (a) $C + O_2 \longrightarrow CO_2$

(c) $CuBr_2 + Cl_2 \longrightarrow CuCl_2 + Br_2$

(e) $2\,NaNO_3 \xrightarrow{\Delta} 2\,NaNO_2 + O_2$

20. (a) 2 mol of Na react with 1 mol of Cl_2 to produce 2 mol of NaCl and release 822 kJ of energy. Exothermic

(b) 1 mol of PCl_5 absorbs 92.9 kJ of energy to produce 1 mol of PCl_3 and 1 mol of Cl_2. Endothermic

22. (a) $Ca(s) + 2\,H_2O(l) \longrightarrow Ca(OH)_2(aq) + H_2(g) + 635.1$ kJ

(b) $2\,BrF_3 + 601.6$ kJ $\longrightarrow Br_2 + 3\,F_2$

24. (a) single displacement,
$\qquad Ni(s) + Pb(NO_3)_2(aq) \longrightarrow Pb(s) + Ni(NO_3)_2(aq)$

(c) decomposition, $2\,HgO(s) \longrightarrow 2\,Hg(l) + O_2(g)$

25. Combinations that form precipitates
$Ca(NO_3)_2(aq) + (NH_4)_2SO_4(aq) \longrightarrow$
$\qquad\qquad CaSO_4(s) + 2\,NH_4NO_3(aq)$

$Ca(NO_3)_2(aq) + (NH_4)_2CO_3 \longrightarrow CaCO_3(s) + 2\,NH_4NO_3(aq)$

$AgNO_3(aq) + NH_4Cl(aq) \longrightarrow AgCl(s) + NH_4NO_3(aq)$

$2\,AgNO_3(aq) + (NH_4)_2SO_4 \longrightarrow Ag_2SO_4(s) + 2\,NH_4NO_3(aq)$

$2 \text{AgNO}_3(aq) + (\text{NH}_4)_2\text{CO}_3(aq) \longrightarrow$
$$\text{Ag}_2\text{CO}_3(s) + 2 \text{NH}_4\text{NO}_3(aq)$$

26. $\text{P}_4\text{O}_{10} + 12 \text{HClO}_4 \longrightarrow 6 \text{Cl}_2\text{O}_7 + 4 \text{H}_3\text{PO}_4$

58 atoms O on each side

34. (a) $4 \text{Cs} + \text{O}_2 \longrightarrow 2 \text{Cs}_2\text{O}$

(c) $\text{SO}_3 + \text{H}_2\text{O} \longrightarrow \text{H}_2\text{SO}_4$

37. (a) $2 \text{ZnO} \xrightarrow{\Delta} 2 \text{Zn} + \text{O}_2$

(c) $\text{Na}_2\text{CO}_3 \xrightarrow{\Delta} \text{Na}_2\text{O} + \text{CO}_2$

38. (a) $\text{Mg}(s) + 2 \text{HCl}(aq) \longrightarrow \text{H}_2(g) + \text{MgCl}_2(aq)$

(c) $3 \text{Zn}(s) + 2 \text{Fe(NO}_3)_3(aq) \longrightarrow 2 \text{Fe}(s) + 3 \text{Zn(NO}_3)_2(aq)$

39. (a) $2 (\text{NH}_4)_3\text{PO}_4(aq) + 3 \text{Ba(NO}_3)_2(aq) \longrightarrow$
$$\text{Ba}_3(\text{PO}_4)_2(s) + 6 \text{NH}_4\text{NO}_3(aq)$$

(c) $\text{CuSO}_4(aq) + \text{Ca(ClO}_3)_2(aq) \longrightarrow$
$$\text{CaSO}_4(s) + \text{Cu(ClO}_3)_2(aq)$$

(e) $\text{H}_3\text{PO}_4(aq) + 3 \text{KOH}(aq) \longrightarrow \text{K}_3\text{PO}_4(aq) + 3 \text{H}_2\text{O}(l)$

42. (a) $\text{CH}_4 + 2 \text{O}_2 \longrightarrow \text{CO}_2 + 2 \text{H}_2\text{O}$

(b) $2 \text{C}_3\text{H}_6 + 9 \text{O}_2 \longrightarrow 6 \text{CO}_2 + 6 \text{H}_2\text{O}$

(c) $\text{C}_6\text{H}_5\text{CH}_3 + 9 \text{O}_2 \longrightarrow 7 \text{CO}_2 + 4 \text{H}_2\text{O}$

CHAPTER 9

Exercises

2. (a) 25.0 mol NaHCO_3 (c) 16 mol CO_2

4. (a) 1.31 g NiSO_4 (e) 18 g K_2CrO_4

(c) 373 g Bi_2S_3

6. HCl

8. (a) $\dfrac{6 \text{ mol O}_2}{1 \text{ mol C}_4\text{H}_9\text{OH}}$ (d) $\dfrac{1 \text{ mol C}_4\text{H}_9\text{OH}}{4 \text{ mol CO}_2}$

(c) $\dfrac{4 \text{ mol CO}_2}{5 \text{ mol H}_2\text{O}}$ (f) $\dfrac{4 \text{ mol CO}_2}{6 \text{ mol O}_2}$

10. (a) 34 mol NaOH   (b) 11 mol Na_2SO_4

12. (a) 8.33 mol H_2O (b) 0.800 mol Al(OH)_3

14. $2 \text{Al} + 6 \text{HBr} \longrightarrow 2 \text{AlBr}_3 + 3 \text{H}_2$

249 g AlBr_3

16. 117 g H_2O, 271 g Fe

18. (a) 1.9 mol CaS   (e) 2.50×10^3 g CaS

(c) 0.4179 mol CaO

20. (a)

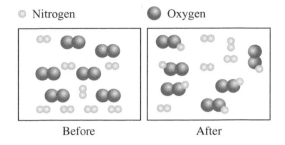

Li

I

neither is limiting

(b)

Ag

Cl

Ag is limiting

22. (a) Oxygen is the limiting reactant.

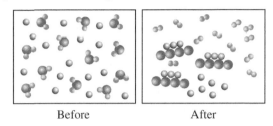

Nitrogen   Oxygen

Before   After

(b) Water is the limiting reactant.

Before   After

24. (a) H_2S is the limiting reactant and $\text{Bi(NO}_3)_3$ is in excess.

(b) H_2O is the limiting reactant and Fe is in excess.

26. (a) 0.193 mol PCl_3

(b) 71 g PCl_3; P_4 is in excess

(c) 23 mol PCl_3 will be produced; 9 mol P_4 unreacted

28. Zinc

30. 89.02%

32. (a) 0.32 mol FeCl_3 and 0.48 mol H_2O

(b) 9 g Fe_2O_3 in excess

(c) 48 g FeCl_3 actual yield

36. (a) 0.19 mol KO_2 (b) 28 g O_2/hr

39. 70.7 g O_2

41. (a) 0.16 mol MnCl_2 (e) 11 g KMnO_4 unreacted

(c) 82% yield

44. 46.97 g Ca(OH)_2

46. (a) 5.0 mol CO_2, 7.5 mol H_2O

(b) 430. g CO_2 , 264 g H_2

48. (a) 2.0 mol Cu, 2.0 mol FeSO_4 , 1 mol CuSO_4

(b) 15.9 g Cu, 38.1 g FeSO_4, 6.0 g Fe

50. (a) 3.2×10^2 g $\text{C}_2\text{H}_5\text{OH}$

(b) 1.10×10^3 g $\text{C}_6\text{H}_{12}\text{O}_6$

52. 3.7×10^2 kg Li_2O

55. 223.0 g H_2SO_4; 72.90% yield

58. 67.2% KClO_3

CHAPTER 10

Exercises

2. (a) Na   11 total electrons; 1 valence electron

(c) P   15 total electrons; 5 valence electrons

4. (a) Mn $1s^2 2s^2 2p^6 3s^2 3p^6 4s^2 3d^5$

(c) Ga $1s^2 2s^2 2p^6 3s^2 3p^6 4s^2 3d^{10} 4p^1$

6. Bohr said that a number of orbits were available for electrons, each corresponding to an energy level. When an electron falls from a higher energy orbit to a lower orbit, energy is given off as a specific wavelength of light. Only those energies in the visible range are seen in the hydrogen spectrum. Each line corresponds to a change from one orbit to another.

8. 18 electrons in third energy level; 2 in s, 6 in p, 10 in d

10. (a) $^{28}_{14}Si$

(c) $^{40}_{18}Ar$

(e) $^{31}_{15}P$

12. (a) Li $1s^2 2s^1$
(c) Zn $1s^2 2s^2 2p^6 3s^2 3p^6 4s^2 3d^{10}$
(e) K $1s^2 2s^2 2p^6 3s^2 3p^6 4s^1$

14. (a) correct
(c) incorrect

16. (a) N   (c) Ca

18. (a) boron, B   (c) lead, Pb

20. (a) Phosphorus (P)

(c) Calcium (Ca)

(e) Potassium (K)

22. (a) Cl

(c) Ni

(e) Ba

24. (a) ⟨13p 14n⟩ $2e^- 8e^- 3e^-$ $^{27}_{13}Al$

(b) ⟨22p 26n⟩ $2e^- 8e^- 8e^- 4e^-$ $^{48}_{22}Ti$

26. The last electron in potassium is located in the fourth energy level because the 4s orbital is at a lower energy level than the 3d orbital. Also the properties of potassium are similar to the other elements in Group 1A.

28. Noble gases each have filled s and p orbitals in the outermost energy level.

30. The elements in a group have the same number of outer energy level electrons. They are located vertically on the periodic table.

32. Valence shell electrons
(a) 5   (c) 6   (e) 3

34. All of these elements have an $s^2 d^{10}$ electron configuration in their outermost energy levels.

36. (a) and (f)   (e) and (h)

38. 7, 33 since they are in the same periodic group.

40. (a) nonmetal, I   (c) metal, Mo

42. Period 4, Group 3B

44. Group 3A contains 3 valence electrons. Group 3B contains 2 electrons in the outermost level and 1 electron in an inner d orbital. Group A elements are representative, while Group B elements are transition elements.

46. (a) Pb   (b) Sm   (c) Ga   (d) Ir
48. (a) Mg $1s^2 2s^2 2p^6 3s^2$
(c) K $1s^2 2s^2 2p^6 3s^2 3p^6 4s^1$
(d) F $1s^2 2s^2 2p^5$
(f) N $1s^2 2s^2 2p^3$

50. (a) 7A, Halogens   (e) 8A, Noble Gases
(c) 1A, Alkali Metals

56. (a) Any orbital can hold a maximum of two electrons.
(c) The third principal energy level can hold two electrons in 3s, six electrons in 3p, and ten electrons in 3d for a total of eighteen electrons.
(e) An f sublevel can hold a maximum of fourteen electrons.

59. (a) Ne   (c) F
(b) Ge   (d) N

61. Transition elements are found in Groups 1B–8B, lanthanides and actinides.

63. Elements 7, 15, 33, 51, 83 all have 5 electrons in their valence shell.

65. (a) sublevel p   (c) sublevel f
(b) sublevel d

67. If 36 is a noble gas, 35 would be in periodic Group 7A and 37 would be in periodic Group 1A.

CHAPTER 11

Exercises

2. Drawing 1 Cl atom, drawing 2 Cl⁻ ion
4. (a) Fe^{2+} (e) Rubidium ion.
(c) Chloride ion.
6.
(a) H⁺ Cl⁻   (e) Cs⁺ I⁻
(c) C⁺ Cl⁻
8. (a) ionic   (c) covalent
10. (a) $K \longrightarrow K^+ + 1\,e^-$
(b) $S + 2\,e^- \longrightarrow S^{2-}$
12. (a)

(b)

14. (a) Pb (4)   (d) Cs (1)
(c) O (6)   (f) Ar (8)

16. (a) sulfur atom, gain 2 e⁻
(b) calcium atom, lose 2 e⁻
(c) nitrogen atom, gain 3 e⁻
(d) iodide ion, none

18. (a) Nonpolar covalent compound; O_2.
(c) Polar covalent compound; H_2O.

20. (a) SbH_3, Sb_2O_3 (c) HCl, Cl_2O_7

22. $BeBr_2$, beryllium bromide

    $MgBr_2$, magnesium bromide

    $SrBr_2$, strontium bromide

    $BaBr_2$, barium bromide

    $RaBr_2$, radium bromide

24. (a) Ga: (b) $[Ga]^{3+}$ (c) $[Ca]^{2+}$

26. (a) covalent   (c) covalent

    (b) ionic   (d) covalent

28. (a) covalent   (c) covalent

    (b) covalent

30. (a) :Ö::Ö: (b) :Br:Br: (c) :I:I:

32. (a) :S:H   (c) H:N:H
       H   H

34. (a) $\left[\,:\ddot{I}:\,\right]^-$ (e) $\left[:\ddot{O}:N::O:\right]^-$
                                           :O:

    (c) $\left[:\ddot{O}:C::\ddot{O}:\right]^{2-}$
              :O:

36. (a) H_2, nonpolar   (c) CH_3OH, polar

    (b) NI_3, polar   (d) CS_2, nonpolar

38. (a) 3 electron pairs, trigonal planar

    (b) 4 electron pairs, tetrahedral

    (c) 4 electron pairs, tetrahedral

40. (a) tetrahedral   (c) tetrahedral

    (b) trigonal pyramidal

42. (a) tetrahedral   (b) bent   (c) bent

44. potassium

47. N_2H_4 14 e⁻   :N—N: HN_3 16 e⁻   H—N=N=N̈
(with H above and below each N of N₂H₄)

50. (a) Be   (d) F

    (b) He   (e) Fr

    (c) K   (f) Ne

51. (a) Cl   (c) Ca

55. $SnBr_2$, $GeBr_2$

58. This structure shown is incorrect since the bond is ionic. It should be represented as:

$\left[Na\right]^+ \left[:\ddot{O}:\right]^{2-} \left[Na\right]^+$

59. Answer: Fluorine, oxygen, nitrogen, chlorine

64. (a) 109.5° (actual angle is closer to 105)   (c) 109.5°

68. Empirical formula is SO_3.

      :Ö:
       |
 :Ö—S=Ö:

70. (a) ionic   (c) covalent

    (b) both   (d) covalent

CHAPTER 12

Exercises

2.

	mm Hg	lb/in.²	atmospheres
a.	789	15.3	1.04
b.	1700	32	2.2
c.	1100	21	1.4

4. (a) 86.5 kPa   (c) 2770 mm Hg   (e) 82.1 cm Hg

    (b) 0.0500 atm   (d) 1.06 atm

6. (a) 2.1 atm   (b) 1600 torr   (c) 210 kPa

8. (a) 1330 torr   (b) 40.0 torr

10. 21.2 L

12. (a) 691 mL   (c) 737 mL

    (b) 633 mL

14. 30.8 L

16. 33.4 L CO_2

18. −150°C

20. 719 mm Hg

22. 1.450×10^3 torr

24. 1.19 L C_3H_8

26. 132 L

28. (a) 67.0 L SO_3 (c) 7.96 L Cl_2

    (b) 170 L C_2H_6

30. 1.78 g C_3H_6

32. 2.82×10^{23} molecules CO_2

34. 2.1 g CH_4

36. 1.8×10^3 L CH_4

38. 0.362 mol CO_2

40. 209 K

42. (a) 9.91 g/L Rn   (c) 3.575 g/L SO_3

    (b) 2.054 g/L NO_2 (d) 1.252 g/L C_2H_4

44. (a) 0.85 g/L C_2H_4 (b) 0.154 g/L He

46. (a) 3.95×10^4 mL H_2 (b) 0.0737 mol HCl

48. (a) 36 L O_2 (c) 12 L H_2O vapor

    (b) 210 g CO_2

50. 1.12×10^3 L CO_2

54. image (a)

55. (a) the pressure will be cut in half

    (c) the pressure will be cut in half

59. 22.4 L

62. SF_6 has the greatest density.

64. (a) CH_3

    (b) C_2H_6

             H   H
             | |
    (c) H—C—C—H
             | |
             H   H

67. 2.3×10^7 K

70. 327°C

72. 211 K (−62°C)

74. 3.55 atm

78. 1.03×10^4 mm (33.8 ft)

79. 330 mol O_2

81. 43.2 g/mol (molar mass)

83. (a) 8.4 L H_2 (c) 8.48 g/L CO_2

85. 279 L H_2 at STP

86. C_4H_8

CHAPTER 13

Exercises

2. $H_2Se < H_2S < H_2O$

4. $CO_2 < SO_2 < CS_2$

6. (a) HI will not hydrogen bond; hydrogen is not bonded to fluorine, oxygen, or nitrogen.

  (b) NH_3 will hydrogen bond; hydrogen is bonded to nitrogen.

  (c) CH_2F_2 will not hydrogen bond; hydrogen is not bonded to fluorine, oxygen, or nitrogen.

  (d) C_2H_5OH will hydrogen bond; one of the hydrogens is bonded to oxygen.

  (e) H_2O will hydrogen bond; hydrogen is bonded to oxygen.

8. (b) H—N—H ······ N—H NH_3

  (d) H—C—C—O—H ······ O—C—C—H C_2H_5OH

  (e) H—O—H ······ O H_2O

10. Water forming beaded droplets is an example of cohesive forces. The water molecules have stronger attractive forces for other water molecules than they do for the surface.

12. (a) magnesium ammonium phosphate hexahydrate

  (b) iron(II) sulfate heptahydrate

  (c) tin(IV) chloride pentahydrate

14. 0.0655 mol $Na_2B_4O_7 \cdot 10\ H_2O$

16. (a) 56.0 g H_2O

  (b) 69.0 g $AlCl_3$

18. 20.93% H_2O

20. The formula is $NiCl_2 \cdot 6\ H_2O$.

22. 1.57×10^5 J

24. 42 g of steam needed; not enough steam (35 g)

26. The system will be at 0°C. It will be a mixture of ice and water.

28. Steam molecules will cause a more severe burn. Steam molecules contain more energy at 100°C than water molecules at 100°C due to the energy absorbed during the vaporization state (heat of vaporization).

30. When one leaves the swimming pool, water starts to evaporate from the skin of the body. Part of the energy needed for evaporation is absorbed from the skin, resulting in the cool feeling.

36. $MgSO_4 \cdot 7\ H_2O$ $Na_2HPO_4 \cdot 12\ H_2O$

43. 6.78×10^5 J or 1.62×10^5 cal

44. 40.7 kJ/mol

46. 2.30×10^6 J

48. 40.2 g H_2O

50. 1.00 mole of water vapor at STP has a volume of 22.4 L (gas); 1.00 mole of liquid water has a volume of 18.0 mL.

52. 3.9×10^3 J

55. 2.71×10^4 J

56. 5.2×10^4 J

57. $2\ H_2O(l) \longrightarrow 2\ H_2(g) + O_2(g)$

CHAPTER 14

Exercises

2. Generally soluble:

  (b) $Cu(NO_3)_2$

  (d) $NH_4C_2H_3O_2$

  (f) $AgNO_3$

4. (a) 16.7% $NaNO_3$

  (c) 39% K_2CrO_4

6. 143 g iron(III) oxide solution

8. (a) 9.0 g $BaCl_2$

  (b) 66 g solvent

10. (a) 63.59% $C_{12}H_{22}O_{11}$

  (b) 47.3% CH_3OH

12. (a) 13.6% butanol

  (b) 16% methanol

  (c) 6.00% isoamyl alcohol

14. (a) 4.0 M

  (c) 1.97 M $C_6H_{12}O_6$

16. (a) 1.1 mol HNO_3

  (b) 7.5×10^{-3} mol $NaClO_3$

  (c) 0.088 mol LiBr

18. (a) 2.1×10^3 g H_2SO_4

  (b) 6.52 g $KMnO_4$

  (c) 1.2 g $Fe_2(SO_4)_3$

20. (a) 3.4×10^3 mL

  (b) 1.88×10^3 mL

  (c) 1.37 mL

22. (a) 1.2 M

  (b) 0.070 M

  (c) 0.333 M

24. (a) 25 mL 18 M H_2SO_4

  (b) 5.0 mL 15 M NH_3

26. (a) 1.2 M HCl

  (b) 4.21 M HCl

28. (a) 3.6 mol Na_2SO_4

  (c) 0.625 mol NaOH

  (e) 38.25 mL H_2SO_4

30. (a) 1.88×10^{-3} mol H_2O

  (c) 90.2 mL $HC_2H_3O_2$

  (e) 1.8 L CO_2

32. (a) 1.67 m $CaCl_2$

  (b) 0.026 m $C_6H_{12}O_6$

  (c) 6.44 m $(CH_3)_2CHOH$

34. (a) 10.74 m

  (b) 105.50°C

  (c) −20.0°C

36. 163 g/mol

38. Concord grape juice and stainless steel

40. Red paint and oil and vinegar salad dressing are not a true solution because they will separate out if they are not shaken or stirred.

42. (a) The amino acid will dissolve faster in the solvent at 75°C because the rate of dissolving increases with increasing temperature.

(b) The powdered sodium acetate will dissolve faster because it has a smaller particle size.

(c) The carton of table salt will dissolve faster because it has a smaller particle size and the temperature is higher.

(d) The acetaminophen will dissolve faster in the infant pain medication because it has less acetaminophen already dissolved in it.

44. 1.092 M $HgCl_2$

51. 0.15 M NaCl

53. (a) 160 g sugar

(b) 0.47 M $C_{12}H_{22}O_{11}$

(c) 0.516 m $C_{12}H_{22}O_{11}$

55. 16.2 m HCl

57. 66 mL C_2H_5OH [ethyl alcohol]

59. (a) 4.5 g NaCl

(b) 450. mL H_2O must evaporate.

61. 2.94 L solution

63. 15 M H_3PO_4

67. 1.20 g $Mg(OH)_2$

69. 6.2 m H_2SO_4

     5.0 M H_2SO_4

70. (a) 2.9 m

(b) 101.5°C

72. (a) 8.04×10^3 g $C_2H_6O_2$

(b) 7.24×10^3 mL $C_2H_6O_2$

(c) −4.0°F

73. 47% $NaHCO_3$

74. (a) 7.7 L H_2O must be added

(b) 0.0178 mol H_2SO_4

(c) 0.0015 mol H_2SO_4 in each mL

77. 2.84 g $Ba(OH)_2$ is formed.

78. (a) 0.011 mol Li_2CO_3

(c) 3.2×10^2 mL solution

84. 53 m sugar

CHAPTER 15

Exercises

2. Conjugate acid–base pairs:

(a) $H_2S − HS^-$; $NH_3 − NH_4^+$

(c) $HBr − Br^-$; $CH_3O^- − CH_3OH$

4. (a) $Fe_2O_3(s) + 6\,HBr(aq) \longrightarrow 2\,FeBr_3(aq) + 3\,H_2O(l)$

(c) $2\,NaOH(aq) + H_2CO_3(aq) \longrightarrow Na_2CO_3(aq) + 2\,H_2O(l)$

(e) $Mg(s) + 2\,HClO_4(aq) \longrightarrow Mg(ClO_4)_2(aq) + H_2(g)$

6. (a) $Fe_2O_3 + (6\,H^+ + 6\,Br^-) \longrightarrow (2\,Fe^{3+} + 6\,Br^-) + 3\,H_2O$

     $Fe_2O_3 + 6\,H^+ \longrightarrow 2\,Fe^{3+} + 3\,H_2O$

(c) $(2\,Na^+ + 2\,OH^-) + H_2CO_3 \longrightarrow (2\,Na^+ + CO_3^{2-}) + 2\,H_2O$

     $2\,OH^- + H_2CO_3 \longrightarrow CO_3^{2-} + 2\,H_2O$

(e) $Mg + (2\,H^+ + 2\,ClO_4^-) \longrightarrow (Mg^{2+} + 2\,ClO_4^-) + H_2$

     $Mg + 2\,H^+ \longrightarrow Mg^{2+} + H_2$

8. (a) $2\,HBr + Mg(OH)_2 \longrightarrow 2\,H_2O + MgBr_2$

(b) $H_3PO_4 + 3\,KOH \longrightarrow 3\,H_2O + K_3PO_4$

(c) $H_2SO_4 + 2\,NH_4OH \longrightarrow 2\,H_2O + (NH_4)_2SO_4$

10. $Ca(OH)_2$ and H_2CO_3; $Ca(OH)_2 + H_2CO_3 \longrightarrow 2\,H_2O + CaCO_3$

12. (a) $C_6H_{12}O_6$ — nonelectrolyte

(c) NaClO — electrolyte

(e) C_2H_5OH — nonelectrolyte

14. (a) 2.25 M Fe^{3+}, 6.75 M Cl^-

(c) 0.75 M Na^+, 0.75 M $H_2PO_4^-$

16. (a) 12.6 g Fe^{3+}, 23.9 g Cl^-

(c) 1.7 g Na^+, 7.3 g $H_2PO_4^-$

18. (a) $[H^+] = 1 \times 10^{-7}$

(b) $[H^+] = 5 \times 10^{-5}$ M

(c) $[H^+] = 2 \times 10^{-6}$ M

(d) $[H^+] = 5 \times 10^{-11}$ M

20. (a) $[Na^+] = 0.25\ M$, $[Cl^-] = 0.25\ M$

(c) $[Ba^{2+}] = 0.062\ M$, $[Ag^+] = 0.081\ M$, $[NO_3^-] = 0.20\ M$

22. $HCN + H_2O \rightleftharpoons H_3O^+ + CN^-$, weak electrolyte and weak acid

24. (a) 0.147 M NaOH

(b) 0.964 M NaOH

(c) 0.4750 M NaOH

26. (a) $Mg(s) + Cu^{2+}(aq) \longrightarrow Cu(s) + Hg^{2+}(aq)$

(b) $H^+(aq) + OH^-(aq) \longrightarrow H_2O(l)$

(c) $SO_3^{2-}(aq) + 2\,H^+(aq) \longrightarrow H_2O(l) + SO_2(g)$

28. (a) 2 M HCl

(b) 1 M H_2SO_4

30. 0.894 g of $Al(OH)_3$

32. 7.0% NaCl in the sample

34. 0.936 L H_2

36. (a) pH = 2.70

(b) pH = 7.15

(c) pH = −0.48

38. (a) pH = 4.30

(b) pH = 10.47

40. (a) weak acid

(b) strong base

(c) strong acid

(d) strong acid

42. (a) BrO_3^-

(b) NH_3

(c) HPO_4^{2-}

44. $S^{2-}(aq) + H_2O(l) \longrightarrow HS^-(aq) + OH^-(aq)$

46. $H_2SO_4(aq) + CaCO_3(s) \longrightarrow CaSO_4(s) + H_2O(l) + CO_2(g)$

48. (a) basic

(c) neutral

(e) acidic

51. 0.218 M H_2SO_4

55. Freezing point depression is directly related to the concentration of particles in the solution.

highest freezing point	$C_{12}H_{22}O_{11}$ > $HC_2H_3O_2$ > HCl > $CaCl_2$	lowest freezing point
	1 mol 1 mol + 2 mol 3 mol	
	(particles in solution)	

57. As the pH changes by 1 unit, the concentration of H^+ in solution changes by a factor of 10. For example, the pH of 0.10 M HCl is 1.00, while the pH of 0.0100 M HCl is 2.00.

58. 1.77% solute, 98.23% H_2O

59. 0.201 M HCl

61. 0.673 g KOH

63. 0.462 M HCl

65. pH = 1.1, acidic

67. (a) $2\,NaOH(aq) + H_2SO_4(aq) \longrightarrow Na_2SO_4(aq) + 2\,H_2O(l)$

   (b) 1.0×10^2 mL NaOH

   (c) 0.71 g Na_2SO_4

70. acidic pH = 0.82

75. 806 mL

CHAPTER 16

Exercises

2. (a) $I_2(s) \Longleftrightarrow I_2(g)$

   (b) $NaNO_3(s) \Longleftrightarrow Na^+(aq) + NO_3^-(aq)$

4. (a) Reaction is exothermic.

   (b) Reaction shifts to the right. [HCl] will be decreased; $[O_2]$, $[H_2O]$, and $[Cl_2]$ will be increased.

   (c) Reaction will shift left.

6. (a) left   I   I   I (add NH_3)

   (b) left   I   I   D (increase volume)

   (c) no change N   N   N (add catalyst)

   (d) ?   ?   I   I (add H_2 and N_2)

8.

Reaction	Increase temperature	Increase pressure	Add catalyst
(a)	right	left	no change
(b)	left	left	no change
(c)	left	left	no change

10. Equilibrium shift

   (a) no change   (b) left   (c) right   (d) right

12. (a) $K_{eq} = \dfrac{[H^+][H_2PO_4^-]}{[H_3PO_4]}$ (c) $K_{eq} = \dfrac{[N_2O_5]^2}{[NO_2]^4[O_2]}$

   (b) $K_{eq} = \dfrac{[CH_4][H_2S]^2}{[CS_2][H_2]^4}$

14. (a) $K_{sp} = [Mg^{2+}][CO_3^{2-}]$ (c) $K_{sp} = [Tl^{3+}][OH^-]^3$

   (b) $K_{sp} = [Ca^{2+}][C_2O_4^{2-}]$ (d) $K_{sp} = [Pb^{2+}]^3[AsO_4^{3-}]^2$

16. If H^+ is increased,

   (a) pH is decreased   (c) OH^- is decreased

   (b) pOH is increased   (d) K_W, remains unchanged

18. When excess base gets into the bloodstream, it reacts with H^+ to form water. Then H_2CO_3 ionizes to replace H^+, thus maintaining the approximate pH of the blood.

20. (a) $[H^+] = 4.6 \times 10^{-3}\,M$ (c) 18% ionized

   (b) pH = 2.34

22. $K_a = 2.3 \times 10^{-5}$

24. (a) 0.79% ionized; pH = 2.10

   (b) 2.5% ionized; pH = 2.60

   (c) 7.9% ionized; pH = 3.10

26. $K_a = 7.3 \times 10^{-6}$

28. $[H^+] = 3.0\,M$; pH = -0.48; pOH = 14.48; $[OH^-] = 3.3 \times 10^{-15}$

30. (a) pOH = 3.00; pH = 11.00

   (b) pH = 0.903; pOH = 13.10

   (c) pH = 5.74; pOH = 8.26

32. (a) $[OH^-] = 2.5 \times 10^{-6}$

   (c) $[OH^-] = 4.5 \times 10^{-10}$

34. (a) $[H^+] = 2.2 \times 10^{-13}$

   (b) $[H^+] = 1.9 \times 10^{-6}$

36. (a) 1.2×10^{-23}

   (c) 1.81×10^{-18}

38. (a) $1.1 \times 10^{-4}\,M$

   (b) $9.2 \times 10^{-6}\,M$

40. (a) 3.3×10^{-3} g $PbSO_4$

   (b) 2.3×10^{-4} g $BaCrO_4$

42. Precipitation occurs.

44. 2.6×10^{-12} mol AgBr will dissolve.

46. pH = 4.74

48. Change in pH = $4.74 - 4.72 = 0.02$ units in the buffered solution. Initial pH = 4.74.

52. 4.20 mol HI

54. 0.500 mol HI, 2.73 mol H_2, 0.538 mol I_2

56. 128 times faster

58. pH = 4.57

60. Hypochlorous acid: $K_a = 3.5 \times 10^{-8}$
    Propanoic acid: $K_a = 1.3 \times 10^{-5}$
    Hydrocyanic acid: $K_a = 4.0 \times 10^{-10}$

62. (a) Precipitation occurs.

   (b) Precipitation occurs.

   (c) No precipitation occurs.

64. No precipitate of $PbCl_2$

66. $K_{eq} = 1.1 \times 10^4$

68. 8.0 M NH_3

70. $K_{sp} = 4.00 \times 10^{-28}$

72. (a) The temperature could have been cooler.

   (b) The humidity in the air could have been higher.

   (c) The air pressure could have been greater.

74. (a) $K_{eq} = \dfrac{[O_3]^2}{[O_2]^3}$ (c) $K_{sp} = [CO_2]$

   (b) $K_{eq} = \dfrac{[H_2O(l)]}{[H_2O(g)]}$ (d) $K_{sp} = \dfrac{[H^+]^6}{[Bi^{3+}]^2[H_2S]^3}$

76. $K_{eq} = 450$

78. 1.1 g $CaSO_4$

81. (a) shift right   (b) shift left   (c) shift right   (d) shift left

83. (a) $HCO_3^-(aq) + H^+(aq) \Longleftrightarrow H_2CO_3(aq)$

   (b) $HCO_3^-(aq) + OH^-(aq) \Longleftrightarrow H_2O(l) + CO_3^{2-}(aq)$

CHAPTER 17

Exercises

2. (a) CHF_3 C = +2; H = +1; F = −1

   (c) SF_6 S = +6; F = −1

   (e) CH_3OH C = −2; H = +1; O = −2

4. (a) $\underline{C}O_3^{2-}$ +4

   (c) $NaH_2\underline{P}O_4$ +5

6. (a) Cu +2; S +6   (b) +7   (c) +4   (d) +6

8. (a) $Cu^{2+} + e^- \longrightarrow Cu^{1+}$

   reduction

   (c) $2\,IO_4^- + 16\,H^+ + 14\,e^- \longrightarrow I_2 + 8\,H_2O$

   reduction

10. (a) C is oxidized, O is reduced.

   CH_4 is the reducing agent, O_2 is the oxidizing agent.

   (b) Mg is oxidized, Fe is reduced.

   Mg is the reducing agent, $FeCl_3$ is the oxidizing agent.

12. (a) incorrectly balanced

   $3\,MnO_2(s) + 4\,Al(s) \longrightarrow 3\,Mn(s) + 2\,Al_2O_3(s)$

   (c) correctly balanced

14. (a) $Cu + 2\,AgNO_3 \longrightarrow 2\,Ag + Cu(NO_3)_2$

   (c) $4\,HCl + O_2 \longrightarrow 2\,Cl_2 + 2\,H_2O$

   (e) $2\,KMnO_4 + 5\,CaC_2O_4 + 8\,H_2SO_4 \longrightarrow$
   $K_2SO_4 + 2\,MnSO_4 + 5\,CaSO_4 + 10\,CO_2 + 8\,H_2O$

16. (a) $6\,H^+ + ClO_3^- + 6\,I^- \longrightarrow 3\,I_2 + Cl^- + 3\,H_2O$

   (c) $2\,H_2O + 2\,MnO_4^- + 5\,SO_2 \longrightarrow$
   $4\,H^+ + 2\,Mn^{2+} + 5\,SO_4^{2-}$

   (e) $8\,H^+ + Cr_2O_7^{2-} + 3\,H_3AsO_3 \longrightarrow$
   $2\,Cr^{3+} + 3\,H_3AsO_4 + 4\,H_2O$

18. (a) $H_2O + 2\,MnO_4^- + 3\,SO_3^{2-} \longrightarrow$
   $2\,MnO_2 + 3\,SO_4^{2-} + 2\,OH^-$

   (c) $8\,Al + 3\,NO_3^- + 18\,H_2O + 5\,OH^- \longrightarrow$
   $3\,NH_3 + 8\,Al(OH)_4^-$

   (e) $2\,Al + 6\,H_2O + 2\,OH^- \longrightarrow 2\,Al(OH)_4^- + 3\,H_2$

20. (a) $5\,Mo_2O_3 + 6\,MnO_4^- + 18\,H^+ \longrightarrow$
   $10\,MoO_3 + 6\,Mn^{2+} + 9\,H_2O$

   (b) $3\,BrO^- + 2\,Cr(OH)_4^- + 2\,OH^- \longrightarrow$
   $3\,Br^- + 2\,CrO_4^{2-} + 5\,H_2O$

   (c) $3\,S_2O_3^{2-} + 8\,MnO_4^- + H_2O \longrightarrow$
   $6\,SO_4^{2-} + 8\,MnO_2 + 2\,OH^-$

24. (a) $Pb + SO_4^{2-} \longrightarrow PbSO_4 + 2\,e^-$

   $PbO_2 + SO_4^{2-} + 4\,H^+ + 2\,e^- \longrightarrow PbSO_4 + 2\,H_2O$

   (b) The first reaction is oxidation (Pb^0 is oxidized to Pb^{2+}).

   The second reaction is reduction (Pb^{4+} is reduced to Pb^{2+}).

   (c) The first reaction (oxidation) occurs at the anode of the battery.

26. Zinc is a more reactive metal than copper, so when corrosion occurs, the zinc preferentially reacts. Zinc is above hydrogen in the Activity Series of Metals; copper is below hydrogen.

28. 4.23 L CO_2; $H_2C_2O_4$ oxidized, $K_2S_2O_8$ reduced

32. 2.94 g Zn

34. 5.560 mol H_2

36. The electrons lost by the species undergoing oxidation must be gained (or attracted) by another species, which then undergoes reduction.

38. Sn^{4+} can only be an oxidizing agent.

   Sn^0 can only be a reducing agent.

   Sn^{2+} can be both oxidizing and reducing agents.

40. Equations (a) and (b) represent oxidations.

42. (a) $F_2 + 2\,Cl^- \longrightarrow 2\,F^- + Cl_2$

   (b) $Br_2 + Cl^- \longrightarrow NR$

   (c) $I_2 + Cl^- \longrightarrow NR$

   (d) $Br_2 + 2\,I^- \longrightarrow 2\,Br^- + I_2$

44. $4\,Zn + NO_3^- + 10\,H^+ \longrightarrow 4\,Zn^{2+} + NH_4^+ + 3\,H_2O$

46. (a) Pb is the anode.

   (c) oxidation occurs at Pb (anode).

   (e) Electrons flow from the lead through the wire to the silver.

CHAPTER 18

Exercises

2.

	Protons	Neutrons	Nucleons
(a) $^{128}_{52}Te$	52	76	128
(b) $^{32}_{16}S$	16	16	32

4. Its atomic number increases by one, and its mass number remains unchanged.

6. Equations for alpha decay:

   (a) $^{238}_{90}Th \longrightarrow {}^4_2He + {}^{234}_{88}Ra$

   (b) $^{239}_{94}Pu \longrightarrow {}^4_2He + {}^{235}_{92}U$

8. Equations for beta decay:

   (a) $^{28}_{13}Al \longrightarrow {}^{\,\,\,0}_{-1}e + {}^{28}_{14}Si$

   (b) $^{239}_{93}Np \longrightarrow {}^{\,\,\,0}_{-1}e + {}^{239}_{94}Pu$

10. (a) gamma-emission

   (b) alpha-emission then beta-emission

   (c) alpha-emission then gamma-emission

12. $^{32}_{15}P \longrightarrow {}^{\,\,\,0}_{-1}e + {}^{32}_{16}S$

14. (a) $^{27}_{13}Al + {}^4_2He \longrightarrow {}^{30}_{15}P + {}^1_0n$

   (c) $^{12}_{6}C + {}^2_1H \longrightarrow {}^{13}_{7}N + {}^1_0n$

16. The year 2064; 1/8 of Sr-90 remaining

18. $^{228}_{90}Th \xrightarrow{-\alpha} {}^{224}_{88}Ra \xrightarrow{-\alpha} {}^{220}_{86}Rn \xrightarrow{-\alpha} {}^{216}_{84}Po \xrightarrow{-\alpha} {}^{212}_{82}Pb$

20. (a) 5.4×10^{11} J/mol

   (b) 0.199% mass loss

21. (a) 24 protons; 27 neutrons; 24 electrons

   (c) 46 protons; 57 neutrons; 46 electrons

23. 1.50×10^{10} months

25. 61.59% neutrons by mass; 0.021% electrons by mass

27. 11,460 years old

29. (a) 0.0424 g/mol (mass defect)

   (b) 3.8×10^{12} J/mol (binding energy)

32. 0.16 mg remaining

33. 112 days

38. (a) $^{235}_{92}U + {}^1_0n \longrightarrow {}^{143}_{54}Xe + 3\,{}^1_0n + {}^{90}_{38}Sr$

   (b) $^{235}_{92}U + {}^1_0n \longrightarrow {}^{102}_{39}Y + 3\,{}^1_0n + {}^{131}_{53}I$

   (c) $^{14}_{7}N + {}^1_0n \longrightarrow {}^1_1H + {}^{14}_{6}C$

40. $^{236}_{92}U \longrightarrow {}^{90}_{38}Sr + 3\,{}^1_0n + {}^{143}_{54}Xe$

42. 7680 g

44. (a) 0.500 g left

   (c) 0.0625 g left

46. (a) 2.29×10^4 years

CHAPTER 19

Exercises

2. Lewis structures:

(a) CH_4 H:C̈:H (with H above and below)

(b) C_3H_8 H:C̈:C̈:C̈:H (with H above and below each carbon)

(c) C_5H_{12} H:C̈:C̈:C̈:C̈:C̈:H (with H above and below each carbon)

4. The same compound is represented by formulas (a), (c), and (f).

6. The formulas in Exercise 4 contain the following numbers of methyl groups:

(a) 3   (b) 2   (c) 3   (d) 4   (e) 4   (f) 3

8. hexane $CH_3CH_2CH_2CH_2CH_2CH_3$ $CH_3CH_2CH_2CHCH_3$
                                                                  |
                                                                CH_3

$CH_3CH_2CHCH_2CH_3$ $CH_3CH_2CCH_3$ $CH_3CHCHCH_3$
          | | | |
        CH_3 CH_3 CH_3 CH_3
                     (middle one has two CH_3 on the C)

10. (a) CH_3Br, one: CH_3Br

(b) C_2H_5Cl, one: C_2H_5Cl

(c) C_4H_9I, four: $CH_3CH_2CH_2CH_2I$ $CH_3CH_2CHICH_3$
         $(CH_3)_2CHCH_2I$ $(CH_3)_3CI$

(d) C_3H_6BrCl, five: $CH_3CH_2CHBrCl$ $CH_3CHClCH_2Br$
             $CH_3CHBrCH_2Cl$ $CH_2ClCH_2CH_2Br$
             $CH_3CBrClCH_3$

12. (a) 7   (b) 7   (c) 6

14. IUPAC names

(a) chloroethane

(b) 1-chloro-2-methylpropane

(c) 2-chlorobutane

(d) methylcyclopropane

(e) 2,4-dimethylpentane

16. Tertiary carbon atoms

(a)
$$CH_2CH_3$$
$$CH_3CHCHCH_3$$ (with circles around the two central CH)
$$CH_2CHCH_3$$
$$CH_3$$

(b)
$$CH_2CH_2CH_3$$
$$CH_3-C-CH_2CH_3$$
$$CH_2CH_2CH_3$$

(c)
$$CH_3CHCH_2CH_3$$ (with circle around CH)
$$CH_3-C-CH_3$$
$$CH_2CH_3$$

18. (a)
$$CH_3$$
$$CH_3CH_2CHCH_2CHCH_3$$
$$CH_2CH_3$$

(b)
$$CH_3CH_2CH_2CHCH_2CH_2CH_3$$
$$C(CH_3)_3$$

(c)
$$CH_3 \quad CH_2CH_3 \quad CHCH_3$$
$$CH_3CHCH_2CCH_2CH_2CHCHCH_2CH_3$$ (with CH_3 branch above CHCH_3)
$$CH_3 \qquad CH_3$$

(d)
$$H_3C \quad CH_2CH_3$$
$$CH_3-C-CHCH_2CH_2CH_2CH_3$$
$$CH_3$$

(e)

20. (a) 3-methyl-5-ethyloctane $CH_3CH_2CHCH_2CHCH_2CH_2CH_3$
                                                  | |
                                               CH_3 CH_2CH_3

Ethyl should be named before methyl (alphabetical order): The numbering is correct. The correct name is 5-ethyl-3-methyloctane.

(b) 3,5,5-triethylhexane $CH_3CH_2CHCH_2CCH_3$
                                          | |
                                        CH_2 CH_2CH_3 (with CH_2CH_3 above the C)
                                          |
                                        CH_3

The name is not based on the longest carbon chain (7 carbons). The correct name is 3,5-diethyl-3-methylheptane.

(c) 4,4-dimethyl-3-ethylheptane $CH_3CH_2CH-CCH_2CH_2CH_3$
                                                      | |
                                                 CH_3CH_2 CH_3 (with CH_3 above the C)

Ethyl should be named before dimethyl (alphabetical order). The correct name is 3-ethyl-4,4-dimethylheptane.

(d) 1,6-dimethylcyclohexane

(cyclohexane ring with CH_3 substituents)

The ring should be numbered to give the smallest possible values to the substituents. The correct name is 1,2-dimethylcyclohexane.

22. (a) 2-methylbutane, $CH_3CHCH_2CH_3$
                                            |
                                          CH_3

(b) 2,2 dimethylbutane, $CH_3CCH_2CH_3$
                                         |
                                       CH_3 (with CH_3 above the C)

24. Isomers are shown in (a) and (b)

26. (a) 2-bromo-2,3-dimethylbutane;
  (b) 2-bromo-2-methylbutane.

28. (a) $CH_3C(CH_3)_2CH_3$, 2,2-dimethylpropane
  (b) $CH_3CH_2CH_2CH_2CH_3$, pentane

30. (a) Three isomers:

1,2-dibromocyclopentane   1,3-dibromocyclopentane

1,1-dibromocyclopentane

(b) Seven isomers:

$CHBr_2-\overset{\underset{|}{CH_3}}{\underset{|}{CH_3}}{C}-CH_2-CH_3$

1,1-dibromo-2,2-dimethylbutane

$H_3C-\overset{\underset{|}{CH_3}}{\underset{|}{CH_3}}{C}-CH_2-CHBr_2$

1,1-dibromo-3,3-dimethylbutane

$CH_2Br-\overset{\underset{|}{CH_3}}{\underset{|}{CH_3}}{C}-CHBr-CH_3$

1,3-dibromo-2,2-dimethylbutane

$H_3C-\overset{\underset{|}{CH_3}}{\underset{|}{CH_3}}{C}-CHBr-CH_2Br$

1,2-dibromo-3,3-dimethylbutane

$H_3C-\overset{\underset{|}{CH_3}}{\underset{|}{CH_3}}{C}-CBr_2-CH_3$

2,2-dibromo-3,3-dimethylbutane

$CH_2Br-\overset{\underset{|}{CH_3}}{\underset{|}{CH_2Br}}{C}-CH_2-CH_3$

1-bromo-2-bromomethyl-2-methylbutane

$CH_2Br-\overset{\underset{|}{CH_3}}{\underset{|}{CH_3}}{C}-CH_2-CH_2Br$

1,4-dibromo-2,2-dimethylbutane

32. (a)

(b)   (c) CH_3CH_2

34. (a) chair   (b) boat

35. $C_{12}H_{26}$

36. $FCH_2CH_2F + Cl_2 \longrightarrow FCH_2CHFCl + HCl$

38. (a) elimination   (b) substitution   (c) addition

CHAPTER 20

Exercises

2. (a) propane   (b) propene   (c) propyne

H:C:C:C:H   H:C:C::C:H   H:C:C:::C:H

sp sp sp³ sp³ sp³

4. $HC\equiv C-CH_2CH_2CH_3$

6. (a) C_3H_5Cl

trans-1-chloropropene   *cis*-1-chloropropene

$CH_3CCl=CH_2$
2-chloropropene

$CH_2ClCH=CH_2$
3-chloropropene

(b) chlorocyclopropane

8. (a) $CH_2=CHCCH_2CH_3$ with CH_2CH_3 and CH_3 substituents   (c) $CH\equiv CCHCH_3$

(e) cyclohexene with CH_3

10. (a) 23 sigma bonds, 1 pi bond
  (b) 27 sigma bonds, 7 pi bonds
  (c) 20 sigma bonds, 5 pi bonds
  (d) 13 sigma bonds, 1 pi bond
  (e) 19 sigma bonds, 1 pi bond
  (f) 21 sigma bonds, 1 pi bond

12. (a) 3-phenyl-1-butyne;
  (b) 2-methyl-2-hexene;
  (c) *cis*-3,4-dimethyl-3-hexene;

14. all the pentynes, C_5H_8

1-pentyne   2-pentyne   3-methyl-1-butyne

$CH_3CH_2CH_2C\equiv CH$ $CH_3CH_2C\equiv CCH_3$ $CH_3CHC\equiv CH$ with CH_3

16. (a) 4-methyl-2-pentyne;
  (b) 4-methyl-2-hexyne;
  (c) 3-bromo-1-butyne;

18. *Cis-trans* isomers exist for (b) only.

20. (a) *trans*   (b) *trans*   (c) neither

22. (a) $CH_3CH_2CH_2CH=CH_2 + H_2O \xrightarrow{H^+} CH_3CH_2CH_2CHCH_3$
with OH below the CHCH₃

(b) $CH_3CH_2CH=CHCH_3 + HBr \longrightarrow$
$CH_3CH_2CHBrCH_2CH_3 + CH_3CH_2CH_2CHBrCH_3$

(c) $CH_2=CHCl + Br_2 \longrightarrow CH_2BrCHClBr$

(d) CH=CH₂ benzene ring +HCl ⟶ CHClCH₃ benzene ring

(e) $CH_2=CHCH_2CH_3 + KMnO_4 \xrightarrow[\text{cold}]{H_2O} CH_2CHCH_2CH_3$
with OH OH below

24. (a) $CH_3C≡CH + H_2(1\text{ mol}) \xrightarrow[\text{1 atm}]{Pt, 25°C} CH_3CH=CH_2$

(b) $CH_3C≡CCH_3 + Br_2(2\text{ mol}) \longrightarrow CH_3CBr_2CBr_2CH_3$

(c) two-step reaction:
$CH_3C≡CH + HCl \longrightarrow CH_3CCl=CH_2 \xrightarrow{HCl}$
$CH_3CCl_2CH_3$

26. When cyclopentene, [cyclopentene structure] reacts with

(a) Cl_2 the product is [cyclopentane ring with Cl, Cl] 1,2-dichlorocyclopentane

(b) HBr the product is [cyclopentane ring with Br] bromocyclopentane

(c) H_2, Pt the product is [cyclopentane ring] cyclopentane

(d) H_2O, H^+ the product is [cyclopentane ring with OH] cyclopentanol

28. (a) $CH≡C-\overset{\overset{\displaystyle CH_3}{|}}{\underset{\underset{\displaystyle CH_3}{|}}{C}}-CH_2CH_3 + Cl_2$

$\longrightarrow CH=C-C-CH_2CH_3$ with Cl, Cl, CH₃ above and CH₃ below

(b) $CH≡C-C-CH_2CH_3 + HCl$ with CH₃ above and CH₃ below

$\longrightarrow CH_2=C-C-CH_2CH_3$ with Cl, CH₃ above and CH₃ below

(c) $CH≡C-C-CH_2CH_3 + 2\,HCl$ with CH₃ above and CH₃ below

$\longrightarrow CH_3-C-C-CH_2CH_3$ with Cl, CH₃ above and Cl, CH₃ below

30. (a) *para*   (b) *meta*   (c) *para*

32. (b) [benzene ring with Cl, Cl, Cl substituents]

(d) [benzene ring with CH=CH₂]

(f) [benzene ring with NO₂]

34. (a) trichlorobenzenes

[three benzene ring structures]

1,2,3-trichlorobenzene   1,2,4-trichlorobenzene   1,3,5-trichlorobenzene

36. (a) styrene   (c) 2,4-dibromobenzoic acid
(b) *m*-nitrotoluene   (d) isopropylbenzene

38. (a) 2,3-dibromophenol
(b) 1,3,5-trichlorobenzene
(c) *m*-iodotoluene
(e) 2,4,6-tribromophenol

40. (a) [benzene ring] + CH_3CHCH_3 (with Cl below) $\xrightarrow{AlCl_3}$ [benzene ring with CHCH₃ and CH₃ above] + HCl

isopropylbenzene

(b) [benzene ring with CH₃] + $KMnO_4 \xrightarrow{H_2O}$ [benzene ring with COOH]

benzoic acid

44. (a) $CH_3\overset{+}{C}H_2$ primary

(b) $CH_3\overset{+}{C}HCH_3$ secondary

(c) $CH_3-\overset{\overset{}{+}}{\underset{\underset{\displaystyle CH_3}{|}}{C}}-CH_3$ tertiary

47. (a) $CH_3CHClCH_2CH_3 \xrightarrow{-HCl}$
$CH_3CH=CHCH_3 + CH_2=CHCH_2CH_3$

(b) $CH_2ClCH_2CH_2CH_2CH_3 \xrightarrow{-HCl} CH_2=CHCH_2CH_2CH_3$

(c) [cyclohexane with Cl] $\xrightarrow{-HCl}$ [cyclohexene]

54. (a) Four isomers:
$CH_2=CHCH_2CH_3$ 1-butene
$CH_3CH=CHCH_3$ 2-butene (cis and trans)
$CH_2=C(CH_3)_2$ 2-methyl-1-propene

(b) One isomer

$$\underset{\text{cyclopentene}}{\overset{\displaystyle HC\!\!\underset{H_2C\!-\!CH_2}{\overset{C}{\diagup}\overset{H}{\diagdown}\!CH_2}}{}}$$

56. Carbon-2 has two methyl groups on it. The configuration of two of the same groups on a carbon of a carbon–carbon double bond does not show cis-trans isomerism.

57. (a) alkyne or cycloalkene
(b) alkene or cycloalkane
(c) alkane
(d) alkyne or cycloalkene

CHAPTER 21

Exercises

2. 350,000 g/mol

4. (a) $-\!(CH_2\!-\!CCl_2)_{\overline{n}}$ (c) $-\!(CH_2\!-\!CH)_{\overline{n}}$

(b) $-\!(CH_2\!-\!CH)_{\overline{n}}$ (d) $-\!(CH_2\!-\!CH)_{\overline{n}}$
       | |
      CH_3 CN

6. $ROCH_2\!-\!CH\!-\!CH_2\!-\!CH\bullet$
              | |
             CH_3 CH_3

8. (a) ethylene $-\!(CH_2\!-\!CH_2)_{\overline{n}}$

(b) chloroethene $-\!(CH_2CHCl)_{\overline{n}}$

(c) 1-butene $-\!\left(CH_2CH\!-\!\underset{CH_2CH_3}{\overset{}{|}}\right)_{\!n}$

10. Two possible ways in which acrylonitrile can polymerize to form Orlon are:

$$-\!\left(CH_2CHCH_2CHCH_2CHCH_2CH\right)_{\!n}$$
$$\quad\;\; |\quad\;\; |\quad\;\; |\quad\;\; |$$
$$\quad CN\quad CN\quad CN\quad CN$$

$$-\!\left(CH_2CH\!-\!CHCH_2CH_2CH\!-\!CHCH_2\right)_{\!n}$$
$$\quad\; |\quad\;\; |\qquad\quad\;\; |\qquad |$$
$$\quad CN\quad CN\qquad CN\quad CN$$

12. polypropylene, $CH_2\!=\!CH$
                               |
                              CH_3

14. $-\!(CH_2\!-\!CH\!-\!CH_2\!-\!\underset{\underset{CH_3}{|}}{\overset{\overset{CH_3}{|}}{C}})_{\overline{n}}$

16. Gutta percha (all trans).

18. Yes, styrene–butadiene rubber contains carbon–carbon double bonds and is attacked by the ozone in smog, causing "age hardening" and cracking.

20. (a) synthetic natural rubber: $CH_2\!=\!CCH\!=\!CH_2$
                                                        |
                                                       CH_3

(b) neoprene rubber: $CH_2\!=\!CCl\!-\!CH\!=\!CH_2$

22. (a) Isotactic polypropylene

$$-\!\left(CH_2CHCH_2CHCH_2CHCH_2CH\right)_{\!n}$$
$$\quad\;\; |\qquad |\qquad |\qquad |$$
$$\quad CH_3\;\; CH_3\;\; CH_3\;\; CH_3$$

(b) Another form of polypropylene

$$-\!\left(CH_2CHCH_2\overset{\overset{CH_3}{|}}{C}HCH_2CHCH_2\overset{\overset{CH_3}{|}}{C}H\right)_{\!n}$$
$$\quad\;\; |\qquad\qquad\qquad |$$
$$\quad CH_3\qquad\qquad\quad CH_3$$

(other structures are possible)

24. (a) one double bond $-\!CH_2CH\!=\!CHCH_2\!-$ (b) none

26. (a) *trans*   (b) *cis*   (c) *cis*

27. Polystyrene has the highest mass percent carbon.

$-\!(CH_2\!-\!CH)_{\overline{n}}$ C_8H_8 molar mass $= 104.1$ g/mol

$$\frac{96.08 \text{ g C}}{104.1 \text{ g}} \times 100\% = 92.30\% \text{ C}$$

CHAPTER 22

Exercises

2. (a) [cyclopentane]—OH

(b) $CH_3\overset{\overset{OH}{|}}{C}CH_2CH_3$
          |
         CH_3

(c) $CH_3\overset{\overset{CH_3}{|}}{\underset{\underset{CH_3}{|}}{C}}\!-\!CHCH_2CH_2CH_3$

(d) $CH_3\overset{\overset{OH}{|}}{C}HCH_2CH_2OH$

(e) $CH_2\!-\!OH$
        |
    $CH\!-\!OH$
        |
    $CH_2\!-\!OH$

(f) $CH_3\overset{\overset{OH}{|}}{\underset{\underset{CH_3}{|}}{C}}\!-\!\overset{\overset{CH_3}{|}}{C}CH_2CH_3$

4. There are only eight isomers:

$HOCH_2\overset{\overset{CH_3}{|}}{C}HCH_2CH_2CH_3$

$CH_3\overset{\overset{CH_3}{|}}{\underset{\underset{OH}{|}}{C}}CH_2CH_2CH_3$

$CH_3\overset{\overset{CH_3}{|}}{C}HCHCH_2CH_3$
                    |
                   OH

$CH_3\overset{\overset{CH_3}{|}}{C}H\overset{\overset{OH}{|}}{C}H_2CHCH_3$

$CH_3\overset{\overset{CH_3}{|}}{C}HCH_2CH_2CH_2OH$

$HOCH_2CH_2\overset{\overset{CH_3}{|}}{C}HCH_2CH_3$

$CH_3\overset{\overset{CH_3}{|}}{C}HCHCH_2CH_3$
                    |
                   OH

$CH_3CH_2\overset{\overset{CH_3}{|}}{\underset{\underset{OH}{|}}{C}}CH_2CH_3$

6. (a) primary alcohols: d, e
   (b) secondary alcohols: a, c, d, e
   (c) tertiary alcohols: b, f
   (d) diols: d;
   (e) triols: e

8. (a) ethanol (ethyl alcohol)   (e) 3-pentanol
   (b) 2-phenylethanol   (f) 1,2-propanediol
   (c) 3-methyl-3-pentanol   (g) 4-ethyl-2-hexanol
   (d) 1-methylcyclopentanol

10. (a)

1-methylcyclopentene

   (b) $CH_3CH{=}CHCH_3$ 2-butene

   (c)   2-methyl-2-pentene

12. (a)

   1,2-dimethylcyclohexanol

   (b) $HOCH_2CH_2CH_2CCH_3$
       4,4-dimethyl-1-pentanol

   (c) $CH_3CH_2CHCH_2CH_3$
       3-pentanol

14. (a) HCOOH, methanoic acid, formic acid.
   (b) NR
   (c) CH_3COOH, ethanoic acid, acetic acid
   (d) $CH_3CH_2CCH_2CH_2CH_3$
       3-hexanone

16. (a) —OH   cyclopentanol

   (b) $HO{-}CH_2{-}CH{-}CH_2$ 2-methyl-1-propanol

   (c) CH_3OH methanol

18. (a) $CH_3CHCH_2CH_3$ 2-butanol

   (b) $CH_3CHCHCH_2CH_3$ 3-ethyl-2-pentanol

   (c) —OH   cyclopentanol

20. (a) $2\ CH_3CH_2OH + 2\ Na \longrightarrow 2\ CH_3CH_2O^-Na^+ + H_2$

   (b) $CH_3CH_2CH_2CH_2OH \xrightarrow[H_2SO_4]{K_2Cr_2O_7} CH_3CH_2CH_2C{-}OH$

   (c)

(d) $CH_3CH_2C{-}OCH_3 + NaOH \longrightarrow$

$CH_3CH_2C{-}O^-Na^+ + CH_3OH$

22. (a) Methanol, $CH_3{-}OH$

   (b) 2,2-dimethyl-1-propanol

   (c) 3,3-dimethyl-1-pentanol

24. (a) cyclopentanol   (c) 2-methyl-2-propanol
   (b) 2-propanol

26. (a)

   (b)

   (c)

28. (a) p-dihydroxybenzene (hydroquinone)
   (b) 2,4-dimethylphenol
   (c) 2,4-dinitrophenol
   (d) m-hexylphenol

30. Order of decreasing solubility in water:
   [a (highest), d, c, b (lowest)]
   (a) $CH_3CH(OH)CH(OH)CH_2OH$
   (d) $CH_3CH(OH)CH_2CH_2OH$
   (c) $CH_3CH_2CH_2CH_2OH$
   (b) $CH_3CH_2OCH_2CH_3$

32. boiling points, c < b < a.

34. Each of these molecules has about the same molar mass. 1-propanol can hydrogen bond to itself while ethyl methyl ether can not. Thus, ethyl methyl ether will have the lower boiling point.

   boiling point for ethyl methyl ether = 8°C,

   boiling point for 1-propanol = 97.4°C

36. (a) common, ethyl methyl ether;
       IUPAC, methoxyethane.
   (b) common, ethyl isobutyl ether;
       IUPAC, 1-ethoxy-2-methylpropane.
   (c) common, ethyl cyclohexyl ether;
       IUPAC, ethoxycyclohexane.

38. The six isomeric ethers of $C_5H_{12}O$ are:

$CH_3OCH_2CH_2CH_2CH_3$
methyl *n*-butyl ether
(1-methoxybutane)

$\overset{\displaystyle CH_3}{\underset{\displaystyle |}{CH_3OCHCH_2CH_3}}$
methyl sec-butyl ether
(2-methoxybutane)

$\overset{\displaystyle CH_3}{\underset{\displaystyle |}{CH_3OCH_2CHCH_3}}$
isobutyl methyl ether
(1-methoxy-2-methylpropane)

$\overset{\displaystyle CH_3}{\underset{\displaystyle |}{\underset{\displaystyle CH_3}{\overset{\displaystyle |}{CH_3OCCH_3}}}}$
t-butyl methyl ether
(2-methoxy-2-methylpropane)

$CH_3CH_2OCH_2CH_2CH_3$
ethyl *n*-propyl ether
(1-ethoxypropane)

$\overset{\displaystyle CH_3}{\underset{\displaystyle |}{CH_3CH_2OCHCH_3}}$
ethyl isopropyl ether
(2-ethoxypropane)

40. These are possible combinations of reactants to make the following ethers by the Williamson syntheses:

(a) $CH_3CH_2CH_2OCH_2CH_2CH_3$
$CH_3CH_2CH_2ONa + CH_3CH_2CH_2Cl$

(b) $\overset{\displaystyle CH_3}{\underset{\displaystyle |}{HCOCH_2CH_2CH_3}}$
$\overset{\displaystyle CH_3}{\underset{\displaystyle |}{CH_3}}$

$\overset{\displaystyle CH_3}{\underset{\displaystyle |}{HCONa + CH_3CH_2CH_2Cl}}$
$\overset{\displaystyle |}{CH_3}$ or $CH_3CH_2CH_2ONa + \overset{\displaystyle CH_3CHCH_3}{\underset{\displaystyle |}{Cl}}$

(c)

Cannot use a 2° alkyl halide in the Williamson synthesis.

42. IUPAC names
(a) 2-methylcyclopentanethiol
(b) 2,3-dimethyl-2-pentanethiol
(c) 2-propanethiol
(d) 3-ethyl-2,2,4-trimethyl-3-pentanethiol

43. The name is 4-hexylresorcinol or 4-hexyl-1,3-dihydroxybenzene.

47. Oxidation products from ethylene glycol include

$\overset{\displaystyle O}{\overset{\displaystyle \|}{HOCH_2-CH}}$ $HOCH_2COOH$ $HOOCCOOH$

$\overset{\displaystyle O\ \ O}{\overset{\displaystyle \|\ \ \|}{HC-CH}}$ $\overset{\displaystyle O}{\overset{\displaystyle \|}{HC-COOH}}$

53. Only compound (a), phenol, will react with NaOH.

(benzene ring with OH) $+ NaOH \longrightarrow$ (benzene ring with ONa) $+ H_2O$

54. Order of increasing boiling points.
1-pentanol < 1-octanol < 1,2-pentanediol
   138°C   194°C   210°C

All three compounds are alcohols. 1-pentanol has the lowest molar mass and hence the lowest boiling point. 1-octanol has a higher molar mass and therefore a higher boiling point than 1-pentanol. 1,2-pentanediol has two —OH groups and therefore forms more hydrogen bonds than the other two alcohols, which causes its higher boiling point.

CHAPTER 23

Exercises

2. (a) ethanal, acetaldehyde
(b) butanal
(c) benzaldehyde
(d) 2-chloro-5-isopropyl-benzaldehyde
(e) 3-hydroxybutanal

4. (a) butanone, methyl ethyl ketone (MEK)
(b) 3,3-dimethylbutanone, *t*-butyl methyl ketone
(c) 2,5-hexanedione
(d) 1-phenyl-2-propanone, benzyl methyl ketone

6. (a) $\overset{\displaystyle O}{\overset{\displaystyle \|}{HOCH_2CH_2C-H}}$

(b) $\overset{\displaystyle O}{\overset{\displaystyle \|}{CH_3CH_2CCHCH_2CH_3}}$
$\underset{\displaystyle |}{\underset{\displaystyle CH_3}{}}$

(c) (cyclohexanone with =O)

(d) $\overset{\displaystyle O}{\overset{\displaystyle \|}{CH_3CHCH_2CHCH_2CHC-H}}$
$\underset{\displaystyle Cl}{\underset{\displaystyle |}{}}\underset{\displaystyle Cl}{\underset{\displaystyle |}{}}\underset{\displaystyle Cl}{\underset{\displaystyle |}{}}$

(e) $\overset{\displaystyle O}{\overset{\displaystyle \|}{CH_3CH=CHCH_2C-H}}$

8. (a) 2-methylpropanal   (b) methanal
(c) 3-hexanone

10. (a) butanone   (b) 2-butanol
(c) 2-pentanone   (d) 1,2-propanediol

12. (a) 3-hydroxypentanal   (b) cyclohexanone
(c) propanone

14. (a) 1-propanol:

$CH_3CH_2CH_2OH \xrightarrow[H_2SO_4]{K_2Cr_2O_7} \overset{\displaystyle O}{\overset{\displaystyle \|}{CH_3CH_2C-H}}$ or CH_3CH_2COOH

$CH_3CH_2CH_2OH + O_2 \xrightarrow[\Delta]{Cu} \overset{\displaystyle O}{\overset{\displaystyle \|}{CH_3CH_2C-H}}$

(b) 2,3-dimethyl-2-butanol:

$\overset{\displaystyle OH}{\underset{\displaystyle |}{CH_3CHCCH_3}} + O_2 \xrightarrow[\Delta]{Ag}$ No reaction (3° alcohol)
$\underset{\displaystyle H_3C}{\underset{\displaystyle |}{}}\underset{\displaystyle CH_3}{\underset{\displaystyle |}{}}$ with either oxidizing agent

16. (a)

(b) ⁻O—C(=O)—CH₂CH₂—C(=O)—O⁻

(c) CH₃—CH₂CH₂—C(=O)—OH

18. (a) formaldehyde (methanal)   CH₂(=O)

(b) propanal   CH₃—CH₂—CH(=O)

(c) propanal   CH₃—CH₂—CH(=O)

20. (a) An aldehyde group, —C(H)=O must be present to give a positive Fehling test.

(b) The visible evidence for a positive Fehling test is the formation of brick-red Cu_2O, which precipitates during the reaction.

(c) $CH_3C(H)=O + 2 Cu^{2+} \xrightarrow[H_2O]{NaOH}$

$CH_3COONa + Cu_2O(s)$ (brick red)

22. (a) CH₃CH₂CH(CH₃)CH₂OH

(b) $CH_3CO^- \ Na^+$

(c) CH₃CH(OH)CH₃

(d) CH₃CH₂—CH(CH₂CH₃)—CO⁻ NH₄⁺

24. (a) HOCH₂COOH

(b) CH₃CH₂CH₂CH₂—C(OH)(CH₃)—COOH

(c) CH₃—C(CH₃)(CH₃)—CH(OH)—COOH

26. (a) 3-pentanone:

$2\ CH_3CH_2CCH_2CH_3 \xrightarrow{\text{dilute NaOH}} CH_3CH_2C(OH)(CH_2CH_3)—CH(CH_3)—CCH_2CH_3$ (with =O)

(b) propanal:

$2\ CH_3CH_2C(H)=O \xrightarrow{\text{dilute NaOH}} CH_3CH_2CH(OH)CH(CH_3)C(H)=O$

28. (a) $CH_3CH_2C(H)(OH)=O + CH_3CH_2CH_2OH \xrightleftharpoons{\text{dry HCl}}$

$CH_3CH_2C(H)—OCH_2CH_2CH_3 + H_2O$

(b) cyclohexanone $+ CH_3OH \xrightleftharpoons{H^+}$ 1-methoxycyclohexanol (OH, OCH₃)

(c) $CH_3CH_2CH_2CH(OCH_3)_2 \xrightleftharpoons[H^+]{H_2O}$

$CH_3CH_2CH_2C(H)=O + 2\ CH_3OH$

30. (a) (phenyl)—C(H)=O $+ HCN \xrightarrow{OH^-}$ (phenyl)—CH(OH)—CN

(b) (phenyl)—CH(OH)—CN $+ H_2O \xrightarrow{H^+}$ (phenyl)—CH(OH)—COOH

(c) (phenyl)—CH(OH)—COOH $\xrightarrow[H_2SO_4]{K_2Cr_2O_7}$ (phenyl)—C(=O)—COOH

31. tetrahydrofuran-2-ol (cyclic O, H, OH)

33. Four aldol condensation products from a mixture of ethanal (E) and propanal (P) are possible: EE PP EP and PE.

EE is $CH_3CHCH_2C(=O)—H$ (OH)   PP is $CH_3CH_2CHCHC(=O)—H$ (CH₃, OH)

EP is $CH_3CHCHC(=O)—H$ (CH₃, OH)   PE is $CH_3CH_2CHCH_2C(=O)—H$ (OH)

38. Pyruvic acid is changed to lactic acid by a reduction reaction.

39. Alcohols that should be oxidized to give the ketones listed.
   (a) 3-pentanol
   (b) 2-butanol
   (c) 4-phenyl-2-butanol

CHAPTER 24

Exercises

2. (a) *m*-toluic acid   (c) butyric acid
   (b) β-chloropropionic acid   (d) glutaric acid

4. (a) propanoic acid
  (b) 2,4-dimethylpentanoic acid
  (c) butanedioic acid
  (d) 2-hydroxybutanoic acid

6. (a) HOOCCH₂COOH

  (b) CH_3CH_2—$\overset{\overset{\displaystyle OH}{|}}{CH}$—$CH_2$—$\overset{\overset{\displaystyle CH_2CH_3}{|}}{CH}$—$COOH$

  (c) CH_3—$\overset{\overset{\displaystyle Cl}{|}}{CH}$—$COOH$

  (d)

  (e) HOOC—⟨ ⟩—COOH

  (f) CH₃CH₂COOH

  (g) $CH_3CH_2CH_2$—$\overset{\overset{\displaystyle O}{\|}}{C}$$O^-$ Li$^+$

8. (a) 3-bromobutanoic acid   (b) 2-hydroxypropanoic acid
  (c) 3-ethylpentanoic acid

10. Decreasing pH means increasing acidity:

  KOH > NH₃ > KBr > ⟨OH⟩ > HCOOH > HBr

  decreasing pH →

12. (a) ethanoic acid   (c) ethanoic acid
  (b) propanoic acid   (d) malonic acid

14. (a) methyl methanoate   methyl formate
  (b) propyl benzoate   propyl benzoate
  (c) ethyl propanoate   ethyl propionate

16. (a) $CH_3\overset{\overset{\displaystyle O}{\|}}{C}$—$OCH_2CH_2CH_3$ (b) ⟨ ⟩—$\overset{\overset{\displaystyle O}{\|}}{C}$—$OCH_3$

  (c) $CH_3CH_2CH_2CH_2CH_2\overset{\overset{\displaystyle O}{\|}}{C}$—$OCH_2CH_3$

18. (a) Compounds are different: methyl benzoate and phenyl acetate
  (b) Compounds are different: methyl acetate and methyl propanoate
  (c) Compounds are the same

20. (a) methanol and propanoic acid: $CH_3CH_2\overset{\overset{\displaystyle O}{\|}}{C}$—$OCH_3$

  (b) 1-octanol and acetic acid: $CH_3\overset{\overset{\displaystyle O}{\|}}{C}$—$OCH_2(CH_2)_6CH_3$

  (c) ethanol and butanoic acid: $CH_3CH_2CH_2\overset{\overset{\displaystyle O}{\|}}{C}$—$OCH_2CH_3$

22. (a) isopropyl formate: $CH_3\overset{\overset{\displaystyle }{}}{\underset{\underset{\displaystyle OH}{|}}{CH}}CH_3$ + HCOOH

(b) diethyl adipate: CH_3CH_2OH + $\underset{\underset{\displaystyle (CH_2)_4}{|}}{\overset{\overset{\displaystyle COOH}{|}}{}}$ COOH

(c) benzyl benzoate: ⟨ ⟩—CH₂OH + ⟨ ⟩—COOH

24. (a) ⟨ ⟩—$\overset{\overset{\displaystyle O}{\|}}{C}$$O^-$ Na$^+$

  sodium benzoate

  (b) CH₃CH₂CH₂COOH

  butanoic acid

  (c) CH_3CH_2—$\overset{\overset{\displaystyle O}{\|}}{C}$$O^-$ Na$^+$

  sodium propanoate

26. (a) CH₃CH₂COOH

  (b) CH_3—$\overset{\overset{\displaystyle O}{\|}}{C}$—$OCH_2CH_2CH_3$

  (c) H—$\overset{\overset{\displaystyle O}{\|}}{C}$—$OCH_2CH_3$

28. (a) Benzoic acid and ethyl benzoate: benzoic acid is an odorless solid; ethyl benzoate is a fragrant liquid.
  (b) Succinic acid and fumaric acid: fumaric acid has a carbon–carbon double bond and will readily add and decolorize bromine; succinic acid will not decolorize bromine.

30. (a) $CH_3\overset{\overset{\displaystyle CH_3}{|}}{CH}CH_2COOH$ + SOCl₂ ⟶

  $CH_3\overset{\overset{\displaystyle CH_3}{|}}{CH}CH_2\overset{\overset{\displaystyle O}{\|}}{C}Cl$ + SO₂ + HCl

  (b) $CH_3\overset{\overset{\displaystyle CH_3}{|}}{CH}CH_2COOH$ + CH₃CH₂CH₂OH ⟶

  $CH_3\overset{\overset{\displaystyle CH_3}{|}}{CH}CH_2\overset{\overset{\displaystyle O}{\|}}{C}OCH_2CH_2CH_3$ + H₂O

32. (a) $CH_3\overset{\overset{\displaystyle OH}{|}}{CH}CH_3$ + CH₃CH₂COOH

  (b) CH₃OH + $CH_3CH_2CH_2CH_2CH_2$—$\overset{\overset{\displaystyle O}{\|}}{C}$$O^-$ Na$^+$

34. (a) $CH_3CH_2\overset{\overset{\displaystyle O}{\|}}{C}OCH_2CH_3$ + KOH $\xrightarrow[\Delta]{H_2O}$

  $CH_3CH_2\overset{\overset{\displaystyle O}{\|}}{C}O^-K^+$ + CH₃CH₂OH

  (b) $CH_3CH_2CH_2\overset{\overset{\displaystyle O}{\|}}{C}OCH_2CH_2CH_3$ + H₂O $\xrightarrow{HCl}$

  $CH_3CH_2CH_2\overset{\overset{\displaystyle O}{\|}}{C}OH$ + CH₃CH₂CH₂OH

36. (a) $CH_3(CH_2)_{16}COOH$

(b) $\overset{\displaystyle CH_2OH}{\underset{\displaystyle CH_2OH}{\overset{|}{\underset{|}{CHOH}}}}$ + 3 $CH_3(CH_2)_{10}CH_2OH$

(c) $\overset{\displaystyle CH_2OH}{\underset{\displaystyle CH_2OH}{\overset{|}{\underset{|}{CHOH}}}}$ + 3 $CH_3(CH_2)_{14}COOH$

38.

40. Sodium lauryl sulfate would be more effective as a detergent in hard water than sodium propyl sulfate because the hydrocarbon chain is only three carbons long in the latter, not long enough to dissolve grease well.

42. Only (c), $CH_3(CH_2)_{10}CH_2O(CH_2CH_2O)_7CH_2CH_2OH$, would be a good detergent in water. It is nonionic.

44. (a) $CH_3O-\overset{\displaystyle O}{\overset{\|}{\underset{\underset{\displaystyle OCH_3}{|}}{P}}}-OCH_3$ + 3 H_2O

(b) $CH_3O-\overset{\displaystyle O}{\overset{\|}{\underset{\underset{\displaystyle OH}{|}}{P}}}-\overset{\displaystyle CH_3}{\overset{|}{OCHCH_2CH_3}}$

47. The ester is propyl propanoate

$CH_3CH_2\underset{\underset{\displaystyle O}{\|}}{C}-OCH_2CH_2CH_3$

Compound A is an acid; B is an alcohol. If B is oxidized to an acid which is the same as A then A and B both have the same carbon structure, three carbon atoms each. The acid A must be propanoic acid, CH_3CH_2COOH. The alcohol can be 1-propanol or 2-propanol. Only 1-propanol can be oxidized to propanoic acid which is the same as compound A.

53. $\overset{\displaystyle CH_2O-\overset{\overset{\displaystyle O}{\|}}{C}(CH_2)_{10}CH_3}{\underset{\displaystyle CH_2O-\overset{\overset{\displaystyle O}{\|}}{C}(CH_2)_7CH=CH(CH_2)_7CH_3}{\overset{|}{\underset{|}{CHO-\overset{\overset{\displaystyle O}{\|}}{C}(CH_2)_{14}CH_3}}}}$

There would be two other triacylglycerols containing all three of these acids. Each of the three acids can be at the middle position.

60. The statement is false. When methyl propanoate is hydrolyzed, propanoic acid and methanol are formed.

CHAPTER 25

Exercises

2. (a) $CH_3CH_2CH_2CH_2-\overset{\displaystyle O}{\overset{\|}{C}}-\overset{\displaystyle CH_3}{\overset{|}{N}}-CH_3$

(b) $CH_3-\overset{\displaystyle O}{\overset{\|}{C}}-NH_2$

(c) $CH_3CH_2-\overset{\displaystyle CH_3}{\overset{|}{CH}}-\overset{\displaystyle CH_3}{\overset{|}{CH}}-\overset{\displaystyle O}{\overset{\|}{C}}-NH_2$

(d) $\langle\!\!\!\bigcirc\!\!\!\rangle-\overset{\displaystyle O}{\overset{\|}{C}}-NH-CH_2CH_3$

4. (a) benzamide
   (b) *N,N*-dibutylethanamide
   (c) common, *N*-methylacetamide, IUPAC, *N*-methylethanamide

6. water solubility: (c) < (a) < (b)

8.

10. Organic products

(a) $CH_3\overset{\displaystyle O}{\overset{\|}{C}}-N(CH_2CH_3)_2$

(b) $\langle\!\!\!\bigcirc\!\!\!\rangle\!\!-CH_2COOH$ + $CH_3\overset{+}{N}H_2CH_3$

(c) $CH_3\overset{\displaystyle CH_3}{\overset{|}{CH}}CH_2\overset{\displaystyle O}{\overset{\|}{C}}-NHCH_3$

12. (a) $CH_3\overset{\displaystyle O}{\overset{\|}{C}}-NHCH_2CH_3$ + NaOH

(b) $CH_3CH_2\overset{\displaystyle O}{\overset{\|}{C}}-OH$ + CH_3NHCH_3

(c) $CH_3\overset{\displaystyle O}{\overset{\|}{C}}-NH_2$ + HCl + H_2O

14. Structures of amines with formula C_3H_9N:

| $1°$ | $1°$ | $2°$ | $3°$ |

16. (a) secondary   (c) secondary
     (b) tertiary   (d) tertiary

18. The isopropylamine solution in 1.0 *M* KOH would have the more objectionable odor because it would be in the form of the free amine, while in the acid solution the amine would form a salt that will have little or no odor.

20. (a) *N*-ethylaniline   (d) ethylammonium bromide
     (b) 2-butanamine   (e) pyridine
     (c) diphenylamine   (f) *N*-ethylacetamide

22. (a) $CH_3CH_2CH_2CH_2NCH_2CH_2CH_3$
                           $CH_2CH_2CH_2CH_3$

(b)

(c) $CH_3CH_2NH_3^+Cl^-$

(d) $CH_3CH_2CH_2CHCH_2OH$
                    NH_2

(e) $CH_3CH_2CH_2C - CH - NH -$ 〈benzene ring〉
                 $CH_3 \; CH_3$

(f) $H_2NCH_2CH_2NH_2$

24. (a) 2-propanamine
     (b) *N*-ethylethanamine
     (c) ethanamide

26. (a) $(CH_3)_3N$, trimethylamine (*N,N*-dimethylmethanamine)

(b) H_3C〈ring〉NH_2 3,4-dimethylaniline
     H_3C

(c) $CH_3CH_2NHCH_3$, *N*-methylethanamine
                         (ethylmethylamine)

28. (a) Organic molecule A
                CH_3
       $H_3C - CH - CH_2 - NH_2$

       2-methyl-1-propanamine
     Organic molecule B
                CH_3
       $H_3C - CH - CH_2 - NH_3^+OH^-$

       2-methyl-1-propanammonium hydeoxide

30. (a) neither
     (b) acid
     (c) neither
     (d) base
     (e) base
     (f) acid

CHAPTER 26

Exercises

2. $-92°$

4. (b), (c) and (d) are chiral

6. (a) 0   (b) 2   (c) 1   (d) 3

8. (a) $CH_3CHCHCH_2CHCH_3$, optically active
            CH_3 CH_3
                      CH_3

(b) $CH_2ICH_2CH_2CH_2CH_2CH_3$

(c) $CH_3CH_2CHCH_2CH_2CH_3$
            CH_2CH_3

(d) $CH_3CHICHClCH_2CH_2CH_3$, optically active

10. (a) 2   (b) 1   (c) 2

12.

14. The two projection formulas (A) and (B) are the same compound, for it takes two changes to make (B) identical to (A).

16. (+)-alanine $H_2N - \overset{COOH}{\underset{CH_3}{|}} - H$ (−)-alanine $H - \overset{COOH}{\underset{CH_3}{|}} - NH_2$

(+)-alanine (b, c, d); (−)-alanine (a, e, f).

18.

20.

22. 8 isomers

24. (a) 2,3-dichlorobutane

enantiomers   meso compound

(b) 2,4-dibromopentane

enantiomers   meso compound

(c) 3-hexanol

enantiomers

26. All the stereoisomers of 3,4-dichloro-2-methylpentane:

Compounds A and B and C and D are pairs of enantiomers. There are no meso compounds. Pairs of diastereomers are A and C, A and D, B and C, and B and D.

28. The four stereoisomers of 2-chloro-3-hexene:

The two *cis* compounds are enantiomers and the two trans compounds are enantiomers.

30. Assume (+)-2-chlorobutane is

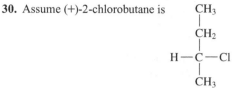

All possible isomers formed when (+)-2-chlorobutane is further chlorinated to dichlorobutane are

Compounds A, B, and E would be optically active: C does not have a chiral carbon atom; D is a meso compound.

32. If 1-chlorobutane and 2-chlorobutane were obtained by chlorinating butane, and then distilled, they would be separated into the two fractions, because their boiling points are different. 1-Chlorobutane has no chiral carbon, so would not be optically active. 2-Chlorobutane would exist as a racemic mixture (equal quantities of enantiomers) because substitution of Cl for H on carbon 2 gives equal amounts of the two enantiomers. Distillation would not separate the enantiomers because their boiling points are identical. The optical rotation of the two enantiomers of the 2-chlorobutane fraction would exactly cancel and, thus, would not show optical activity.

34. Compound (d) is meso.

36. (a) diastereomers (b) enantiomers (c) diastereomers

38. (a)   (CH₃)₂CHCH₂— ⬡ —C—COOH   chiral carbon

(b) enantiomer.

(CH₃)₂CHCH₂— ⬡ —C—COOH

40. (a) (+)–carvone (from caraway seeds)   chiral carbon

(b) The enantiomer has the mirror-image arrangement of groups around the chiral carbon.

enantiomer of (+)–carvone (from spearmint)

42.

44. Stereoisomer structures

(a) 2-bromo-3-chlorobutane

(b) 2,3,4-trichloro-1-pentanol

There are no meso compounds.

47.

The similarity is that the chiral carbon in each compound is bonded to an NH_2, a COOH, and an H group.

CHAPTER 27

Exercises

2.

4. L-Aldopentose. The chiral carbon furthest from the aldehyde group has the —OH on the left in the Fischer projection formula.

6. A common carbohydrate with the formula, $C_6H_{12}O_6$, can be either

aldohexose   ketohexose

but not an aldopentose. The correct answer is the ketohexose since it has three chiral carbons.

8.

10. (a) An epimer differs at one chiral carbon. For example,

(b) The enantiomer of D-fructose is

(c) A diastereomer is any stereoisomer that is not a mirror image. For example,

12. Since D-galactose and D-mannose are diasteroemers, they are not mirror-image stereoisomers. They may differ at one or more chiral carbons but they cannot be enantiomers.

14. (a) (b) (c)

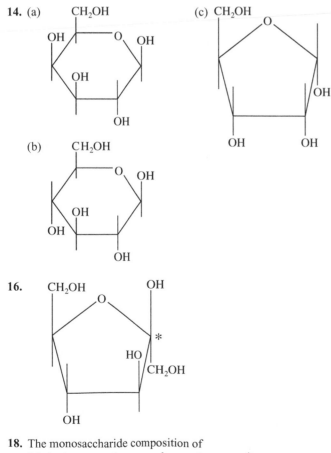

16.

18. The monosaccharide composition of
  (a) lactose: one glucose and one galactose unit
  (b) amylopectin: many glucose units
  (c) cellulose: many glucose units
  (d) sucrose: one glucose and one fructose unit

20. Both maltose and isomaltose are disaccharides composed of two glucose units. The glucose units in maltose are linked by an α-1,4-glycosidic bond while the glucose units of isomaltose are linked by an α-1,6-glycosidic bond.

22. Both maltose and isomaltose will show mutarotation. Both disaccharides contain a hemiacetal structure that will open, allowing mutarotation.

24. maltose,   lactose,

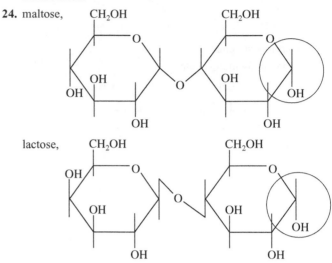

26. maltose, α-D-glucopyranosyl-(1,4)-α-D-glucopyranose; lactose, β-D-galactopyranosyl-(1,4)-α-D-glucopyranose.

28. (a) (b)

30.

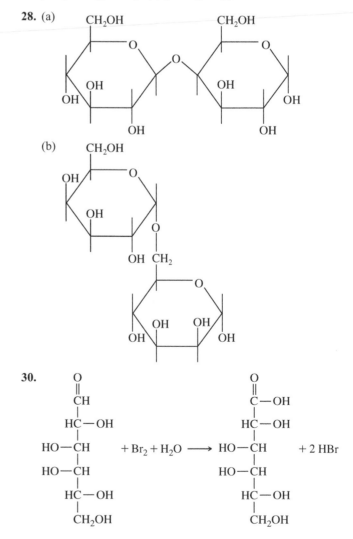

32.

CH₂OH
HO—C—H
HO—C—H
H—C—OH
H—C—OH
CH₂OH

34.

COOH
H—C—OH
H—C—OH
H—C—OH
COOH

36. (a) D-Ribose and D-ribulose share the same structure except that D-ribose is an aldose while D-ribulose is a ketose (and, thus, has one less chiral carbon).

(b) Maltose and isomaltose share the same structure except that maltose contains a (1,4) acetal bond while isomaltose contains a (1,6) acetal bond.

(c) Cellulose and amylose share the same structure except that cellulose has β-anomer glucose units while amylose has α-anomer glucose units.

38.

cellobiose

40.

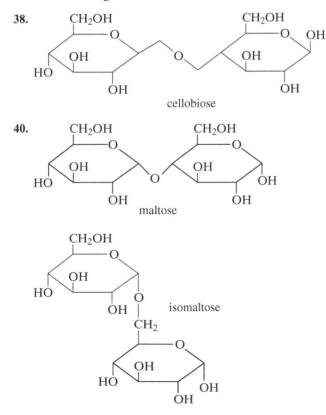

maltose

isomaltose

41. Glucose is called blood sugar because it is the most abundant carbohydrate in the blood and is carried by the bloodstream to all parts of the body.

48. A nonreducing disaccharide composed of two molecules of α-D-galactopyranose can have no hemiacetal structures. Thus, the hemiacetal structure of one α-D-galactopyranose must be used to form the glycosidic link to the hemiacetal structure of the other α-D-galactopyranose unit forming an acetal structure.

51. No, the classmate should not be believed. Although D-glucose and D-mannose are related as epimers, it is pairs of enantiomers that have equal and opposite optical rotation.

CHAPTER 28

Exercises

2.

$$CH_2O-\overset{O}{\overset{\|}{C}}-(CH_2)_7-CH=CH-CH_2-CH=CH-CH_2-CH=CH-CH_2CH_3$$
CHOH
CH₂OH

(Linolenic acid can be located at any one of the hydroxyls of glycerol.)

$$CH_2O-\overset{O}{\overset{\|}{C}}-(CH_2)_7-CH=CH-CH_2-CH=CH-CH_2-CH=CH-CH_2CH_3$$
CHOH
$$CH_2O-\overset{O}{\overset{\|}{C}}-(CH_2)_7-CH=CH-CH_2-CH=CH-CH_2-CH=CH-CH_2CH_3$$

(Linolenic acid can be located at any two of the three hydroxyls on glycerol.)

4.

$$CH_2O-\overset{O}{\overset{\|}{C}}(CH_2)_{14}CH_3 \qquad \text{palmitic acid}$$
$$CHO-\overset{O}{\overset{\|}{C}}(CH_2)_{14}CH_3 \qquad \text{palmitic acid}$$
$$CH_2O-\overset{O}{\overset{\|}{C}}(CH_2)_7CH=CH(CH_2)_7CH_3 \quad \text{oleic acid}$$

There is one other possible triacylglycerol with the same components.

6. No. A phospholipid contains functional groups that attract water (e.g., phosphate) and this lipid is less hydrophobic than a triacylglycerol.

8.
$$2\ CH_3(CH_2)_{16}COOH\ +\ \begin{array}{l}CH_2OH\\ CHOH\\ CH_2OH\end{array}\ \longrightarrow$$

$$CH_2O-\overset{O}{\overset{\|}{C}}(CH_2)_{16}CH_3$$
CHOH
$$CH_2O-\overset{O}{\overset{\|}{C}}(CH_2)_{16}CH_3 \qquad +\ 2\ H_2O$$

the stearic acids may be connected at any two of the three glycerol hydroxyl groups

10. $CH_3(CH_2)_{14}\overset{\overset{\displaystyle O}{\|}}{C}-O-CH_2(CH_2)_{28}CH_3$

12.
$$\begin{array}{l} CH_2O-\overset{\overset{\displaystyle O}{\|}}{C}-(CH_2)_7\overset{CH=CH}{\diagup\diagdown}(CH_2)_7-CH_3 \\ CHOH \\ CH_2OH \end{array}$$

(The oleic acid may be located at any one of the three hydroxyls on glycerol.)

14.
$$\begin{array}{l} CH_2O-\overset{\overset{\displaystyle O}{\|}}{C}(CH_2)_{16}CH_3 \\ CHO-\overset{\overset{\displaystyle O}{\|}}{C}(CH_2)_{16}CH_3 \\ CH_2O-\overset{\overset{\displaystyle O}{\|}}{\underset{\underset{\displaystyle O^-}{|}}{P}}-OCH_2CH_2\overset{\overset{\displaystyle CH_3}{|}}{\underset{\underset{\displaystyle CH_3}{|}}{N^+}}-CH_3 \end{array}$$

16.
$$\begin{array}{l} \overset{\overset{\displaystyle OH}{|}}{CHCH}=CH(CH_2)_{12}CH_3 \\ CHNH-\overset{\overset{\displaystyle O}{\|}}{C}(CH_2)_{16}CH_3 \\ CH_2O-\overset{\overset{\displaystyle O}{\|}}{\underset{\underset{\displaystyle O^-}{|}}{P}}-OCH_2CH_2\overset{+}{N}H_3 \end{array}$$

18.
$$\begin{array}{l} CH_2O-\overset{\overset{\displaystyle O}{\|}}{C}(CH_2)_{14}CH_3 \\ CHO-\overset{\overset{\displaystyle O}{\|}}{C}(CH_2)_{14}CH_3 \\ CH_2O-\overset{\overset{\displaystyle O}{\|}}{C}(CH_2)_{14}CH_3 \end{array}$$

20.
$$\begin{array}{l} CH_2O-\overset{\overset{\displaystyle O}{\|}}{C}(CH_2)_{14}CH_3 \\ CHO-\overset{\overset{\displaystyle O}{\|}}{C}(CH_2)_{14}CH_3 \\ CH_2O-\overset{\overset{\displaystyle O}{\|}}{\underset{\underset{\displaystyle O^-}{|}}{P}}-OCH_2CH_2\overset{+}{N}H_3 \end{array}$$

22. HDL (high density lipoprotein) differs from LDL (low density lipoprotein) in that

(a) LDL has a lower density than HDL.

(b) LDL delivers cholesterol to peripheral tissues while HDL scavenges cholesterol and returns it to the liver.

(c) LDL is often described as "bad" cholesterol because it causes atherosclerosis while HDL is described as "good" cholesterol because it aids in removing cholesterol from the body.

24. (a) Both compounds have two long hydrophobic chains.

(b) For both compounds, the primary alcohol can react further with either acids (to form esters) or sugars (to form acetals).

26. Phosphate ion will move from a region of low concentration to a region of high concentration as it moves from a 0.1 M solution across a membrane to 0.5 M solution. This process requires energy and can be accomplished by active transport.

28. Prostaglandins, thromboxanes, or prostacyclins.

30. (a) triacylglycerol (triglyceride); palmitic acid, oleic acid, linoleic acid

(b) glycolipid; stearic acid

32. Diacylglycerol (diglyceride). A diacylglycerol contains only glycerol and two fatty acids (linked to the glycerol by ester bonds).

36. This meal is changed by increasing the fat content from 10 grams to 15 grams, an increase of 5 grams. Since each gram of fat yields an average of 9.5 Cal, an increase of 5 grams equates to an increase of 47.5 Cal. Thus, the meal will now contain 282 Cal.

38. $CH_3(CH_2)_7CH=CH(CH_2)_7COOH$
oleic acid or 9-octadeceneoic acid

CHAPTER 29

Exercises

2.
$$\begin{array}{l} NH_2-\overset{\overset{\displaystyle COOH}{|}}{\underset{\underset{\displaystyle CH_2}{|}}{C}}-H \qquad H-\overset{\overset{\displaystyle COOH}{|}}{\underset{\underset{\displaystyle CH_2}{|}}{C}}-NH_2 \end{array}$$

　　L-phenylalanine　　　　　　D-phenylalanine

The benzene ring causes phenylalanine to be hydrophobic and, thus, this amino acid prefers to be inside proteins and away from water.

4. Polar, uncharged. The amide functional group causes the amino acid side chain to be polar but uncharged.

6. Gln = glutamine. $NH_2\overset{\overset{\displaystyle O}{\|}}{C}CH_2CH_2\overset{\overset{\displaystyle}{}}{\underset{\underset{\displaystyle \overset{+}{N}H_3}{|}}{C}}HCOO^-$

8. For tryptophan:

(a) Zwitterion formula

(b) formula in 0.1 M H_2SO_4

(c) formula in 0.1 M NaOH

10.

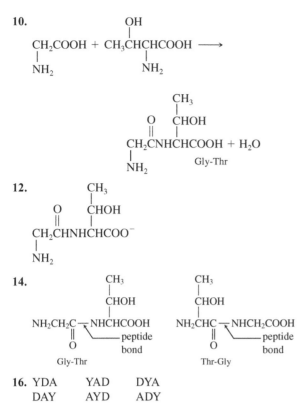

12.

14.

Gly-Thr   Thr-Gly

16. YDA   YAD   DYA
DAY   AYD   ADY

18. Hydrolysis breaks the peptide bonds. One water molecule will react with each peptide bond; a hydrogen atom attaches to the nitrogen to complete the amino group and an —OH group attaches to the carboxyl carbon. The tripeptide Ala-Glu-Tyr will hydrolyze to yield the following:

20.

22.

24. Epidermal growth factor (EGF) has a regulatory function. Cells change their metabolism in response to EGF. This protein signals cells to grow and differentiate.

26. (a) The ribbon structure of the epidermal growth factors shows four strands of beta-pleated sheet.
(b) The space-filling model shows the epidermal growth factor (EGF) to be a compact protein. EGF is a globular protein.

28. The tripeptide, Gly-Ser-Asp, will
(a) react with $CuSO_4$ (biuret test) to give a violet color. The tripeptide has the required two peptide bonds.
(b) not react to give a positive xanthoproteic test because there are no benzene rings in this tripeptide.
(c) react with ninhydrin to give a blue solution.

30. $6.8 \times 10^4 \; \frac{g}{mole}$ (molar mass of hemoglobin)

32. Phe-Ala-Ala-Leu-Phe-Gly-Tyr

34. This newly discovered protein is probably not a structural-support protein because it is globular in shape and has secondary structure (beta-pleated sheet) at its core. Thus, it is more likely to be a binding protein.

36. A domain is a compact piece of protein structure of about 20,000 g/mole. The newly discovered protein with two domains is more likely to have a molar mass between 40,000 and 60,000 g/mole.

38. The silk protein, fibroin, has a high percentage of the secondary structure, beta-pleated sheet. This secondary structure is like a sheet of paper in that it is flexible but not stretchable. Thus, fibroin is not easily stretched.

39. The amino acid sequence of the nonapeptide is
Arg-Pro-Pro-Gly-Phe-Ser-Pro-Phe-Arg

43. The stereoisomers of threonine:

46. thirty-nine dipeptides

CHAPTER 30

Exercises

2. $4 \times 10^{-5} \; M/s$

4. (a) $0.0041 \; M/min$ (b) $4100 \; \mu M/min$

6. Approximately $3.1 \times 10^{-3} \; M/min$

8. Approximately $3.1 \; mM/min$

10. $104/sec$

12. 1.1×10^3 reactants converted to products by three pepsin molecules

14. The hexokinase active site attracts both glucose and ATP. By bringing the two reactants together, the reaction is made quicker by proximity catalysis.

16. For proximity catalysis, active site attraction brings the reactants together; for the strain hypothesis, active site attraction forces the reactant shape to change toward the product shape.

18. Very low pH destroys the natural three-dimensional enzyme shape (denaturation) and the enzyme becomes inactive.

20. Enzyme A: At very large (substrate), Enzyme A has a much larger velocity than Enzyme B. Thus, Enzyme A has a larger V_{max}.

22. Since pepsin is produced in the stomach, this enzyme probably has a pH optimum around 2. When pepsin moves into the small intestine (pH = 7), the enzyme's activity probably decreases.

24. Trypsin probably has a pH optimum around 7 so the enzyme will be optimally active in its natural environment, the small intestine.

26. Condition B is the same as Condition A except that the activation energy is lower (15 kcal/mole for Condition B versus 20 kcal/mole for Condition A). Condition B's lower activation energy will allow for a faster reaction.

28. Although ribose has four hydroxyls that could react, only the hydroxyl at C-2 does react with ATP. The enzyme must orient ribose so that only the C-2 hydroxyl reacts. This is an example of the productive binding hypothesis.

30. Glutamine is a starting material [reactant] for the liver metabolic pathway that produces urea. Thus, glutamine control of this pathway must be "feedforward." Since an increase in glutamine concentration causes the metabolic pathway to speed up, this control must be feedforward activation.

32. Blood clots in the brain are the major cause of strokes. Specific proteases are used to dissolve these blood clots to alleviate the cause of strokes.

34. Amylase is present in laundry detergents to digest starchy residues.

36. Sucrase converts sucrose to a mixture of glucose and fructose. Since fructose is sweeter than sucrose, a sweeter solution is created.

37. The turnover number measures the number of substrate molecules converted to product by one enzyme molecule under optimum conditions. Chymotrypsin can convert one glycine-containing substance to product every 20 seconds while the enzyme can convert 200 L-tyrosine-containing substrates to products each second. Chymotrypsin is a much more efficient catalyst for the L-tyrosine-containing substrate.

CHAPTER 31

Exercises

2.

guanine

4. (a) G, guanosine
   (b) GMP, guanosine-5′-monophosphate
   (c) dGDP, deoxyguanosine-5′-diphosphate
   (d) CTP, cytidine-5′-triphosphate

6. (a) U

   (b) UMP

   (c) CTP

(d) dTMP

8. (a) deoxyguanosine
   (b) thymidine-2′-monophosphate

10.

12. Two different small nucleic acids can be made from AMP and UMP.

or

14.

16. mRNA provides the information or "message" that dictates the protein amino acid sequence (the 1° structure).

18. Transcription is the process of making RNA using a DNA template, whereas translation is a process for making protein using an mRNA template.

20. Both mRNA and rRNA can be found in the ribosomes. rRNA serves as part of the ribosome structure, whereas mRNA serves as a template for protein synthesis.

22. (a) CGAAUCUGGACU
(b) Arg-Ile-Trp-Thr

24. Translation makes a polymer of amino acids by forming amide bonds to connect the amino acids to each other. The amide bond combines an amine with a carboxylic acid.

26. Translation initiation occurs when the ribosome reaches a special AUG or GUG codon along the mRNA. Since there is commonly more than one AUG or GUG codon, the ribosome must use other information to choose the special AUG or GUG. This codon is the starting point for protein synthesis and is bound by either a special tRNA carrying *N*-formyl methionine (in procaryotes) or a tRNA carrying methionine (in eucaryotes).

28. (a) GCG   (c) CUA
(b) UGU   (d) AAG

30. Both snRNA and snoRNA are small RNAs that aid posttranscriptional modification of RNA in the nucleus. snoRNA specifically helps modify rRNA in the nucleolus while snRNA is found in other parts of the nucleus and modifies other RNA.

32. (b) protein engineering. This science works to modify proteins by changing individual amino acids in the protein's primary structure.

These specific changes are caused by selective changes in the genetic code.

34. The original mRNA sequence codes for the amino acids ... Val-Gln-Lys ... The mutation changes the second codon to a termination or nonsense codon UAA. The protein will end at this point and may cause a major disruption of the protein function.

36. "Nonsense" means the codon does not code for an amino acid. Instead, this codon causes translation to stop. (It is also known as a termination codon.)

38. The genome is the sum of all hereditary material contained in a cell. The genome contains many genes. Each gene is a segment of DNA that controls the formation of a molecule of RNA.

39. This isomer of thymine will more easily (strongly) H-bond to guanine rather than form its normal base pair with adenine.

isomer of thymine   guanine

CHAPTER 32

Exercises

2. (a) 132 g   (b) 1464 mg   (c) 31.5 mg

4. (a) fat, 333 kcal; carbohydrate, 100 kcal
(b) 19% of the teacher's EER

6. 20% of the iron DRI.

8. 31% of the riboflavin DRI.

10. protein (70 g), > 100% of the DRI; carbohydrate (25 g), 18% of the DRI (except for infants); fat (37 g), DRI not determined (except for infants).

12. major elements: Na, K , Mg, Ca total major element mass: 1458 mg (1.458 g).

14. When food enters the stomach, it triggers the release of gastric juice that contains, among other things, hydrochloric acid and the digestive enzymes pepsin and lipase. The main digestive function of the stomach is the partial digestion of proteins aided by the enzyme pepsin.

16. The three classes of nutrients that commonly supply energy for the cells are proteins, carbohydrates, and lipids.

18. Cellulose is important as dietary fiber. Although it is not digested, cellulose absorbs water and provides dietary bulk, which helps maintain a healthy digestive tract.

20. Pancreatic juice is slightly basic.

22. Lecithin acts as an emulsifying agent.

24. Pepsin digests proteins.

26. Vegetables should be the second most abundant food group in our diet.

28. Vitamin B_1 (thiamin) is the vitamin that is lost in beriberi.

30. The tomato soup serving size is reported as 1 cup (240 g). One serving (1 cup) provides 2 g of fiber. Thus two servings (2 cups) are needed for 4 g of fiber.

$$(4 \text{ g fiber})/(2 \text{ g fiber/cup}) = 2 \text{ cups}$$

32. There is 0.5 g of fat in one serving of this tomato soup. Saturated fat represents 0% of the total fat.

    (0 g saturated fat/serving)/(0.5 g total fat/serving)(100%) = 0%

34. No, this new diet is not reasonable. To lose this much fat, the person would have to use more energy than is possible in a week.

    Since a kilogram of fat contains about 9000 kcal of energy, 9 kilograms will contain about 81,000 kcal. This diet proposes using this much energy in one week. A typical adult only uses between 2000 and 3000 kcal/day or between 14,000 and 21,000 kcal/week. A person cannot "burn" enough energy to lose 9 kilograms of fat/week.

35. A complete protein contains all essential amino acids. There are 10 essential amino acids that cannot be synthesized by human cells and that must be supplied in the diet.

CHAPTER 33

Exercises

2. The average oxidation state of carbon in ethanal is −2. The average oxidation state of carbon in acetic acid is 0. The carbons in ethanal, being in a lower oxidation state, will deliver more energy in biological redox reactions.

4. The carbons in a fat are more reduced than those in a carbohydrate. These more reduced carbons can be oxidized more extensively and, thus, can provide more metabolic energy.

6. superoxide, O_2^-

8. "Substrate" refers to an organic compound that is an intermediate in a metabolic pathway. During substrate-level phosphorylation, substrates contribute phosphates to ADP, making ATP.

10. Both oxidized forms of the coenzymes (NAD^+ and FAD) are on the same side of the equation. For a reaction to occur one reduced coenzyme (NADH or $FADH_2$) must be paired with one of the oxidized coenzymes.

12. The conversion of acetate to long-chain fatty acids is anabolic. A smaller molecule (acetate) is converted to a large molecule (long-chain fatty acid) and the acetate carbons are progressively reduced as they are converted to the long-chain fatty acid.

14. Oxidative phosphorylation creates ATP and is a catabolic process, not an anabolic one.

16. Chloroplasts carry out photosynthesis, not oxidative phosphorylation.

18. The chemical changes in the chloroplasts are anabolic. Smaller carbon dioxide molecules are converted to larger glucose molecules, the carbons become progressively more reduced, and this process requires an input of energy (from sunlight).

20. Three important characteristics of a catabolic process are (1) complex substances are broken down into simpler substances; (2) carbons are often oxidized; (3) cellular energy is often produced.

22. The flavin ring is the reactive center of FAD.

24. Since the conversion of $FADH_2$ to FAD is oxidation, some pathway metabolites are being reduced. A pathway that reduces carbon compounds is anabolic.

26. 0.34 mol O_2

28. 0.18 mol e^-

30. zero

32. Energy is required. Figure 33.10 shows that the electrons must increase in energy before converting $NADP^+$ to NADPH. The energy comes from light.

34. Since the phosphorylated substrate 1,3-diphosphoglycerate contains only one high-energy phosphate bond, substrate-level phosphorylation can produce only one ATP.

36. 12 ATPs

38. According to the sliding filament model, calcium initiates muscle contraction. By blocking calcium release, botulism toxin stops the initial step in muscle contraction. Myosin does not react with ATP and the muscles remain relaxed.

40. FAD has one phosphate anhydride.

42. Myosin moves into its "kinked" structure in Figure 33.8a, part iii. Myosin changes its shape when ATP is reacted with water and released.

CHAPTER 34

Exercises

2. 170 kcal/day.

4. 47 g/day.

6. The liver will lose its ability to maintain the blood-glucose levels needed for skeletal muscle work. Additionally, the liver will not be able to remove the blood lactate derived from skeletal muscle work.

8. When the liver takes lactate and converts it to glucose, this is anabolic metabolism. First, a smaller molecule, lactate, is converted to a larger molecule, glucose. Second, this process requires an input of ATP.

10. Gluconeogenesis and glycogenesis must work together to convert lactate to glycogen. This is an anabolic process as the smaller lactate is reacted to form the much larger glycogen. Also, ATP is required for this process.

12. The Embden–Meyerhof pathway uses substrate-level phosphorylation to produce ATP. That is, following carbon oxidation a phosphate group is transferred from a substrate to ADP, forming ATP.

14. Although no molecular oxygen (O_2) is used in the citric acid cycle, reduced coenzymes NADH and $FADH_2$ are produced. These reduced coenzymes must be oxidized by electron transport so that the citric acid cycle can continue. And it is electron transport that uses molecular oxygen. Thus, the citric acid cycle depends on the presence of molecular oxygen and is considered to be aerobic.

16. 1.7 mol ATP

18. The end product of the anaerobic catabolism of glucose in muscle tissue is lactate.

20. The gluconeogenesis pathway is considered to be anabolic because (a) smaller, noncarbohydrate precursors such as lactate are converted to the larger product, glucose, and (b) as this conversion takes place, the carbons become progressively more reduced.

22. The glycolysis pathway uses substrate-level phosphorylation to produce ATP and thus does not need electron transport and oxidative phosphorylation.

24. One pass through the citric acid cycle uses 1 acetyl-CoA and yields 3 NADH, 1 $FADH_2$, and 1 ATP. Each NADH yields a maximum of 3 ATP in electron transport and oxidative phosphorylation. Each $FADH_2$ yields a maximum of 2 ATP in electron transport and oxidative phosphorylation. Thus, for each acetyl-CoA, the cell produces the following ATP:

    1 ATP directly from the citric acid cycle
    9 ATP from the 3 NADH produced in the citric acid cycle
    2 ATP from the 1 $FADH_2$ produced in the citric acid cycle
    12 ATP/acetyl-CoA

For 0.38 mole of acetyl-CoA, the following moles of ATP will be made:

(0.38 mole acetyl-CoA)(12 moles ATP/mole acetyl-CoA) = 4.6 moles ATP

26. Gluconeogenesis synthesizes glucose from noncarbohydrate precursors while glycogenesis is the process that makes glycogen from glucose.

28. When pyruvate is converted to lactate, a carbonyl group is changed to an hydroxyl group. The carbon in these functional groups loses a bond to oxygen and gains a bond to hydrogen. So, the carbon is reduced. Simultaneously, NADH is converted to NAD^+, losing electrons and becoming oxidized.

30. While insulin decreases blood-glucose levels and stimulates glycogen synthesis, glucagon increases blood-glucose levels and stimulates glycogen breakdown.

32. The polypeptide hormone is vasopressin.

33. 1200 kcal/day

38. CH$_3$CHCOO$^-$
        |
        OH

    lactate

All three carbons of lactate are more reduced than the carbon in CO_2. Thus, lactate can provide more cellular energy upon further oxidation of the carbons.

40. In the first step of this sequence, pyruvate is converted to acetaldehyde and carbon dioxide, causing dough to rise for bakers. In the second step, acetaldehyde is changed to ethanol, creating alcoholic beverages for brewers.

CHAPTER 35

Exercises

2. (CH$_3$CH$_2$)CH$_2$CH$_2$CH$_2$COOH; the two carbons circled remain.

4. CH$_3$(CH$_2$)$_{10}$*CH$_2$CH$_2$COOH

6. 8 acetyl-CoA

8. 0.60 kg will be lost.

10. The liver will increase urea production. During a fast, muscle protein is broken down to amino acids. The carbon skeletons of these amino acids are used for energy while the nitrogen is excreted as part of urea.

12. (a) ACP is a protein whereas CoA is a coenzyme

(b) ACP is used in fatty acid synthesis whereas CoA is used in the β-oxidation pathway.

14. A diet of protein and carbohydrate (but no fat) will not make the office worker "fat deficient." The human liver can convert both proteins and carbohydrates into fat.

16. After surgery, part of the healing process involves protein synthesis. More nitrogen will be consumed than excreted and a positive nitrogen balance will occur.

18. (a)
$$HOOCCH_2\overset{\overset{\displaystyle O}{\|}}{C}COOH$$

(b)
⟨benzene ring⟩—$CH_2\overset{\overset{\displaystyle O}{\|}}{C}COOH$

20.
          COOH
          |
          CH$_2$
          |
    (H$_2$N)—CH—COOH

22. One mole of urea is produced for every mole of L-aspartic acid used. 0.84 moles of aspartic acid will yield 0.84 moles of urea. One mole of L-glutamic acid is used for every mole of L-aspartic acid. 0.84 moles of aspartic acid uses 0.84 moles of glutamic acid.

24. Although this is part of the nitrogen cycle, it is not nitrogen fixation. The bacteria are starting with ammonia rather than elemental nitrogen as is required in nitrogen fixation.

25. As shown in Figure 35.5, proteins and fats can be converted to acetyl CoA. However, there can be no net synthesis of glucose from acetyl CoA (the conversion of glucose to acetyl CoA is a one way process).

27. In step 3, the carbonyl group is reacted to form an hydroxyl group. The reactant's carbonyl carbon has two bonds to oxygen while the product's hydroxyl carbon has only one bond to oxygen (and one bond to hydrogen). Thus, the carbon is reduced.

28. β-hydroxybutyric acid:

    CH$_3$CHCH$_2$COOH
        |
        OH

32. $(1.0 \text{ mol palmitic acid})\left(\dfrac{256.4 \text{ g}}{\text{mol palmitic acid}}\right) = 2.6 \times 10^2 \text{ g}$

$\left(\dfrac{9 \text{ kcal}}{\text{g}}\right)(2.6 \times 10^2 \text{ g}) = 2 \times 10^3 \text{ kcal}$

APPENDIX VII

Answers to Putting It Together Review Exercises

CHAPTERS 1–4

Multiple Choice: 1. d 2. a 3. d 4. b 5. d 6. c 7. a
8. d 9. a 10. b 11. a 12. d 13. b 14. c 15. a 16. d
17. c 18. b 19. d 20. c 21. c 22. a 23. b 24. c 25. c
26. a 27. d 28. d 29. c 30. a 31. b 32. a 33. c 34. c
35. c 36. d 37. d 38. c 39. c 40. b 41. b 42. c 43. b
44. b

Free Response:

1. $(1.5 \text{ m})\left(\dfrac{100 \text{ cm}}{1 \text{ m}}\right)\left(\dfrac{1 \text{ in.}}{2.54 \text{ cm}}\right)\left(\dfrac{1 \text{ ft}}{12 \text{ in.}}\right) = 4.9 \text{ ft}$

$(4 \text{ m})\left(\dfrac{100 \text{ cm}}{1 \text{ m}}\right)\left(\dfrac{1 \text{ in.}}{2.54 \text{ cm}}\right)\left(\dfrac{1 \text{ ft}}{12 \text{ in.}}\right) = 13 \text{ ft}$

$(27°C \times 1.8) + 32 = 81°F$

2. Jane needs to time how long it took from starting to heat to when the butter is just melted. From this information, she can determine how much heat the pot and butter absorbed. Jane can look up the specific heat of copper. Jane should weigh the pot and measure the temperature of the pot and the temperature at which the butter just melted. This should allow Jane to calculate how much heat the pot absorbed. Then she simply has to subtract the heat the pot absorbed from the heat the stove put out to find out how much heat the butter absorbed.

3. $CaCO_3 \longrightarrow CaO + CO_2$
   75 g   42 g   X

X = 75 g − 42 g = 33 g
44 g CO_2 occupies 24 dm^3
Therefore, 33 g CO_2 occupies

$(33 \text{ g})\left(\dfrac{24 \text{ dm}^3}{44 \text{ g}}\right)\left(\dfrac{1 \text{ L}}{1 \text{ dm}^3}\right) = 18 \text{ L}.$

4. (a), (b), Picture (2) best represents a homogeneous mixture. Pictures (1) and (c) (3) show heterogeneous mixtures, and picture (4) does not show a mixture, as only one species is present.

   Picture (1) likely shows a compound, as one of the components of the mixture is made up of more than one type of "ball." Picture (2) shows a component with more than one part, but the parts seem identical, and therefore it could be representing a diatomic molecule.

5. (a) Picture (3) because fluorine gas exists as a diatomic molecule.
   (b) Other elements that exist as diatomic molecules are oxygen, nitrogen, chlorine, hydrogen, bromine, and iodine.
   (c) Picture (2) could represent SO_3 gas.

6. (a) Tim's bowl should require less energy. Both bowls hold the same volume, but since snow is less dense than a solid block of ice, the mass of water in Tim's bowl is less than the mass of water in Sue's bowl. (Both bowls contain ice at 12°F.)

(b) $\dfrac{12°F - 32}{1.8} = -11°C$

   Temperature change: −11°C to 25°C = 36°C
(c) temperature change: −11°C to 0°C = 11°C
   specific heat of ice = 2.059 J/g°C

   vol. of H_2O = 1 qt = $(0.946 \text{ L})\left(\dfrac{1000 \text{ mL}}{\text{L}}\right)$
   = 946 mL

   mass of ice = mass of water = $(946 \text{ mL})\left(\dfrac{1 \text{ g}}{1 \text{ mL}}\right)$
   = 946 g

   heat required = (m)(sp. ht.)(Δt)
   = $(946 \text{ g})\left(\dfrac{2.059 \text{ J}}{\text{g°C}}\right)(11°C)\left(\dfrac{1 \text{ kJ}}{1000 \text{ J}}\right) = 21 \text{ kJ}$

(d) Physical changes

7. (a) Let x = RDA of iron
   60% of x = 11 mg Fe
   $x = \dfrac{11 \text{ mg Fe} \times 100\%}{60\%} = 18 \text{ mg Fe}$

(b) density of iron = 7.86 g/mL
   $V = \dfrac{m}{d} = (11 \text{ mg Fe})\left(\dfrac{1 \text{ g}}{1000 \text{ mg}}\right)\left(\dfrac{1 \text{ mL}}{7.86 \text{ g}}\right)$
   = 1.4×10^{-3} mL Fe

8. If Alfred inspects the bottles carefully, he should be able to see whether the contents are solid (silver) or liquid (mercury). Alternatively, since mercury is more dense than silver, the bottle of mercury should weigh more than the bottle of silver (the question indicated that both bottles were of similar size and both were full). Density is mass/volume.

9. (a) Container holds a mixture of sulfur and oxygen.
   (b) No. If the container were sealed, the total mass would remain the same whether a reaction took place or not. The mass of the reactants must equal the mass of the products.
   (c) No. Density is mass/volume. The volume is the container volume, which does not change. Since the total mass remains constant even if a reaction has taken place, the density of the container, including its contents, remains constant. The density of each individual component within the container may have changed, but the total density of the container is constant.

CHAPTERS 5–6

Multiple Choice: 1. b 2. d 3. b 4. d 5. b 6. b 7. a
8. b 9. d 10. c 11. b 12. d 13. a 14. c 15. d
Names and Formulas: The following are correct: 1, 2, 4, 5, 6, 7, 9, 11, 12, 15, 16, 17, 18, 19, 21, 22, 25, 28, 30, 32, 33, 34, 36, 37, 38, 40.

A-48

316

Free Response:

1. (a) An ion is a charged atom or group of atoms. The charge can be either positive or negative.

   (b) Electrons have negligible mass compared with the mass of protons and neurons. The only difference between Ca and Ca^{2+} is two electrons. The mass of those two electrons is insignificant compared with the mass of the protons and neutrons present (and whose numbers do not change).

2. (a) Let x = abundance of heavier isotope.

   $$303.9303(x) + 300.9326(1 - x) = 303.001$$
   $$303.9303x - 300.9326x = 303.001 - 300.9326$$
   $$2.9977x = 2.068$$
   $$x = 0.6899$$
   $$1 - x = 0.3101$$

   % abundance of heavier isotope = 68.99%

   % abundance of lighter isotope = 31.01%

   (b) $^{304}_{120}Wz$, $^{301}_{120}Wz$

   (c) mass number − atomic number = 303 − 120

   $\qquad\qquad\qquad\qquad\qquad\qquad = 183$ neutrons

3. Cl_2O_7 Cl: $17p \times 2 = \underline{34}$ protons

   $\qquad\quad$ O: $\ 8p \times 7 = \underline{56}$ protons

   $\qquad\qquad\qquad\qquad\ 90$ protons in Cl_2O_7

   Since the molecule is electrically neutral, the number of electrons is equal to the number of protons, so Cl_2O_7 has 90 electrons. The number of neutrons cannot be precisely determined unless it is known which isotopes of Cl and O are in this particular molecule.

4. Phosphate has a −3 charge; therefore, the formula for the ionic compound is $M_3(PO_4)_2$.

   P has 15 protons; therefore, $M_3(PO_4)_2$ has 30 phosphorus protons.

   $$3 \text{ (number of protons in M)} = \frac{30 \times 6}{5}$$

   $$= 36 \text{ protons in 3 M}$$

   $$\text{number of protons in M} = \frac{36}{3} = 12 \text{ protons}$$

   from the periodic table, M is Mg.

5. (a) Iron can form cations with different charges (e.g., Fe^{2+} or Fe^{3+}). The Roman numeral indicating which cation of iron is involved is missing. This name cannot be fixed unless the particular cation of iron is specified.

   (b) $K_2Cr_2O_7$. Potassium is generally involved in ionic compounds. The naming system used was for covalent compounds. The name should be potassium dichromate. (Dichromate is the name of the $Cr_2O_7^{2-}$ anion.)

   (c) Sulfur and oxygen are both nonmetals and form a covalent compound. The number of each atom involved needs to be specified for covalent compounds. There are two oxides of sulfur—SO_2 and SO_3. Both elements are nonmetals, so the names should be sulfur dioxide and sulfur trioxide, respectively.

6. No. Each compound, SO_2 and SO_3, has a definite composition of sulfur and oxygen by mass. The law of multiple proportions says that two elements may combine in different ratios to form more than one compound.

7. (a) Electrons are not in the nucleus.

   (b) When an atom becomes an anion, its size increases.

   (c) An ion of Ca (Ca^{2+}) and an atom of Ar have the same number of electrons.

8. (a) 12 amu $\times$ 7.18 = 86.16 amu

   (b) The atom is most likely Rb or Sr. Other remote possibilities are Kr or Y.

   (c) Because of the possible presence of isotopes, the atom cannot be positively identified. The periodic table gives average masses.

   (d) M forms a +1 cation and is most likely in Group 1A. The unknown atom is most likely $^{86}_{37}Rb$.

9. The presence of isotopes contradicts Dalton's theory that all atoms of the same element are identical. Also, the discovery of protons, neutrons, and electrons suggests that there are particles smaller than the atom and that the atom is not indivisible.

   Thomson proposed a model of an atom with no clearly defined nucleus.

   Rutherford passed alpha particles through gold foil and inspected the angles at which the alpha particles were deflected. From his results, he proposed the idea of an atom having a small dense nucleus.

CHAPTERS 7–9

Multiple Choice: 1. a   2. a   3. d   4. d   5. a   6. b   7. a
8. b   9. b   10. d   11. a   12. d   13. b   14. c   15. c   16. d
17. d   18. b   19. b   20. a   21. b   22. c   23. d   24. b
25. b   26. a   27. d   28. c   29. c   30. b   31. c   32. c
33. b   34. d   35. b   36. d   37. c   38. b   39. c   40. d
41. a   42. c   43. c   44. b   45. b   46. a   47. d   48. b
49. b   50. a

Free Response:

1. (a) $104 \text{ g } O_2 = (104 \text{ g } O_2)\left(\dfrac{1 \text{ mol}}{32.00 \text{ g}}\right) = 3.25 \text{ mol } O_2$

   $$\begin{array}{ccccccc} X & + & O_2 & \longrightarrow & CO_2 & + & H_2O \\ & & 3.25 \text{ mol} & & 2 \text{ mol} & & 2.5 \text{ mol} \end{array}$$

   $\qquad\qquad\qquad\qquad\qquad\qquad$ (multiply moles by 4)

   $4X + 13 \, O_2 \longrightarrow 8 \, CO_2 + 10 \, H_2O$

   Oxygen is balanced. By inspection, X must have 8/4 C atoms and 20/4 H atoms (2 C and 5 H).

   Empirical formula is C_2H_5.

   (b) Additional information needed is the molar mass of X.

2. (a)

   (b) $25 \text{ g } SO_2\left(\dfrac{1 \text{ mol}}{64.07 \text{ g}}\right) = 0.39 \text{ mol } SO_2$

   $\quad 5 \text{ g } O_2\left(\dfrac{1 \text{ mol}}{32.00 \text{ g}}\right) = 0.16 \text{ mol } O_2$

   $\quad \text{mol ratio} = \dfrac{0.39}{0.16} = \dfrac{2.4 \text{ mol } SO_2}{1 \text{ mol } O_2}$

   O_2 is the limiting reagent.

(c) False. The percentages given are not mass percentages. The percent composition of S in SO_2 is $(32/64) \times 100 = 50.\%$ S. The percent composition of S in SO_3 is $(32/80) \times 100 = 40.\%$ S.

3. (a) $\%O = 100 - (63.16 + 8.77) = 28.07\%$ O

Start with 100 g compound Z

C: $(63.16 \text{ g})\left(\dfrac{1 \text{ mol}}{12.01 \text{ g}}\right) = 5.259 \text{ mol}$

$\dfrac{5.259 \text{ mol}}{1.75 \text{ mol}} = 2.998$

H: $(8.77 \text{ g})\left(\dfrac{1 \text{ mol}}{1.008 \text{ g}}\right) = 8.70 \text{ mol}$

$\dfrac{8.70 \text{ mol}}{1.754 \text{ mol}} = 4.96$

O: $(28.07 \text{ g})\left(\dfrac{1 \text{ mol}}{16.00 \text{ g}}\right) = 1.754 \text{ mol}$

$\dfrac{1.754 \text{ mol}}{1.754 \text{ mol}} = 1.000$

The ratio of C:H:O is $3:5:1$.

The empirical formula is C_3H_5O.

molar mass = 114; mass of empirical formula is 57

Therefore, the molecular formula is $C_6H_{10}O_2$.

(b) $2 C_6H_{10}O_2 + 15 O_2 \longrightarrow 12 CO_2 + 10 H_2O$

4. (a) $Ca_3(PO_4)_2$:

molar mass = $3(40.08) + 2(30.97) + 8(16.00)$

$= 310.3$ %Ca in $Ca_3(PO_4)_2 = \dfrac{3(40.08)}{310.3}(100) = 38.7\%$

Let x = mg $Ca_3(PO_4)_2$

38.7% of x = 162 mg Ca

$x = \dfrac{(162 \text{ mg})(100)}{38.7} = 419 \text{ mg } Ca_3(PO_4)_2$

(b) $Ca_3(PO_4)_2$ is a compound.

(c) Convert 120 mL to cups

$(120 \text{ mL})\left(\dfrac{1 \text{ L}}{1000 \text{ mL}}\right)\left(\dfrac{1.059 \text{ qt}}{1 \text{ L}}\right)\left(\dfrac{4 \text{ cups}}{1 \text{ qt}}\right) = 0.51 \text{ cup}$

13% of x = 0.51 cup

$x = \dfrac{(0.51 \text{ cup})(100)}{13} = 3.9 \text{ cups}$

5. (a) Compound A must have a lower activation energy than compound B because B requires heat to overcome the activation energy for the reaction.

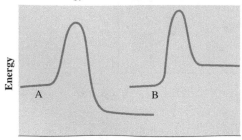

Reaction progress

(b) (i) $2 NaHCO_3 \longrightarrow Na_2CO_3 + H_2O + CO_2$

Decomposition of 0.500 mol $NaHCO_3$ requires 85.5 kJ of heat.

If 24.0 g CO_2 is produced, then

$(24.0 \text{ g } CO_2)\left(\dfrac{1 \text{ mol } CO_2}{44.01 \text{ g}}\right)\left(\dfrac{1 \text{ mol } H_2O}{1 \text{ mol } CO_2}\right)\left(\dfrac{18.02 \text{ g}}{1 \text{ mol } H_2O}\right)$

$= 9.83 \text{ g } H_2O$ produced

0.500 mol $NaHCO_3$ produces

$(0.500 \text{ mol } NaHCO_3)\left(\dfrac{1 \text{ mol } CO_2}{2 \text{ mol } NaHCO_3}\right)\left(\dfrac{44.01 \text{ g } CO_2}{1 \text{ mol } CO_2}\right)$

$= 11.0 \text{ g } CO_2$

Producing 11.0 g CO_2 required 85.5 kJ

Producing 24.0 g CO_2 requires $\left(\dfrac{24.0 \text{ g}}{11.0 \text{ g}}\right)(85.5 \text{ kJ})$

$= 187 \text{ kJ}$

(ii) $NaHCO_3$ could be compound B. Since heat was absorbed for the decomposition of $NaHCO_3$, the reaction was endothermic. Decomposition of A was exothermic.

6. (a) Double-displacement reaction

(b) $2 NH_4OH(aq) + CoSO_4(aq) \longrightarrow$

$(NH_4)_2SO_4(aq) + Co(OH)_2(s)$

(c) 8.09 g is 25% yield

Therefore, 100% yield = $(8.09 \text{ g } (NH_4)_2SO_4)\left(\dfrac{100\%}{25\%}\right)$

$= 32.4 \text{ g } (NH_4)_2SO_4$

(theoretical yield)

(d) molar mass of $(NH_4)_2SO_4 = 132.2 \text{ g/mol}$

theoretical moles $(NH_4)_2SO_4 = (32.4 \text{ g})\left(\dfrac{1}{132.2 \text{ g/mol}}\right)$

$= 0.245 \text{ mol } (NH_4)_2SO_4$

Calculate the moles of $(NH_4)_2SO_4$ produced from 38.0 g of each reactant.

$(38.0 \text{ g } NH_4OH)\left(\dfrac{1 \text{ mol}}{35.05 \text{ g}}\right)\left(\dfrac{1 \text{ mol } (NH_4)_2SO_4}{2 \text{ mol } NH_4OH}\right)$

$= 0.542 \text{ mol } (NH_4)_2SO_4$

$(38.0 \text{ g } CoSO_4)\left(\dfrac{1 \text{ mol}}{155.0 \text{ g}}\right)\left(\dfrac{1 \text{ mol } (NH_4)_2SO_4}{1 \text{ mol } CoSO_4}\right)$

$= 0.254 \text{ mol } (NH_4)_2SO_4$

Limiting reactant is $CoSO_4$; NH_4OH is in excess.

7. (a) $C_6H_{12}O_6 \longrightarrow 2 C_2H_5OH + 2 CO_2(g)$

Calculate the grams of $C_6H_{12}O_6$ that produced 11.2 g C_2H_5OH.

$(11.2 \text{ g } C_2H_5OH)\left(\dfrac{1 \text{ mol}}{46.07 \text{ g}}\right)\left(\dfrac{1 \text{ mol } C_6H_{12}O_6}{2 \text{ mol } C_2H_5OH}\right)\left(\dfrac{180.1 \text{ g}}{1 \text{ mol}}\right)$

$= 21.9 \text{ g } C_6H_{12}O_6$

$25.0 \text{ g} - 21.9 \text{ g} = 3.1 \text{ g } C_6H_{12}O_6$ left unreacted

Volume of CO_2 produced:

$(11.2 \text{ g } C_2H_5OH)\left(\dfrac{1 \text{ mol}}{46.07 \text{ g}}\right)\left(\dfrac{2 \text{ mol } CO_2}{2 \text{ mol } C_2H_5OH}\right)\left(\dfrac{24.0 \text{ L}}{\text{mol}}\right)$

$= 5.83 \text{ L}$

The assumptions made are that the conditions before and after the reaction are the same and that all reactants went to the products.

(b) The theoretical yield is

$(25.0 \text{ g } C_6H_{12}O_6)\left(\dfrac{1 \text{ mol}}{180.1 \text{ g}}\right)\left(\dfrac{2 \text{ mol } C_2H_5OH}{1 \text{ mol } C_6H_{12}O_6}\right)\left(\dfrac{46.07 \text{ g}}{\text{mol}}\right)$

$= 12.8 \text{ g } C_2H_5OH$

$$\% \text{ yield} = \left(\frac{11.2 \text{ g}}{12.8 \text{ g}}\right)(100) = 87.5\%$$

(c) decomposition reaction

8. (a) double decomposition (precipitation)

(b) lead(II) iodide (PbI_2)

(c) $Pb(NO_3)_2(aq) + 2\ KI(aq) \longrightarrow 2\ KNO_3(aq) + PbI_2(s)$

If $Pb(NO_3)_2$ is limiting, the theoretical yield is

$$(25 \text{ g } Pb(NO_3)_2)\left(\frac{1 \text{ mol}}{331.2 \text{ g}}\right)\left(\frac{1 \text{ mol } PbI_2}{1 \text{ mol } Pb(NO_3)_2}\right)\left(\frac{461.0 \text{ g}}{\text{mol}}\right)$$
$$= 35 \text{ g } PbI_2$$

If KI is limiting, the theoretical yield is

$$(25 \text{ g } KI)\left(\frac{1 \text{ mol}}{166.0 \text{ g}}\right)\left(\frac{1 \text{ mol } PbI_2}{2 \text{ mol } KI}\right)\left(\frac{461.0 \text{ g}}{\text{mol}}\right) = 35 \text{ g } PbI_2$$

$$\text{percent yield} = \left(\frac{7.66 \text{ g}}{35 \text{ g}}\right)(100) = 22\%$$

9. (a) Balance the equation

$$2\ XNO_3 + CaCl_2 \longrightarrow 2\ XCl + Ca(NO_3)_2$$

$$(30.8 \text{ g } CaCl_2)\left(\frac{1 \text{ mol}}{111.0 \text{ g}}\right)\left(\frac{2 \text{ mol } XCl}{1 \text{ mol } CaCl_2}\right) = 0.555 \text{ mol } XCl$$

Therefore, the molar mass of the XCl is

$$\frac{79.6 \text{ g}}{0.555 \text{ mol}} = 143 \text{ g/mol}$$

$$\text{mass of } (X + Cl) = \text{mass of } XCl$$
$$\text{mass of } X = 143 - 35.45 = 107.6$$
$$X = Ag \text{ (from periodic table)}$$

(b) No. Ag is below H in the activity series.

10. (a) $2\ H_2O_2 \longrightarrow 2\ H_2O + O_2$

There must have been eight H_2O_2 molecules and four O_2 molecules in the flask at the start of the reaction.

(b) The reaction is exothermic.

(c) Decomposition reaction.

(d) The empirical formula is OH.

CHAPTERS 10–11

Multiple Choice: 1. c   2. a   3. b   4. a   5. a   6. b   7. b
8. b   9. c   10. a   11. d   12. d   13. a   14. b   15. c   16. c
17. b   18. c   19. d   20. d   21. d   22. a   23. c   24. c
25. b   26. d   27. b   28. a   29. b   30. c   31. c   32. d
33. a   34. a   35. c   36. d   37. b   38. c   39. c   40. c   41. a

Free Response:

1. The compound will be ionic because there is a very large difference in electronegativity between elements in Group 2A and those in Group 7A of the periodic table. The Lewis structure is

$$[M]^{2+} \quad \begin{matrix} [:\ddot{X}:]^- \\ [:\ddot{X}:]^- \end{matrix}$$

2. Having an even atomic number has no bearing on electrons being paired. An even atomic number means only that there is an even number of electrons. For example, carbon is atomic number six, and it has two unpaired p electrons: $1s^2 2s^2 2p_x^1 2p_y^1$.

3. False. The noble gases do not have any unpaired electrons. Their valence shell electron structure is ns^2np^6 (except He).

4. The outermost electron in potassium is farther away from the nucleus than the outermost electrons in calcium, so the first ionization energy of potassium is lower than that of calcium.

However, once potassium loses one electron, it achieves a noble gas electron configuration and, therefore, taking a second electron away requires considerably more energy. For calcium, the second electron is still in the outermost shell and does not require as much energy to remove it.

5. The ionization energy is the energy required to *remove* an electron. A chlorine atom forms a chloride ion by *gaining* an electron to achieve a noble gas configuration.

6. The anion is Cl^-; therefore, the cation is K^+ and the noble gas is Ar. K^+ has the smallest radius, while Cl^- will have the largest. K loses an electron, and therefore, in K^+, the remaining electrons are pulled in even closer. Cl was originally larger than Ar, and gaining an electron means that, since the nuclear charge is exceeded by the number of electrons, the radius will increase relative to a Cl atom.

7. The structure shown in the question implies covalent bonds between Al and F, since the lines represent shared electrons. Solid AlF_3 is an ionic compound and, therefore, probably exists as an Al^{3+} ion and three F^- ions. Only valence electrons are shown in Lewis structures.

8. Carbon has four valence electrons; it needs four electrons to form a noble gas electron structure. By sharing four electrons, a carbon atom can form four covalent bonds.

9. NCl_3 is pyramidal. The presence of three pairs of electrons and a lone pair of electrons around the central atom (N) gives the molecule a tetrahedral structure and a pyramidal shape. BF_3 has three pairs of electrons and no lone pairs of electrons around the central atom (B), so both the structure and the shape of the molecule are trigonal planar.

10. The atom is Br ($35e^-$), which should form a slightly polar covalent bond with sulfur.

The Lewis structure of Br is $:\ddot{Br}\cdot$

CHAPTERS 12–14

Multiple Choice: 1. b   2. a   3. b   4. c   5. a   6. d   7. d
8. b   9. a   10. b   11. c   12. a   13. c   14. c   15. d   16. a
17. c   18. a   19. a   20. d   21. b   22. c   23. a   24. a   25. d
26. d   27. a   28. b   29. c   30. a   31. a   32. c   33. c   34. c
35. a   36. b   37. b   38. c   39. d   40. a   41. c   42. d
43. b   44. c   45. c   46. c   47. a   48. c   49. d   50. b   51. a
52. c   53. d   54. b   55. b   56. a   57. d   58. c   59. b   60. b

Free Response:

1. 10.0% (m/v) has 10.0 g KCl per 100. mL of solution:

Therefore, KCl solution contains

$$\left(\frac{10.0 \text{ g } KCl}{100. \text{ mL}}\right)(215 \text{ mL})\left(\frac{1 \text{ mol}}{74.55 \text{ g}}\right) = 0.288 \text{ mol } KCl$$

NaCl solution contains

$$\left(\frac{1.10 \text{ mol } NaCl}{L}\right)\left(\frac{1 \text{ L}}{1000 \text{ mL}}\right)(224 \text{ mL}) = 0.246 \text{ mol } NaCl$$

The KCl solution has more particles in solution and will have the higher boiling point.

2. Mass of CO_2 in solution

$$= (\text{molar mass})(\text{moles}) = (\text{molar mass})\left(\frac{PV}{RT}\right)$$

$$= \left(\frac{44.01 \text{ g } CO_2}{\text{mol}}\right)\left(\frac{1 \text{ atm} \times 1.40 \text{ L}}{\dfrac{0.08206 \text{ L atm}}{\text{mol K}} \times 298 \text{ K}}\right) = 2.52 \text{ g } CO_2$$

$$\text{mass of soft drink} = (345 \text{ mL})\left(\frac{0.965 \text{ g}}{\text{mL}}\right) = 333 \text{ g}$$

$$\text{ppm of CO}_2 = \left(\frac{2.52 \text{ g}}{333 \text{ g} + 2.52 \text{ g}}\right)(10^6)$$

$$= 7.51 \times 10^3 \text{ ppm}$$

3. 10% KOH m/v solution contains 10 g KOH in 100 mL solution.

10% KOH by mass solution contains 10 g KOH + 90 g H_2O.

The 10% by mass solution is the more concentrated solution and therefore would require less volume to neutralize the HCl.

4. (a) $\dfrac{0.355 \text{ mol}}{0.755 \text{ L}} = 0.470 \text{ M}$

(b) The lower pathway represents the evaporation of water; only a phase change occurs; no new substances are formed. The upper path represents the decomposition of water. The middle path is the ionization of water.

5. Zack went to Ely, Gaye went to the Dead Sea, and Lamont was in Honolulu. Zack's bp was lowered, so he was in a region of lower atmospheric pressure (on a mountain). Lamont was basically at sea level, so his bp was about normal. Since Gaye's boiling point was raised, she was at a place of higher atmospheric pressure and therefore was possibly in a location below sea level. The Dead Sea is below sea level.

6. The particles in solids and liquids are close together (held together by intermolecular attractions), and an increase in pressure is unable to move them significantly closer to each other. In a gas, the space between molecules is significant, and an increase in pressure is often accompanied by a decrease in volume.

| Liquid | Solid | Gas |

7. (a) The CO_2 balloon will be heaviest, followed by the Ar balloon. The H_2 balloon would be the lightest. Gases at the same temperature, pressure, and volume contain the same number of moles. All balloons will contain the same number of moles of gas molecules, so when moles are converted to mass, the order from heaviest to lightest is CO_2, Ar, H_2.

(b) Molar mass: O_2, 32.00; N_2, 28.02; Ne, 20.18

Using equal masses of gas, we find that the balloon containing O_2 will have the lowest number of moles of gas. Since pressure is directly proportional to moles, the balloon containing O_2 will have the lowest pressure.

8. Ray probably expected to get 0.050 mole $Cu(NO_3)_2$, which is

$$(0.050 \text{ mol Cu(NO}_3)_2)\left(\frac{187.6 \text{ g}}{\text{mol}}\right) = 9.4 \text{ g Cu(NO}_3)_2$$

The fact that he got 14.775 g meant that the solid blue crystals were very likely a hydrate containing water of crystallization.

9. For most reactions to occur, molecules or ions need to collide. In the solid phase, the particles are immobile and therefore do not collide. In solution or in the gas phase, particles are more mobile and can collide to facilitate a chemical reaction.

10. $\Delta t_b = 81.48°C - 80.1°C = 1.38°C$

$$K_b = 2.53 \frac{°C \text{ kg solvent}}{\text{mol solute}}$$

$$\Delta t_b = mK_b$$

$$1.38°C = m\left(2.53 \frac{°C \text{ kg solvent}}{\text{mol solute}}\right)$$

$$0.545 \frac{\text{mol solute}}{\text{kg solvent}} = m$$

Now we convert molality to molarity.

$$\left(\frac{5.36 \text{ g solute}}{76.8 \text{ g benzene}}\right)\left(\frac{1000 \text{ g benzene}}{1 \text{ kg benzene}}\right)\left(\frac{1 \text{ kg benzene}}{0.545 \text{ mol solute}}\right)$$

$$= 128. \text{ g/mol}$$

CHAPTERS 15–17

Multiple Choice: 1. c 2. d 3. d 4. c 5. c 6. d 7. a 8. d 9. b 10. c 11. a 12. d 13. c 14. b 15. b 16. d 17. c 18. a 19. a 20. a 21. b 22. c 23. a 24. c 25. c 26. d 27. a 28. b 29. a 30. b 31. a 32. c 33. a 34. b 35. c 36. c 37. b 38. d 39. a 40. c 41. a 42. b 43. a 44. b 45. a 46. a 47. d 48. a 49. c 50. d 51. b 52. a 53. a 54. b

Balanced Equations:

55. $3 P + 5 HNO_3 \longrightarrow 3 HPO_3 + 5 NO + H_2O$

56. $2 MnSO_4 + 5 PbO_2 + 3 H_2SO_4 \longrightarrow$
$$2 HMnO_4 + 5 PbSO_4 + 2 H_2O$$

57. $Cr_2O_7^{2-} + 14 H^+ + 6 Cl^- \longrightarrow 2 Cr^{3+} + 7 H_2O + 3 Cl_2$

58. $2 MnO_4^- + 5 AsO_3^{3-} + 6 H^+ \longrightarrow 2 Mn^{2+} + 5 AsO_4^{3-} + 3 H_2O$

59. $S^{2-} + 4 Cl_2 + 8 OH^- \longrightarrow SO_4^{2-} + 8 Cl^- + 4 H_2O$

60. $4 Zn + NO_3^- + 6 H_2O + 7 OH^- \longrightarrow 4 Zn(OH)_4^{2-} + NH_3$

61. $2 KOH + Cl_2 \longrightarrow KCl + KClO + H_2O$

62. $4 As + 3 ClO_3^- + 6 H_2O + 3 H^+ \longrightarrow 4 H_3AsO_3 + 3 HClO$

63. $2 MnO_4^- + 10 Cl^- + 16 H^+ \longrightarrow 2 Mn^{2+} + 5 Cl_2 + 8 H_2O$

64. $Cl_2O_7 + 4 H_2O_2 + 2 OH^- \longrightarrow 2 ClO_2^- + 4 O_2 + 5 H_2O$

Free Response:

1. $2 Bz + 3 Yz^{2+} \longrightarrow 2 Bz^{3+} + 3 Yz$

Bz is above Yz in the activity series.

2. (a) $2 Al(s) + 3 Fe(NO_3)_2(aq) \longrightarrow 2 Al(NO_3)_3(aq) + 3 Fe(s)$

(b) The initial solution of $Fe(NO_3)_2$ will have the lower freezing point. It has more particles in solution than the product.

3. (a) $pH = -\log[H^+] = -\log[0.10] = 1.00$

(b) mol HCl $= 0.050 \text{ L} \times \dfrac{0.10 \text{ mol}}{\text{L}} = 0.0050 \text{ mol HCl}$

Flask A

$Zn(s) + 2 HCl(aq) \longrightarrow ZnCl_2(aq) + H_2(g)$

HCl is the limiting reactant, so no HCl will remain in the product.

pH = 7.0

Flask B

No reaction occurs in flask B, so the pH does not change.

pH = 1.00

4. (a) $2 NaOH(aq) + H_2S(aq) \longrightarrow Na_2S(aq) + 2 H_2O(l)$

(b) $H_2S \rightleftharpoons 2H^+ + S^{2-}$ (aqueous solution)

$Na_2S \longrightarrow 2 Na^+ + S^{2-}$ (aqueous solution)

The addition of S^{2-} to a solution of H_2S will shift the equilibrium to the left, reducing the $[H^+]$ and thereby increasing the pH (more basic).

5. (a) Yes. The K_{eq} of AgCN indicates that it is slightly soluble in water, so a precipitate will form.

Net ionic equation:

$Ag^+(aq) + CN^-(aq) \rightleftharpoons AgCN(s)$

(b) NaCN is a salt of a weak acid and a strong base and will hydrolyze in water.

$CN^-(aq) + H_2O(l) \rightleftharpoons HCN(aq) + OH^-(aq)$

The solution will be basic due to increased OH^- concentration.

6. (a)

$\square$ = $PbSO_4(s)$

(b)

No reaction—contents
are merely mixed.

7. (a) $2\,A_3X \rightleftharpoons 2\,A_2X + A_2$

$$K_{eq} = \frac{(A_2X)^2(A_2)}{(A_3X)^2} = \frac{(3)^2(6)}{(4)^2} = 3.375$$

(b) The equilibrium lies to the right. $K_{eq} > 1$

(c) Yes, it is a redox reaction because the oxidation state of A has changed. The oxidation state of A in A_2 must be 0, but the oxidation state of A in A_3X is not 0.

8. (a) $X_2 + 2\,G \rightleftharpoons X_2G_2$

$$K_{eq} = \frac{(X_2G_2)}{(X_2)(G)^2} = \frac{(1)}{(3)(2)^2} = 8.33 \times 10^{-2}$$

(b) Exothermic. An increase in the amount of reactants means that the equilibrium shifted to the left.

(c) An increase in pressure will cause an equilibrium to shift by reducing the number of moles of gas in the equilibrium. If the equilibrium shifts to the right, there must be fewer moles of gas in the product than in the reactants.

9. The pH of the solution is 4.5. (Acid medium)

$5\,Fe^{2+} + MnO_4^- + 8\,H^+ \longrightarrow 5\,Fe^{3+} + Mn^{2+} + 4\,H_2O$

CHAPTER 18

Multiple Choice: 1. b **2.** d **3.** a **4.** a **5.** d **6.** b **7.** a **8.** c **9.** c **10.** c **11.** a **12.** c **13.** b **14.** b **15.** c **16.** d **17.** b

Free Response:

1. The nuclide lost two alpha particles and one beta particle in any order. One series could be $^{223}_{87}Fr \xrightarrow{-\alpha} {}^{219}_{85}At \xrightarrow{-\beta} {}^{219}_{86}Rn \xrightarrow{-\alpha} {}^{215}_{84}Po$. $^{215}_{84}Po$ is the resulting nuclide.

2. $96\,g \longrightarrow 48\,g \longrightarrow 24\,g \longrightarrow$
   $12\,g \longrightarrow 6\,g \longrightarrow 3\,g \longrightarrow 1.5\,g$

   Each change involves a half-life. Six (6) half-lives are required to go from 96 g to 1.5 g. The half-life is about four days.

3. (a) The process is transmutation.

   (b) Transmutation produces a different element by bombarding an element with a small particle such as hydrogen, deuterium, or a neutron. Radioactive decay is the formation of a different element by the loss of an alpha or beta particle from the nucleus of a radioactive element.

   (c) No. Nuclear fission involves the bombardment of a heavy element with a neutron, causing the element to split (fission) into two or more lighter elements and produces two or more neutrons. A large amount of energy also is formed in a nuclear fission.

CHAPTERS 19–21

Multiple Choice: 1. c **2.** b **3.** c **4.** a **5.** c **6.** d **7.** a **8.** a **9.** a **10.** d **11.** b **12.** a **13.** b **14.** c **15.** d **16.** a **17.** c **18.** d **19.** b **20.** d **21.** a **22.** c **23.** d **24.** c **25.** c **26.** d **27.** c **28.** d **29.** d **30.** a **31.** d **32.** d **33.** b **34.** a **35.** d **36.** c **37.** b **38.** a **39.** b **40.** a **41.** c **42.** d **43.** a **44.** a **45.** c **46.** b **47.** c **48.** c **49.** c **50.** b **51.** b **52.** d **53.** a **54.** b **55.** a **56.** b **57.** d **58.** d **59.** c **60.** b **61.** a **62.** b

Free Response:

1. Disagree. The second molecule is aromatic and, thus, the double bonds do not easily undergo addition reactions.

2. The two compounds are not isomers but are two drawings of the same molecule. They share the same carbon connectivity as well as the same molecular formula.

3. Compounds that are used to make addition polymers contain double bonds. This functional group participates in addition reactions needed for polymerization.

4. Each of these compounds will react with bromine but if the unknown is either of compounds I and II, additional reagents/conditions will be needed. In all situations the disappearance of the bromine color will indicate a reaction (positive result) and therefore the identity of the unknown. Add bromine to the unknown. A positive result indicates compound III is the unknown. If there is a negative result, try adding $FeBr_3$. A positive result indicates compound I. Two negative results indicate compound II.

This can be verified by adding bromine in the presence of light or high heat to compound III and looking for a positive result.

5. Alkynes cannot have geometric isomers because they have only one group attached to the alkyne carbons and they are linear compounds around the alkyne bond. Cycloalkanes with substituents on different carbons can have geometric isomers.

6. Because each pair of compounds are hydrocarbons with approximately the same molar mass and relatively similarly shaped, predicting a significant difference in boiling point or solubility would be difficult. Their intermolecular attractions are similar and no molecule is significantly more polar. In actuality, their boiling points are very similar. All would be expected to be insoluble in water, again because they have similar types of intermolecular forces. However, their chemical properties are markedly different, for example:

(a) Reaction with $Br_2/FeBr_3$—benzene will react, cyclohexane will not.

(b) Reaction with $KMnO_4$—1-hexyne will react, hexane will not.

(c) Reaction with $KMnO_4$—cyclohexene will react, cyclohexane will not unless subjected to harsh conditions.

7. Because there is only one monomer involved, Plexiglass is likely an addition polymer. The structure of the monomer therefore probably has a double bond (alkene) which is used in the addition reaction.

$$CH_3$$
$$|$$
$$C=CH_2$$
$$|$$
$$CO_2CH_3$$

8.

chloroethane   ethylbenzene

benzoic acid

CHAPTERS 22–23

Multiple Choice: 1. b   2. d   3. b   4. d   5. b   6. c   7. a
8. c   9. b   10. c   11. a   12. a   13. b   14. c   15. b   16. c
17. d   18. b   19. c   20. b   21. d   22. b   23. c   24. b   25. d
26. d   27. d   28. c   29. c   30. b   31. a   32. c   33. c   34. c
35. d   36. a   37. b   38. c   39. d   40. c   41. b   42. b   43. b
44. a   45. d   46. b   47. c   48. a   49. a   50. c   51. a   52. b
53. c   54. a   55. d   56. b   57. b   58. c   59. d   60. d   61. b
62. c

Free Response:

1. Based on the formula, and the other conditions given, the compound cannot be an alcohol or an ether. Therefore it must be either an aldehyde or a ketone. Try oxidizing a sample of the compound with dichromate. If a color change from orange to green is obtained, the compound underwent oxidation and is an aldehyde. If there is no color change, the compound did not oxidize and is a ketone.

2. Aldehydes and ketones have a carbon that is attached to only three different atoms and therefore involve a pi bond. Addition reactions

generally involve the breaking of a pi bond and the formation of a sigma bond, adding a new atom to each of the original participants in the pi bond.

3. (a) $CH_3CH_2CH_2COOH$

$$OH$$
$$|$$
(b) $CH_3CH_2CH_2CHCN$

(c) $CH_3CH_2CH_2CH_2OH$

$$OH \quad CH_3$$
$$|\qquad |$$
(d) $CH_3CH_2CH_2CHOCHCH_2CH_3$

4.
$$CH_3$$
$$|$$
$$CH_3CHCH_2OH$$

$$CH_3CH_2CH_2CH_2OH$$

$$OH$$
$$|$$
$$CH_3CH_2CHCH_3$$

The circled compound is a tertiary alcohol that is not oxidized by $K_2Cr_2O_7$.

5. The most soluble should be the one that is able to participate most effectively in hydrogen bonding with water, that is, 1-propanol. The least soluble compound should be the least polar compound, in this case. butene. Butene has no polar groups and is unable to effectively associate with water.

6.

cyclobutanol   butanal   butanone

$CH_2=CHOCH_2CH_3$ plus several others
vinyl ethyl ether

7.

8.

9. Aldehydes and ketones of the same molar mass are difficult to distinguish from each other based on boiling points so they will

need to be identified based on a chemical test, such as a Tollens test, which will give a positive result (silver mirror) for the aldehyde. The rest of the compounds should boil in the following order from lowest boiling point to highest:

dipropyl ether < 1-pentanethiol < 1-hexanol
   91°C   126°C   155°C

These boiling points would be based on the strengths of the intermolecular attractions. The alcohol has hydrogen-bonding, while the thiol is more polar than the symmetrical ether. Note that the thiol may be difficult to distinguish from the aldehyde and ketone in terms of boiling point also, but can probably be fairly easily identified based on odor.

10. (a) phenol and 1-hexanol—treat with NaOH and see which becomes miscible with water (phenol); or treat with $K_2Cr_2O_7$/H_2SO_4 (or $KMnO_4$ in alkaline solution) and look for a color change (hexanol)

   (b) phenol and hexanal—treat with NaOH and see which becomes miscible with water (phenol); or perform the Tollens test and look for a positive result (hexanal)

   (c) 1-hexanol and 3-hexanone—treat with Na and see which bubbles (reacts with hexanol to produce H_2); or treat with $K_2Cr_2O_7$/H_2SO_4 (or $KMnO_4$ in alkaline solution) and look for a color change (hexanol)

11.

CHAPTERS 24–25

Multiple Choice: 1. a   2. c   3. c   4. c   5. c   6. b   7. a
8. c   9. d   10. d   11. d   12. a   13. c   14. b   15. c   16. b
17. c   18. b   19. b   20. c   21. d   22. c   23. c   24. b   25. a
26. c   27. c   28. c   29. a   30. c   31. b   32. a   33. c   34. d
35. b   36. a   37. a   38. c   39. b   40. a   41. b   42. b   43. a
44. b   45. d   46. d   47. d   48. c   49. a   50. d   51. b   52. c
53. c   54. b   55. d

Free Response:

1. Fatty acid I is most likely synthetically produced since most naturally occurring unsaturated fatty acids contain *cis* double bonds, not *trans* double bonds.

2. Succinic acid undergoes an elimination reaction (dehydrogenation) to produce fumaric acid. Fumaric acid is hydrated (an addition reaction) to produce malic acid.

$$HOOC-CH_2-CH_2-COOH \longrightarrow$$
   succinic acid

$$HOOC-CH=CH-COOH \xrightarrow[H_2SO_4]{H_2O}$$
        fumaric acid
          (trans)

$$HOOC-CH_2-CH-COOH$$
                          |
                         OH
              malic acid

3.

phenyl benzoate   →(NaOH)   sodium benzoate   +   sodium phenoxide

Yes, one of the organic products would be different if a weaker base were used. The carboxylate salt would still be obtained but the alcohol would most likely be obtained as the neutral alcohol and not as the alkoxide; that is, phenol would be the product. Phenol is not as acidic as carboxylic acids and will not be deprotonated by weak bases.

4. (a)
$$CH_3-\overset{\overset{\displaystyle CH_3}{|}}{\underset{\underset{\displaystyle COOH}{|}}{C}}-\overset{\overset{\displaystyle OH}{|}}{CH}-COOH$$
1,3: carboxyl groups
2: hydroxyl group

   (b)
$$CH_3O-\overset{O}{\overset{||}{C}}-\overset{\overset{\displaystyle CH_3}{|}}{\underset{\underset{\displaystyle CH_3}{|}}{C}}-\overset{O}{\overset{||}{C}}-CH_2OH$$
1: ester group
2: carbonyl group
3: hydroxyl group

   (c)
$$HO-\overset{O}{\overset{||}{C}}-\overset{\overset{\displaystyle CH_3}{|}}{\underset{\underset{\displaystyle CH_3}{|}}{C}}-\overset{\overset{\displaystyle OH}{|}}{CH}-\overset{O}{\overset{||}{CH}}$$
1: carboxyl group
2: hydroxyl group
3: carbonyl group

5. (d) > (c) > (a) > (b) All the compounds have about the same molar mass but they differ with respect to their functional groups. Salts are more water soluble than acids, which are more water soluble than esters. The compound in (d) is the most soluble because it combines a salt and an acid group.

6. Oxidation: I = either $CH_3\overset{\overset{\displaystyle CH_3}{|}}{C}HCH_2CH_2OH$ or

$$CH_3\overset{\overset{\displaystyle CH_3}{|}}{C}HCH_2-\overset{O}{\overset{||}{C}}H$$

   Esterification: II = $CH_3\overset{\overset{\displaystyle CH_3}{|}}{C}HCH_2OH$

   Saponification: III = $CH_3\overset{\overset{\displaystyle CH_3}{|}}{C}HCH_2-\overset{O}{\overset{||}{C}}O^-\ Na^+$

   IV = $CH_3\overset{\overset{\displaystyle CH_3}{|}}{C}HCH_2OH$

7. Acid halides are much more reactive than carboxylic acids. Also, the initial reaction between a carboxylic acid and ammonia (or an amine) is an acid–base reaction forming a salt, not the desired amide. In order for the amide to form, the initially produced salt

must be strongly heated and not all compounds or other functional groups are always stable to high heat conditions.

8.

CHAPTERS 26–28

Multiple Choice: 1. c 2. c 3. a 4. b 5. a 6. c 7. d
8. b 9. a 10. d 11. c 12. b 13. b 14. c 15. d 16. a
17. b 18. b 19. d 20. c 21. b 22. a 23. d 24. d 25. c
26. a 27. b 28. a 29. b 30. d 31. a 32. b 33. a 34. c
35. d 36. c 37. b 38. b 39. d 40. c 41. b 42. a 43. b
44. d 45. a 46. c 47. b 48. d 49. a 50. d 51. d 52. b
53. c 54. c 55. b 56. b

Free Response:

1. Fatty acid B would be more likely to give a softer margarine spread. Fatty acid A contains one *cis* double bond and one *trans* double bond while fatty acid B contains two *cis* double bonds. *Cis* fatty acid isomers tend to have lower melting points. Thus, fatty acid B should give the softer margarine.

2. Disagree. The carbohydrate isolated from goat's milk is not D-glucose.
   (a) The molecular formula suggests that this carbohydrate is a hexose.
   (b) The Benedict test indicates a reducing sugar; the unknown carbohydrate is probably a monosaccharide.
   (c) Since the sugar alcohol product has no optical activity, it is likely a meso compound. The sugar alcohol of D-glucose is not a meso compound and will have optical activity.

3. (a) Monosaccharides like β-D-sedoheptulopyranose reduce Cu^{2+} in the Benedict test and are classified as reducing sugars.
   (b) The starred carbon (C*) is part of both an ether and an alcohol and is directly bonded to two other carbons. Thus, the starred carbon is part of a hemiketal.
   (c) β-D-sedoheptulopyranose has five chiral carbons. The number of stereoisomers is equal to 2^n where n is the number of chiral carbons.

$$2^n = 2^5 = 32 \text{ stereoisomers}$$

4. The molecules are geometric isomers of each other. The only difference is the cis/trans orientation of the double bonds in the lower fatty acid chain.

5. (a) The lipid is made up from a triglycerol structure.
   (b) The substituent on the phosphate group does not represent an aldohexose as there is no oxygen in the ring. It is not a pyranose ring, and there is no hemiacetal or acetal group present.

6. The fatty acid has a total of 20 carbons and is therefore arachidic acid. The sphingosine backbone has an amine group and therefore a condensation reaction between the amine of sphingosine and the carboxylic acid group of the fatty acid should result in the amide functional group shown in the molecule.

7. The three fatty acids involved are (from the top down) myristic acid, linoleic acid (an ω-6 fatty acid) and palmitoleic acid. The only chiral carbon in this lipid is the middle carbon of the glycerol unit, and therefore there are only two possible optical isomers.

8.

In the reduction a new chiral carbon is formed and therefore since the reaction is not selective, a mix of the two products shown above will be formed. These two compounds are diastereomers, or more specifically, epimers of each other, differing only at the second carbon. The molecule on the left (A) will not have optical activity as it is a meso compound, while the molecule on the right (B) should exhibit optical activity.

9. Compound A is a glucose polymer, specifically cellulose (has β-1,4-linkages). Although it has many sites for hydrogen bonding, they are usually occupied with hydrogen bonding to other cellulose strands; due to that and to its large size, cellulose is insoluble in water.

   Compound B is a monosaccharide, specifically a ketohexose. It is small and has many sites for hydrogen bonding with water and is thus expected to be soluble in water.

   Compound C is a large molar-mass ester and therefore could be classified as lipid, specifically a wax. The only significant polarity in the molecule, the ester group, is not sufficient to compensate for the large nonpolar portions of the molecule in terms of water solubility and is therefore insoluble in water.

10. The functional group connecting the carbohydrate and the sphingosine structure is an acetal (ether). The carbohydrate used is β-D-galactose. There are 7 chiral carbons in the molecule (as shown by the *).

CHAPTERS 29–31

Multiple Choice: 1. a 2. c 3. b 4. d 5. b 6. c 7. d
8. b 9. c 10. a 11. a 12. b 13. a 14. c 15. d 16. c
17. d 18. b 19. a 20. d 21. a 22. c 23. b 24. a 25. a
26. b 27. b 28. a 29. b 30. d 31. c 32. a 33. c 34. d
35. c 36. b 37. d 38. c 39. d 40. c 41. a 42. d 43. b
44. b 45. b 46. a 47. d 48. b 49. a 50. c

Free Response:

1. In the first step, ethylene glycol is being oxidized to an aldehyde. An oxidoreductase enzyme is involved (specifically alcohol dehydrogenase).

2. Enzyme A can be classified as a hydrolase or as a transferase (depending on what happened to the phosphate group).
Enzyme B can be classified as an isomerase (epimerase).
Enzyme C can be classified as a transferase (phosphotransferase).

3.

   ser-met-pro or serylmethionylproline-termination

4. Polar, acidic or basic amino acids are more likely to be found on the outside as these side chains are the ones that will interact with water. Hydrophobic (nonpolar) side chains will not have favorable interactions with water and would be more likely to be folded toward the inside of a globular protein.

5.

   At pH = 7 only the terminal amine and terminal carboxyl groups will be ionized. The charges cancel out making the molecule a zwitterion.

6. The iron-binding protein could be classified as a
   Defense protein: By binding iron, this protein protects these bacteria from other microorganisms that use the iron to outgrow them.
   Transport protein: After binding iron, this protein might move the iron back into these bacterial cells.
   Storage protein: After binding iron, this protein might retain the iron for future use by these bacteria.

7. Gene therapy is described as causing a permanent change because a change in DNA remains through the life of the cell and is transmitted to succeeding generations. RNA interference is described as causing a temporary change because the affected RNA is only present in the cell for a short time span.

8. The dipeptides are not the same as peptides, which are always named from the N-terminal to the C-terminal end. In phe-asp there is an N-terminal phe group and a C-terminal asp group while in asp-phe there is an N-terminal asp group and a C-terminal phe group. So asp-phe is not the same as phe-asp. Both peptides will give a positive xanthoproteic test as they contain phe that has an aromatic side group. Possible codon sequences for asp-phe are GAUUUU, GAUUUC, GACUUU or GACUUC.

9.

CHAPTERS 32–35

Multiple Choice: 1. b 2. a 3. d 4. c 5. a 6. c 7. b
8. c 9. b 10. c 11. a 12. c 13. b 14. a 15. b 16. d
17. b 18. c 19. a 20. b 21. a 22. a 23. d 24. b 25. c
26. b 27. c 28. a 29. b 30. d 31. c 32. c 33. b 34. d
35. b 36. b 37. a 38. b 39. a 40. c 41. d 42. d 43. c
44. b 45. c 46. c 47. b 48. b 49. a 50. d 51. c 52. c
53. a 54. b 55. c 56. c 57. c 58. b 59. b 60. a

Free Response:

1. The vitamin is water soluble. The relatively small size of the molecule and the presence of three polar, hydrophilic OH groups as well as an NH group should enable this molecule to hydrogen-bond with water fairly effectively. (The vitamin is pyridoxine or vitamin B_6.)

2. Disagree. Photosynthesis is an anabolic process, building larger molecules (glucose) from smaller precursors (carbon dioxide) with an energy input (sunlight). A catabolic process breaks down larger biomolecules to smaller products and releases metabolic energy.

3.
   $$H_2C-OH$$
   $$HC-OH + 3\ CH_3(CH_2)_{16}COOH$$
   $$H_2C-OH$$
   glycerol   stearic acid

   $$H_2C-OH$$
   $$HC-OH + 3\ CH_3(CH_2)_7CH=CH(CH_2)_7COOH$$
   $$H_2C-OH$$
   glycerol   oleic acid

   The molecules represent triacylglycerols, which are lipids. Lipids are macronutrients. The above molecules specifically represent a fat (glycerol and stearic acid products) and an oil (glycerol and oleic acid products). The fat provides a little more cellular energy than the oil because its carbons are in a more reduced state. Both have the same number of carbon atoms, but the unsaturated carbons in the oil are in a more oxidized state than the saturated carbons in the fat.

4. Under normal circumstances, the liver maintains blood-glucose levels while skeletal muscle uses blood-glucose as an energy

supply to carry out work. Without a glycogen supply, the liver can no longer replenish blood glucose and the ability of skeletal muscle to do work will be compromised.

5. The goal of fatty acid beta oxidation is to increase cellular ATP levels, yet this pathway only produces reduced coenzymes, NADH and FADH$_2$. These coenzymes must be reacted with molecular oxygen in electron-transport/oxidative phosphorylation to make ATP. Beta oxidation is classified as aerobic because ATP is only produced in conjunction with electron-transport/oxidative phosphorylation.

6. Fatty acid catabolism (breakdown) occurs two carbon atoms at a time. Each set of two carbons cleaved from the fatty acid produces a molecule of acetyl-CoA. Each mole of acetyl-CoA produces 12 moles of ATP from the citric acid cycle. Therefore if 96 moles of ATP are produced, 8 moles of acetyl-CoA entered the citric acid cycle. The fatty acid had 16 carbons and must have been palmitic acid.

carbohydrate $\xrightarrow[\text{mouth or saliva}]{\alpha\text{-amylase}}$

7.

maltose $\xrightarrow{\text{intestines}}$ glucose

glucose $\xrightarrow[\text{pathaway}]{\text{Embden–Meyerhof}}$ pyruvate $\longrightarrow$

acetyl-CoA $\xrightarrow[\text{cycle}]{\text{citric acid}}$ CO$_2$

8. glu-phe-asp-asn-val-
-tyr-trp-ala-val-phe- $\xrightarrow{\text{A. stomach}}$ glu-phe
-asp-asn-val-tyr-
trp-ala-val-phe

glu
phe
asp
asn
val $\xleftarrow{\text{B. intestines}}$ tyr $\xrightarrow{\text{C. liver}}$ urea
trp
ala
val
phe

GLOSSARY

A

absolute zero $-273°C$, the zero point on the Kelvin (absolute) temperature scale. *See also* Kelvin temperature scale. [12.3]

acetal With an excess of alcohol, two alcohols can react with a carbonyl to form an acetal (from an aldehyde) and a ketal (from a ketone). The carbon in an acetal or ketal is bonded to two ether oxygens. [23.4]

achiral Molecules that are superimposable on their mirror images are described as achiral. [26.2]

acid ionization constant (K_a) The equilibrium constant for the ionization of a weak acid in water. [16.6]

activation energy The amount of energy needed to start a chemical reaction. [8.4, 16.3]

active transport Active transport is aided by a protein and also requires energy. [28.6]

activity series of metals A listing of metallic elements in descending order of reactivity. [17.4]

actual yield The amount of product actually produced in a chemical reaction (compared with the theoretical yield). [9.5]

addition polymer An addition polymer (e.g., polyethylene) uses an addition reaction to connect monomers together. [21.3]

addition reaction In an addition reaction, two reactants add together to form a single product. [19.9]

adenosine diphosphate (ADP) The ester may be a monophosphate (MP), a diphosphate (DP), or a triphosphate (TP). [31.2]

adenosine triphosphate (ATP) The ester may be a monophosphate (MP), a diphosphate (DP), or a triphosphate (TP). [31.2]

aerobic metabolism Biochemical reactions that depend on the presence of O_2. [34.1]

alcohol An alcohol is an organic compound that contains the hydroxyl functional group. [22.1]

aldehyde Aldehydes have at least one hydrogen atom bonded to a carbonyl carbon. [23.1]

aldol condensation In an aldol condensation, two carbonyl-containing molecules (either aldehydes or ketones) connect together. [23.4]

aldose A monosaccharide that contains an aldehyde functional group. [27.2]

aliphatic Compounds that contain benzene rings are aromatic, while all other organic compounds are classified as aliphatic. [19.4]

alkali metal An element (except H) from Group 1A of the periodic table. [3.2]

alkaline earth metal An element from Group 2A of the periodic table. [3.2]

alkaloid Basic compounds that are derived from plants and show physiological activity are known as alkaloids. [25.8]

alkane Alkanes are saturated hydrocarbons. [19.5]

alkene Alkenes are hydrocarbons that contain carbon–carbon double bonds. [20.1]

alkoxide ion An alkoxide ion is formed when an alcohol is deprotonated. [22.4]

alkyl group Alkyl groups have one less hydrogen than the corresponding alkanes. Their formulas are C_nH_{2n+1}. [19.8]

alkyl halide Alkyl halides are formed when alkanes react with halogens. [19.10]

alkyne Alkynes are hydrocarbons that contain carbon–carbon triple bonds. [20.1]

alpha (α) amino acid Amino acids found in proteins are called alpha (α) amino acids because the amine group is bonded to the first or α-carbon, adjacent to the carboxyl group. [29.2]

alpha particle (α) A particle emitted from a nucleus of an atom during radioactive decay; it consists of two protons and two neutrons with a mass of about 4 amu and a charge of $+2$; it is considered to be a doubly charged helium atom. [18.2]

amide Amides are neutral, nonionic compounds that contain the following characteristic structure:

$$-\overset{\overset{\displaystyle O}{\|}}{C}-\overset{|}{N}- \text{ [25.1]}$$

amine An amine is a substituted ammonia molecule bonded to at least one alkyl or aryl group (R). [25.5]

amines are bases Like ammonia, amines are bases. Amines accept a proton from water, forming substituted ammonium ions. When the nitrogen is protonated, the *-amine* ending is changed to *-ammonium* and the *-aniline* is changed to *-anilinium*. Amines are only weak bases like ammonia. [25.7]

amino acid pool The amino acid pool supplies other nitrogen pools such as the tissue proteins. [35.6]

amorphous A solid without shape or form. [1.3]

amphoteric A substance having properties of both an acid and a base. [15.2]

amphoteric (or amphiprotic) A compound that can react as either an acid or a base. [29.2]

anabolism Anabolism is the process by which simple substances are synthesized into complex substances. [33.1]

anaerobic metabolism Biochemical reactions that do not depend the presence of O_2. [34.1]

anion A negatively charged ion. *See also* ion. [3.3]

anode The electrode where oxidation occurs in an electrochemical reaction. [17.5]

anomer When two cyclic isomers differ only in their stereo arrangement at a new chiral carbon, they are called anomers. [27.6]

apoenzyme Some enzymes are conjugated proteins; the protein part is the apoenzyme, and the nonprotein part is the coenzyme. As a whole, the conjugated protein is termed a holoenzyme. [30.1]

apoptosis Apoptosis is cell instigated self-destruction. [31.8]

aromatic compound Aromatic compounds are hydrocarbons that contain benzene rings. [20.1]

artificial radioactivity Radioactivity produced in nuclides during some types of transmutations. Artificial radioactive nuclides behave like natural radioactive elements in two ways: They disintegrate in a definite fashion, and they have a specific half-life. Sometimes called *induced radioactivity*. [18.3]

asymmetric carbon atom Optical activity is commonly associated with asymmetric carbon atoms. An asymmetric carbon atom is bonded to four different groups. [26.2]

1 atmosphere The standard atmospheric pressure, that is, the pressure exerted by a column of mercury 760 mm high at a temperature of 0°C. *See also* atmospheric pressure. [12.1]

atmospheric pressure The pressure experienced by objects on Earth as a result of the layer of air surrounding our planet. A pressure of 1 atmosphere (1 atm) is the pressure that will support a column of mercury 760 mm high at 0°C. [12.1]

atom The smallest particle of an element that can enter into a chemical reaction. [3.1]

atomic mass The average relative mass of the isotopes of an element referred to the atomic mass of carbon-12. [5.6]

atomic mass unit (amu) A unit of mass equal to one-twelfth the mass of a carbon-12 atom. [5.6]

atomic number (Z) The number of protons in the nucleus of an atom of a given element. *See also* isotopic notation. [5.4]

Avogadro's law Equal volumes of different gases at the same temperature and pressure contain equal numbers of molecules. [12.4]

Avogadro's number 6.022×10^{23}; the number of formula units in 1 mole. [7.1]

axial hydrogen The conformations of cyclohexane hold the molecule's hydrogen atoms in either the plane of the ring (equatorial hydrogens) or roughly perpendicular to the ring (axial hydrogens). [19.11]

B

balanced diet A diet that supplies all the necessary nutrients is said to be "balanced." [32.9]

balanced equation A chemical equation having the same number of each kind of atom and the same electrical charge on each side of the equation. [8.2]

barometer A device used to measure atmospheric pressure. [12.1]

basal metabolic rate The basic energy cost for maintaining life. [34.1]

bent structure Molecular structure in which the molecule looks like a V. The electron structure is tetrahedral but there are 2 pairs of nonbonding electrons. [11.10]

beta oxidation Beta oxidation, or the two-carbon chop, is a series of reactions whereby the first two carbon atoms of the fatty acid chain become the acetyl group in a molecule of acetyl-CoA. Beta oxidation repeats a set of reactions (oxidation, hydration, oxidation, cleavage) until the whole fatty acid chain has been converted into acetyl-CoA molecules. [35.2]

beta particle (β) A particle identical in charge (-1) and mass to an electron. [18.2]

binary compounds Compounds which are composed of two different elements. [6.4]

biodegradable Biodegradable refers to organic substances that are readily decomposed by microorganisms in the environment. [24.10]

bioenergetics Bioenergetics is the study of the transformation, distribution, and utilization of energy by living organisms. [33.1]

biogenic amines Biogenic amines are derived from amino acids and act as neurotransmitters and hormones in animals. [25.8]

boiling point The temperature at which the vapor pressure of a liquid is equal to the pressure above the liquid. It is called the normal boiling when the pressure is 1 atmosphere. [13.3]

Boyle's law The relationship between pressure and volume of a gas. At constant temperature, the volume of a fixed mass of gas is inversely proportional to the pressure ($PV = $ constant). [12.2]

buffer solution A solution that resists changes in pH when diluted or when small amounts of a strong acid or strong base are added. [16.8]

C

calorie (cal) A commonly used unit of heat energy; 1 calorie is a quantity of heat energy that will raise the temperature of 1 g of water 1°C (e.g., from 14.5 to 15.5°C). Also, 4.184 joules $=$ 1 calorie exactly. *See also* joule. [4.5]

capillary action The spontaneous rising of a liquid in a narrow tube, which results from the cohesive forces within the liquid and the adhesive forces between the liquid and the walls of the container. [13.2]

carbocation The alkene addition reaction follows a series of steps (a reaction mechanism) that involves a carbocation. A carbocation is a positively charged carbon ion. [20.5]

carbohydrate Carbohydrates are among the most important classes of biochemicals. Carbohydrates are generally defined as polyhydroxy aldehydes or polyhydroxy ketones or substances that yield these compounds when hydrolyzed. [27.1]

carbonyl group Both aldehydes and ketones contain the carbonyl group, $\diagdown C{=}O$, a carbon–oxygen double bond. [23.1]

carboxyl group Carboxylic acids contain the carboxyl group, which can be represented as follows:

$$-\overset{\overset{\displaystyle O}{\|}}{C}{-}OH \text{ or } -COOH \text{ or } -CO_2H. \text{ [24.1]}$$

catabolism Catabolism is the process by which complex substances are broken down into simpler substances. [33.1]

catalyst A substance that influences the rate of a reaction and can be recovered essentially unchanged at the end of the reaction. [16.3]

cathode The electrode where reduction occurs in an electrochemical reaction. [17.5]

cation A positively charged ion. *See also* ion. [3.3]

chain reaction A self-sustaining nuclear or chemical reaction in which the products cause the reaction to continue or to increase in magnitude. [18.5]

Charles' law At constant pressure, the volume of a fixed mass of any gas is directly proportional to the absolute temperature (V/T = constant). [12.3]

chemical change A change producing products that differ in composition from the original substances. [4.2]

chemical equation A shorthand expression showing the reactants and the products of a chemical change (e.g., $2\,H_2O = 2\,H_2 + O_2$). [4.2, 8.1]

chemical equilibrium The state in which the rate of the forward reaction equals the rate of the reverse reaction in a chemical change. [16.2]

chemical formula A shorthand method for showing the composition of a compound, using symbols of the elements. [3.3]

chemical kinetics The study of reaction rates and reaction mechanisms. [16.1]

chemical properties The ability of a substance to form new substances either by reaction with other substances or by decomposition. [4.1]

chemistry The science of the composition, structure, properties, and reactions of matter, especially of atomic and molecular systems. [1.1]

chiral A molecule that is not superimposable on its mirror image is said to be chiral. [26.2]

chiral carbon atom An asymmetric carbon atom can also be described as a chiral carbon atom. [26.2]

chromatographic method The components of a mixture are separated by means of differences in their distributions between two phases. [29.8]

***cis-trans* isomers** Molecules having the same bonded order of atoms but differing in the spatial arrangement of these atoms. Also known as geometric isomers. [20.3]

citric acid cycle The citric acid cycle is a cyclic metabolic pathway that converts the acetate carbons of acetyl-CoA to carbon dioxide. [34.3]

codon Each code word in DNA is a three-nucleotide sequence and is called a codon. Almost every codon signals a specific amino acid. Three codons are nonsense or termination codons and signal the end of protein synthesis. [31.9]

coenzyme Some enzymes are conjugated proteins; the protein part is the apoenzyme, and the nonprotein part is the coenzyme. As a whole, the conjugated protein is termed a holoenzyme. [30.1]

colligative properties Properties of a solution that depend on the number of solute particles in solution and not on the nature of the solute (examples: vapor pressure lowering, freezing point depression, boiling point elevation). [14.5]

combination reaction A direct union or combination of two substances to produce one new substance. [8.3]

common energy currency (ATP) An easily accessible and readily released energy store usable by many metabolic reactions. [33.4]

common ion effect The shift of a chemical equilibrium caused by the addition of an ion common to the ions in the equilibrium. [16.7]

complementary base pairs (AT, GC) Although the nucleotide composition may vary among different DNAs, the ratios of A to T and G to C are always essentially 1:1. [31.5]

complete protein A complete protein provides all the essential amino acids. [32.3]

compound A distinct substance composed of two or more elements combined in a definite proportion by mass. [3.3]

concentrated solution A solution containing a relatively large amount of dissolved solute. [14.4]

concentration of a solution A quantitative expression of the amount of dissolved solute in a certain quantity of solvent. [14.2]

condensation The process by which molecules in the gaseous state return to the liquid state. [13.2]

condensation polymer A condensation polymer (e.g., nylon) is formed when monomers bond together with a loss of water (a substitution reaction). [21.3]

condensation reaction A reaction in which two molecules (e.g., two 1° alcohols) are combined by removing a small molecule (e.g., water) is known as a condensation reaction. [22.4]

condensed structural formula In contrast to inorganic compounds, organic compounds are often written in structural or condensed structural formulas. [19.6]

conformation Cycloalkanes have well-defined three-dimensional shapes known as conformations. [19.11]

conjugated protein Conjugated proteins yield amino acids and additional products upon hydrolysis. [29.1]

copolymer A copolymer is made up of two different kinds of monomers. A copolymer's properties depend on the ratio of the two different monomers in the mixture. [21.6]

covalent bond A chemical bond formed between two atoms by sharing a pair of electrons. [11.5]

conversion factor A ratio of equivalent quantities. [2.5]

cracking A cracking process breaks saturated hydrocarbons into smaller pieces by heating the molecules to high temperatures in the presence of a catalyst. [20.5]

critical mass The minimum quantity of mass required to support a self-sustaining chain reaction. [18.5]

curie (Ci) A unit of radioactivity indicating the rate of decay of a radioactive substance: 1 Ci $= 3.7 \times 10^{10}$ disintegrations per second. [18.4]

cyanohydrin Cyanohydrins are formed by the addition of HCN to a carbonyl group. The cyanohydrin carbon is bonded to an hydroxyl group and a cyano ($-$CN) group. [23.4]

cycloalkane Cycloalkanes are cyclic structures with the general formula C_nH_{2n}. [19.11]

cycloalkene Cycloalkenes are cyclic compounds that contain a double bond in the ring. [20.4]

D

Dalton's atomic model The first modern atomic theory to state that elements are composed of minute individual particles called *atoms*. [5.1]

Dalton's law of partial pressures The total pressure of a mixture of gases is the sum of the partial pressures exerted by each of the gases in the mixture. [12.7]

D-amino acids D-amino acids have the amine group on the right side of the α-carbon. [29.2]

decomposition reaction A breaking down, or decomposition, of one substance into two or more different substances. [8.3]

dehydration Dehydration removes water from alcohols to form alkenes. [20.5]

denaturation If a protein loses only its natural three-dimensional conformation, the process is referred to as denaturation. [29.7]

density The mass of an object divided by its volume. [2.8]

deoxyribonucleic acid (DNA) Deoxyribonucleic acid (DNA) is a polynucleotide that, upon hydrolysis, yields deoxyribose, phosphoric acid, and the four purine and pyrimidine bases adenine, guanine, cytosine, and thymine. [31.4]

dextrorotatory If the plane-polarized light is rotated in a clockwise manner as it passes through a solution, the solute is dextrorotatory. [26.2]

diastereomer Stereoisomers that are not mirror images (enantiomers) are called diastereomers. [26.6]

diatomic molecules The molecules of elements that always contain two atoms. Seven elements occur as diatomic molecules: H_2, N_2, O_2, F_2, Cl_2, Br_2, and I_2. [3.2]

diet A diet is the food and drink that we consume. [32.1]

Dietary Reference Intake (DRI) The Dietary Reference Intake (DRI) takes into account the many different types of nutrient data needed to judge a healthful diet. It is based generally on either a Recommended Dietary Allowance or an Adequate Intake. [32.1]

digestion Digestion is a series of enzyme-catalyzed reactions by which large molecules are hydrolyzed to molecules small enough to be absorbed through the intestinal membranes. [32.10]

dilute solution A solution containing a relatively small amount of dissolved solute. [14.4]

dipole A molecule that is electrically asymmetrical, causing it to be oppositely charged at two points. [11.6]

dipole–dipole attractions Forces of attraction between polar molecules as a result of the dipole moment within each molecule. [13.5]

disaccharide A disaccharide yields two monosaccharides when hydrolyzed. [27.2]

dissociation The process by which a salt separates into individual ions when dissolved in water. [15.4]

DNA polymerase chain reaction (PCR) The enzyme, DNA polymerase, is used to synthesize specific genes in large amounts even in the presence of other genetic material. [31.10]

double-displacement reaction A reaction of two compounds to produce two different compounds by exchanging the components of the reacting compounds. [8.3]

double helix According to the structure proposed by Watson and Crick, the structure of DNA consists of two polymeric strands in the form of a double helix with both nucleotide strands coiled around the same axis. [31.5]

E

Edman degradation The Edman degradation uses phenylisothiocyanate to sequentially remove the N-terminal amino acid from a protein. [29.9]

electrolysis The process whereby electrical energy is used to bring about a chemical change. [17.5]

electrolyte A substance whose aqueous solution conducts electricity. [15.4]

electrolytic cell An electrolysis apparatus in which electrical energy from an outside source is used to produce a chemical change. [17.5]

electron A subatomic particle that exists outside the nucleus and carries a negative electrical charge. [5.3]

electron configuration The orbital arrangement of electrons in an atom. [10.4]

electronegativity The relative attraction that an atom has for a pair of shared electrons in a covalent bond. [11.6]

electrophoresis Basic amino acids have isoelectric points from 7.8 to 10.8, neutral amino acids have isoelectric points from 4.8 to 6.3, and acidic amino acids have isoelectric points from 2.8 to 3.3. [29.2]

element A basic building block of matter that cannot be broken down into simpler substances by ordinary chemical changes; in 1994, there were 111 known elements. [3.1]

elimination reaction An elimination reaction is a reaction in which a single reactant is split into two products and one of the products is eliminated. [19.9]

Embden–Meyerhof pathway The Embden–Meyerhof pathway is the anaerobic conversion of glucose to pyruvate. [34.2]

empirical formula A chemical formula that gives the smallest whole-number ratio of atoms in a compound—that is, the relative number of atoms of each element in the compound; also known as the simplest formula. [7.4]

enantiomer Chiral molecules that are mirror images of each other are stereoisomers and are called enantiomers. [26.4]

endothermic reactions A chemical reaction that absorbs heat. [8.4]

energy The capacity of matter to do work. [4.4]

enzyme Enzymes are proteins that catalyze biochemical reactions. [30.1]

enzyme activation Enzyme activation means an increase in enzyme activity. [30.7]

enzyme active site A small portion of an enzyme surface where catalysis occurs. [30.5]

enzyme inhibition Enzyme inhibition means a decrease in enzyme activity. [30.7]

epimer Any two monosaccharides that differ in configuration around a single carbon atom are called epimers. [27.5]

equatorial hydrogen The conformations of cyclohexane hold the molecule's hydrogen atoms in either the plane of the ring (equatorial hydrogens) or roughly perpendicular to the ring (axial hydrogens). [19.11]

equilibrium A dynamic state in which two or more opposing processes are taking place at the same time and at the same rate. [16.2]

equilibrium constant (K_{eq}) A constant representing the concentrations of the reactants and the products in a chemical reaction at equilibrium. [16.4]

essential amino acids Ten of the common amino acids are essential amino acids because they are needed for good health and cannot be synthesized in the human body. [29.2]

essential fatty acids A source for both omega-6 and omega-3 fatty acids. [32.3]

ester Esters are derivatives of carboxylic acids with the general formula RCOOR'. [24.4]

esterification The reaction of an acid with an alcohol to yield two molecules, water and an ester. [24.4]

Estimated Energy Requirement (EER) The Estimated Energy Requirement (EER) is the average dietary intake that is required to maintain energy balance for good health. [32.2]

ether Ethers have the general formula ROR. Simple ether names combine the names of the alkyl groups attached to the ether O followed by *ether*. [22.8]

eucaryote Eucaryotes are cells that contain internal, membrane-bound bodies called organelles. [33.1]

evaporation The escape of molecules from the liquid state to the gas or vapor state. [13.2]

exothermic reactions A chemical reaction in which heat is released as a product. [8.4]

F

facilitated diffusion Facilitated diffusion is transport across a lipid bilayer with the aid of a protein but without the need for energy input. [28.6]

fats and oils Fast and oils are esters of glycerol and predominately long-chain carboxylic acids (fatty acids). [28.2, 24.9]

feedback inhibition When an initial enzyme-catalyzed step is inhibited by a product of subsequent metabolism feedback inhibition is said to apply. [30.7]

feedforward activation When the product of an initial enzyme-catalyzed step activates a subsequent enzyme-catalyzed step, feedforward activation applies. [30.7]

Fehling and Benedict tests In the Fehling and Benedict tests, Cu^{2+} is reduced to form Cu_2O, a reddish-brown precipitate. Aldehydes are oxidized; simple ketones do not react. [23.4]

fibrous protein Fibrous proteins have highly developed secondary structures and often function in support roles. [29.6]

Fischer projection formula Projection formulas depict a three-dimensional molecule as a flat, two-dimensional drawing. [26.3]

fluid-mosaic model The fluid-mosaic model pictures a biological membrane as a fluid lipid bilayer with many imbedded proteins. [28.6]

food additives Food additives are chemicals that are added to foods during processing. [32.8]

formula equation A chemical equation in which all the reactants and products are written in their molecular, or normal, formula expression; also called a molecular equation. [15.7]

free radical A free radical is an atom or group of atoms that has an unpaired electron. [19.10]

freezing point *See* melting point. [13.3]

frequency A measurement of the number of waves that pass a particular point per second. [10.1]

functional group Functional groups represent different classes of compounds. [19.3]

G

gamma ray (γ) High-energy photons emitted by radioactive nuclei; they have no electrical charge and no measurable mass. [18.2]

gas A state of matter that has no shape or definite volume so that the substance completely fills its container. [1.3]

Gay-Lussac's law of combining volumes When measured at the same temperature and pressure, the ratios of the volumes of reacting gases are small whole numbers. [12.4]

gene A gene is a segment of the DNA chain that controls the formation of a molecule of RNA. [31.6]

genetic engineering Genetic engineering is a process for introducing controlled genetic change. [31.10]

genome The genome is the sum of all hereditary material contained in a cell. [31.6]

geometric isomers Geometric isomers differ in their molecular geometry but not in the bonded order of their atoms, also called *cis–trans* isomers. [20.3]

globular protein Globular proteins have a more complex tertiary structure and a compact shape. Globular proteins provide more complex biochemical functions than do fibrous proteins. [29.6]

glucogenic amino acid Glucogenic amino acids can be used to produce glucose. [35.7]

gluconeogenesis Gluconeogenesis is the formation of glucose from noncarbohydrate precursors. [34.4]

glycogenesis Glycogenesis is the synthesis of glycogen from glucose. [34.1]

glycogenolysis Glycogenolysis is the catabolic pathway that converts glycogen to glucose. [34.1]

glycolipids Glycolipids yield sphingosine and a carbohydrate as well as a fatty acid upon hydrolysis. [28.4]

glycolysis Glycolysis produces lactate from glucose by combining the Embden–Meyerhof pathway with a reaction that reduces pyruvate to lactate. [34.2]

glycoside When a monosaccharide hemiacetal reacts with an alcohol, the product is an acetal; this product is a glycoside in carbohydrate terminology. [27.7]

glycosuria Any condition where glucose is excreted in the urine. [27.4]

ground state The lowest available energy level within an atom. [10.2]

groups or families (of elements) Vertical groups of elements in the periodic table (1A, 2A, and so on). Families of elements that have similar outer-orbital electron structures. [3.2, 10.5]

H

half-life ($t_{1/2}$) The time required for one-half of a specific amount of a radioactive nuclide to disintegrate; half-lives of the elements range from a fraction of a second to billions of years. [18.1]

halogens Group 7A of the periodic table; consists of the elements fluorine, chlorine, bromine, iodine, and astatine. [3.2]

heat Flow of energy due to a temperature difference. [2.7]

heat of fusion The energy required to change 1 gram of a solid into a liquid at its melting point. [13.4]

heat of reaction The quantity of heat produced by a chemical reaction. [8.4]

heat of vaporization The amount of heat required to change 1 gram of a liquid to a vapor at its normal boiling point. [13.4]

hemiacetal A hemiacetal is formed when an alcohol adds across an aldehyde carbonyl double bond. If an alcohol adds to a ketone, a hemiketal is produced. [23.4]

hemiketal The carbon in a hemiacetal or hemiketal is bonded to both an ether oxygen and an alcohol oxygen. [23.4]

heredity Heredity is the process by which the physical and mental characteristics of parents are transferred to their offspring. [31.6]

heterocyclic compound Heterocyclic compounds are ring structures where the atoms forming the ring are not all alike. Many nitrogen-containing heterocyclic compounds are present in naturally occurring biochemicals. [25.5]

heterogeneous Matter without a uniform composition—having two or more components or phases. [1.4]

high-energy phosphate bonds Bonds to phosphate that are transportable throughout the cell and allow work to be done. [33.4]

holoenzyme Some enzymes are conjugated proteins; the protein part is the apoenzyme, and the nonprotein part is the coenzyme. As a whole, the conjugated protein is termed a holoenzyme. [30.1]

homogeneous Matter that has uniform properties throughout. [1.4]

homologous series A functional group of compounds in which successive members differ by a CH_2 group. [19.5]

hormones Hormones are chemical substances that act as control agents in the body, often regulating metabolic pathways. [34.6]

hybridization A specific number of different atomic orbitals (e.g., s and p orbitals) are mixed to form the same number of equivalent hybrid orbitals. [19.2]

hydrate A solid that contains water molecules as a part of its crystalline structure. [13.6]

hydrocarbon Compounds that contain only hydrogen and carbon are called hydrocarbons. [19.4]

hydrocarbons Compounds composed entirely of carbon and hydrogen. [8.4, 19.2]

hydrogen bond The intermolecular force acting between molecules that contain hydrogen covalently bonded to the highly electronegative elements F, O, and N. [13.5]

hydrogenolysis Hydrogenolysis breaks a triacylglycerol into glycerol and three long-chain primary alcohols. [24.9]

hydronium ion The result of a proton combining with a polar water molecule to form a hydrated hydrogen ion, H_3O^+. [15.1]

hydrophilic The fatty acid anion combines properties described as hydrophilic (water-loving) and hydrophobic (water-fearing). [24.10]

hydrophobic The fatty acid anion combines properties described as hydrophilic (water-loving) and hydrophobic (water-fearing). [24.10]

hypothesis A tentative explanation of certain facts to provide a basis for further experimentation. [1.2]

I

ideal gas A gas that behaves precisely according to the kinetic-molecular theory; also called a perfect gas. [12.6]

ideal gas law $PV = nRT$; that is, the volume of a gas varies *directly* with the number of gas molecules and the absolute temperature and *inversely* with the pressure. [12.6]

immiscible Incapable of mixing; immiscible liquids do not form a solution with one another. [14.2]

induced-fit model The active site structure changes slightly in response to substrate binding. This is called the induced-fit model. [30.5]

induced radioactivity *See* artificial radioactivity. [18.3]

intermolecular forces Forces of attraction between molecules. [13.5]

International System *See* SI, Systeme International. [2.5]

intramolecular forces Forces of attractions within a molecule, for example a covalent bond. [13.5]

invert sugar Invert sugar is made by hydrolyzing sucrose to form a mixture of glucose and fructose. [27.10]

ion A positively or negatively charged atom or group of atoms. *See also* cation, anion. [3.3]

ionic bond The chemical bond between a positively charged ion and a negatively charged ion. [11.3]

ionization The formation of ions, which occurs as the result of a chemical reaction of certain substances with water. [15.4]

ionization energy The energy required to remove an electron from an atom, an ion, or a molecule. [11.1]

ionizing radiation Radiation with enough energy to dislocate bonding electrons and create ions when passing through matter. [18.7]

ion product constant for water (K_w) An equilibrium constant defined as the product of the H^+ ion concentration and the OH^- ion concentration, each in moles per liter. $K_w = [H^+][OH^-] = 1 \times 10^{-14}$ at 25°C. [16.5]

isoelectric point The pH at which an amino acid has no overall charge (and will not migrate in an electrolytic cell) is called the isoelectric point. [29.2]

isomer Molecules with different structural formulas that have the same molecular formula are isomers of each other. [19.7]

isomerism Isomerism is the phenomenon that two or more different compounds have the same molecular formula but different structures. [19.7]

isotope An atom of an element that has the same atomic number but a different atomic mass. Since their atomic numbers are identical, isotopes vary only in the number of neutrons in the nucleus. [5.5]

IUPAC System The IUPAC System derives a name using a set of rules based on an organic compound's structural formula. [19.8]

J

joule (J) The SI unit of energy. *See also* calorie. [4.5]

K

ketal With an excess of alcohol, two alcohols can react with a carbonyl to form an acetal (from an aldehyde) and a ketal (from a ketone). The carbon in an acetal or ketal is bonded to two ether oxygens. [23.4]

ketogenic amino acid Some amino acids can be directly converted to acetyl-CoA and can cause an increase in ketone body concentrations; these amino acids are ketogenic amino acids. [35.7]

ketone Ketones have only alkyl or aryl groups bonded to the carbonyl carbon. [23.1]

ketone bodies When the human body is low in glucose, ketone bodies are produced as a partial substitute. [35.4]

ketose A monosaccharide that contains a ketone functional group. [27.2]

Kiliani–Fischer synthesis A laboratory conversion that extends an aldose chain by one carbon via a carbonyl addition reaction with hydrogen cyanide. [27.5]

kilogram (kg) The standard unit of mass in the metric system; 1 kilogram equals 2.205 pounds. [2.5]

kinetic energy (KE) The energy that matter possesses due to its motion; $KE = 1/2\ mv^2$. [4.4]

kinetic-molecular theory (KMT) A group of assumptions used to explain the behavior and properties of gases. [12.6]

kwashiorkor Protein malnutrition. [32.3]

L

L-amino acids L-amino acids have the amine group on the left side of the α-carbon. [29.2]

law of conservation of energy Energy can be neither created nor destroyed, though it can be transferred from one form to another. [4.4]

law of conservation of mass No change is observed in the total mass of the substances involved in a chemical reaction; that is, the mass of the products equals the mass of the reactants. [8.1]

law of definite composition A compound always contains two or more elements in a definite proportion by mass. [3.3]

law of multiple proportions Atoms of two or more elements may combine in different ratios to produce more than one compound. [3.3]

Le Châtelier's principle If a stress is applied to a system in equilibrium, the system will respond in such a way as to relieve that stress and restore equilibrium under a new set of conditions. [16.3]

levorotatory If the plane-polarized light is rotated in a counter-clockwise manner as it passes through a solution, the solute is levorotatory. [26.2]

Lewis structure A method of indicating the covalent bonds between atoms in a molecule or an ion such that a pair of electrons (:) represents the valence electrons forming the covalent bond. [11.2]

limiting reactant A reactant that limits the amount of product formed because it is present in insufficient amount compared with the other reactants. [9.5]

line spectrum Colored lines generated when light emitted by a gas is passed through a spectroscope. Each element possesses a unique set of line spectra. [10.2]

line structures Line structures simplify structural formulas and are often used for molecules that are complex or that contain rings. [19.6]

linear structure In the VSEPR model, an arrangement where the pairs of electrons are arranged 180° apart for maximum separation. [11.10]

lipases Lipases are enzymes that digest lipids. [30.4]

lipid bilayer A lipid bilayer is composed of two adjoining layers of compound lipid molecules so that their hydrophobic portions form the bilayer interior while their hydrophilic portions form the bilayer exterior. [28.6]

lipids Lipids are water-insoluble, oily, or greasy biochemicals. Lipids are described as hydrophobic (water fearing). [28.1]

lipogenesis The biosynthesis of fatty acids from acetyl-CoA is called lipogenesis. [35.3]

liquid A state of matter in which the particles move about freely while the substance retains a definite volume; thus, liquids flow and take the shape of their containers. [1.3]

liter (L) A unit of volume commonly used in chemistry; $1 L = 1000$ mL; the volume of a kilogram of water at 4°C. [2.5]

lock-and-key hypothesis Enzyme specificity is partly due to a complementary relationship between the structure of the active site and the structure of the substrate; this is the lock-and-key hypothesis. [30.5]

logarithm (log) The power to which 10 must be raised to give a certain number. The log of 100 is 2.0. [15.5]

London dispersion forces Attractive forces between nonpolar molecules which result from instantaneous formation of dipoles in the electron cloud. [13.5]

M

macromolecules Macromolecules commonly contain thousands of atoms. [21.1]

macronutrient Carbohydrates, lipids, and proteins are classified as macronutrients because they are used in relatively large amounts by cells. [32.1]

marasmus A wasting disease due to starvation. [32.2]

Markovnikov's rule Markovnikov's rule states that when a hydrogen-containing unsymmetric molecule (HX) adds to a double bond, the hydrogen will add to the carbon with the greatest number of hydrogens. Markovnikov's rule can be explained based on the stability of carbocations. [20.5]

mass The quantity or amount of matter that an object possesses. [2.5]

mass defect The difference between the actual mass of an atom of an isotope and the calculated mass of the protons and neutrons in the nucleus of that atom. [18.6]

mass number (A) The sum of the protons and neutrons in the nucleus of a given isotope of an atom. [5.5]

matter Anything that has mass and occupies space. [1.3]

measurement A quantitative observation which requires both a number and a unit. [2.1]

mechanism The mechanism for a reaction is the path it takes to go from reactants to products. [19.10]

meiosis Meiosis occurs when the cell splits in such a way as to reduce the number of chromosomes to one-half the normal amount. [31.6]

melting point (or freezing point) The temperature at which the solid and liquid states of a substance are in equilibrium. [13.3]

meniscus The shape of the surface of a liquid when placed in a glass cylinder. It can be concave or convex. [13.2]

mercaptan Thiols or mercaptans are organic compounds that contain the — SH group. [22.10]

meso compound Stereoisomers that contain chiral carbon atoms and are superimposable on their mirror images are called meso compounds or meso structures. Meso compounds are not optically active and are achiral compounds. [26.6]

meso structure Stereoisomers that contain chiral carbon atoms and are superimposable on their mirror images are called meso compounds or meso structures. [26.6]

metabolic pathway A metabolic pathway is a series of biochemical reactions that serves a specific purpose. [34.1]

metabolism Metabolism is the sum of all chemical reactions that occur within a living organism. [33.1]

metal An element that is solid at room temperature and whose properties include luster, ductility, malleability, and good conductivity of heat and electricity; metals tend to lose their valence electrons and become positive ions. [3.2]

metalloid An element having properties that are intermediate between those of metals and nonmetals (e.g., silicon); these elements are useful in electronics. [3.2]

meter (m) The standard unit of length in the SI and metric systems; 1 meter equals 39.37 inches. [2.5]

metric system A decimal system of measurements. *See also* SI. [2.5]

micronutrient Vitamins and minerals are used in relatively small amounts and are classed as micronutrients. [32.1]

minerals in the diet Minerals are micronutrients that come from inorganic sources. [32.5]

miscible Capable of mixing and forming a solution. [14.2]

mitosis Mitosis occurs during normal cell division when each daughter cell gains the full genetic code that was present in the parent. [31.6]

mixture Matter containing two or more substances, which can be present in variable amounts; mixtures can be homogeneous (sugar water) or heterogeneous (sand and water). [1.4]

molality (m) An expression of the number of moles of solute dissolved in 1000 g of solvent. [14.5]

molarity (M) The number of moles of solute per liter of solution. [14.4]

molar mass The mass of Avogadro's number of atoms or molecules. The sum of the atomic masses of all the atoms in an element, compound, or ion. The mass of a mole of any formula unit. It is also known as the molecular weight. [7.1, 9.1]

molar volume The volume of 1 mol of a gas at STP equals 22.4 L/mol. [12.5]

mole The amount of a substance containing the same number of formula units (6.022×10^{23}) as there are in exactly 12 g of ^{12}C. One mole is equal to the molar mass in grams of any substance. [7.1]

molecular formula The total number of atoms of each element present in one molecule of a compound; also known as the true formula. *See also* empirical formula. [7.5]

molecule The smallest uncharged individual unit of a compound formed by the union of two or more atoms. [3.3]

mole ratio A ratio between the number of moles of any two species involved in a chemical reaction; the mole ratio is used as a conversion factor in stoichiometric calculations. [9.1]

monomer A monomer is a small bonded group of atoms that forms polymers by reacting with other monomers. [21.1]

monosaccharide A monosaccharide is a carbohydrate that cannot be hydrolyzed to simpler carbohydrate units. [27.2]

monosubstitution Substituting one halogen atom for a hydrogen atom in an alkane is an example of a monosubstitution reaction. [19.10]

mutagen A mutagen is an agent that causes a mutation. [31.10]

mutarotation Mutarotation is the process by which anomers are interconverted. [27.6]

mutation Mutations are traits that are generally the result of genetic or chromosomal changes. [31.10]

N

natural law A statement summarizing general observations regarding nature. [3.3]

negative nitrogen balance A fasting or starving person ingests less nitrogen than is excreted and is in a negative nitrogen balance. [35.6]

net ionic equation A chemical equation that includes only those molecules and ions that have changed in the chemical reaction. [15.7]

neutralization The reaction of an acid and a base to form a salt plus water. [15.6]

neutron A subatomic particle that is electrically neutral and is found in the nucleus of an atom. [5.3]

nitrogen balance When the amount of excreted nitrogen equals the amount of nitrogen ingested, nitrogen balance is achieved. [35.6]

nitrogen cycle The nitrogen cycle describes the process by which nitrogen is circulated and recirculated from the atmosphere through living organisms and back to the atmosphere. [35.5]

nitrogen fixation Nitrogen fixation is the conversion of diatomic nitrogen to a biochemically usable form. [35.5]

noble gases A family of elements in the periodic table—helium, neon, argon, krypton, xenon, and radon—that contains a particularly stable electron structure. [3.2]

nonelectrolyte A substance whose aqueous solutions do not conduct electricity. [15.4]

nonmetal An element that has properties the opposite of metals: lack of luster, relatively low melting point and density, and generally poor conduction of heat and electricity. Nonmetals may or may not be solid at room temperature (examples: carbon, bromine, nitrogen); many are gases. They are located mainly in the upper right-hand corner of the periodic table. [3.2]

nonpolar covalent bond A covalent bond between two atoms with the same electronegativity value; thus, the electrons are shared equally between the two atoms. [11.6]

normal boiling point The temperature at which the vapor pressure of a liquid equals 1 atm or 760 torr pressure. [13.3]

nuclear binding energy The energy equivalent to the mass defect; that is, the amount of energy required to break a nucleus into its individual protons and neutrons. [18.6]

nuclear fission A nuclear reaction in which a heavy nucleus splits into two smaller nuclei and two or more neutrons. [18.5]

nuclear fusion The uniting of two light elements to form one heavier nucleus, which is accompanied by the release of energy. [18.5]

nucleic acid Nucleic acids are polymers of nucleotides that contain either the sugar deoxyribose (deoxyribonucleic acid, DNA) or the sugar ribose (ribonucleic acid, RNA). [31.1]

nucleon A collective term for the neutrons and protons in the nucleus of an atom. [18.1]

nucleoprotein Chromosomes consist largely of protein bonded to nucleic acid, a nucleoprotein. [31.1]

nucleoside A nucleoside is formed when either a purine or a pyrimidine base is linked to a sugar molecule, either D-ribose or D-deoxyribose. [31.1]

nucleotide Nucleotides are phosphate esters of nucleosides. [31.2]

nucleus The central part of an atom that contains all its protons and neutrons. The nucleus is very dense and has a positive electrical charge. [5.4]

nuclide A general term for any isotope of any atom. [18.1]

nutrient Nutrients are components of the food we eat that make body growth, maintenance, and repair possible. [32.1]

Nutrition Facts Many food packages contain a Nutrition Facts label. [32.7]

O

oligosaccharide An oligosaccharide is composed of two to six monosaccharide units. [27.2]

oncogenes Oncogenes cause the cell to lose control and become cancerous. [31.8]

optically active Compounds that are able to rotate polarized light are said to be optically active. [26.2]

orbital A cloudlike region around the nucleus where electrons are located. Orbitals are considered to be energy sublevels (s, p, d, f) within the principal energy levels. *See also* principal energy levels. [10.2]

orbital diagram A way of showing the arrangement of electrons in an atom, where boxes with small arrows indicating the electrons represent orbitals. [10.4]

organelle Eucaryotes are cells that contain internal, membrane-bound bodies called organelles. [33.1]

organic chemistry Organic chemistry is the chemistry of carbon compounds. [19.1]

osmosis The diffusion of water, either pure or from a dilute solution, through a semipermeable membrane into a solution of higher concentration. [14.6]

osmotic pressure The difference between atmospheric pressure and an applied pressure that is required to prevent osmosis from occurring. [14.6]

oxidation An increase in the oxidation number of an atom as a result of losing electrons. [17.1]

oxidation number A small number representing the state of oxidation of an atom. For an ion, it is the positive or negative charge on the ion; for covalently bonded atoms, it is a positive or negative number assigned to the more electronegative atom; in free elements, it is zero. [17.1]

oxidation–reduction A chemical reaction wherein electrons are transferred from one element to another; also known as redox. [17.1]

oxidation state *See* oxidation number. [17.1]

oxidative phosphorylation Oxidative phosphorylation directly uses energy from redox reactions to form ATP. [33.5]

oxidizing agent A substance that causes an increase in the oxidation state of another substance. The oxidizing agent is reduced during the course of the reaction. [17.1]

oxonium ion An oxonium ion forms when an alcohol is protonated. [22.4]

P

partial pressure The pressure exerted independently by each gas in a mixture of gases. [12.7]

parts per million (ppm) A measurement of the concentration of dilute solutions now commonly used by chemists in place of mass percent. [14.4]

Pauli exclusion principle An atomic orbital can hold a maximum of two electrons, which must have opposite spins. [10.3]

peptide linkage (bond) An amide bond is formed when a carboxyl group on one amino acid reacts with the α-amine group of a second amino acid to eliminate water. This amide bond links amino acids together and is termed a peptide linkage or peptide bond. [29.3]

percent composition of a compound The mass percent represented by each element in a compound. [7.3]

percent yield The ratio of the actual yield to the theoretical yield multiplied by 100. [9.5]

period The horizontal groupings (rows) of elements in the periodic table. [10.5]

pH A method of expressing the H^+ concentration (acidity) of a solution; $pH = -\log[H^+]$, $pH = 7$ is a neutral solution, $pH < 7$ is acidic, and $pH > 7$ is basic. [15.5]

phase A homogeneous part of a system separated from other parts by a physical boundary. [1.4]

phenol A phenol contains a hydroxyl group bound to an aromatic ring. Phenols are named as aromatic compounds. [22.6]

phosphate ester A phosphate ester combines a phosphoric acid with an alcohol. [24.11]

phospholipids Phospholipids yield a phosphate and a nitrogen-containing base as well as glycerol and fatty acids upon hydrolysis. [28.4]

phosphorylation The production of high-energy phosphate bonds. [33.5]

photons Theoretically, a tiny packet of energy that streams with others of its kind to produce a beam of light. [10.1]

photosynthesis Photosynthesis is a process by which energy from the Sun is converted to chemical energy that is stored in chemical bonds. [33.7]

physical change A change in form (such as size, shape, or physical state) without a change in composition. [4.2]

physical properties Inherent physical characteristics of a substance that can be determined without altering its composition: color, taste, odor, state of matter, density, melting point, boiling point. [4.1]

pi (π) bond A pi (π) bond is formed by the sideways overlap of two *p* orbitals and consists of two electron clouds: one above and one below the sigma bond. [20.1]

plane-polarized light Plane-polarized light is light vibrating in only one plane. [26.2]

polar covalent bond A covalent bond between two atoms with differing electronegativity values, resulting in unequal sharing of bonding electrons. [11.5]

polyamide Polyamides form when a carboxylic acid from one monomer reacts with an amine from a second monomer, forming an amide bond and splitting out water. One of the most common commercial polyamides is Nylon-66, formed from a six-carbon dicarboxylic acid (adipic acid) and a six-carbon diamine (1,6-hexanediamine). [25.3]

polyatomic ion An ion composed of more than one atom. [6.5]

polycyclic or fused aromatic ring system Polycyclic or fused aromatic ring systems contain two or more benzene rings (*polycyclic*) in which two carbon atoms are common to two rings (*fused*). [20.9]

polyhydroxy alcohol Polyhydroxy alcohols (or polyols) have more than one hydroxyl group per molecule. [22.1]

polymer A polymer is a macromolecule made up of many monomers. [21.1]

polymerization Polymerization is the chemical reaction that bonds monomers together to make a polymer. [21.1]

polypeptides Polymers containing up to about 50 amino acids are called polypeptides. [29.3]

polysaccharide A polysaccharide is a macromolecule that can be hydrolyzed to yield many monosaccharide units. [27.2]

positive nitrogen balance A growing child ingests more nitrogen than is excreted; the child is in a positive nitrogen balance. [35.6]

potential energy (PE) Stored energy, or the energy of an object due to its relative position. [4.4]

pressure Force per unit area; expressed in many units, such as mm Hg, atm, $lb/in.^2$, torr, and pascal. [12.1]

primary (1°), secondary (2°), and tertiary (3°) amines Alkylation of ammonia (with alkyl halides) will successively form primary, secondary, and tertiary amines. [25.6]

primary alcohol A hydroxyl-group carbon of a primary alcohol is bonded to one other carbon (methanol is grouped with the 1° alcohols). [22.1]

primary structure The primary structure of a protein is the amino acid sequence of that protein. [29.4]

principal energy levels Existing within the atom, these energy levels contain orbitals within which electrons are found. *See also* electron, orbital. [10.3]

procaryote Procaryotes are cells without internal membrane-bound bodies and have a minimum amount of spatial organization. [33.1]

productive binding hypothesis The productive binding hypothesis proposes that as reactants bind to the enzyme active site, they align for optimum reaction. [30.5]

products A chemical substance produced from reactants by a chemical change. [4.2, 8.1]

properties The characteristics, or traits, of substances that give them their unique identities. Properties are classified as physical or chemical. [4.1]

proteases Proteases are enzymes that break down proteins. [30.4]

protein domain Larger proteins are often composed of several globular sections about the size of myoglobin or carboxypeptidase A called protein domains. [29.6]

proton A subatomic particle found in the nucleus of the atom that carries a positive electrical charge and a mass of about 1 amu. An H^+ ion is a proton. [5.3]

proximity catalysis Proximity catalysis occurs when reactants are drawn together at the enzyme active site. [30.5]

Q

quanta Small discrete increments of energy. From the theory proposed by physicist Max Planck that energy is emitted in energy *quanta* rather than a continuous stream. [10.2]

quaternary ammonium salt Many well-known biologically active compounds are quaternary ammonium salts. [25.6]

quaternary structure A quaternary structure is found in proteins with more than one peptide chain and refers to the relative three-dimensional arrangement of these peptides with respect to each other. [29.4]

R

racemic mixture A mixture containing equal amounts of a pair of enantiomers is known as a racemic mixture. [26.5]

rad (radiation *a*bsorbed *d*ose) A unit of absorbed radiation indicating the energy absorbed from any ionizing radiation; 1 rad = 0.01 J of energy absorbed per kilogram of matter. [18.4]

radioactive decay The process by which a radioactive element emits particles or rays and is transformed into another element. [18.1]

radioactivity The spontaneous emission of radiation from the nucleus of an atom. [18.1]

reactants A chemical substance entering into a reaction. [4.2, 8.1]

reactive oxygen species (ROS) Oxygen-containing species (hydrogen peroxide, superoxide, hydroxyl radical) that can react and destroy many vital cell molecules. [33.3]

recombinant DNA The modified and repaired genome now contains a new gene and is called recombinant DNA. [31.10]

Recommended Dietary Allowance (RDA) The Recommended Dietary Allowance (RDA) is defined as the daily dietary intake that is sufficient to meet the requirements of nearly all individuals in a specific age and gender group. [32.1]

redox *See* oxidation–reduction. [17.1]

redox coenzymes Organic compounds that are used and reused to help an enzyme-catalyzed, oxidation-reduction reaction. [33.2]

reducing agent A substance that causes a decrease in the oxidation state of another substance; the reducing agent is oxidized during the course of a reaction. [17.1]

reducing sugar Many clinical tests monitor glucose as a reducing sugar. [27.11]

reduction A decrease in the oxidation number of an element as a result of gaining electrons. [17.1]

rem (*r*oentgen *e*quivalent to *m*an) A unit of radiation-dose equivalent taking into account that the energy absorbed from different sources does not produce the same degree of biological effect. [18.4]

replication Replication is the biological process for duplication of the DNA molecule. [31.6]

representative element An element in one of the A groups in the periodic table. [3.2, 10.5]

resonance structure A molecule or ion that has multiple Lewis structures. *See also* Lewis structure. [11.8]

reversible chemical reaction A chemical reaction in which the products formed react to produce the original reactants. A double arrow is used to indicate that a reaction is reversible. [16.2]

ribonucleic acid (RNA) Ribonucleic acid (RNA) is a polynucleotide that, upon hydrolysis, yields ribose, phosphoric acid, and the four purine and pyrimidine bases adenine, guanine, cytosine, and uracil. [31.4]

roentgen (R) A unit of exposure of gamma radiation based on the quantity of ionization produced in air. [18.4]

rounding off numbers The process by which the value of the last digit retained is determined after dropping nonsignificant digits. [2.3]

S

Sanger's reagent Sanger's reagent, 1-fluoro-2,4-dinitrobenzene, reacts with the α-amino group of the N-terminal residue to tag and separate that specific amino acid with a yellow color. [29.9]

saponification When a strong base is used to speed up hydrolysis, the process is called alkaline hydrolysis or saponification. [24.8]

saturated compound In a saturated compound, each carbon atom is bonded to four other atoms by single bonds with bond angles of about 109.5°. [19.2]

saturated solution A solution containing dissolved solute in equilibrium with undissolved solute. [14.2]

Saytzeff's rule Saytzeff's rule states that when there is a choice of positions for the carbon–carbon double bond, the more highly substituted alkene is preferred. [22.4]

scientific laws Simple statements of natural phenomena to which no exceptions are known under the given conditions. [1.2]

scientific method A method of solving problems by observation; recording and evaluating data of an experiment; formulating hypotheses and theories to explain the behavior of nature; and devising additional experiments to test the hypotheses and theories to see if they are correct. [1.2]

scientific notation A convenient way of expressing large and small numbers using powers of 10. To write a number as a power of 10 move the decimal point in the original number so that it is located after the first nonzero digit, and follow the new number by a multiplication sign and 10 with an exponent (called its *power*) that is the number of places the decimal point was moved. Example: $2468 = 2.468 \times 10^3$. [2.1]

secondary alcohol For a secondary alcohol, two carbons are bonded to the hydroxyl-group carbon; three carbons are bonded to the hydroxyl-group carbon for a tertiary alcohol. [22.1]

secondary structure The secondary structure of a protein can be characterized as a regular, three-dimensional structure held together by hydrogen bonds between the components of the peptide linkages (the $>C=O$ and the $H-N<$). [29.4]

semipermeable membrane A membrane that allows the passage of water (solvent) molecules through it in either direction but prevents the passage of larger solute molecules or ions. [13.7, 14.6]

SI (*Systeme International*, or International System) An agreed-upon standard system of measurements used by scientists around the world. *See also* metric system. [2.5]

sigma bond Sigma bonds occur when two atoms share two electrons along a line drawn between the two nuclei. [19.2]

significant figures The number of digits that are known plus one estimated digit are considered significant in a measured quantity; also called significant digits. [2.2, Appendix I]

simple protein Simple proteins yield only amino acids upon hydrolysis. [29.1]

single-displacement reaction A reaction of an element and a compound that yields a different element and a different compound. [8.3]

sliding filament model Muscle contraction occurs as actin repeatedly slides along myosin filaments. [33.6]

soap Soaps are salts of long-chain fatty acids. [24.10]

solid A state of matter having a definite shape and a definite volume, whose particles cohere rigidly to one another, so that a solid can be independent of its container. [1.3]

solubility An amount of solute that will dissolve in a specific amount of solvent under stated conditions. [14.2]

solubility product constant (K_{sp}) The equilibrium constant for the solubility of a slightly soluble salt. [16.7]

solute The substance that is dissolved—or the least abundant component—in a solution. [14.1]

solution A system in which one or more substances are homogeneously mixed or dissolved in another substance. [14.1]

solution map An outline for the path of a unit conversion. [2.5]

solvent The dissolving agent or the most abundant component in a solution. [14.1]

specific gravity The ratio of the density of one substance to the density of another substance taken as a standard. Water is usually the standard for liquids and solids; air, for gases. [2.8]

specific heat The quantity of heat required to change the temperature of 1 g of any substance by 1°C. [4.5]

specific rotation The specific rotation is the number of degrees that polarized light is rotated by passing through 1 decimeter (dm) of a solution whose concentration is 1 g/mL. [26.2]

spectator ion An ion in solution that does not undergo chemical change during a chemical reaction. [15.6]

speed A measurement of how fast a wave travels through space. [10.1]

sphingolipids Sphingolipids yield an unsaturated amino alcohol (sphingosine) and a carbohydrate or phosphate and nitrogen base in addition to a fatty acid upon hydrolysis. [28.4]

spin A property of an electron that describes its appearance of spinning on an axis like a globe; the electron can spin in only two directions, and, to occupy the same orbital, two electrons must spin in opposite directions. *See also* orbital. [10.3]

standard conditions *See* standard temperature and pressure. [12.5]

standard temperature and pressure (STP) 0°C (273 K) and 1 atm (760 torr); also known as standard conditions. [12.5]

stereoisomer Stereoisomers have the same structural formula but differ in their spatial arrangement. [26.1]

stereoisomerism In stereoisomerism the isomers have the same structural formula but differ in the spatial arrangement of atoms. [26.1]

steroids Steroids are compounds that have the steroid nucleus. Steroids possess the steroid nucleus—a 17-carbon structure consisting of four fused carbocyclic rings. [28.5]

Stock System A system that uses Roman numerals to name elements that form more than one type of cation. (For example: Fe^{2+}, iron(II); Fe^{3+}, iron(III).) [6.4]

stoichiometry The area of chemistry that deals with the quantitative relationships among reactants and products in a chemical reaction. [9.1]

strain hypothesis The strain hypothesis states that the binding forces that draw a reactant to the enzyme active site also force the reactant to change into the transition state. [30.5]

strong electrolyte An electrolyte that is essentially 100% ionized in aqueous solution. [15.4]

subatomic particles Particles found within the atom, mainly protons, neutrons, and electrons. [5.3]

sublevels Each principal energy level is divided into sublevels. [10.3]

sublimation The process of going directly from the solid state to the vapor state without becoming a liquid. [13.2]

subscript Number that appears partially below the line and to the right of a symbol of an element (example: H_2SO_4). [3.3]

substance Matter that is homogeneous and has a definite, fixed composition; substances occur in two forms—as elements and as compounds. [1.4]

substitution reaction A substitution reaction occurs when an atom bonded to carbon is replaced by a different atom or group of atoms. [19.9]

substrate The substance acted on by an enzyme is called the substrate. [30.1]

substrate-level phosphorylation Substrate-level phosphorylation uses energy derived from oxidation to form high-energy phosphate bonds on substrates, biochemicals in metabolic pathways. [33.5]

superimposable Superimposable means that, when we lay one object upon another, all parts of both objects coincide exactly. [26.2]

supersaturated solution A solution containing more solute than needed for a saturated solution at a particular temperature. Supersaturated solutions tend to be unstable; jarring the container or dropping in a "seed" crystal will cause crystallization of the excess solute. [14.2]

surface tension The resistance of a liquid to an increase in its surface area. [13.2]

symbol In chemistry, an abbreviation for the name of an element. [3.1]

synthetic detergent, syndet A synthetic detergent (syndet) is an organic molecule that has been synthesized in a chemical factory and acts as a cleansing agent. [24.10]

system A body of matter under consideration. [1.4]

T

temperature A measure of the intensity of heat, or of how hot or cold a system is; the SI unit is the kelvin (K). [2.7]

tertiary alcohol For a secondary alcohol, two carbons are bonded to the hydroxyl-group carbon; three carbons are bonded to the hydroxyl-group carbon for a tertiary alcohol. [22.1]

tertiary structure The tertiary structure of a protein refers to the distinctive and characteristic conformation, or shape, of a protein molecule. The tertiary structure is held together by interactions between amino acid side chains. [29.4]

tetrahedral structure An arrangement of the VSEPR model where four pairs of electrons are placed 109.5° degrees apart to form a tetrahedron. [11.10]

theoretical yield The maximum amount of product that can be produced according to a balanced equation. [9.5]

theory An explanation of the general principles of certain phenomena with considerable evidence to support it; a well-established hypothesis. [1.2]

thermal energy A form of energy associated with the motion of small particles. [2.7]

thermoplastic polymers Thermoplastic polymers soften and can be remolded every time they are heated. [21.3]

thermosetting polymers Thermosetting plastics set to an infusible solid upon heating and do not soften upon reheating. [21.3]

thiol Thiols or mercaptans are organic compounds that contain the —SH group. Naming thiols is analogous to naming alcohols except that the suffix -*thiol* is used in place of the suffix -*ol*. [22.10]

Thomson model of the atom Thomson asserted that atoms are not indivisible but are composed of smaller parts; they contain both positively and negatively charged particles—protons as well as electrons. [5.3]

titration The process of measuring the volume of one reagent required to react with a measured mass or volume of another reagent. [15.6]

Tollens test In the Tollens test, Ag^+ is reduced to form metallic silver as an aldehyde is oxidized. [23.4]

total ionic equation An equation that shows compounds in the form in which they actually exist. Strong electrolytes are written as ions in solution, whereas nonelectrolytes, weak electrolytes, precipitates, and gases are written in the un-ionized form. [15.7]

transamination Transamination is the transfer of an amino group from an alpha amino acid to an alpha keto acid:

$$RCH-COOH + R'C-COOH \rightleftharpoons RC-COOH + R'CHCOOH$$

[35.7]

transcription Transcription is the making of RNA from DNA. [31.7]

transition elements The metallic elements characterized by increasing numbers of *d* and *f* electrons. These elements are located in Groups 1B–8B of the periodic table. [3.2, 10.5]

transition state When the reactant reaches the highest energy point during reaction, it reaches the transition state—an unstable structure with characteristics of both the reactant and the product. [30.2]

translation Translation is the production of a polypeptide by means of an mRNA. [31.9]

transmutation The conversion of one element into another element. [18.3]

transuranium elements An element that has an atomic number higher than that of uranium (>92). [18.3]

triacylglycerol A triacylglycerol or triglyceride is a glycerol that has been esterified with three fatty acids, generally three *different* fatty acids. [24.9]

triglyceride A triacylglycerol or triglyceride is a glycerol that has been esterified with three fatty acids, generally three *different* fatty acids. [24.9]

trigonal planar structure An arrangement of atoms in the VSEPR model where the three pairs of electrons are placed 120° apart on a flat plane. [11.10]

tumor-suppressor genes Tumor-suppressor genes actively block cancer development; tumor-suppressor genes will trigger commands that lead to cell destruction if normal cellular control fails. [31.8]

turnover number The turnover number, the number of substrates an enzyme can react in a given time span, is a measure of an enzyme's catalytic ability. [30.3]

U

unsaturated compound An unsaturated compound contains double and/or triple bonds between carbon atoms. [19.2]

unsaturated solution A solution containing less solute per unit volume than its corresponding saturated solution. [14.2]

urea Urea is a simple diamide of the structure

$$H_2N-\overset{\overset{\textstyle O}{\|}}{C}-NH_2$$

Urea is also a valuable fertilizer and industrial chemical. [25.4]

urea cycle The urea cycle is the metabolic pathway that creates urea for nitrogen excretion and takes place in the liver. [35.8]

V

valence electrons An electron in the outermost energy level of an atom; these electrons are the ones involved in bonding atoms together to form compounds. [10.4]

vaporization *See* evaporation. [13.2]

vapor pressure The pressure exerted by a vapor in equilibrium with its liquid. [13.2]

vapor pressure curve A graph generated by plotting the temperature of a liquid on the *x*-axis and its vapor pressure on the *y*-axis. Any point on the curve represents an equilibrium between the vapor and liquid. [13.3]

vital-force theory The theory that organic compounds were formed only by living organisms. [19.1]

vitamin Vitamins are a group of naturally occurring organic compounds that are essential for good nutrition and that must be supplied in the diet. [32.4]

volatile A substance that evaporates readily; a liquid with a high vapor pressure and a low boiling point. [13.2]

voltaic cell A cell that produces electric current from a spontaneous chemical reaction. [17.5]

volume The amount of space occupied by matter; measured in SI units by cubic meters (m^3) but also commonly in liters and milliliters. [2.5]

vulcanization process Rubber polymers are cross-linked with sulfur to extend rubber's useful temperature range and to improve rubber's abrasion resistance. [21.6]

W

water of crystallization Water molecules that are part of a crystalline structure, as in a hydrate; also called water of hydration. [13.6]

water of hydration *See* water of crystallization. [13.6]

wavelength The distance between consecutive peaks and troughs in a wave; symbolized by the Greek letter lambda. [10.1]

wax Waxes are esters of fatty acids and a high-molar-mass alcohol (up to about 30 carbons long). Waxes are extremely water insoluble and serve a protective function on leaves, feathers, fruit, and fur. [28.2]

weak electrolyte A substance that is ionized to a small extent in aqueous solution. [15.4]

weight A measure of Earth's gravitational attraction for a body (object). [2.5]

Williamson synthesis A synthesis of ethers by a substitution reaction between alkyl halides and sodium alkoxides. [22.9]

Z

zwitterion In neutral solutions, amino acids form dipolar ions called zwitterions. [29.2]

INDEX

Names, Formulas, and Charges of Common Ions

Positive Ions (Cations)

Charge	Name	Formula
1+	Ammonium	NH_4^+
	Copper(I) (Cuprous)	Cu^+
	Hydrogen	H^+
	Potassium	K^+
	Silver	Ag^+
	Sodium	Na^+
2+	Barium	Ba^{2+}
	Cadmium	Cd^{2+}
	Calcium	Ca^{2+}
	Cobalt(II)	Co^{2+}
	Copper(II) (Cupric)	Cu^{2+}
	Iron(II) (Ferrous)	Fe^{2+}
	Lead(II)	Pb^{2+}
	Magnesium	Mg^{2+}
	Manganese(II)	Mn^{2+}
	Mercury(II) (Mercuric)	Hg^{2+}
	Nickel(II)	Ni^{2+}
	Tin(II) (Stannous)	Sn^{2+}
	Zinc	Zn^{2+}
3+	Aluminum	Al^{3+}
	Antimony(III)	Sb^{3+}
	Arsenic(III)	As^{3+}
	Bismuth(III)	Bi^{3+}
	Chromium(III)	Cr^{3+}
	Iron(III) (Ferric)	Fe^{3+}
	Titanium(III) (Titanous)	Ti^{3+}
4+	Manganese(IV)	Mn^{4+}
	Tin(IV) (Stannic)	Sn^{4+}
	Titanium(IV) (Titanic)	Ti^{4+}
5+	Antimony(V)	Sb^{5+}
	Arsenic(V)	As^{5+}

Negative Ions (Anions)

Charge	Name	Formula
1−	Acetate	$C_2H_3O_2^-$
	Bromate	BrO_3^-
	Bromide	Br^-
	Chlorate	ClO_3^-
	Chloride	Cl^-
	Chlorite	ClO_2^-
	Cyanide	CN^-
	Fluoride	F^-
	Hydride	H^-
	Hydrogen carbonate (Bicarbonate)	HCO_3^-
	Hydrogen sulfate (Disulfate)	HSO_4^-
	Hydrogen sulfite (Bisulfite)	HSO_3^-
	Hydroxide	OH^-
	Hypochlorite	ClO^-
	Iodate	IO_3^-
	Iodide	I^-
	Nitrate	NO_3^-
	Nitrite	NO_2^-
	Perchlorate	ClO_4^-
	Permanganate	MnO_4^-
	Thiocyanate	SCN^-
2−	Carbonate	CO_3^{2-}
	Chromate	CrO_4^{2-}
	Dichromate	$Cr_2O_7^{2-}$
	Oxalate	$C_2O_4^{2-}$
	Oxide	O^{2-}
	Peroxide	O_2^{2-}
	Silicate	SiO_3^{2-}
	Sulfate	SO_4^{2-}
	Sulfide	S^{2-}
	Sulfite	SO_3^{2-}
3−	Arsenate	AsO_4^{3-}
	Borate	BO_3^{3-}
	Phosphate	PO_4^{3-}
	Phosphide	P^{3-}
	Phosphite	PO_3^{3-}

Prefixes and Numerical Values for SI Units

Prefix	Symbol	Numerical value	Power of 10 equivalent
exa	E	1,000,000,000,000,000,000	10^{18}
peta	P	1,000,000,000,000,000	10^{15}
tera	T	1,000,000,000,000	10^{12}
giga	G	1,000,000,000	10^{9}
mega	M	1,000,000	10^{6}
kilo	k	1,000	10^{3}
hecto	h	100	10^{2}
deka	da	10	10^{1}
—	—	1	10^{0}
deci	d	0.1	10^{-1}
centi	c	0.01	10^{-2}
milli	m	0.001	10^{-3}
micro	μ	0.000001	10^{-6}
nano	n	0.000000001	10^{-9}
pico	p	0.000000000001	10^{-12}
femto	f	0.000000000000001	10^{-15}
atto	a	0.000000000000000001	10^{-18}

SI Units and Conversion Factors

Length

SI unit: meter (m)

1 meter	=	1000 millimeters
	=	1.0936 yards
1 centimeter	=	0.3937 inch
1 inch	=	2.54 centimeters (exactly)
1 kilometer	=	0.62137 mile
1 mile	=	5280 feet
	=	1.609 kilometers
1 angstrom	=	10^{-10} meter

Mass

SI unit: kilogram (kg)

1 kilogram	=	1000 grams
	=	2.20 pounds
1 gram	=	1000 milligrams
1 pound	=	453.59 grams
	=	0.45359 kilogram
	=	16 ounces
1 ton	=	2000 pounds
	=	907.185 kilograms
1 ounce	=	28.3 grams
1 atomic mass unit	=	1.6606×10^{-27} kilograms

Volume

SI unit: cubic meter (m^3)

1 liter	=	1000 milliliters
	=	$10^{-3}\,m^3$
	=	1 dm^3
	=	1.0567 quarts
1 gallon	=	4 quarts
	=	8 pints
	=	3.785 liters
1 quart	=	32 fluid ounces
	=	0.946 liter
	=	4 cups
1 fluid ounce	=	29.6 mL

Temperature

SI unit: kelvin (K)

0 K	=	$-273.15°C$
	=	$-459.67°F$
K	=	$°C + 273.15$
$°C$	=	$\dfrac{(°F - 32)}{1.8}$
$°C$	=	$\dfrac{5}{9}(°F - 32)$
$°F$	=	$1.8(°C) + 32$

Energy

SI unit: joule (J)

1 joule	=	1 kg m^2/s^2
	=	0.23901 calorie
1 calorie	=	4.184 joules

Pressure

SI unit: pascal (Pa)

1 pascal	=	1 kg/(ms^2)
1 atmosphere	=	101.325 kilopascals
	=	760 torr
	=	760 mm Hg
	=	14.70 pounds per square inch (psi)